ANIMAL PHYSIOLOGY

Bradley T. Scheer
Professor of Biology
University of Oregon

ANIMAL

John Wiley & Sons, Inc., New York · London

PHYSIOLOGY

Preface

One function of a preface is to inform the prospective reader concerning the nature of the contents of the book, and the intentions of the author in writing it. My intention was to prepare a summary of the leading ideas and concepts of the physiology of animals that would be suitable for use as a textbook in a course at the level of the junior or senior year in college. Since I have already written two books with the same general intention, some justification might be appropriate for a third. The best justification is that, with the rapid growth of knowledge, especially physiological knowledge, any textbook in the field requires frequent revision, if the facts and concepts presented are to be reasonably current. Besides this, my own knowledge and thought have changed, I hope progressively, with the years to the extent that I now interpret some of the facts and concepts, old and new, differently and present them differently in my own teaching.

Most existing textbooks in physiology are written from one of three viewpoints: homocentric, comparative, or cellular. The emphasis on human physiology which is appropriate in a medical school seems less so in a liberal arts college, where most undergraduate courses in physiology are taught. The strictly comparative or strictly cellular approaches severely limit the presentation in other ways. Comparative physiology, no matter how well taught, tends to emphasize details and differences and lose general principles. Cellular physiology, in concentrating on the cell, loses sight of organic and organismal principles. There are good arguments in favor of each of the three approaches, but I have preferred a different one.

In this book, I have tried to make a synthesis, not alone of human or cellular or comparative physiology, but of the physiology of animals. The synthesis begins at the level of molecules and of energy and moves upward through a scale of increasing complexity, from molecules to cells, from cells to organs, and finally to the integration of all these into activities of organisms. The synthesis utilizes both the "general" and the "comparative" method, noting both significant generalizations and important variations. The task I have thus undertaken is not a small one, and I have approached it in all humility. Some of my colleagues will doubtless be annoyed, even perhaps offended, by the casual treatment or even neglect of important areas of interest, and by what may seem overemphasis on some of my own partialities. I can only plead that I have written about what I know best; the result is, inevitably, a personal synthesis. It is as general, as solidly based in fact, and as representative of current thought as I can make it in the limits of space I have set for myself. The lists of references are selected to help the student, his teacher, and any more general reader who may find matter of interest here to find other views and other interpretations, and to find the details of fact which I could not include fully here.

The student who hopes to follow my argument must come prepared with certain minimum tools and abilities. In a few places, he will be asked to follow elementary algebraic arguments; he must have a good knowledge of chemistry, including the chemistry of organic compounds. He should know something of physics, and of the biology of the principal kinds of animals, and be familiar with their structure and appearance. In the curricular pattern of American colleges and universities, these tools are not usually acquired before the junior year. The student should have the opportunity, while he is reading about physiology, to do at least one good physiological experiment. The aims of the laboratory work in physiology should, in my opinion, not be primarily illustrating a principle, teaching elaborate techniques, or leading a student by the hand through a classical experiment. Rather, the student should be required to follow through the process of physiological discovery himself—to formulate a problem, devise the means for its solution, and go through the mental process of critical analysis of experimental results. With such an aim, no formal laboratory exercises need be specified, and I have included none here. Instead, the teacher must provide the student with living organisms and such equipment for their observation as he may be able to command; with these provisions, his role should be that of counselor, not director.

The student should be brought to realize that neither this textbook nor any other book is the real source of physiological information. The first source is the laboratory and, derived from that, the accounts of laboratory investigations which make up the original literature of physiology. The bulk of this literature is so great, however, that it seems unwise to give specific literature references to original sources in a book as short as this one. Instead, I have provided references to review articles from which the student may readily find the original literature, prior to the date of the review. He should be encouraged to follow the literature of more recent date when it is available to him.

Eugene, Oregon   Bradley T. Scheer
February 1963

Acknowledgments

My first expression of gratitude must go to my wife, Marlin Ann Ray Scheer, for her forbearance, encouragement, support, and assistance during the five years in which this book was in gestation. The labor of preparing the manuscript for the press was performed with skill by Mrs. Marjorie Turbyfill, Mrs. Barbara Stearns, and Mrs. Donna Tyvoll. The many colleagues and their publishers, who generously permitted use of their original materials, have been most gracious, and their contributions are acknowledged in the proper places. The initial development of the book was carried out during tenure of a Guggenheim Memorial Fellowship, and the generous support of the General Secretary and Board of the Guggenheim Foundation is appreciated.

B.T.S.

Contents

Introduction:

the nature of physiology

Physiology is, in one sense, the oldest of the sciences. The first physiologists (*physiologoi*) were the Ionian Greek philosophers who, over 2000 years ago, made the first attempt to explain the universe in rational terms. The task of the modern physiologist is more limited: it is the explanation, in a scientific sense, of vital processes. To a modern scientist, the word explanation has a very distinct and limited meaning. The scientist is concerned with phenomena, that is with observable happenings or events. His concern is to connect these phenomena in a chain of cause and effect: to be able to say, reliably, that phenomenon A always accompanies or is followed by phenomenon B, or at any rate that the two occur together with a certain predictable frequency. Such a statement is a statement of scientific fact. In physi-ology we may establish that the contraction or beat of the heart is always accompanied by ejection of blood into the aorta, or that the application of an electric shock of a certain strength to a point on a nerve is always followed by propagation of a wave of electrical potential change along the nerve.

When we have a number of facts relating several phenomena, we can proceed to the next step and link up these facts into a hypothesis. In this process we use, consciously or unconsciously, the process of logical reasoning, and in physiology our logic normally follows mechanistic patterns; that is, we develop, in abstract terms, a mechanism or machine, a model which will have the same properties we have observed in the living organism. Thus William Harvey, observing the action of the heart in forcing blood

1

into the blood vessels, at once thought of this action in terms of a pump, and we have ever since used this model in our thinking about heart action. In many cases, there is no known machine which will do what the organism or cell does, and we must imagine or invent the machinery. The action of nerve cells in conducting electrical impulses is not similar to the action of any man-made device—though some of the properties may be imitated by an iron wire in a nitric acid solution—but we have built up in our minds a model of nerve action that will behave like a nerve cell. The only limitation on this kind of model-building is that the principles involved in operation of the model must be the tested principles of natural science, themselves based on observations through the same processes of logical reasoning we use in physiology.

When we have a hypothetical model, we must then test it. The model will have properties which we have imagined rather than observed, and these properties will suggest observations to be made on the cell or organism. Each such observation may either confirm the existence of the imagined property in the natural system or show that the property is not exhibited by the natural system, and that we must revise our model accordingly. When our model coincides with the natural system in a great many points, we have an explanation. We can now describe, say, heart action or nerve action in terms of a rational system in which all the phenomena are related in an intelligible fashion in accordance with established scientific principles. Such an explanation has great utility. It permits us to manipulate and use the phenomena that we understand. For this reason, physiology in the modern

sense of the word has always been closely associated with medicine, and modern medicine relies heavily and continuously on physiological knowledge. We must remember, however, that we truly understand only the model that we have constructed. The real living system may, and frequently does, surprise us by revealing properties we have not built into our model, or by failing to exhibit properties which we have built into our model without adequate basis in observation or testing. When that happens, we have to rebuild our model, sometimes from the very beginning, but each new model brings us closer to the real, living organism which is our primary interest. For the research physiologist, whether he works in a medical school or a college of liberal arts, on men or dogs or crabs or frogs, this is the ultimate aim of physiology: an understanding of the real living organism in its relation to the universe.

The task of understanding vital processes is no small one. These processes are enormously complex and varied. We must accordingly analyze the processes, and select among them those we are interested in and those that are accessible to study. Physiologists commonly choose to study only a limited number of types of organisms, or limited aspects of vital activity. Thus there are mammalian physiologists and insect physiologists, cellular physiologists and neurophysiologists, biochemists and biophysicists. For convenience we restrict ourselves here to animals, but not to any specific aspect of animal physiology. The problems are still myriad, and we shall have to look at them briefly, and one at a time. For convenience, again, we begin with the group of processes we call metabolic. By the word metabolism we mean the exchanges of matter and energy that occur in the organism. It will soon become evident that the most fundamental aspects of these exchanges occur in the cells, and hence we can focus our attention on cells, and try to understand something of what goes on here before taking up the larger question of the metabolism of the whole organism.

In our thinking about metabolism, we can use, at first, a very simple model of the cell as a collection of enzymes capable of catalyzing certain complex systems of chemical reactions. This model will soon prove inadequate, and we must learn something about cellular structure and the changes of the cell in time, so that we can build a better model. Most cells, we will find, have the property of irritability, in that sudden changes in the environment provoke equally sudden, but disproportionate, changes in the cell. We shall look at a few kinds of cells in which this property is highly developed, to learn something of its characteristics and its mechanism. In the whole organism, the changes of irritability are often adaptive in that they ultimately lead to a response of the whole organism, enabling it to adjust its activities in relation to the environmental change. This adjustment involves integration, a process in which the effects of a variety of influences, arising both within and outside the organism, are interrelated to produce a continuing pattern of action of the whole organism, modified continuously as these influences change. In our mental progression from cellular events of metabolism to the integrative mechanisms, we shall have to incorporate our model of the cell into an infinitely more complex model of a highly adapted organism. This organism, though continually changing in detail, nevertheless remains remarkably constant in most of its properties. The maintenance of this constancy is called regulation, and we shall conclude by examining a number of instances of regulation and the relevant mechanisms.

We shall not, in this book or in our lifetimes, achieve the task of the physiologist. Many vital processes remain unexplained, and the challenge of physiology lies in these unexplored areas. We can only point out some of the important phenomena for future exploration. Of the vital processes of which we already know something, space and time restrict us to a series of short sketches. The student who finds these sketches attractive can look forward to an exciting intellectual adventure in more advanced courses where the model will be made more detailed, filled in, and rounded out. He may seek even more adventure in research, in the construction of new and better models for the edification and welfare of humanity. The student whose major interests lie elsewhere may still hope to derive from this book something of the picture which one physiologist has of the living world, a picture which may help him to use physiological concepts in other fields.

References

The books and articles listed below are all reviews, symposia, or advanced textbooks which cover the material discussed in this book or closely related subjects, usually in more detail or at a more advanced level. Most of the references are to material published within the last decade, but occasionally other works are included because of their special merits or historical importance. For most topics discussed in this book, original articles of more recent date than those listed in this bibliography have also been used by the author;

the student should be encouraged to seek these out for himself and to find more recent original papers, which may require alteration of some of the conclusions I have reached.

General References

The following books are concerned with topics which are discussed in several chapters of this book.

Baldwin, E. 1957. *Dynamic Aspects of Biochemistry.* (3rd edn.) Univ. Press, Cambridge, England.

Baldwin, E. 1949. *An Introduction to Comparative Biochemistry.* (3rd edn.) Univ. Press, Cambridge, England.

Brown, M. E. (ed.) 1957. *The Physiology of Fishes.* (2 vols.) Academic Press, New York.

Davson, H. 1959. *A Textbook of General Physiology.* (2nd edn.) Little, Brown, Boston.

Florkin, M. 1949. *Biochemical Evolution.* (transl. S. Morgulis) Academic Press, New York.

Florkin, M. and Mason, H. S. (eds.) 1960. *Comparative Biochemistry* (3 vols.) Academic Press, New York.

Fruton, J. S., and Simmonds, S. 1958. *General Biochemistry.* (2nd edn.) Wiley, New York.

Jessop, W. J. B. 1961. *Fearon's Introduction to Biochemistry.* Academic Press, New York.

Marshall, A. J. (ed.) 1960–1961. *Biology and Comparative Physiology of Birds.* (2 vols.) Academic Press, New York.

Prosser, C. L. (ed.) 1950. *Comparative Animal Physiology.* Saunders, Philadelphia.

Prosser, C. L., and Brown, F. A. Jr. 1961. *Comparative Animal Physiology* (2nd edn.) Saunders, Philadelphia.

Ramsay, J. A. 1952. *A Physiological Approach to the Lower Animals.* Univ. Press; Cambridge, England.

Roeder, K. D. (ed.) 1953. *Insect Physiology.* Wiley, New York.

Scheer, B. T. 1948. *Comparative Physiology.* Wiley, New York.

Scheer, B. T. 1953. *General Physiology.* Wiley, New York.

Scheer, B. T. (ed.) 1957. *Recent Advances in Invertebrate Physiology.* U. Oregon Press, Eugene, Ore.

Tracey, M. V. 1954. *Principles of Biochemistry.* Pitman, London.

Umbreit, W. W. 1960. *Metabolic Maps.* (2nd edn.) Minneapolis, Minn.

Waterman, T. H. (ed.) 1960. *The Physiology of Crustacea.* (2 vols.) Academic Press, New York.

Specific references will be made at the end of individual chapters to the following volumes which contain review articles on a number of topics by several authors.

Barron, E. S. G. (ed.) 1952. *Modern Trends in Physiology and Biochemistry.* Academic Press, New York. (*Mod. Trends. Physiol. Biochem.*)

Bourne, G. H. (ed.) 1960. *Structure and Function of Muscle.* (3 vols.) Academic Press, New York. (*Struc. Func. Musc.*)

Bourne, G. H. and Kidder, G. W. (eds.) 1953. *Biochemistry and Physiology of Nutrition* (2 vols.) Academic Press, New York. (*Biochem. Physiol. Nutr.*)

Brachet, I. and Mirsky, A. E. (eds.) 1959. *The Cell.* (5 vols.) Academic Press, New York.

Field, J. (ed.) 1960. *Handbook of Physiology. Section 1: Neurophysiology* (3 vols.) American Physiological Society, Washington. (*Hdbk. Physiol. I Neurophysiol.*)

Green, D. E. (ed.) 1948. *Currents in Biochemical Research.* Interscience, New York. (*Curr. Biochem. Res.*)

Green, D. E. (ed.) 1956. *Currents in Biochemical Research 1956.* Interscience, New York. (*Curr. Biochem. Res. 1956.*)

Greenberg, D. M. (ed.) 1954. *Chemical Pathways of Metabolism.* Academic Press, New York. (*Chem. Path. Metab.*)

Pincus, G. and Thimann, K. V. (eds.) 1948–1955. *The Hormones.* (3 vols.) Academic Press, New York.

Scheer, B. T. (ed.) 1957. *Recent Advances in Invertebrate Physiology.* U. of Oregon Publ., Eugene. (*Rec. Adv. Inv. Physiol.*)

Stewart, C. P., and Strengers, T. (eds.) 1961. *Symposium on Water and Electrolyte Metabolism.* Elsevier, Amsterdam. (*Symp. Water Electrolyte Metab.*)

Williams, P. C., and Austin, C. R. (eds.) 1961. *Cell Mechanisms of Hormone Production and Action.* Univ. Press, Cambridge, England. (*Cell Mech. Horm. Prod. Act.*)

Original Literature

The serious student of physiology should familiarize himself with those periodicals in which the original observations, which are the real source of physiological knowledge, are published. A selected annotated list follows:

Académie des Sciences, Comptes Rendus: General Science, in French by French authors; one of the oldest scientific periodicals.

Acta Physiologica Scandinavica: Physiology, mostly in English by Scandinavian authors.

American Journal of Physiology: Official journal of the American Physiological Society, in English mostly by American authors.

Archives des Sciences Physiologiques: Physiology, in French by French and Belgian authors.

Archives of Biochemistry and Biophysics: Mostly biochemistry, in English by American authors.

Biochemical Journal: In English, mostly by British authors.

Biochemische Zeitschrift: Biochemistry, mostly in German by northern and central European authors.

Biochemistry: New journal of American Chemical Society, in English.

Biochimica et Biophysica Acta: International: English, French, or German.

Biological Bulletin: General Biology with considerable comparative physiology, in English; published by the Marine Biological Laboratory, Woods Hole, Mass. and reports work done there and elsewhere.

Biologisches Zentralblatt: General Biology, usually in German.

Comparative Biochemistry and Physiology: International, mostly in English.

Endocrinology: In English, American authors.

Experientia: General science, international, in English, French, German, or Italian.

Experimental Cell Research: International, mostly in English.

General and Comparative Endocrinology: International, mostly in English.

Hoppe-Seyler's Zeitschrift für Physiologische Chemie: One of the oldest biochemical journals, mostly in German.

Journal of Biological Chemistry: Official Journal of American Society of Biological Chemists; in English, American authors.

Journal of Biophysical and Biochemical Cytology: in English, mostly American authors; official publication of the Rockefeller Institute.

Journal of Cellular and Comparative Physiology: in English, mostly American authors.

Journal of Endocrinology: in English, mostly British authors; official journal of the Endocrine Society (British).

Journal of Experimental Biology: in English, mostly British authors; official journal of the Society for Experimental Biology (British).

Journal of General Physiology: in English mostly

American authors; official publication of the Rockefeller Institute.

Journal of Insect Physiology: International, mostly in English.

Journal of Neurochemistry: International, mostly in English.

Journal of Neurophysiology: In English, mostly American authors.

Journal of Physiology: In English, mostly British authors, official journal of the Physiological Society (British).

Marine Biological Association of the United Kingdom, Journal: General marine biology, including some physiology; published by the laboratory of the M.B.A., Plymouth, England; reports mostly work done there.

National Academy of Sciences, Proceedings: General Science; official journal of the Academy (U.S.A.).

Nature: General Science, in English, by international authors.

Die Naturwissenschaffen: General Science, mostly in German, international.

Pflügers Archiv für die gesamte Physiologie: One of the oldest physiological journals, mostly in German.

Physiological Zoology: In English, mostly American authors.

Quarterly Journal of Experimental Physiology: Mammalian physiology, in English.

Royal Society of London, Proceedings, series B: General biology, with much physiology, in English, British authors; official publication, with the *Philosophical Transactions,* of the oldest scientific society with a continuous history.

Science: General science, in English, American authors; official publication of the American Association for the Advancement of Science.

Société de Chimie Biologique, Bulletin: Biochemistry, in French, French authors.

Société de Biologie, Comptes Rendus: General biology, especially experimental, in French; French and other Latin authors, short papers.

Society for Experimental Biology and Medicine, Proceedings: Medical biology, in English, American authors, short papers.

Zeitschrift für Vergleichende Physiologie: Comparative physiology, mostly in German.

Zeitschrift für Zellforschung und Mikroskopische Anatomie: Cell biology, histology, physiology; mostly in German.

part I
Metabolism

1 The nature of biological oxidations

The beginnings of our knowledge of metabolism go back to seventeenth century England. Here a group of men made a practice of gathering together to perform scientific experiments, and out of their gatherings grew the Royal Society of London, the oldest existing scientific society with a continuous history. These men, and notably Robert Hooke, Robert Boyle, and John Mayow, were interested in gases. In antiquity and in the Middle Ages the universe was believed to be made up of four elements—earth, air, fire, and water. But in the early seventeenth century it became clear that there are several kinds of "air" with distinct properties, and the word *gas* was introduced to distinguish these various kinds of air. The English scientists studied the behavior of gases with the aid of the air pump invented by Hooke, under increased and reduced pressure, and from these studies emerged Boyle's law relating the pressure and the volume of a gas. They were also interested in the role of gases in animal respiration and in combustion. Animals were enclosed in chambers from which the air was then pumped out, or in which a candle was burning. In either chamber, the animal died. These observations led to the conclusion that there is some component of the air which is essential to both life and combustion.

Over a century later, these experiments were repeated and expanded by others, but the accumulated knowledge of the intervening period made possible a more complete understanding of the results. Through the work of Joseph Priestley and Antoine Lavoisier, it became clear that air is a mixture of two

9

gases at least, and that one of these is essential for life and combustion, while the other will not support either process. Lavoisier made the major contribution by recognizing that oxygen, which Priestley had first prepared, is an element in that it cannot be further broken down to simpler substances. He recognized also that in reactions involving oxygen, which we now call oxidations, the oxygen combines with the substance oxidized to form a compound. If the substances contain carbon, the product is now known to be carbon dioxide. Lavoisier also carried out experiments with animals, showing that in their metabolism they use oxygen and liberate carbon dioxide and water, and develop heat, just as does combustion of wood, coal, or a candle. His demonstration that heat is liberated in combustion or respiration, and liberated in direct proportion to the amount of oxygen consumed, utilized

the ice calorimeter, in which the chamber containing the animal, or in which the combustion is taking place, is enclosed in ice, and the heat produced is measured by measuring the amount of ice melted in a given time (Figure 1.1).

The Fuel: Carbohydrates, Proteins, and Lipids

Lavoisier did not know the nature of the substances burned in animal metabolism. He guessed that the fuel was a "hydrocarbonous fluid." The final establishment of our present concepts was the work of a long series of biochemical studies which we cannot discuss here. These studies led to classification of foodstuffs and of such body constituents as carbohydrates, proteins, and lipids and to proof of the composition and, in many cases, the structure of each of these constituents.

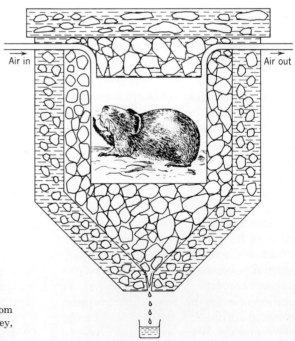

Fig. 1.1 Lavoisier's ice calorimeter (From Kleiber, M., 1961, *The Fire of Life,* Wiley, New York.)

Carbohydrates

Carbohydrates are compounds of carbon, hydrogen, and oxygen, in which the proportions of hydrogen to oxygen are the same as in water (2:1). The basic units of the carbohydrate molecule are known as monosaccharides (Figure 1.2), and glucose is the most important of these. It has the crude formula $C_6H_{12}O_6$, and its normal structure is that of a 6-membered ring involving 5 of the carbon atoms and 1 oxygen, as shown in the diagram. In all the monosaccharides each carbon atom typically has 1 H and 1 OH group attached, and the individual compounds differ in the pattern of arrangement of these groups, as to whether they project above or below the plane of the ring. In addition to the 6-carbon sugars—hexoses—there are sugars with 3, 4, 5, and 7 carbon atoms; there are also hexoses such as fructose in which the ring has only 5 members.

The monosaccharides can be linked together by specific enzyme systems into higher polymers (Figure 1.3). The process involves removal of the elements of water, H from one monosaccharide unit and OH from the other, to form a C—O bond, usually in the 1,4′, or 1,6′ positions. The reaction is not a simple dehydration but involves phosphorylated intermediates. This synthesis is endergonic and requires coupling with an energy-donating reaction. Among the common disaccharides are maltose, sucrose, and galactose. Addition of successive glucose units to maltose forms a chain which is the basis for the most common animal polysaccharide, glycogen. Glycogen consists of relatively short chains of α-1,6′ linkages with frequent branchings due to 1,4′ linkages. Starch, the common plant polysaccharide, is similarly constructed but with longer chains and fewer branches. The "molecules" of these polysaccharides are of indefinite size, since units are continually added to or split off from a central core in the course of cellular activities. In recent years it has become evident that a large class of polysaccharides, known as mucopolysaccharides because they were first discovered as constituents of mucus, are of considerable physiological importance; these substances generally contain two or three different monosaccharide units and usually nitrogen and sulfate groups as well, and the structure is known for only a few of them. The oxidation of 1 gram of carbohydrate as fuel liberates 3.8 to 4.1 kilogram calories (kcal) of energy.

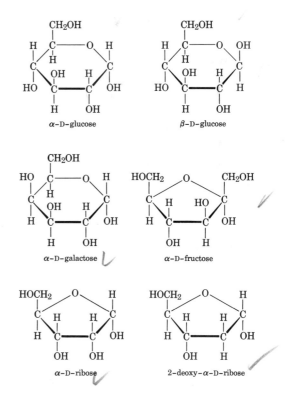

Fig. 1.2   Structure of monosaccharides.

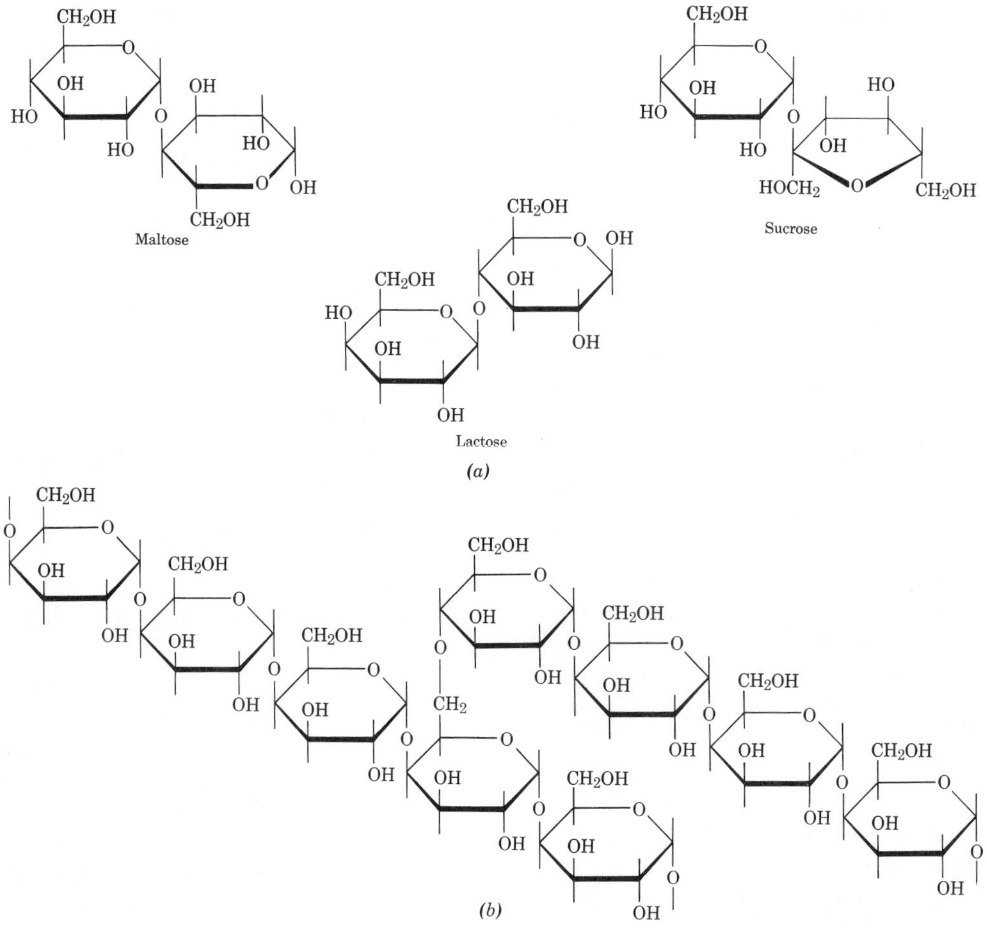

Fig. 1.3 Structure of disaccharides and polysaccharides. (*a*) The disaccharides maltose, sucrose, and lactose. (*b*) A portion of the chain of starch or glycogen.

The kilogram calorie is 4.184 abs. joules, or approximately the amount of heat needed to raise the temperature of 1000 grams of water 1°C.

Proteins

Proteins are compounds of carbon, hydrogen, oxygen, nitrogen, and sulfur, with in some cases other elements. The basic structural units in the protein molecule are the α-amino acids, of which more than twenty are known to occur naturally as components of proteins (Figures 1.4, 1.5). The amino acids are linked together in the protein molecule in chains; each amino acid in the chain is linked to the next by a peptide bond, a covalent bond formed synthetically by elimination of —H from the amino group of one amino acid and —OH from the carboxyl group of the next. Again the synthetic process is complex, endergonic, and must be coupled with an exergonic process. The peptide chains are

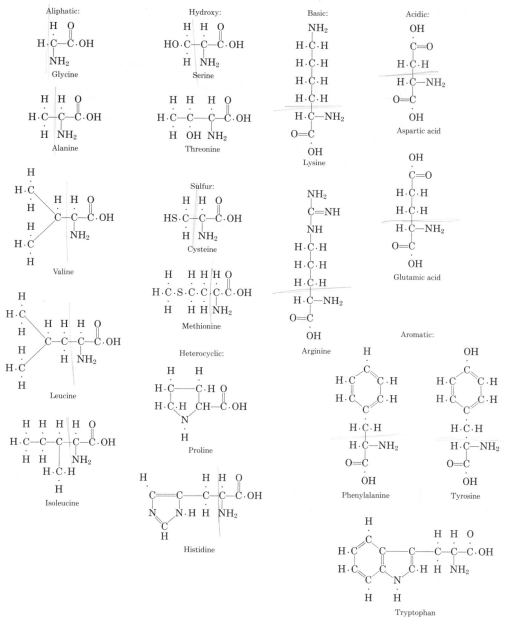

Fig. 1.4 Amino acids.

twisted into a spiral by formation of secondary bonds known as hydrogen bonds between the —C=O and —N—H groups of the peptide bonds. The individual spirals may be held together in groups, or further twisted on them-selves, by salt bonds between the terminal carboxyl groups of dicar-boxylic amino acids such as aspartic and glutamic, and the amino groups of diamino acids such as arginine and lysine, or by covalent bonds of the

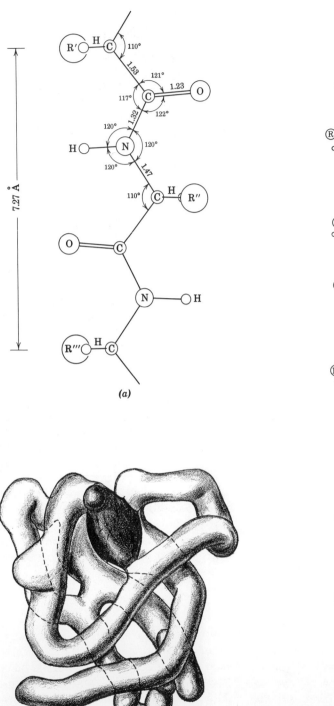

(a)

(c)

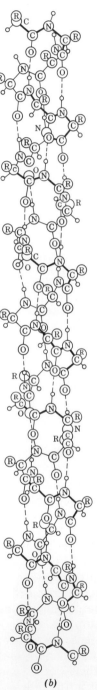

(b)

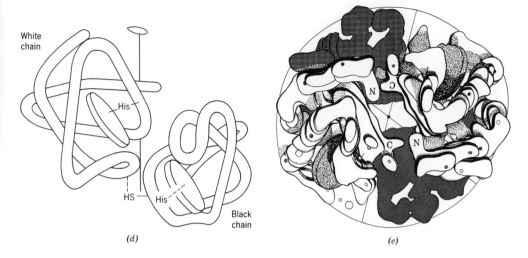

White
chain

His

HS — His

Black
chain

(d)

N

C

N

(e)

Fig. 1.5 The structure of proteins. (*a*) The peptide bond, showing dimensions and angles. (From Pauling, Corey and Branson, 1951, *Proc. Nat. Acad. Sci.* **37** 205). (*b*) The α-helix structure, with 3.7 amino acid residues per turn of the spiral (*ibid.*). (*c*) A model of the myoglobin molecule; the dark portion at the top represents the heme group. (From Kendrew et al., 1960, *Nature* **185** 426). (*d*) Outline drawing of two component chains in the hemoglobin molecule; the terms "white" and "black" are used merely to identify the chains, which are shown in a three-dimensional model in (*e*). (From Perutz, M. F. et al., 1960, *Nature* **185** 420.)

—S—S— type formed by dehydrogenation of the —SH groups of cysteine. Typical proteins may have molecular weights of the order of 50,000 to 100,000 and contain large numbers of amino acid residues in each molecule. The possibilities of structural complexity are therefore enormous.

This complexity is of particular significance in relation to enzyme action and to the specific protein interactions involved in immunity to disease and related phenomena. The specificity in both cases is clearly related to a complex protein structure which, in some critical portion of the molecule, exactly matches, in its configuration, the configuration of the substance on which the enzyme acts, or the foreign protein with which the antibody reacts. The specificity of structure is quite readily lost in the process of denatura-

tion. Heating of protein solutions, treatment with dehydrating agents such as alcohol or acetone, or exposure to ultraviolet light will rupture the hydrogen bonds which hold the molecule in its specific α-helix configuration and hence destroy its chemical specificity, though the total composition remains unchanged. The oxidation of 1 gram of protein as fuel liberates between 3.1 and 4.4 kcal of energy.

Lipids

Lipids comprise a rather heterogeneous group of compounds characterized by solubility in nonpolar solvents such as ether, alcohol, and chloroform. Most lipids are either esters, alcohols, or compounds derived from these, and they contain carbon, hydrogen, oxygen, and often other elements such as

Saturated Acids:

$$CH_3-CH_2-CH_2-CH_2-CH_2-CH_2-CH_2-CH_2-CH_2-CH_2-CH_2-CH_2-CH_2-COOH$$

$$C_{13}H_{27}-COOH$$

Myristic acid

$$CH_3-CH_2-CH_2-CH_2-CH_2-CH_2-CH_2-CH_2-CH_2-CH_2-CH_2-CH_2-CH_2-CH_2-COOH$$

$$C_{15}H_{31}-COOH$$

Palmitic acid

$$CH_3-CH_2-CH_2-CH_2-CH_2-CH_2-CH_2-CH_2-CH_2-CH_2-CH_2-CH_2-CH_2-CH_2-CH_2-CH_2-COOH$$

$$C_{17}H_{35}-COOH$$

Stearic acid

Unsaturated Acids:

$$CH_3-CH_2-CH_2-CH_2-CH_2-CH_2-CH_2-CH_2-CH=CH-CH_2-CH_2-CH_2-CH_2-CH_2-CH_2-CH_2-COOH$$

$$C_{17}H_{33}-COOH$$

Oleic acid; 9-octadecenoic acid

$$CH_3-CH_2-CH_2-CH_2-CH_2-CH_2-CH_2-CH_2-CH=CH-CH_2-CH=CH-CH_2-CH_2-CH_2-CH_2-COOH$$

$$C_{17}H_{31}-COOH$$

Linoleic acid; 9,12-octadecadienoic acid

$$CH_3-CH_2-CH_2-CH_2-CH_2-CH_2-CH_2-CH_2-CH=CH-CH_2-CH=CH-CH_2-CH=CH-CH_2-COOH$$

$$C_{17}H_{29}-COOH$$

Linolenic acid; 9,12,15-octadecatrienoic acid

$$CH_3-CH_2-CH_2-CH_2-CH=CH-CH_2-CH=CH-CH_2-CH=CH-CH_2-CH=CH-CH_2-CH_2-CH_2-CH_2-COOH$$

$$C_{19}H_{31}-COOH$$

Arachidonic acid; 5,8,11,14-eicosatetraenoic acid

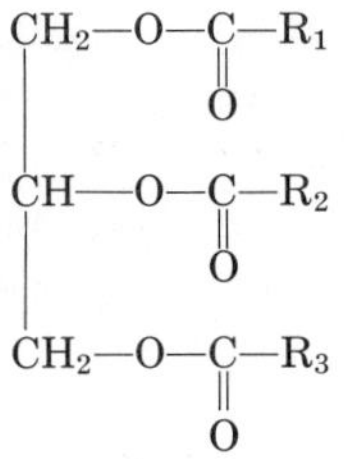

$$CH_2-O-\underset{\underset{O}{\|}}{C}-R_1$$

$$CH-O-\underset{\underset{O}{\|}}{C}-R_2$$

$$CH_2-O-\underset{\underset{O}{\|}}{C}-R_3$$

(b)

Fig. 1.6 Structure of lipids. (a) Common fatty acids. (b) A triglyceride. (c) Phosphatides.

phosphorus and nitrogen; the proportion of carbon and hydrogen to oxygen is generally much higher than in carbohydrates. The most important lipids used as fuel in biological oxidations are the fats, which occur as storage forms of energy in the vertebrates, insects, and some other animals. These compounds are esters of three molecules of long-chain organic acids (fatty acids with an even number, usually 14 to 22, of carbon atoms in

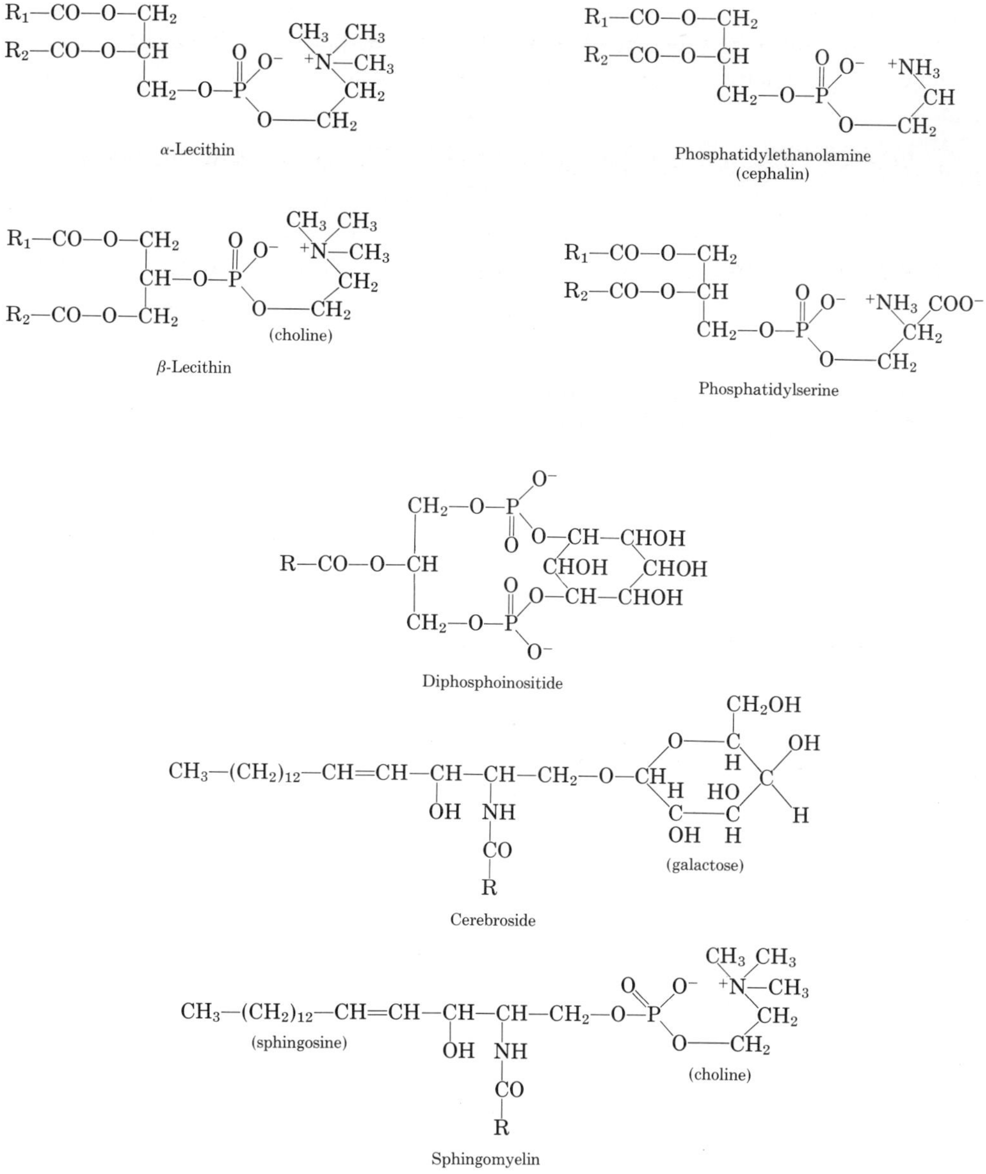

α-Lecithin

Phosphatidylethanolamine
(cephalin)

β-Lecithin

(choline)

Phosphatidylserine

Diphosphoinositide

(galactose)

Cerebroside

(sphingosine)

(choline)

Sphingomyelin

(c)

the chain) with the trihydric alcohol glycerol (Figure 1.6).

Cells normally contain a considerable proportion of phospholipids (phosphatides). These compounds are also glycerides with, typically, one fatty acid replaced by phosphoric acid, which is also combined with a nitrogenous base as in lecithin. Other phosphatides differ more markedly from the triglyceride pattern. Their structure is still under investigation in some cases. A third important group of lipids is the steroids, a group of alcohols with a phenanthrene ring structure. These substances occur as parts of the cell structure, and also in modified form have important effects at very low concentrations as hormones. The oxidation of 1 gram of fat, as fuel, liberates 8.4 to 9 kcal of energy.

Nucleic Acids

While we are discussing chemical structure, we must note another group of compounds, quantitatively less important than the foregoing but of great significance in cellular processes. These are the nucleic acids and their relatives and derivatives. The nucleic acids themselves are substances of high and usually indefinite molecular weight. It was at first considered that they are to be found only in cell nuclei, hence the name. They are now known to be present in both nucleus and cytoplasm. There are two general types of nucleic acids, known as ribonucleic acid or RNA and deoxyribonucleic acid or DNA. On hydrolysis both yield phosphoric acid, a pentose sugar, and several nitrogenous bases. In the case of RNA, the sugar is ribose; in DNA it is deoxyribose. For RNA the nitrogenous bases are adenine, guanine, cytosine, and uracil. In DNA they are adenine, guanine, cytosine, and thymine.

Milder acid hydrolysis of nucleic acids, or enzymatic hydrolysis by suitable enzymes, yields nucleotides (Figure 1.7). These are compounds of a nitrogenous base, a sugar, and phosphoric acid, and it is generally agreed that the nucleotide forms the basic structural unit of the nucleic acid molecule. The model of DNA proposed by Watson and Crick is shown in Figure 1.8. It consists of a double spiral of deoxynucleotides. The spiral is made of a chain of alternating phosphate and deoxyribose units in continuous 3,5' linkages. Projecting toward the axis of the spiral are the nitrogenous bases which form hydrogen bonds between the $-NH_2$ group of adenine and the $-OH$ of thymine, or the $-NH_2$ group of cytosine and the $-OH$ group of guanine. These hydrogen bonds hold the spirals together. The four nucleotides may occur in one spiral in any order, but the order in the other spiral is then determined as a mirror image of the first, if the two spirals are to be held together by the bonds as indicated.

Nucleotides, including some not found in nucleic acid molecules, occur free in cells or combined loosely or tightly with proteins. The most important of these nucleotides are shown in Figure 1.7 along with the related nucleosides (nitrogenous base plus sugar) and nitrogenous bases. The nucleotides, as we shall see, play an extremely important part in biological oxidations and in energy transfer in cells.

Combustion of the Fuel

The final demonstration that the animal organism uses protein, lipid, and carbohydrate as "fuel" came near the end of the last century. At this time, first in Germany and then in the United States, elaborate calorimeters, much more accurate than the ice calorimeter of Lavoisier, were constructed, and studies were made of the production of heat by animals and men. With the information thus obtained, and with information on the amount of heat produced by combustion of the pure compounds outside

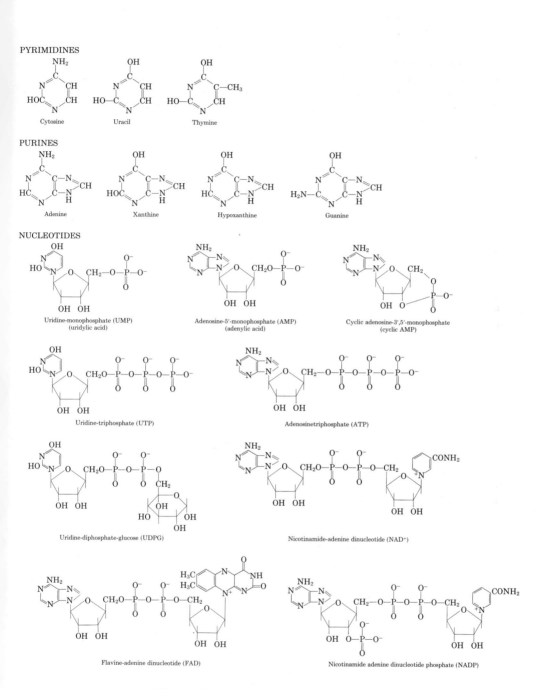

Fig. 1.7 Pyrimidines, purines, and nucleotides.

Guanine   Cytosine

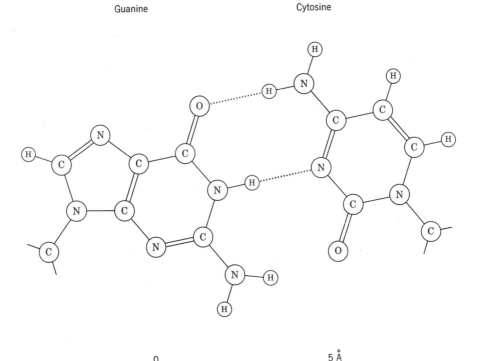

0   5 Å

(a)

Fig. 1.8 Deoxyribonucleic acid (DNA). (a) Hydrogen bonding between the molecules of guanine and cytosine; such bonds are thought to hold the nucleotide chain of DNA in its double spiral form.

the body, measurements of the oxygen consumption, carbon dioxide production, and nitrogen excretion permitted computation of the amounts of each type of fuel burned during any period of measurement. From such studies it became clear that the animal organism may use any of the three types of substance—carbohydrate, protein, or lipid—and normally uses all three. The relative proportions of the three used depend upon the conditions of nutrition and activity, and to some extent on the type of animal. Thus some animals, under conditions of a brief fast, utilize carbohydrate predomi-

nantly, conserving lipid for a short time and protein for a longer time; other kinds of animals may use all three components, or even use protein, and conserve lipid and carbohydrate.

In Lavoisier's study the question arose as to the site of the "combustion." He guessed that it might take place in the lungs, since the blood was known to change color during its passage through the lungs. This could be disproved with relative ease by showing that the blood leaving the lungs of a mammal is somewhat cooler than that which enters the lungs; the hypothesis of combustion in the lungs

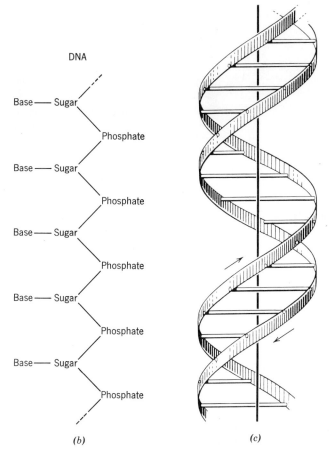

DNA

Base —— Sugar

Phosphate

Base —— Sugar

Phosphate

Base —— Sugar

Phosphate

Base —— Sugar

Phosphate

Base —— Sugar

Phosphate

(b)

(c)

(*b*) The arrangement of nucleotides in a single strand of DNA. (*c*) A diagram of the double helix, made up of two strands of DNA held together by hydrogen bonds. The arrows indicate that the order of nitrogenous bases in one strand is the inverse of that in the other strand. The ribbons represent the sugar-phosphate chains, and the horizontal rods represent the pairs of bases; the vertical line marks the axis of the fiber. (From Watson and Crick, 1953, *Nature* **171** 965)

predicts the reverse. For a long time it was thought that the combustion occurred in the blood as it flowed through the tissues and exhibited a color change the reverse of that in the lungs. There was no real evidence for this site, and the Italian biologist Spallanzani, early in the nineteenth century, showed that isolated tissues of a great variety of animals, including invertebrates which have no red blood, consume oxygen and produce carbon dioxide in the same way as do the intact animals. These observations were ignored for many years, however, until the blood-combustion hypothesis was disproved by demonstrating that the blood itself does not consume much oxygen. About 1850 it became generally accepted that the oxidations of animal metabolism actually take place in the cells of the body.

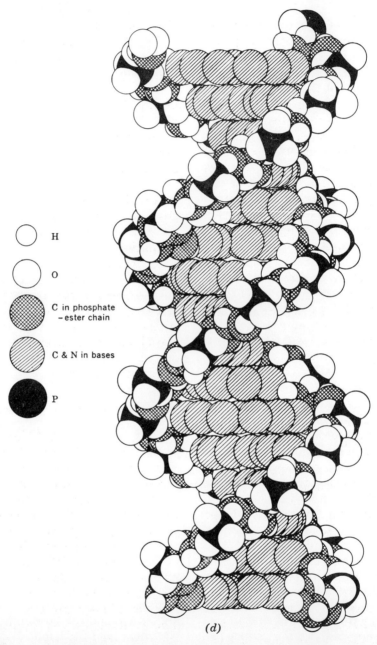

H

O

C in phosphate
– ester chain

C & N in bases

P

(d)

(d) Drawing of a model of DNA, to show the relative positions of the constituent atoms.
(From Feughelman et al., 1955, *Nature* **175** 834.)

The Agents of Oxidation: Enzymes

The nature of the oxidations remained puzzling until the last few decades. Clearly there was no ordinary "burning," with a flame and smoke, as some of the early scientists had almost believed. In the late nineteenth century the discovery was made that "ferments," the (at that time) mysterious constituents of cells responsible for the chemical changes that are uniquely characteristic of life, could be separated from cells and retain their activities. This discovery led almost at once to the suggestion that the cellular combustion is in fact brought about by ferments, or enzymes as they later came to be called in English. The concept of an enzyme (the German language still uses the older term *Ferment*) grew first out of studies of alcoholic fermentation and of digestion. Fermentation has been practiced as a household and industrial art since prehistoric times, and there has been a general belief that some sort of vital principle of ferment is involved in the process. The French chemist and microbiologist Louis Pasteur proved that a living organism (yeast) is responsible for fermentation, and he held the opinion that the intact cell is essential for this process. More or less by accident, the brothers Buchner, in Germany, discovered that crushed yeast cells could be filtered in such a way that the ferment passed through the filter into a cell-free filtrate; the resulting yeast extract was not living, but it could carry on fermentation. The active agents in such extracts, and the similar agents which can be found in the digestive secretions of animals, came to be called enzymes (from Greek, in yeast), and the work of several generations of biochemists

has been devoted to the clarification of the nature and mode of action of these substances.

This clarification is still not complete, but we have a good working knowledge of enzymes, and a relatively large number of these substances have been isolated in crystalline and hence probably chemically pure form. From the beginning it was clear that enzymes are catalysts. A catalyst, to the chemist, is an agent which can alter, usually increasing, the rate of a reaction without itself being permanently changed. Thus a small amount of a catalyst can result in the rapid transformation of a large amount of material in a chemical reaction. In fermentation, for example, a small amount of yeast extract containing the fermentation enzymes is able to bring about the transformation of a large amount of carbohydrate to alcohol and carbon dioxide, while the enzymes remain essentially unchanged.

The Mechanism of Enzyme Action

Every enzyme which has been obtained in crystalline form has proved on analysis to be a protein. Since the properties of the enzymes which have not yet been isolated are in general the same as those of the purified enzymes, we now feel quite safe in concluding that all enzymes are proteins. We have already noted briefly that proteins have large molecules with a complex structure, and this is important to the function of many proteins as enzymes. The available evidence indicates that enzymes act by forming a compound (or complex) with the substances on which they act (their substrates). The evidence for this is indirect but convincing. In general, when abundant substrate is present, the rate of an

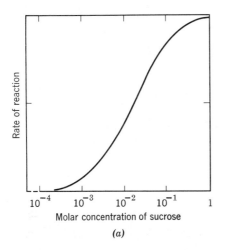

Molar concentration of sucrose

(a)

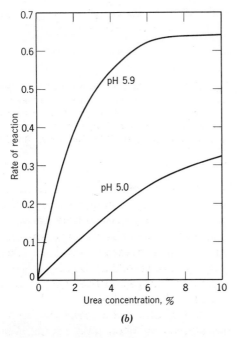

Urea concentration, %

(b)

Fig. 1.9 The relation of substrate concentration to reaction rate in enzyme catalyzed reactions. (*a*) Hydrolysis of sucrose by invertase (sucrase). (From Michaelis and Menten, 1913, *Biochem. Zeitschr.* **49** 333). (*b*) Hydrolysis of urea by crystalline urease. (From Howell and Sumner, 1934, *J. Biol. Chem.* **104** 619.)

enzyme-catalyzed reaction is proportional to the concentration of the enzyme. If the substrate is present in small concentrations, however, with abundant enzyme, the rate of the reaction is proportional to the substrate concentration up to a point beyond which no further increase in rate can be produced by increasing substrate concentration (Figure 1.9). Michaelis and Menten first studied this relation in invertase or sucrase, the enzyme which hydrolyzes the disaccharide sucrose (cane sugar) to its constituent monosaccharides, glucose and fructose. They proposed that the enzyme (E) acts by combining with the sucrose (S) to form a compound (ES). This compound then breaks down into the unchanged enzyme, glucose (G) and fructose (F):

$$E + S \rightleftharpoons ES$$
$$ES + H_2O \longrightarrow E + F + G$$

On the basis of this postulated mechanism, they derived equations for the relations between substrate concentration, enzyme concentration, and the rate of the reaction, and showed by experiments that the equations correctly describe the observed relations. Similar studies have since been made with many enzymes, with comparable results.

The second sort of evidence for this mechanism of action comes from studies of enzyme inhibition. The action of many enzymes is inhibited by the presence of substances which are chemically similar to, but not identical with, the substrate of the enzyme. A classical example is the enzyme acetylcholinesterase, which hydrolyzes the ester acetylcholine to form acetic acid and choline. This enzyme is inhibited by a number of compounds closely related in structure to acetylcholine, and the inhibition is competitive, in that the amount of inhibition depends on the ratio between the concentrations of acetylcholine and the inhibitor. The effectiveness of the inhibitor can be directly related to its chemical structure (Figure 1.10). Acetylcholine carries a positive charge on its molecule because of the quaternary ammonium group. A great variety of other positively charged ions, including quaternary ammonium and other ions, will inhibit cholinesterase. This suggests strongly that the enzyme has an "anionic site," or negatively charged region, which attracts the positively charged substrate to the surface of the enzyme molecule. The part of the molecule on which the enzyme acts, however, is the ester linkage, which is some distance from the positively charged part of the molecule. Other esters are found to act as inhibitors also, as are a variety of other compounds including chemical groupings with properties similar to the —C=O group of the ester linkage. The best inhibitors, however, are those which contain both a —C=O type group and a positive charge, and in the best of these the distance between the two significant parts of the molecule is nearly the same as that which separates the quaternary nitrogen atom from the ester —C=O group in acetylcholine.

The only reasonable conclusion from the very elaborate studies of the relation of structure to the inhibition of cholinesterase is that the enzyme has at its surface two specific binding sites. One of these sites holds the quaternary nitrogen, the other binds the ester group, and both are spaced at the exact distance between the two groups in the substrate molecule. In other words, the enzyme surface has a

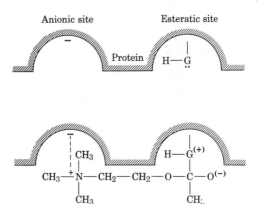

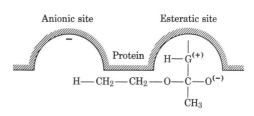

Fig. 1.10 Hypothetical representation of the active site of cholinesterase (top) of the complex with acetylcholine (center) and of the complex with a competitive inhibitor, in this case ethyl acetate. (Wilson, I. B., 1959, *Fed. Proc.* **18** 753.)

specific configuration that is complementary to the configuration of the substrate and serves to hold the substrate on the surface of the enzyme during the enzymatic reaction. The formation of secondary bonds between the ester linkage and the enzyme then weakens the ester linkage, so that the H and OH of a water molecule can be introduced. When this occurs, the bond between substrate and enzyme at the esteratic site is weakened, and the hydrolysis products diffuse away from the enzyme surface. Inhibition studies with other enzymes, though less complete, show that this picture of enzyme action is probably a generally valid one.

The Mechanism of Combustion: Enzymatic Oxidation

It is customary to classify enzymes on the basis of the nature of their actions. Thus we distinguish hydrolytic enzymes, which catalyze reactions of hydrolysis in which chemical bonds are ruptured by introduction of water, and oxidative enzymes, which catalyze oxidative reactions. In the early days of chemical study, oxidations were considered always to involve oxygen, but it soon became clear that the same sort of reaction may be brought about by any of a number of substances known as oxidizing agents, of which oxygen is only one. We assume here that the student is familiar with the chemical concept of oxidation as a reaction in which the valence of the oxidized element is increased, while that of the oxidizing agent is decreased. The concept of oxidation used by the organic chemist and the biological chemist is somewhat different, though it rests upon the same principle. Nearly all of the substances which we find in organisms are carbon compounds in which the valence of carbon is always 4 and does not change in oxidation. All oxidations involve the removal of electrons from the organic compound; the opposite process, reduction, is brought about by adding electrons. In organic oxidations the transfer of electrons is accompanied by transfer of hydrogen, and reduction involves an increase in the proportion of hydrogen to carbon, while oxidation involves a decrease in the hydrogen content of the molecule.

Oxidation of Succinic Acid

An important biological oxidation is that of succinic acid, which is converted upon oxidation to fumaric acid. The reaction is

$$C_4H_6O_4 \longrightarrow C_4H_4O_4 + 2(H)$$

The hydrogen symbol is written enclosed in parentheses because it is not liberated as such but must be transferred to a hydrogen acceptor. In cells the ultimate hydrogen acceptor (actually an electron acceptor) is one of the iron-containing proteins known as cytochromes. The oxidation of succinic acid can be carried out in a test tube using the enzyme succinic dehydrogenase and an artificial hydrogen acceptor, the dye methylene blue. The detailed reaction, with the structure of both succinic and fumaric acids indicated but with methylene blue symbolized simply as MB, is

$$
\begin{array}{c}
\text{COOH} \\
| \\
\text{CH}_2 \\
| \\
\text{CH}_2 \\
| \\
\text{COOH}
\end{array}
+ \text{MB} \longrightarrow
\begin{array}{c}
\text{COOH} \\
| \\
\text{CH} \\
|| \\
\text{CH} \\
| \\
\text{COOH}
\end{array}
+ \text{MBH}_2
$$

Essentially, in this reaction, we have transferred two atoms of hydrogen from succinic acid to methylene blue, which when reduced becomes colorless. The succinic acid is said to be oxidized to fumaric acid because of the change in electron arrangements about the central carbon atom; we may diagram the change thus:

$$
\begin{array}{c}
\text{COOH} \\
\text{H:C:H} \\
\text{H:C:H} \\
\text{COOH}
\end{array}
\longrightarrow
\begin{array}{c}
\text{COOH} \\
\text{C:H} \\
\text{C:H} \\
\text{COOH}
\end{array}
+ 2(\text{H})
$$

with the dots representing electrons. The succinic acid has lost two electrons along with the two hydrogen nuclei (protons), and this loss of electrons we call oxidation.

Cytochrome

As this oxidation occurs in cells, the oxidation follows lines more comparable to those of inorganic oxidations. Cytochrome, the hydrogen acceptor, contains iron in the ferric state (valence 3). The cellular oxidation may be diagrammed thus, with oxidized (ferric) cytochrome represented as $Cyt\text{-}Fe^{3+}$ and reduced (ferrous) cytochrome represented as $Cyt\text{-}Fe^{2+}$:

$$C_4H_6O_4 + 2Cyt\text{-}Fe^{3+} \longrightarrow$$
$$C_4H_4O_4 + 2Cyt\text{-}Fe^{2+} + 2H^+$$

In this reaction, the hydrogen, instead of combining with the cytochrome, is set free as hydrogen ions, and the electrons are accepted by the cytochrome, thus reducing it from the ferric to the ferrous state. Oxidations of both the hydrogen-transfer and the electron-transfer type can occur in cells, depending on the nature of the hydrogen acceptor.

There are a number of substances known as cytochromes in cells. The importance of iron in biological oxidations was emphasized especially during the early part of the present century by the German biochemist Otto Warburg. Eventually the specific iron compounds were identified as the substances responsible for the reddish color of certain cells and tissues and were called cytochromes. Several of these have been isolated in pure form, and others are known by their characteristic absorption spectra to be distinct substances. They are usually designated alphabetically to distinguish them one from another; thus we have in animal respiration cytochromes a, a_3, b, c, and c_1. All of the cytochromes are proteins which contain a nonprotein portion known as the prosthetic group; the prosthetic group of cytochromes

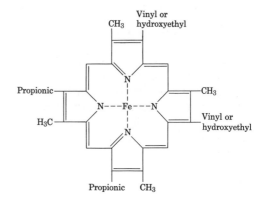

Fig. 1.11 Iron porphyrin structure. Protoporphyrin (hemoglobin) has vinyl radicals in the 2 and 4 positions; hematoporphyrin (cytochrome) has hydroxyethyl radicals in these positions.

b, c, and c_1 is a complex nitrogenous organic compound or heme containing one atom of iron per molecule, and known as protohemin (Figure 1.11). A similar substance is the prosthetic group of the blood protein hemoglobin, which is responsible for the transport of oxygen in vertebrate blood, but the mode of combination between heme and protein is different in the cytochromes from that in hemoglobin, and the proteins are quite different also. The prosthetic group of cytochrome a_3 differs in the nature of the side chains attached to the hemin nucleus.

Through careful studies of the properties of the cytochromes and of their behavior in cells during oxidation processes, it has been established that the cytochromes work in a chain or sequence. In the oxidation of succinic acid, cytochrome c_1 is first reduced; this in turn reduces cytochrome c, and the reduced cytochrome c reduces cytochrome a_3. Finally the reduced cytochrome a_3 is oxidized by oxygen, and the oxidation chain is complete. The reactions may be diagrammed as shown on the next page.

$$C_4H_6O_4 + 2Cyt\text{-}b\text{-}Fe^{3+} \longrightarrow$$
$$C_4H_4O_4 + 2Cyt\text{-}b\text{-}Fe^{2+} + 2H^+$$

$$Cyt\text{-}c_1\text{-}Fe^{2+} + Cyt\text{-}c\text{-}Fe^{3+} \longrightarrow$$
$$Cyt\text{-}c_1\text{-}Fe^{3+} + Cyt\text{-}c\text{-}Fe^{2+}$$

$$Cyt\text{-}c\text{-}Fe^{2+} + Cyt\text{-}a_3\text{-}Fe^{3+} \longrightarrow$$
$$Cyt\text{-}c\text{-}Fe^{3+} + Cyt\text{-}a_3\text{-}Fe^{2+}$$

$$2Cyt\text{-}a_3\text{-}Fe^{2+} + \tfrac{1}{2}O_2 + 2H^+ \longrightarrow$$
$$2Cyt\text{-}a_3\text{-}Fe^{3+} + H_2O$$

The overall reaction is then

$$C_4H_6O_4 + \tfrac{1}{2}O_2 \longrightarrow C_4H_4O_4 + H_2O$$

and the cytochromes have obviously served as catalysts, since they remain unchanged upon completion of the reaction. It is perfectly reasonable to call the cytochromes enzymes, since they are protein catalysts; they are distinguished from most enzymes, however, in that they are not as specific. They will catalyze a great variety of reactions involving many substrates, and in fact over 90% of cellular oxidations involve the cytochromes, but they will only act as catalysts in the presence of a specific oxidizing enzyme; the reaction given requires succinic dehydrogenase, for example, as well as the cytochromes.

The Electron Transport System

In the example of the oxidation of succinic acid, we may consider the series of cytochromes as a kind of biochemical channel along which electrons flow from the substrate (succinic acid) to the final electron acceptor or oxidizing agent (oxygen). The nature of this electron channel or electron transport system varies in different biological oxidations. Succinic dehydrogenase itself is a complex of cytochrome b and the dehydrogenase proper. The latter belongs to the class of enzymes known as flavoproteins, compounds of protein with a prosthetic group including a molecule of flavine combined in a nucleotide; the exact nature of the nucleotide in succinic dehydrogenase is unknown, but it is reduced by electrons derived from the substrate succinate and then oxidized in the reduction of cytochrome b. The malic dehydrogenase system, catalyzing the oxidation of malic acid to oxaloacetic acid, may be symbolized thus:

$$COOH\text{—}CHOH\text{—}CH_2 - COOH$$
(malic acid

$$+\,NAD^+ \longrightarrow COOH\text{—}CO\text{—}CH_2\text{—}COOH$$
+ nicotinamide-adenine dinucleotide $\longrightarrow$ oxaloacetic acid

$$+\,NADH + H^+$$
+ reduced nicotinamide-adenine dinucleotide)

$$NADH + H^+ + FP \longrightarrow NAD^+ + FPH_2$$
(reduced nicotinamide-adenine dinucleotide + flavoprotein $\longrightarrow$ nicotinamide-adenine dinucleotide + reduced flavoprotein

$$FPH_2 + 2Cyt\text{-}b\text{-}Fe^{3+} \longrightarrow$$
$$2Cyt\text{-}b\text{-}Fe^{2+} + FP + 2H^+$$

$$Cyt\text{-}b\text{-}Fe^{2+} + Cyt\text{-}c\text{-}Fe^{3+} \longrightarrow$$
$$Cyt\text{-}b\text{-}Fe^{3+} + Cyt\text{-}c\text{-}Fe^{2+}$$

$$Cyt\text{-}c\text{-}Fe^{2+} + Cyt\text{-}a_3\text{-}Fe^{3+} \longrightarrow$$
$$Cyt\text{-}c\text{-}Fe^{3+} + Cyt\text{-}a_3\text{-}Fe^{2+}$$

$$2Cyt\text{-}a_3\text{-}Fe^{2+} + \tfrac{1}{2}O_2 + 2H^+ \longrightarrow$$
$$2Cyt\text{-}a_3\text{-}Fe^{3+} + H_2O$$

In this scheme, the initial hydrogen acceptor, NAD^+ or nicotinamide-adenine dinucleotide, is called a coenzyme; unlike the heme of the cytochromes, NAD^+ is not firmly bound to the protein of the enzyme malic dehydrogenase, but is nevertheless essential to its action. NAD^+ was formerly known as coenzyme I, and then as diphosphopyridine nucleotide or DPN^+. The flavoprotein, symbolized by FP, is also an enzyme, known as NAD^+ dehydrogenase; the prosthetic group of FP is a flavine adenine dinucleotide.

Electrons are then transferred from the FP to cytochrome *b,* and the rest of the chain is as before. There is a second type of oxidation chain, quite similar to that shown above but involving nicotinamide-adenine dinucleotide phosphate or NADP, formerly known as triphosphopyridine nucleotide or TPN, and a different flavoprotein.

For us at present the important thing is that nearly all biological oxidations are carried out through these three systems, which may be diagrammed in simple form as shown in Figure 1.12.

Electrons derived from oxidation of a substrate by a NAD dehydrogenase pass to a flavoprotein (FP_D) and thence to cytochrome *b;* electrons from succinic dehydrogenase pass to another flavoprotein and thence to coenzyme ubiquinone or coenzyme Q. From this stage on, the pathway is the same for both systems. The significance of ADP and ATP in the system will be discussed later. There is a convergence of oxidative pathways in the cells of nearly all organisms on the cytochrome *c*-cytochrome a_3 pathway whereby electrons are finally transferred to oxygen to form water. The apparent complexity of the oxidative pathways is not meaningless but is closely related to the liberation of energy from oxidative reactions; we shall return to this aspect of the problem later (page 45).

Evidences of Biological Oxidation

We may outline here the experimental evidence on which the foregoing scheme is based, although we cannot give this evidence in detail. Essentially the method has involved the isolation of enzymes, or systems of enzymes, which are capable of carrying out a reaction. In the early days it was possible only to make a partial isolation, but most of the enzymes involved have now been highly purified, and in many cases isolated in crystalline form. The early work with succinic dehydrogenase, for example, showed that tissue extracts could be prepared which would oxidize succinic acid to fumaric acid in the presence of a hydrogen acceptor such as methylene blue. The reaction could be decomposed into two steps by first mixing the tissue extract with the substrate and methylene blue in a vacuum; the methylene blue would then be reduced, becoming colorless. Then, if air was admitted, the methylene blue would again be oxidized by the oxygen. Tissue extracts which would oxidize succinic acid without an artificial hydrogen acceptor, however, proved difficult to find. At the other end of the chain, Warburg first showed that iron is involved in the "activation" of oxygen by tissues. Spectroscopic evidence then showed that the cytochrome of the tissues is reduced in the absence of oxygen, and oxidized again when oxygen is admitted. These changes could be prevented by cyanide, which also inhibits nearly all of the oxygen consumption of tissues, and by carbon monoxide, which has the same effect. The carbon monoxide inhibition, however, could be reversed by light, and the wavelengths of light required to reverse the inhibition were those which are absorbed by the compound of cytochrome and carbon monoxide. When the cytochromes were purified, it was found that tissue extracts would oxidize succinic acid to fumaric in the presence of oxygen if cytochrome was added to the extracts; the reason for this is that, in preparing the extracts,

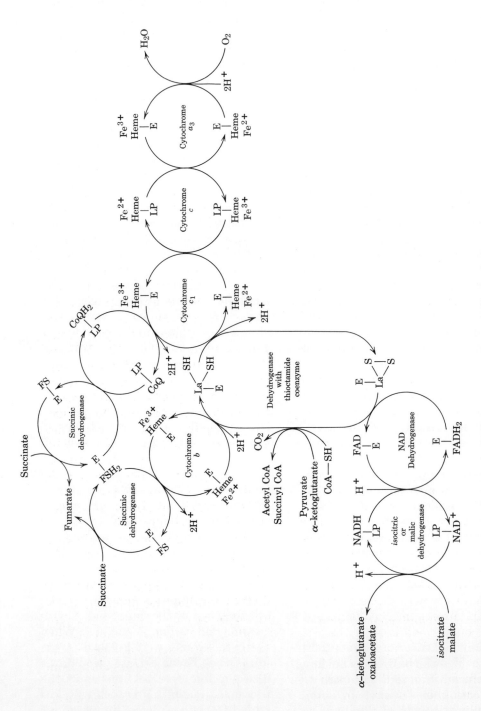

Fig. 1.12 Electron transport system. Abbreviations: CoQ = coenzyme Q, a quinone; NAD = nicotinamide adenine dinucleotide; E = enzyme; FAD = flavine-adenine-dinucleotide; FS = flavoprotein of succinic dehydrogenase system; La = lipoic acid, part of thioctamide; LP = lipoprotein.

the natural cytochrome of the tissues is diluted to such an extent that it can no longer act effectively. Finally it became possible to isolate from tissues the individual components of the succinic oxidase system and to show that the system could be reconstituted by mixing these components together again.

The role of the pyridine nucleotides (NAD, NADP) and of the flavoproteins was worked out in much the same way: purification of enzymes and attempts to reconstitute from purified components systems which would carry out the reactions observed in intact tissues or tissue extracts. As work proceeded on the dehydrogenases, it became clear that succinic dehydrogenase was exceptional in requiring only members of the cytochrome system as intermediates in oxidation. Most of the other dehydrogenases lose their activity very early in the course of attempts at purification. The crucial step here is dialysis. In purifying proteins it is first necessary to precipitate them from solution by some mild treatment which does not destroy their properties. The most commonly used method, especially in the beginning of such studies, was precipitation by concentrated salt solutions (salting out). If we add to most protein solutions an equal volume of a saturated solution of ammonium sulfate, or in more stubborn cases if we saturate the protein solution with this salt, the protein will be precipitated with little damage. The precipitate can then be redissolved in water, but a good deal of the salt comes along, and it is necessary to remove it. This can be done by putting the protein solution in a bag made of sausage casing or "cellophane" and suspending the bag in distilled water. The salt then diffuses out through the

pores of the bag, but the large protein molecules are retained in the bag. When this procedure is applied to most dehydrogenases, the remaining protein molecules are inactive as enzymes, although they survived the precipitation quite well and their physical properties are apparently unaltered. If we now mix the dialysate—that is, the solution outside the bag—with the protein solution, the enzymatic properties are restored. We must therefore conclude that something essential to the enzyme action has diffused out of the bag along with the salt, and this something essential was called a coenzyme.

It soon became clear that, although there are many dehydrogenases, there are only two dehydrogenase coenzymes, and attempts were then made to purify and identify the two. They proved to be NAD and NADP, and every dehydrogenase, with the exception of a few such as succinic dehydrogenase, is specific in two respects: it will act only on a single compound, and it requires a specific coenzyme. In general, we think that dehydrogenases act by combining both with their substrates and with their coenzymes. While they are thus combined into a triple complex, electrons are transferred from the substrate to the coenzyme, and the complex then breaks apart, yielding the oxidized substrate, the reduced coenzyme, and the unchanged enzyme (Figure 1.13). The coenzyme in this case differs from the prosthetic group of a cytochrome, for example, in that it does not remain combined permanently as a part of the enzyme but can readily separate from the latter.

In the early days of enzyme purification, a substance was found which was readily reduced and oxidized in

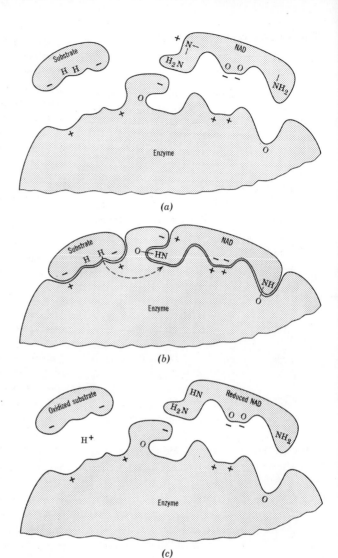

Fig. 1.13 Hypothetical diagram to show the action of a NAD-dehydrogenase. The surface of the enzyme is thought to have specific complementary structures fitting respectively the substrate and the coenzyme (a). The substrate and coenzyme become attached to the specific sites, and hydrogen and electrons are transferred from substrate to coenzyme (b). The oxidized substrate and reduced coenzyme now have a smaller affinity for the enzyme, and so separate from the specific sites (c).

tissues and tissue extracts but did not seem to have any particular specificity. When it was purified, it had a yellow color, and its behavior in tissues could be followed by observing the changes in the absorption spectrum as it was oxidized and reduced; in particular, it was reduced by tissue extracts and oxidized again by the cytochromes. For lack of a better name, it was called the "yellow enzyme." With increasing knowledge of the chemistry of this and related substances, it soon became clear that the prosthetic group of this enzyme was a flavine nucleotide and that other flavine nucleotides occur in tissues as prosthetic groups of oxidizing enzymes. Finally, when the relation of the nicotinamide coenzymes and the dehydrogenases became clear, it was possible to show that the transfer of electrons from NAD or NADP to cytochrome required a flavoprotein, different for each coenzyme.

The Tricarboxylic Acid Cycle

Succinate to Pyruvate

As the nature and mode of action of the oxidizing enzymes became clearer, it became possible to show that the reactions which they catalyze fell into definite patterns. The first such pattern was demonstrated by the Hungarian biochemist Szent-Györgyi, who later emigrated to the United States and now works in Woods Hole, Massachusetts. He showed that, in tissues and tissue extracts, there is a sequence of reactions starting with the dehydrogenation of succinic acid and proceeding as follows:

$$
\begin{array}{ccc}
\begin{array}{l} COOH \\ | \\ CH_2 \\ | \\ CH_2 \\ | \\ COOH \end{array} + \tfrac{1}{2}O_2 \longrightarrow
\begin{array}{l} COOH \\ | \\ CH \\ \| \\ CH \\ | \\ COOH \end{array} + H_2O
\end{array}
$$

succinic acid   fumaric acid

$$
\begin{array}{ccc}
\begin{array}{l} COOH \\ | \\ CH \\ \| \\ CH \\ | \\ COOH \end{array} + H_2O \longrightarrow
\begin{array}{l} COOH \\ | \\ CHOH \\ | \\ CH_2 \\ | \\ COOH \end{array}
\end{array}
$$

fumaric acid   malic acid

$$
\begin{array}{ccc}
\begin{array}{l} COOH \\ | \\ CHOH \\ | \\ CH_2 \\ | \\ COOH \end{array} + \tfrac{1}{2}O_2 \longrightarrow
\begin{array}{l} COOH \\ | \\ CO \\ | \\ CH_2 \\ | \\ COOH \end{array}
\end{array}
$$

malic acid   oxaloacetic acid

$$
\begin{array}{ccc}
\begin{array}{l} COOH \\ | \\ CO \\ | \\ CH_2 \\ | \\ COOH \end{array} \longrightarrow
\begin{array}{l} COOH \\ | \\ CO \\ | \\ CH_3 \end{array} + CO_2
\end{array}
$$

oxaloacetic acid   pyruvic acid

Thus we see that one molecule of succinic acid is converted to one molecule of pyruvic acid by a series of reactions involving, in sequence, oxidation (dehydrogenation), hydration, oxidation, and decarboxylation. We thus begin to see a pattern by which carbon compounds can be broken down stepwise in the tissues, forming eventually carbon dioxide and water. The compounds involved in these reactions, however, are not the ones we are primarily concerned with; the major fuels, as we have already seen, are carbohydrate, protein and lipid, not succinic acid.

The Intermediate Products of Oxidation

By the time the above sequence had been worked out, however, we had a good deal of information concerning at least the preliminary steps in metabolism of the basic fuels. Carbohydrates were known to be readily convertible—in the absence of oxygen—into lactic acid; we shall explore the details of this conversion in the next chapter. Lactic acid, in turn, can be converted to pyruvic acid by a widely distributed enzyme, lactic dehydrogenase:

$$
\begin{array}{l} COOH \\ | \\ CHOH \\ | \\ CH_3 \end{array} + NAD^+ \longrightarrow
$$

lactic acid

$$
\begin{array}{l} COOH \\ | \\ CO \\ | \\ CH_3 \end{array} + NADH + H^+
$$

pyruvic acid

The oxidation of fats was shown to follow a series of steps very similar to those in the succinic acid sequence; the fat is first hydrolyzed to fatty acid and glycerol, and the glycerol can be converted to pyruvic acid, as we shall see later. The fatty acid is oxidized by a process called β-oxidation:

$$R-CH_2-CH_2-CH_2-CH_2-COOH$$
$$\downarrow \quad \text{Dehydrogenation}$$
$$R-CH_2-CH_2-CH=CH-COOH$$
$$\downarrow \quad \text{Hydration}$$
$$R-CH_2-CH_2-CHOH-CH_2-COOH$$
$$\downarrow \quad \text{Dehydrogenation}$$
$$R-CH_2-CH_2-CO-CH_2-COOH$$
$$\downarrow \quad \text{Hydration}$$
$$R-CH_2-CH_2-COOH + CH_3COOH$$

The evidence for this process was indirect at first, and for some time was in dispute, since isolation of the enzymes involved proved difficult. We now know, however, that the sequence shown above is essentially correct. It is clear that the process can be repeated with the shortened chain, thus removing two carbons at a time until the entire chain is converted into 2-carbon units. As we shall see shortly, however, the 2-carbon end product is not in fact acetic acid, but a compound of acetic acid with a coenzyme known as coenzyme A.

For proteins the problem is more complex, since possible separate pathways for each of some 20 amino acids produced by protein hydrolysis must be considered. In most cases, however, the first step in oxidation is oxidative deamination:

$$R-\underset{\underset{NH_2}{|}}{CH}-COOH + \tfrac{1}{2}O_2 \longrightarrow$$

$$R-CO-COOH + NH_3$$

The keto acid ($R-CO-COOH$) produced in this process is then converted, in many cases, to one of three end products: pyruvic acid ($CH_3-CO-COOH$), oxaloacetic acid ($COOH-$ $CO-CH_2-COOH$), or α-ketoglutaric acid ($COOH-CH_2-CH_2-CO-COOH$). In a few cases a derivative of acetic acid is formed, and in a few others the amino acid is oxidized completely by a special set of oxidative enzymes. However, it is now clear that the major intermediate products in the breakdown of all the basic fuel substances in animals are acetic acid, pyruvic acid, oxaloacetic acid, and α-ketoglutaric acid. The basic problem of fuel oxidation then is the problem of oxidizing these four acids.

The Krebs Cycle

This problem was solved in its essentials by H. A. Krebs, a German biochemist who emigrated to England and now works there. He showed that these four acids, and a number of others, participate in a cyclical system of oxidation reactions, now known as the Krebs cycle in his honor. The details of this reactive system are given below:

(1) Oxidative decarboxylation of pyruvic acid: enzyme, pyruvic dehydrogenase; coenzymes; coenzyme A, thiamine pyrophosphate, lipoic acid, and NAD.

$$\underset{\text{pyruvic acid}}{\underset{\underset{COOH}{|}}{\overset{CH_3}{\underset{|}{CO}}}} + NAD^+ + CoA \longrightarrow$$

$$\underset{\text{acetyl-coenzyme A}}{\underset{\underset{CoA}{|}}{\overset{CH_3}{\underset{|}{CO}}}} + NADH + H^+ + CO_2$$

Coenzyme A is a complex substance which includes a sulfhydryl ($-SH$) group in its structure. In this reaction a link is formed by oxidation of the —SH group, with the H transferred to NAD and the S attaching to the acetyl radical. The details of this reaction will be discussed later.

(2) Condensation of acetyl-coenzyme A with oxaloacetic acid to form citric acid: enzyme, citrogenase.

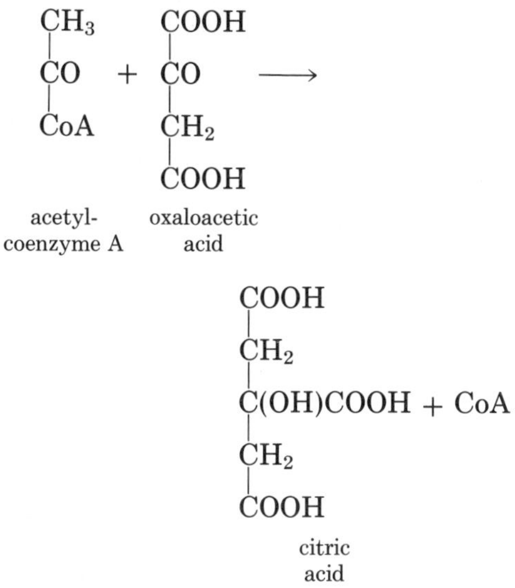

$$
\begin{array}{ccc}
CH_3 & & COOH \\
| & & | \\
CO & + & CO \\
| & & | \\
CoA & & CH_2 \\
& & | \\
& & COOH
\end{array} \longrightarrow
$$

acetyl-   oxaloacetic
coenzyme A   acid

$$
\begin{array}{c}
COOH \\
| \\
CH_2 \\
| \\
C(OH)COOH + CoA \\
| \\
CH_2 \\
| \\
COOH
\end{array}
$$

citric
acid

(3) Isomerization of citric acid to *isocitric* acid: enzyme, aconitase.

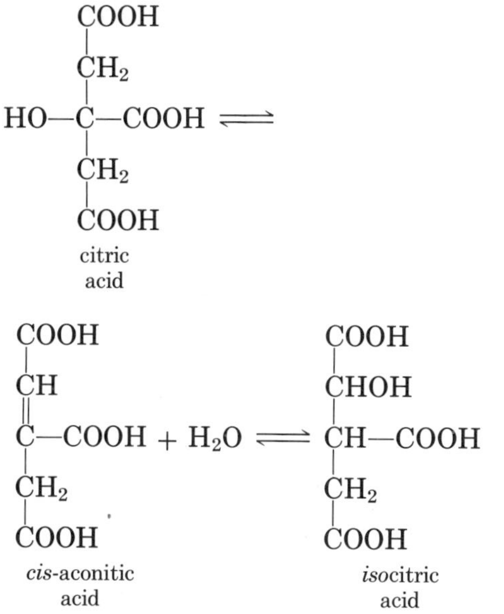

$$
\begin{array}{c}
COOH \\
| \\
CH_2 \\
| \\
HO-C-COOH \rightleftharpoons \\
| \\
CH_2 \\
| \\
COOH
\end{array}
$$

citric
acid

$$
\begin{array}{ccc}
COOH & & COOH \\
| & & | \\
CH & & CHOH \\
\| & & | \\
C-COOH + H_2O & \rightleftharpoons & CH-COOH \\
| & & | \\
CH_2 & & CH_2 \\
| & & | \\
COOH & & COOH
\end{array}
$$

cis-aconitic   *isocitric*
acid   acid

(4) Oxidation of isocitric acid to oxalosuccinic acid, and decarboxylation of oxalosuccinic acid: enzyme *isocitric* dehydrogenase; coenzyme NAD.

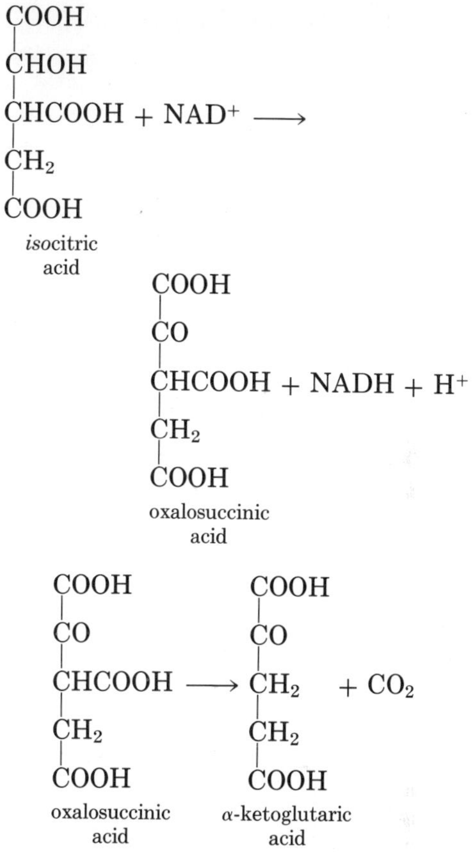

$$
\begin{array}{c}
COOH \\
| \\
CHOH \\
| \\
CHCOOH + NAD^+ \longrightarrow \\
| \\
CH_2 \\
| \\
COOH
\end{array}
$$

isocitric
acid

$$
\begin{array}{c}
COOH \\
| \\
CO \\
| \\
CHCOOH + NADH + H^+ \\
| \\
CH_2 \\
| \\
COOH
\end{array}
$$

oxalosuccinic
acid

$$
\begin{array}{ccc}
COOH & & COOH \\
| & & | \\
CO & & CO \\
| & & | \\
CHCOOH & \longrightarrow & CH_2 \quad + CO_2 \\
| & & | \\
CH_2 & & CH_2 \\
| & & | \\
COOH & & COOH
\end{array}
$$

oxalosuccinic   α-ketoglutaric
acid   acid

(5) Oxidative decarboxylation of α-ketoglutaric acid: enzyme, α-ketoglutaric acid dehydrogenase; coenzymes, NAD, coenzyme A, thiamin pyrophosphate, lipoic acid.

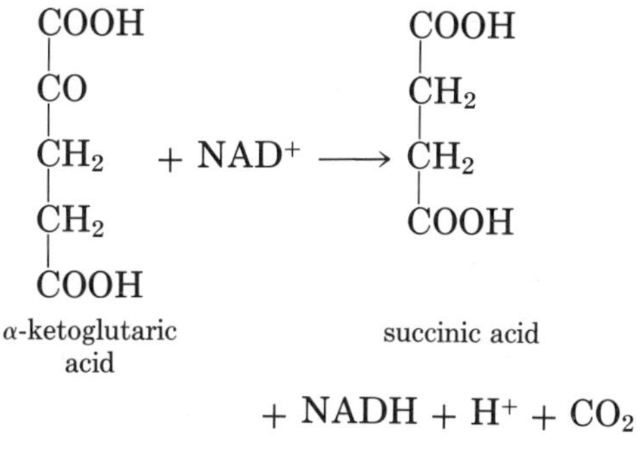

$$
\begin{array}{ccc}
COOH & & COOH \\
| & & | \\
CO & & CH_2 \\
| & & | \\
CH_2 & + NAD^+ \longrightarrow & CH_2 \\
| & & | \\
CH_2 & & COOH \\
| & & \\
COOH & &
\end{array}
$$

α-ketoglutaric   succinic acid
acid

$$+ NADH + H^+ + CO_2$$

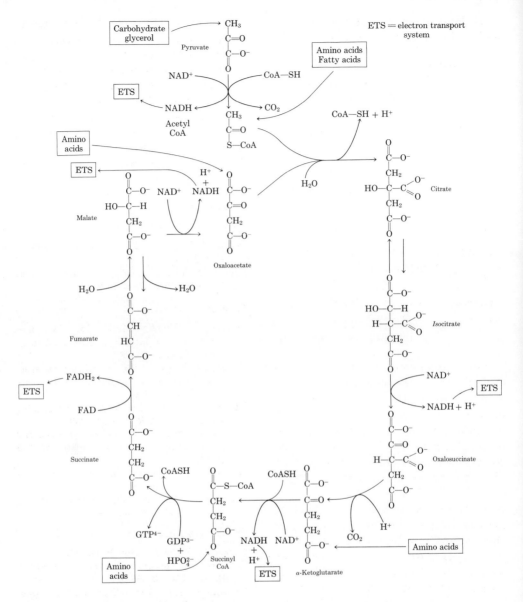

Fig. 1.14 The Krebs tricarboxylic acid cycle of oxidative reactions. ETS refers to the electron transport system, shown in Figure 1.12.

This reaction is also complex, and will be discussed more fully later.

(6) Oxidation of succinic acid to fumaric acid: enzyme, succinic dehydrogenase (FPs); coenzyme, coenzyme Q.

$$
\begin{array}{c}
\text{COOH} \\
| \\
\text{CH}_2 \\
| \\
\text{CH}_2 \\
| \\
\text{COOH}
\end{array}
+ \text{FP}_s \longrightarrow
\begin{array}{c}
\text{COOH} \\
| \\
\text{CH} \\
\| \\
\text{CH} \\
| \\
\text{COOH}
\end{array}
+ \text{FP}_s\text{H}_2
$$

succinic acid   fumaric acid

(7) Hydration of fumaric acid to malic acid: enzyme, fumarase.

$$\begin{array}{c} COOH \\ | \\ CH \\ \| \\ CH \\ | \\ COOH \end{array} \quad + H_2O \longrightarrow \quad \begin{array}{c} COOH \\ | \\ CHOH \\ | \\ CH_2 \\ | \\ COOH \end{array}$$

fumaric acid   malic acid

(8) Oxidation of malic acid to oxaloacetic acid: enzyme, malic dehydrogenase; coenzyme, NAD.

$$\begin{array}{c} COOH \\ | \\ CHOH \\ | \\ CH_2 \\ | \\ COOH \end{array} \quad + NAD^+ \longrightarrow \quad \begin{array}{c} COOH \\ | \\ CO \\ | \\ CH_2 \\ | \\ COOH \end{array}$$

malic acid   oxaloacetic acid

$$+ NADH + H^+$$

This sequence of reactions forms a cycle in which one molecule of pyruvic acid is completely oxidized, and the molecule of oxaloacetic acid which was introduced in reaction 2 is regenerated in reaction 8. Each of the reduced coenzymes is oxidized through the cytochrome chain as was outlined earlier. The details of the Krebs cycle reactions presented above are not of primary importance here as such, but they show how biological oxidations proceed (Figure 1.14). Moreover, as we have pointed out above, all of the major fuel substances are channeled into this cycle of reactions, which thus forms a final oxidative pathway. The entire pattern of relationships is diagrammed in the figure.

Hence we have come a long way from the analogy between combustion and respiration. Combustion is a violent process involving high temperatures and flame, with the liberation of the energy of the fuel entirely in the form of heat. The respiratory combus-tion goes on at normal body temperatures and is a complex process, but a very orderly one, in which the molecules of the fuel are broken down one step at a time. As we shall see in the next chapter, the importance of this elaborate stepwise process is that it permits a substantial fraction of the fuel's energy to be conserved in the form of chemical energy which is usable for biological work.

References

Chemistry of Carbohydrates

Meyer, K. H. 1943. The chemistry of glycogen. *Adv. Enzymol.* **3** 109–135.
Pigman. W. W. (ed.) 1957. *The Carbohydrates.* Academic Press, New York.

Chemistry of Proteins

Cerf, R., and Scheraga, H. A. 1952. Flow birefringence in solutions of macromolecules. *Chem. Rev.* **51** 185–261.
Hollaender, A. (ed.) 1956. Symposium on structure of enzymes and proteins. *J. Cell. Comp. Physiol.* **47** Suppl. I.
Ogston, A. G. 1947. The definition and meaning of pH. *Physiol. Rev.* **27** 228–239.
Pauling, L. 1955. The stochastic method and the structure of proteins. *Am. Scientist* **43** 285–297.
Scheraga, H. A. 1961. *Protein Structure.* Academic Press, New York.
Tuppy, H. 1959. Aminosäure-sequenzen in Proteinen. *Naturwiss.* **46** 35–43.

Chemistry of Lipids

Celmer, W. D., and Carter, H. E. 1952. Chemistry of phosphatides and cerebrosides. *Physiol. Rev.* **32** 167–196.
Dawson, R. M. C. 1957. The animal phospholipids. *Biol. Rev.* **32** 188–229.
Deuel, H. J. 1951–1957. *The Lipids* (3 vols.). Interscience, New York.

Chemistry of Nucleic Acids

Chargaff, E., and Davidson, J. N. (ed.) 1955–1960. *The Nucleic Acids* (3 vols.). Academic Press, New York.
Crick, F. H. C. 1954. Structure and function of DNA. *Discovery* **15** 12–17.
Peacocke, A. R. 1960. The structure and physical chemistry of nucleic acids and nucleoproteins. *Progr. Biophys.* **10** 56–113.

Enzymes

Boyer, P. D., Lardy, H., and Myrbäck, K. (eds.) 1959–1961. *The Enzymes* (2nd ed.) (5 vols.) Academic Press, New York.

Chance, B. 1952. The identification of enzyme-substrate compounds. *Mod. Trends. Physiol. Biochem.* 25–46.

Dixon, M. and Webb, E. C. 1958. *Enzymes.* Academic Press, New York.

Green, D. E. 1946. Biochemistry from the standpoint of enzymes. *Curr. Biochem. Res.* 149–164.

Huennekens, F. M. 1956. The role of nucleotides and coenzymes in enzymatic processes. *Curr. Biochem. Res. 1956.* 493–517.

King, H. K. 1961. Structure and function in proteins. *Sci. Prog.* 49 703–715.

Koshland, D. E. 1953. Stereochemistry and the mechanism of enzymatic reactions. *Biol. Rev.* 28 416–436.

Lehninger, A. L. 1950. Role of metal ions in enzyme systems. *Physiol. Rev.* 30 393–429.

McElroy, W. D., and H. B. Glass (eds.) 1954. *Mechanism of Enzyme Action.* Johns Hopkins Press, Baltimore, Md.

Theorell, H. 1956. Relations between prosthetic groups, coenzymes, and enzymes. *Curr. Biochem. Res. 1956* 275–307.

Williams, R. J. P. 1953. Metal ions in biological systems. *Biol. Rev.* 28 381–415.

Wilson, I. B. 1959. Molecular complementarity in antidotes for nerve gases. *Annals New York Acad. Sci.* 81 307–316.

Yudkin, W. H. 1953. Hydrolytic and phosphorolytic enzymes. *Biochem. Physiol. Nutr.* 2 231–284.

Oxidation, Enzymes

Barron, E. S. G. 1939. Cellular oxidation systems. *Physiol. Rev.* 19 184–239.

Barron, E. S. G. 1952. The mechanism of enzymatic oxidation. *Mod. Trends Physiol. Biochem.* 1–24.

Green, D. E. 1940. *Mechanisms of Biological Oxidations.* Univ. Press, Cambridge, England.

Horecker, B. L., and Kornberg, A. 1953. The respiratory enzymes. *Biochem. Physiol. Nutr.* 2 286–325.

King, H. K. 1960. The cytochromes. *Sci. Prog.* 48 695–709.

Mahler, H. R. 1956. Nature and function of metalloflavoproteins. *Adv. Enzymol.* 17 233–291.

Racker, E. 1955. Mechanism of action and properties of pyridine nucleotide-linked enzymes. *Physiol. Rev.* 35 1–56.

Theorell, H. 1957. The nature and mode of action of oxidation enzymes. *Experientia* 13 2–8.

Oxidation, Pathways

Dixon, M. 1949. *Multi-enzyme Systems.* Univ. Press, Cambridge, England.

Green, D. E. 1951. The cyclophorase complex of enzymes. *Biol. Rev.* 26 410–455.

Greenberg, D. M. (ed.) 1960–1961. *Metabolic Pathways* (2 vols.) Academic Press, New York.

Horecker, B. L. 1958. Le cycle des pentoses et sa signification physiologique. *Bull. Soc. Chim. Biol.* 40 555–578.

Krebs, H. A. 1947. Cyclic processes in living matter. *Enzymologia* 12 88–100.

Krebs, H. A. 1954. The tricarboxylic acid cycle. *Chem. Path. Metab.* 1 109–171.

Krebs, H. A. 1943. The intermediary stages in the biological oxidation of carbohydrate. *Adv. Enzymol.* 3 191–252.

Ochoa, S. 1954. Enzymic mechanisms in the citric acid cycle. *Adv. Enzymol.* 15 183–270.

Wood, H. G. 1955. Significance of alternate pathways in the metabolism of glucose. *Physiol. Rev.* 35 841–859.

2 Energy transformations in cells

In the previous chapter we stated that nearly all the major constituents of cells are converted by one process or another into simple organic acids which are then oxidized through the Krebs cycle. In this chapter we shall be concerned with the way in which the energy liberated in these processes is made available for cellular work. As an initial example we may examine the process known as glycolysis in which carbohydrates are converted to pyruvic acid. This process was worked out by the combined efforts of many biochemists working largely in Germany between 1930 and 1940. Because the major contributions were those of Embden and Meyerhof the process is often known as Embden-Meyerhof glycolysis.

Glycolysis

The basic substrates may be any of the common carbohydrates. We shall consider only glycogen, glucose, and fructose. Before these substances can enter into the reaction of glycolysis they must be activated, a process which involves esterification of one of the hydroxyl groups of the carbohydrate with phosphoric acid.

Activation

The activation reactions are:

(1) Phosphorolysis of glycogen: enzyme, phosphorylase.

$$(C_6H_{10}O_5)_n + HPO_4^{2-} \longrightarrow$$
glycogen   phosphate

$(C_6H_{10}O_5)_{n-1} +$

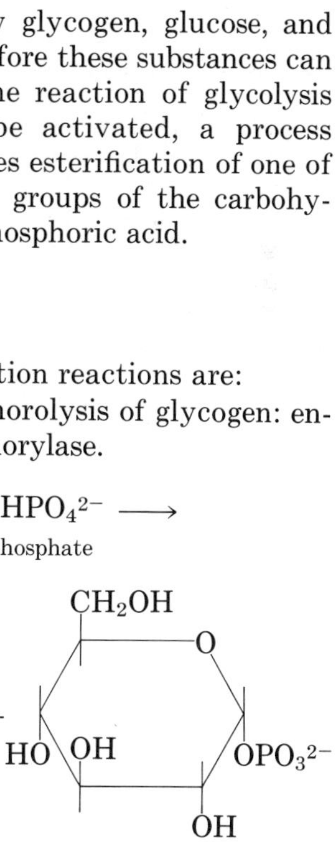

glycogen

glucose-1-phosphate

(2a) Phosphorylation of glucose: enzyme, glucokinase (hexokinase).

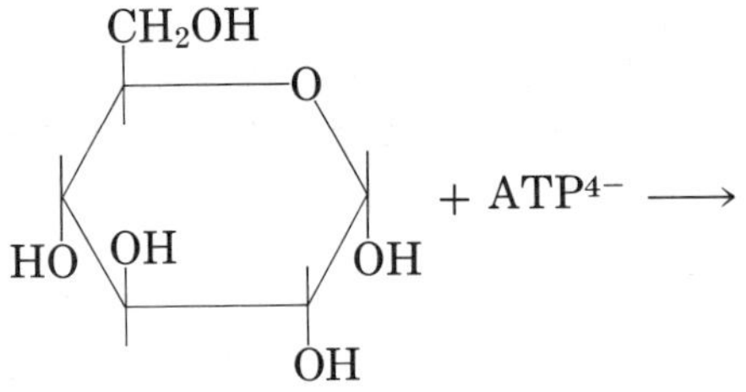

glucose · adenosine triphosphate

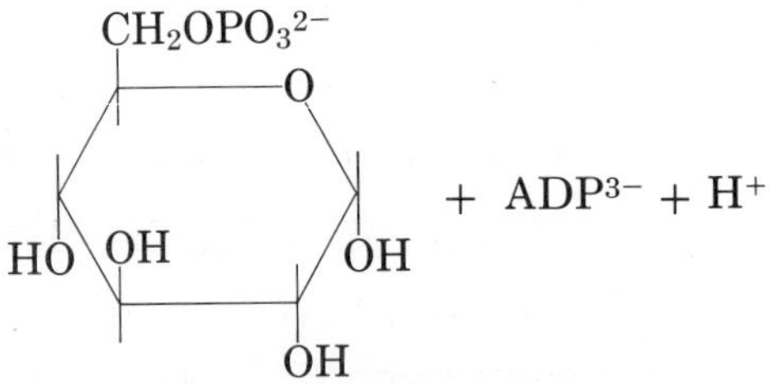

$+ ATP^{4-} \longrightarrow$

glucose-6-phosphate · adenosine diphosphate

$+ ADP^{3-} + H^+$

(2b) Rearrangement of glucose-1-phosphate: enzyme, phosphogluco-mutase.

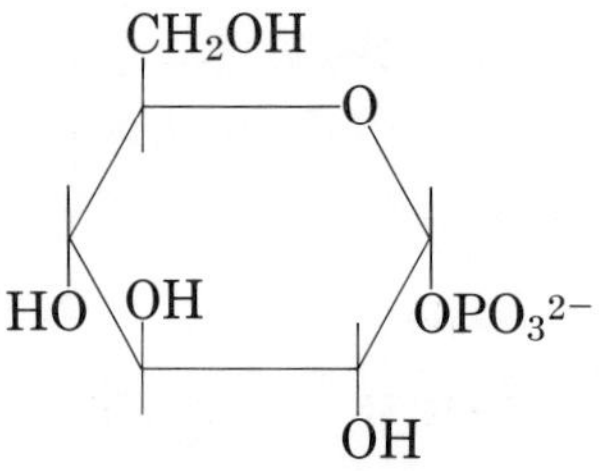

glucose-1-phosphate

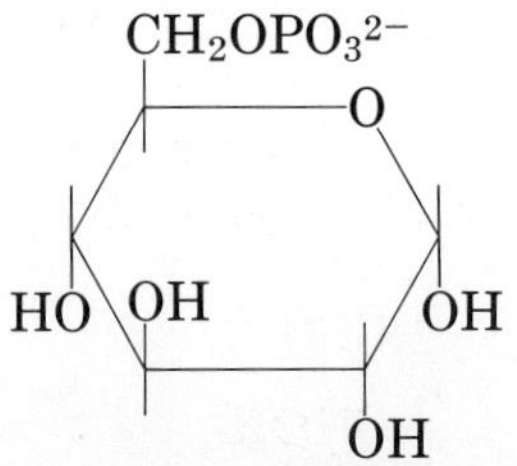

glucose-6-phosphate

(3) Rearrangement of glucose-6-phosphate: enzyme phosphoglucoiso-merase.

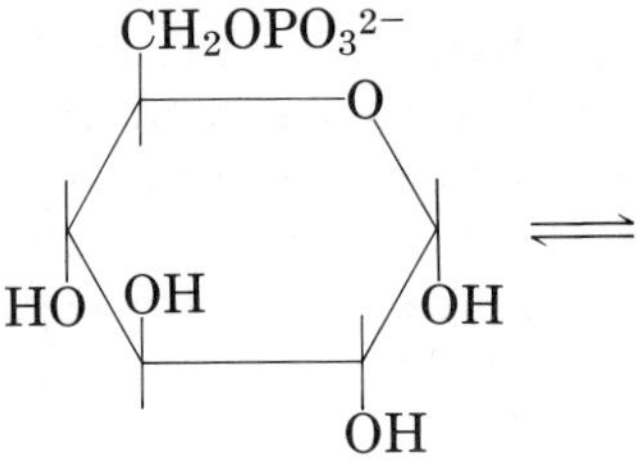

glucose-6-phosphate

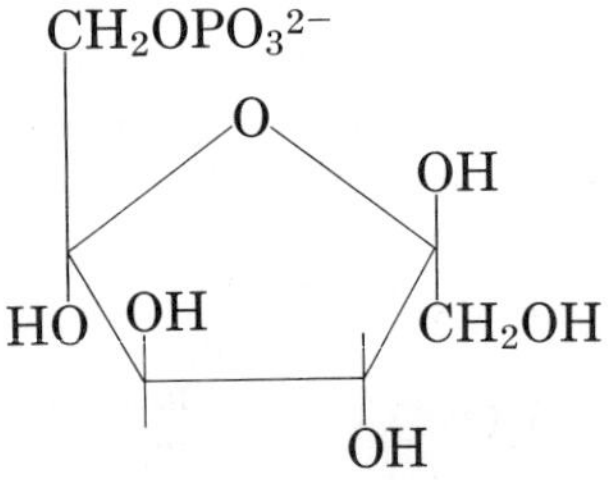

fructose-6-phosphate

(4) Phosphorylation of fructose phosphate: enzyme, phosphofructo-kinase.

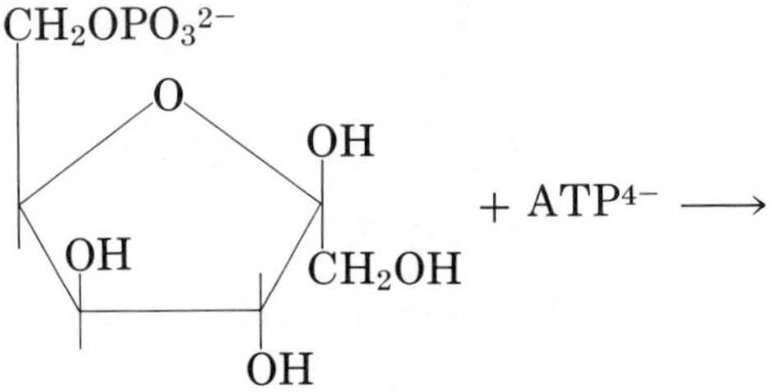

fructose-6-phosphate

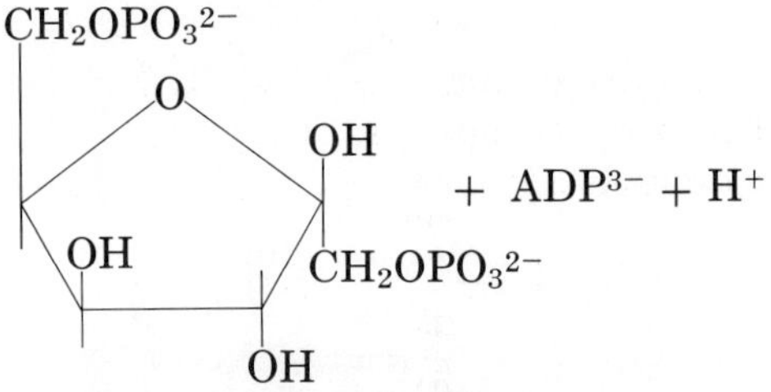

$+ ATP^{4-} \longrightarrow$

fructose-1,6-diphosphate

$+ ADP^{3-} + H^+$

The effect of these reactions is to convert 1 molecule of monosaccharide into 1 molecule of fructose diphosphate. In the process 1 or 2 molecules of ATP are converted to ADP, depending on the starting substrate. Adenosine triphosphate or ATP is an essential catalyst in this entire process and, as we shall see later, is intimately concerned in the transfer of energy. Its primary role in reactions 1 through 4 is as a phosphate donor.

Cleavage

The second major step in glycolysis after activation is cleavage of the hexose molecule.

(5) Cleavage: enzyme, fructo-aldolase.

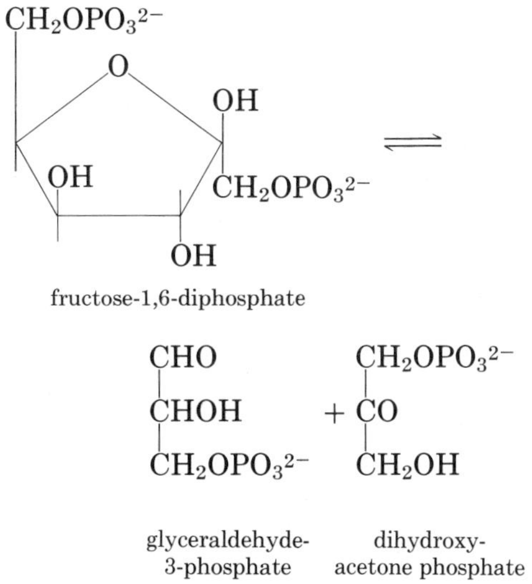

$$CH_2OPO_3^{2-}$$

fructose-1,6-diphosphate

$$
\begin{array}{lll}
CHO & & CH_2OPO_3^{2-} \\
CHOH & + & CO \\
CH_2OPO_3^{2-} & & CH_2OH
\end{array}
$$

glyceraldehyde-   dihydroxy-
3-phosphate   acetone phosphate

(6) Rearrangement of dihydroxyacetone phosphate: enzyme, triose isomerase.

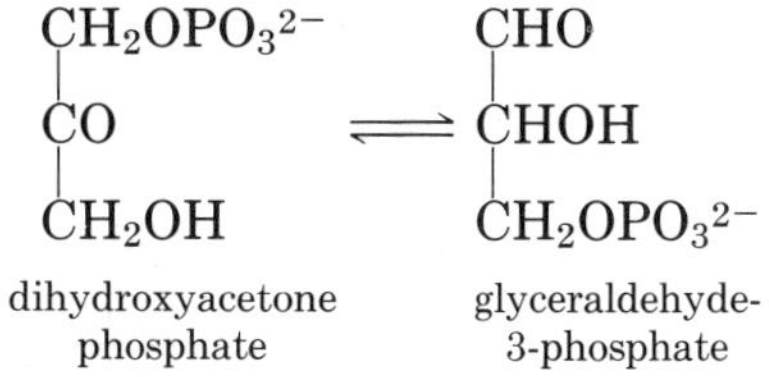

$$
\begin{array}{ll}
CH_2OPO_3^{2-} & CHO \\
CO & \rightleftharpoons \quad CHOH \\
CH_2OH & CH_2OPO_3^{2-}
\end{array}
$$

dihydroxyacetone   glyceraldehyde-
phosphate   3-phosphate

The result of this process (5–6) is conversion of one molecule of hexose diphosphate to two molecules of triose phosphate.

Oxidation

The third major step is an oxidative phosphorylation.

(7) Dehydrogenation and phosphorylation: enzyme, glyceraldehyde phosphate dehydrogenase.

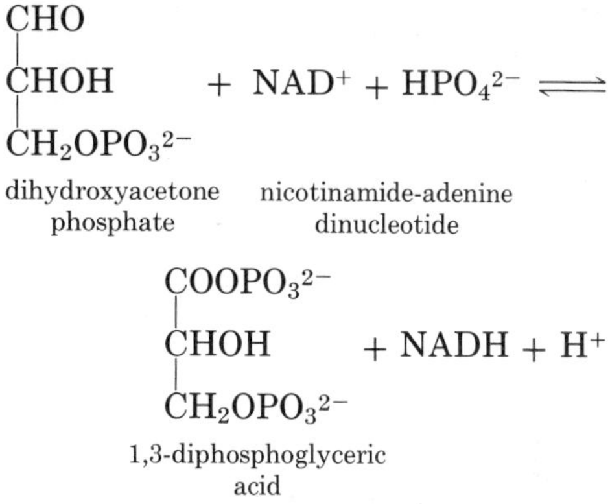

$$
\begin{array}{l}
CHO \\
CHOH \quad + NAD^+ + HPO_4^{2-} \rightleftharpoons \\
CH_2OPO_3^{2-}
\end{array}
$$

dihydroxyacetone   nicotinamide-adenine
phosphate   dinucleotide

$$
\begin{array}{l}
COOPO_3^{2-} \\
CHOH \quad + NADH + H^+ \\
CH_2OPO_3^{2-}
\end{array}
$$

1,3-diphosphoglyceric
acid

(8) Transphosphorylation: enzyme, phosphoglycerate kinase.

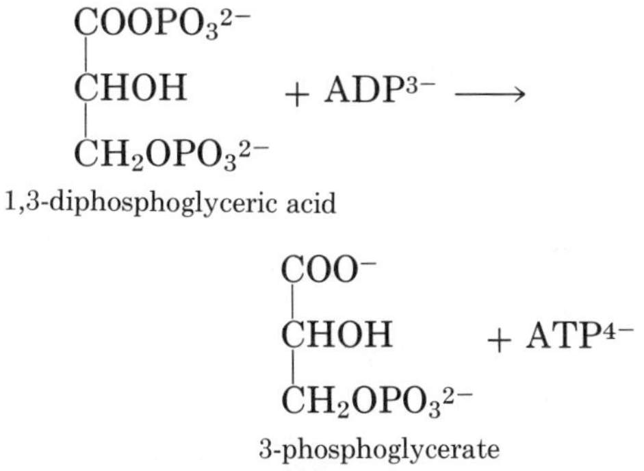

$$
\begin{array}{l}
COOPO_3^{2-} \\
CHOH \quad + ADP^{3-} \longrightarrow \\
CH_2OPO_3^{2-}
\end{array}
$$

1,3-diphosphoglyceric acid

$$
\begin{array}{l}
COO^- \\
CHOH \quad + ATP^{4-} \\
CH_2OPO_3^{2-}
\end{array}
$$

3-phosphoglycerate

(9) Rearrangement of phosphoglycerate: enzyme, phosphoglyceric mutase.

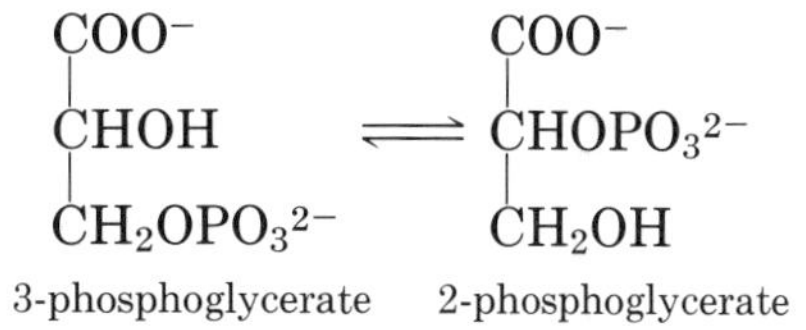

$$
\begin{array}{ll}
COO^- & COO^- \\
CHOH & \rightleftharpoons \quad CHOPO_3^{2-} \\
CH_2OPO_3^{2-} & CH_2OH
\end{array}
$$

3-phosphoglycerate   2-phosphoglycerate

(10) Dehydration (enolization) of phosphoglycerate: enzyme, enolase.

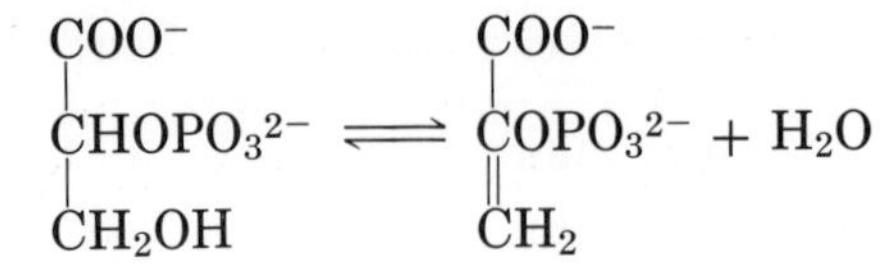

$$\begin{array}{c}\text{COO}^- \\ | \\ \text{CHOPO}_3{}^{2-} \\ | \\ \text{CH}_2\text{OH}\end{array} \rightleftharpoons \begin{array}{c}\text{COO}^- \\ | \\ \text{COPO}_3{}^{2-} + \text{H}_2\text{O} \\ \| \\ \text{CH}_2\end{array}$$

2-phosphoglycerate   2-phosphopyruvate

(11) Transphosphorylation: enzyme, pyruvic kinase.

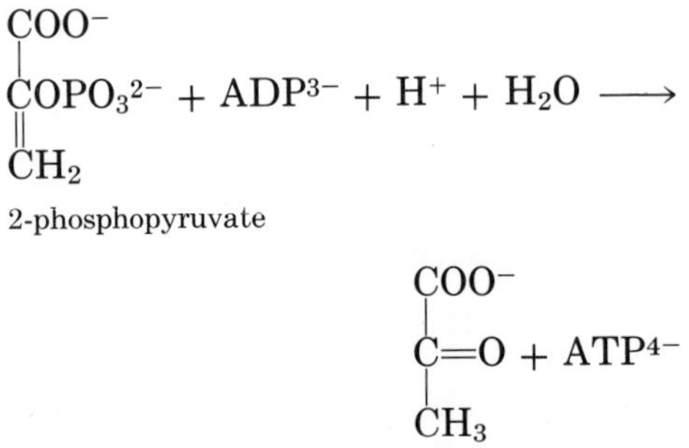

$$\begin{array}{c}\text{COO}^- \\ | \\ \text{COPO}_3{}^{2-} + \text{ADP}^{3-} + \text{H}^+ + \text{H}_2\text{O} \longrightarrow \\ \| \\ \text{CH}_2\end{array}$$

2-phosphopyruvate

$$\begin{array}{c}\text{COO}^- \\ | \\ \text{C}{=}\text{O} + \text{ATP}^{4-} \\ | \\ \text{CH}_3\end{array}$$

pyruvate

The results of this series of reactions (7–11) are threefold: first, the conversion of one molecule of glyceraldehyde-3-phosphate to pyruvic acid; second, the synthesis for each molecule of pyruvate formed of two molecules of ATP; and third, the reduction for each molecule of pyruvate formed of one molecule of NAD (nicotinamide-adenine dinucleotide) as noted in Chapter 1.

Anaerobic glycolysis

The amount of NAD in a cell is very small, and if the process of glycolysis is to continue the reduced NAD must be oxidized. In the presence of oxygen as we discussed earlier, NADH is oxidized through the cytochrome series of reactions. In the absence of oxygen it is oxidized in many animal tissues by the final reaction of glycolysis:

(12) Reduction of pyruvate: enzyme, lactic dehydrogenase.

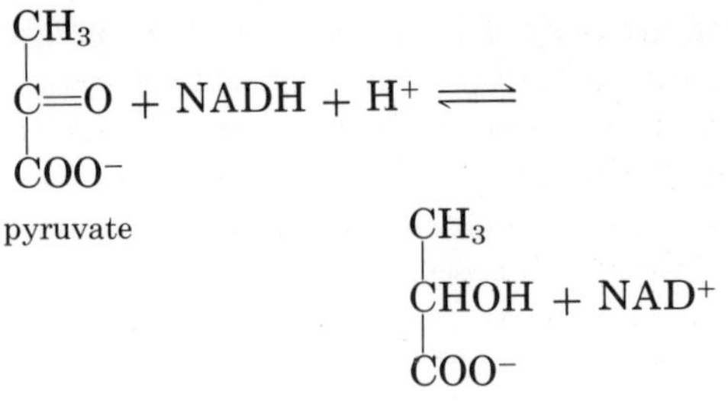

$$\begin{array}{c}\text{CH}_3 \\ | \\ \text{C}{=}\text{O} + \text{NADH} + \text{H}^+ \rightleftharpoons \\ | \\ \text{COO}^-\end{array}$$

pyruvate

$$\begin{array}{c}\text{CH}_3 \\ | \\ \text{CHOH} + \text{NAD}^+ \\ | \\ \text{COO}^-\end{array}$$

lactate

The overall process of anaerobic glycolysis then, if we start with glycogen, involves the conversion of one 6-carbon unit from glycogen into 2 molecules of lactate with the synthesis of 3 molecules of ATP. If we start with glucose we have instead the conversion of 1 molecule of glucose to 2 molecules of lactate with the synthesis of 2 molecules of ATP.

Free Energy and ATP

To understand the significance of this process we must consider not only the chemical changes but also the associated changes in energy. We can determine by appropriate measurements a quantity known as the change in free energy for each of the above reactions. The free-energy change is symbolized by ΔG or ΔF and represents the maximum amount of useful work (chemical, electrical, etc.) which could be obtained from the reaction under ideal conditions. By convention we write the free-energy change ΔG as negative for an exergonic reaction—that is, a reaction which produces energy. Such a reaction will tend to occur spontaneously. The free-energy change of an endergonic reaction which consumes energy is written as positive. The energy consumed in an endergonic reaction must invariably be supplied by another exergonic reaction. In other words an endergonic reaction can occur only if it is coupled to an exergonic reaction which supplies at least as much energy as consumed in the endergonic reaction. This is a somewhat complicated statement of a principle which is no doubt already familiar as the principle of conservation of energy, also known as the first law of thermodynamics.

Table 2.1 gives free-energy changes for each of the glycolytic reactions. The phosphorylation of glucose by ATP, for example, is exergonic, and in the presence of the enzyme hexokinase and adequate quantities of ATP it will occur spontaneously. We can, however, break this reaction down into two parts:

glucose + $HPO_4^{2-} \longrightarrow$ glucose-6-phosphate^{2-} + H_2O	+2.6
ATP^{4-} + $H_2O \longrightarrow ADP^{3-}$ + HPO_4^{2-} + H^+	−8.3
glucose + $ATP^{4-} \longrightarrow$ glucose-6-phosphate^{2-} + ADP^{3-} + H^+	−5.7

TABLE 2.1
Free Energy Changes (ΔG), kcal per mole, for the Reactions of Glycolysis

1. (glycogen)$_n$ + $HPO_4^{2-} \longrightarrow$ (glycogen)$_{n-1}$ + glucose-1-phosphate^{2-}	+0.6
2. glucose + $ATP^{4-} \longrightarrow$ glucose-6-phosphate^{2-} + ADP^{3-} + H^+	−5.7
3. glucose-1-phosphate$^{2-} \longrightarrow$ glucose-6-phosphate^{2-}	−1.7
4. glucose-6-phosphate$^{2-} \longrightarrow$ fructose-6-phosphate^{2-}	+0.5
5. fructose + $ATP^{4-} \longrightarrow$ fructose-6-phosphate^{2-} + ADP^{3-} + H^+	(−5.2)
6. fructose-6-phosphate^{2-} + $ATP^{4-} \longrightarrow$ fructose-1,6-diphosphate^{4-} + ADP^{3-} + H^+	−4.3
1 + 3 + 6. (glycogen)$_n$ + HPO_4^{2-} + $ATP^{4-} \longrightarrow$ (glycogen)$_{n-1}$ + fructose-1,6-diphosphate^{4-} + ADP^{3-} + H^+	−4.9
2 + 4 + 6: glucose + 2$ATP^{4-} \longrightarrow$ fructose-1,6-diphosphate^{4-} + 2ADP^{3-} + 2H^+	−9.5
7. fructose-1,6-diphosphate$^{4-} \longrightarrow$ glyceraldehyde-3-phosphate^{2-} + dihydroxyacetone phosphate^{2-}	+2.8
8. dihydroxyacetone phospate$^{2-} \longrightarrow$ glyceraldehyde-3-phosphate^{2-}	+1.8
7 + 8. fructose-1,6-diphosphate$^{4-} \longrightarrow$ 2 glyceraldehyde-3-phosphate^{2-}	+4.6
9. glyceraldehyde-3-phosphate^{2-} + NAD^+ + $HPO_4^{2-} \longrightarrow$ 1,3-diphosphoglycerate^{4-} + NADH + H^+	+4.2
10. 1,3-diphosphoglycerate^{4-} + ADP^{3-} + $H^+ \longrightarrow$ 3-phosphoglycerate^{2-} + ATP^{4-}	−4.8
11. 3-phosphoglycerate$^{2-} \longrightarrow$ 2-phosphoglycerate^{2-}	+1.1
12. 2-phosphoglycerate$^{2-} \longrightarrow$ 2-phosphopyruvate^{2-} + H_2O	−0.6
13. 2-phosphopyruvate^{2-} + ADP^{3-} + $H_2O \longrightarrow$ pyruvate$^-$ + ATP^{4-}	−5.0
9 to 13. glyceraldehyde-3-phosphate^{2-} + NAD^+ + HPO_4^{2-} + 2$ADP^{3-} \longrightarrow$ pyruvate$^-$ + NADH + 2ATP^{4-}	−5.1
14. pyruvate$^-$ + NADH + $H^+ \longrightarrow$ lactate$^-$ + NAD^+	−10.3
15. ATP^{4-} + $H_2O \longrightarrow ADP^{3-}$ + HPO_4^{2-} + H^+	−8.3

Concentrations of reactants and products 0.2M, pH 7, 25°C.

The first reaction is endergonic and would not occur spontaneously. It is driven by energy supplied by the breakdown of ATP to ADP, an exergonic reaction. ATP serves, in other words, as an energy donor in this and other activation reactions. Similarly the cleavage reactions 6 and 7 are endergonic as are some of the reactions in the oxidative phosphorylation sequence. These, however, are driven by the exergonic reactions preceding and following so that the whole reaction sequence is exergonic.

Efficiency of glycolysis

We noted that ATP may serve as an energy donor for activation of glucose or fructose. We also saw from the glycolysis reactions that the ATP used in the early stages of glycolysis is regenerated in the later reactions, and that 2 or 3 molecules of ATP are synthesized for every hexose unit converted to lactic acid so that there is a net production of ATP for the whole process. This ATP may now serve as energy donor for any of a great variety of biological processes: chemical syntheses, transport processes, production of electrical changes, or mechanical work as in muscular contraction. All of these are driven by energy derived from the hydrolysis of ATP. We may therefore regard the glycolysis reactions as a chemical machine which converts some of the energy of the carbohydrate molecule to the energy of ATP. If we take the free-energy change for the reaction

glucose $\longrightarrow$ 2 lactate$^-$ + 2H$^+$
$$\Delta G = -49.7 \text{ kcal}$$

as an index of the maximum useful energy available from the conversion of glucose to lactate and the free energy change for

$$2ATP^{4-} + H_2O \longrightarrow$$
$$2ADP^{3-} + 2HPO_4^{2-} + 2H^+$$
$$\Delta G = -16.6 \text{ kcal}$$

as an index of the maximum biologically useful free energy derived from this process we can calculate the maximum possible efficiency of the machine as $16.6/49.7 \times 100 = 33.5\%$.

Put in another way, we may say that the total useful energy available from the conversion of 1 mole of glucose to 2 moles of lactate is about 50 kcal. If the reaction were carried out by ordinary chemical processes all of this energy would appear as heat, and it could be turned into work only by using some form of heat engine. In the cell, however, as much as 17 kcal or about one-third of the energy may be conserved in the form of ATP and so can be used directly, doing a variety of biological work; the remaining energy appears as heat.

The biological machine for glycolytic energy transformation works basically by replacing water (H_2O) by phosphoric acid (H_3PO_4). Thus in the activation of glycogen we have phosphorolysis:

$$(C_6H_{10}O_5)_n + HPO_4^{2-} \longrightarrow$$
$$(C_6H_{10}O_5)_{n-1} + C_6H_{11}O_6 \cdot PO_3^{2-}$$

instead of hydrolysis:

$$(C_6H_{10}O_5)_n + H_2O \longrightarrow$$
$$(C_6H_{10}O_5)_{n-1} + C_6H_{12}O_6$$

In the oxidation of glyceraldehyde we have phosphorylation and dehydrogenation:

$$\begin{array}{l} CHO \\ | \\ CHOH \qquad + A + HPO_4^{2-} \longrightarrow \\ | \\ CH_2OPO_3^{2-} \end{array}$$

$$\begin{array}{l} COOPO_3^{2-} \\ | \\ CHOH \qquad + AH_2 \\ | \\ CH_2OPO_3^{2-} \end{array}$$

instead of hydration and dehydrogenation:

$$
\begin{array}{c}
CHO \\
| \\
CHOH \\
| \\
CH_2OH
\end{array}
+ A + H_2O \longrightarrow
\begin{array}{c}
COOH \\
| \\
CHOH \\
| \\
CH_2OH
\end{array}
+ AH_2
$$

and the phosphate introduced into the diphosphoglyceric acid can then be transferred in two successive steps to ATP. The basis of the transfer to ATP is in every case the so-called high-energy phosphate. When a phosphate radical is attached so that its P=O bond is conjugated with another double bond such as C=C, C=O, C=N, or P=O, hydrolysis of the R—O—P bond yields relatively large amounts of energy and the phosphate radical can readily be transferred to ATP or utilized to esterify other compounds in the process generally known as transphosphorylation.

Oxidative Phosphorylation

It is evident that in the products of glycolysis there remains much of the energy of the glucose molecule. This energy is liberated through the oxidative reactions of the Krebs cycle. In that cycle, as we have seen, the NADH formed in the oxidation of the organic acids is oxidized through a series of steps involving the cytochrome system as the final link with oxygen. Each of these steps represents a free-energy decrease. The energy liberated is conserved in the same way as is the energy liberated in glycolysis —by conversion to high-energy phosphate compounds. For glycolysis, we have a rather clear picture of the way in which this is accomplished. For oxidation the picture remains a hypothetical one. Experimentally it is possible to obtain from cells, by methods discussed in the next chapter, a preparation which contains the whole set of enzymes involved in carrying out the complete reactions of the Krebs cycle. When an appropriate substrate such as pyruvic acid is added to such a preparation, and the amounts of oxygen consumed and of high-energy phosphate produced are measured, it is found that in the best preparations the ratio of atoms of phosphorus esterified to atoms of oxygen consumed approaches 3. Present evidence suggests that 1 molecule of ATP is synthesized in the oxidation of NAD, another between flavoprotein and cytochrome c, and a third between cytochrome c and oxygen (Figure 1.12). In the oxidation of succinate to fumarate only the last two of these occur, and in the oxidation of α-ketoglutarate to succinate an extra molecule of ATP is formed in the substrate oxidation process. Thus the overall ratio of 3 ATP to 1 electron pair or oxygen atom is obtained.

Oxidative Decarboxylation

We should at this point consider in more detail some of the reactions in Krebs cycle oxidation, particularly those involving decarboxylation. The latter process involves thiamin pyrophosphate (cocarboxylase) as coenzyme in a reaction which can be depicted by the following equation, where E represents the enzyme, pyruvic dehydrogenase:

$$
(1) \quad
\begin{array}{c}
COO^- \\
| \\
C{=}O \\
| \\
CH_3
\end{array}
+ ThPP + 2H^+ + E \longrightarrow
$$

$$
\left[
\begin{array}{c}
ThPP{-}CH{-}OH \\
| \\
CH_3
\end{array}
\right] {-}E + CO_2
$$

The thiamin pyrophosphate (ThPP) is then displaced from the enzyme-substrate complex by a second coenzyme, lipoic acid, in which the essential structure is a vicinal disulfide group:

$$(2) \quad \begin{bmatrix} \text{ThPP—CH—OH} \\ \quad\quad | \\ \quad\quad \text{CH}_3 \end{bmatrix}\text{—E} + \text{La} \begin{array}{c} \diagup \text{S} \\ \diagdown \text{S} \end{array}$$

lipoic acid

$$\longrightarrow \begin{bmatrix} \quad\quad \text{S—C=O} \\ \text{La} \diagdown \quad | \\ \quad\quad\quad \text{CH}_3 \\ \quad \diagup \\ \text{SH} \end{bmatrix}\text{—E} + \text{ThPP}$$

The sulfur bond between the lipoic acid and the acyl group is then replaced by a sulfur bond with the reduced or sulfhydryl form of coenzyme A. In this process the lipoic acid is reduced, whereas there is in effect an oxidation to form the acetyl group:

$$(3) \quad \begin{bmatrix} \quad\quad \text{S—C=O} \\ \text{La} \diagdown \quad | \\ \quad\quad\quad \text{CH}_3 \\ \quad \diagup \\ \text{SH} \end{bmatrix}\text{—E} + \text{CoASH} \longrightarrow$$

$$\text{CH}_3\text{—CO—SCoA} + \text{La} \begin{array}{c} \quad \text{SH} \\ \diagdown \\ \diagup \\ \quad \text{SH} \end{array} + \text{E}$$

The reduced lipoic acid is then oxidized through the flavine prosthetic group of the pyruvic dehydrogenase enzyme, with NAD as the ultimate hydrogen acceptor:

$$(4) \quad \text{La} \begin{array}{c} \diagup \text{SH} \\ \diagdown \text{SH} \end{array} + \text{E—FAD} \longrightarrow$$

$$\text{La} \begin{array}{c} \diagup \text{S} \\ \diagdown \text{S} \end{array} + \text{E—FADH}_2$$

$$(5) \quad \text{E—FADH}_2 + \text{NAD}^+ \longrightarrow \\ \text{NADH} + \text{H}^+ + \text{E—FAD}$$

The reactions 1–5 take place in a complex with the enzyme. In princi-

ple, this is an oxidative decarboxylation, since acetyl coenzyme A can be hydrolyzed to acetic acid and reduced coenzyme A. The whole process would then be

$$(6) \quad \begin{array}{c} \text{COO}^- \\ | \\ \text{C=O} \\ | \\ \text{CH}_3 \end{array} + \text{H}^+ + \tfrac{1}{2}\text{O}_2 \longrightarrow$$

$$\text{CH}_3\text{COOH} + \text{CO}_2$$

Instead, the sum of reactions 1–5 is

$$(7) \quad \begin{array}{c} \text{COO}^- \\ | \\ \text{C=O} \\ | \\ \text{CH}_3 \end{array} + \text{CoASH} + \text{NAD}^+ \longrightarrow$$

$$\text{CH}_3\text{CO—SCoA} + \text{NADH} + \text{CO}_2$$

The effect is to conserve energy in two ways. Acetyl coenzyme A is at a higher energy level than acetic acid, and NADH oxidation will also yield considerable energy.

The decarboxylation of α-ketoglutarate involves an entirely comparable series of steps which need not be repeated in detail here. These steps are, however, followed by a phosphorylation:

$$\begin{array}{c} \text{CO—SCoA} \\ | \\ \text{CH}_2 \\ | \\ \text{CH}_2 \\ | \\ \text{COO}^- \end{array} + \text{IDP}^{3-} + \text{HPO}_4^{2-} \longrightarrow$$

succinyl   inosine
coenzyme A   diphosphate

$$\begin{array}{c} \text{COO}^- \\ | \\ \text{CH}_2 \\ | \\ \text{CH}_2 \\ | \\ \text{COO}^- \end{array} + \text{ITP}^{4-}$$

succinate   inosine
triphosphate

This step accounts for the "substrate level" phosphorylation, giving a P/O ratio of 4 for the oxidation of α-ketoglutarate.

Efficiency of Oxidative Phosphorylation

For the overall oxidation process, as for glycolysis, we can calculate the efficiency. Starting with lactate, we have

$$\text{lactate}^- + H^+ + 3O_2 \longrightarrow$$
$$3CO_2 + 3H_2O$$
$$\Delta G = -319.4 \text{ kcal}$$

In this process 18 molecules of ATP are formed. The hydrolysis of this ATP would yield a maximum of 151.2 kcal of useful work or a theoretical maximum efficiency for lactic acid oxidation via the Krebs cycle of 47%, somewhat higher than for glycolysis. We may also calculate the overall efficiency for oxidation of 1 mole of glucose via the glycolysis and Krebs reactions assuming that glycolysis is aerobic, that no lactate is formed, and that the NADH formed in glycolysis is oxidized via the flavoprotein-cytochrome mechanism with a P/O ratio of 3. The student should make this calculation himself, given that ΔG for

$$\text{glucose} + 6O_2 \longrightarrow 6CO_2 + 6H_2O$$

is -688.5 kcal.

Of course these are theoretical efficiencies not actually reached in the cell, but it should be clear that the energy yield of glycolysis is lower than that for oxidation from the same amount of substrate and the efficiency is less. Anaerobiosis, in which glycolysis is the main source of energy, is therefore a wasteful kind of metabolism by comparison with aerobiosis. It should also be clear that the living system is capable of operating at a relatively high efficiency. This efficiency is possible because the living machinery is entirely chemical with energy being transferred from one organic compound to another through reactions in a coupled system operating near reversibility.

Oxidation of Lipids and Amino Acids

The fatty acids are oxidized by a sequence of reactions which involve coenzyme A. These may be summarized as follows:

(1) Acyl thiokinase

$$CH_3(CH_2)_nCH_2CH_2CO \cdot OH + ATP$$
$$+ CoASH \longrightarrow CH_3(CH_2)_nCH_2CH_2CO$$
$$\cdot SCoA + AMP + PP$$

(2) Acyl dehydrogenase

$$CH_3(CH_2)_n \cdot CH_2CH_2CO \cdot SCoA$$
$$+ FAD \longrightarrow CH_3(CH_2)_nCH{=}CHCO$$
$$\cdot SCoA + FADH_2$$

(3) Enoyl hydrase

$$CH_3(CH_2)_nCH{=}CH \cdot CO \cdot SCoA$$
$$+ H_2O \longrightarrow CH_3(CH_2)_nCHOH$$
$$\cdot CH_2 \cdot CO \cdot SCoA$$

(4) β-Hydroxyacyl dehydrogenase

$$CH_3(CH_2)_nCHOH \cdot CH_2 \cdot CO \cdot SCoA$$
$$+ NAD^+ \longrightarrow CH_3(CH_2)_n \cdot CO$$
$$\cdot CH_2 \cdot CO \cdot SCoA + NADH + H^+$$

(5) β-Ketoacylthiolase

$$CH_3 \cdot (CH_2)_n \cdot CO \cdot CH_2CO \cdot SCoA$$
$$+ H_2O \longrightarrow CH_3(CH_2)_nCO$$
$$\cdot OH + CH_3 \cdot CO \cdot SCoA$$

The end result of this type of reaction repeated n times is n molecules of acetyl coenzyme A, which can then enter the citric acid cycle and be oxidized, and a molecule of butyryl coenzyme A,

$$CH_3—CH_2—CH_2—CO \cdot SCoA$$

This is oxidized through the same series of reactions to acetoacetyl coenzyme A, $CH_3—CO—CH_2—CO \cdot SCoA$, which is then converted to two molecules of acetyl coenzyme A by the enzyme acetoacetyl thiolase:

(6) $CH_3 \cdot CO \cdot CH_2 \cdot CO \cdot SCoA$

$+ HSCoA \longrightarrow 2CH_3 \cdot CO \cdot SCoA$

For each cycle of reactions 1–5 two molecules of NAD are reduced and subsequently oxidized through the cytochrome system.

The amino acids are also oxidized through the Krebs cycle. The first step is typically that of deamination:

$$R \cdot \underset{\underset{COOH}{|}}{CH} \cdot NH_2 + NAD^+ \longrightarrow$$

$$R \cdot \underset{\underset{COOH}{|}}{C}{=}NH + NADH + H^+$$

$$R \cdot \underset{\underset{COOH}{|}}{C}{=}NH + H_2O \longrightarrow$$

$$R \cdot \underset{\underset{COOH}{|}}{C}{=}O + NH_3$$

The resulting product, a keto acid, is then either in a position to enter directly into the Krebs cycle as pyruvic acid, oxaloacetic acid, etc., or it may be converted by a series of relatively simple reactions into one of the intermediates in the Krebs cycle. A few of the amino acids are converted into acetyl coenzyme A, but all of them are ultimately oxidized through the Krebs cycle or utilized in synthesis. The details are presented in Chapter 12, but the major end products are summarized in Table 2.2.

Synthetic Mechanisms

The best-known synthetic mechanisms are those involving carbohydrates, and we shall devote most of our attention to them. Until recently it was generally believed that the synthesis of polysaccharides such as glycogen from glucose is brought about simply by reversal of phosphorolysis driven by ATP and glucose concentrations at relatively high levels. The free-energy values in the table suggest that this should be possible, and the reaction has been shown to be reversible. However, recent studies make it clear that glycogen synthesis proceeds through another mechanism involving the nucleotides of uridine instead of those of adenine. The terminal phosphate of ATP can be transferred readily to other compounds such as uridine triphosphate (UTP) in the reaction

$$ATP + UDP \longrightarrow ADP + UTP$$

UTP in turn can combine with glucose-1-phosphate to form the nucleotide uridine diphosphoglucose (UDPG);

$$UTP + \text{glucose-1-phosphate} \longrightarrow$$
$$UDPG + \text{phosphate}$$

This combined glucose can now be linked with another glucose molecule to form oligosaccharides:

$$\text{glucose-1-phosphate} + UDPG \longrightarrow$$
$$\text{maltose} + UDP + \text{phosphate}$$

In this way the glycogen molecule can be built up step by step. Note that the energy for this synthesis comes ultimately from ATP.

The synthesis of fats is not as well understood but probably involves the following five steps.

TABLE 2.2
Oxidative Pathways in Amino Acid Metabolism

Amino Acid	Intermediate Products	Oxidizable End Product
Alanine		Pyruvate
Tryptophan	Alanine (part of molecule only)	Pyruvate
Cysteine		Pyruvate + H_2S
Serine		Pyruvate
Serine	Hydroxypyruvate	Glycerol
Cysteine + serine + methionine	Cystathionine	Pyruvate + succinyl CoA
Glycine (+ formate)	Serine	Pyruvate or glycerol
Valine	α-Ketoisovalerate	Succinyl CoA
Threonine	α-Ketobutyrate	Succinyl CoA
Isoleucine	α-Keto-β-methylvalerate	Succinyl CoA + acetyl CoA
Glutamate		α-Ketoglutarate
Proline	Glutamate	α-Ketoglutarate
Histidine	Urocanate $\longrightarrow$ glutamate	α-Ketoglutarate
Arginine	Ornithine $\longrightarrow$ glutamate	α-Ketoglutarate
Lysine	α-Ketoadipate	Acetyl CoA
Leucine	α-Ketoisocaproate	Acetyl CoA
Phenylalanine, tyrosine	Phenylpyruvate	Fumarate
Aspartate		Oxaloacetate

$$
\begin{array}{l}
CH_2OH \\
\!\mid \\
CHOH + ATP^{4-} \longrightarrow \\
\!\mid \\
CH_2OH
\end{array}
$$

$$
\begin{array}{l}
\quad CH_2OH \\
\quad \!\mid \\
\quad CHOH + ADP^{3-} + H^+ \\
\quad \!\mid \\
\quad CH_2OPO_3{}^{2-}
\end{array}
$$

(1) glycerol + ATP $\longrightarrow$
 α-glycerol phosphate + ADP

$$
CH_3(CH_2)_n\,COOH + ATP^{4-}
$$
$$
+ HS \cdot CoA \longrightarrow CH_3(CH_2)_n\,CO \cdot SCoA
$$
$$
+ AMP^{2-} + PP^{3-} + H^+
$$

(2) fatty acid + ATP
 + coenzyme A $\longrightarrow$ acyl coenzyme A
 + adenosine monophosphate
 + pyrophosphate

$$
2CH_3(CH_2)_nCO \cdot SCoA +
\begin{array}{l}
CH_2OH \\
\!\mid \\
CHOH \longrightarrow \\
\!\mid \\
CH_2OPO_3{}^{2-}
\end{array}
$$

$$
\begin{array}{l}
CH_2O \cdot CO(CH_2)_nCH \\
\!\mid \\
CHO \cdot CO(CH_2)_nCH_3 + 2HSCoA \\
\!\mid \\
CH_2OPO_3{}^{2-}
\end{array}
$$

(3) 2 acyl coenzyme A
 + α-glycerol phosphate
 $\longrightarrow$ diacyl phosphatide
 + 2 coenzyme A

$$
\begin{array}{l}
CH_2O \cdot CO(CH_2)_nCH_3 \\
\!\mid \\
CHO \cdot CO(CH_2)_nCH_3 + H_2O \longrightarrow \\
\!\mid \\
CH_2OPO_3{}^{2-}
\end{array}
$$

$$
\begin{array}{l}
CH_2O \cdot CO(CH_2)_n \cdot CH_3 \\
\!\mid \\
CHO \cdot CO(CH_2)_nCH_3 \quad + HPO_4{}^{2-} \\
\!\mid \\
CH_2OH
\end{array}
$$

(4) diacyl phosphatide + $H_2O \longrightarrow$
          diglyceride + phosphate

$$\underset{|}{CH_2O \cdot CO \cdot (CH_2)_n CH_3}$$
$$\underset{|}{CHO \cdot CO(CH_2)_n CH_3}$$
$$CH_2OH$$

$$+ CH_3(CH_2)_n CO \cdot SCoA \longrightarrow$$

$$\underset{|}{CH_2O \cdot CO \cdot (CH_2)_n \cdot CH_3}$$
$$\underset{|}{CHO \cdot CO(CH_2)_n CH_3}$$
$$CH_2O \cdot CO(CH_2)_n CH_3$$

(5) diglyceride + acyl coenzyme A $\longrightarrow$
          triglyceride + coenzyme A

The details of protein synthesis are likewise not completely understood but the basic processes seem to be: (1) activation of the amino acid by formation of a complex with an activating enzyme, the amino acid and ATP; (2) transfer of the amino acid to a complex with a ribonucleic acid with liberation of adenylic acid (AMP); (3) transfer of the amino acid from the ribonucleic acid complex to a protein molecule. Presumably the arrangement of the amino acids in the RNA complex is determined by the arrangement of nucleotide units in the RNA molecule. Details of this problem are considered in Chapter 3.

The synthesis of the three major groups of compounds—polysaccharides, fats, and proteins—from their component units uses energy derived from hydrolysis of ATP. In each case the ATP serves to activate the component unit (monosaccharide fatty acid, glycerol, amino acid) either by phosphorylation (glycerol) or by formation of a complex from which the unit is transferred to its ultimate destination in the polymer molecule.

References

Glycolysis

Dorfman, A. 1943. Pathways of glycolysis. *Physiol. Rev.* 23 124–138.

Lipmann, F. 1946. Metabolic process patterns. *Curr. Biochem. Res.* 137–148.

Meyerhof, O. 1951. Phosphorus metabolism. *Amer. Scientist* 39 682–687.

Stumpf, P. K. 1954. Glycolysis. *Chem. Path. Metab.* 1 67–108.

Oxidation, Energetics

Axelrod, B. 1956. Enzymatic phosphate transfer. *Adv. Enzymol.* 17 159–188.

Baddiley, J. 1955. The structure of coenzyme A. *Adv. Enzymol.* 16 1–21.

Chance, B., and Williams, G. R. 1956. The respiratory chain and oxidative phosphorylation. *Adv. Enzymol.* 17 65–134.

Felix, K. 1953. Die Energieverzehrenden, -liefernden und -übertragenden Reaktionen des intermediären Stoffwechsels. *Naturwiss.* 40 44–49.

George, P., and Rutman, R. J. 1960. The "high energy phosphate bond" concept. *Progr. Biophys.* 10 1–53.

Gillespie, R. J., Maw, G. A., and Vernon, C. A. 1953. The concept of phosphate-bond energy. *Nature* 171 1147–1149.

Green, D. E. 1952. Organized enzyme systems. *J. Cell. Comp. Physiol.* 39 Suppl. 2, 75–111.

Green, D. E. 1954. Fatty acid oxidation in soluble systems of animal tissues. *Biol. Rev.* 29 330–366.

Green, D. E. 1959. Electron transport and oxidative phosphorylation. *Adv. Enzymol.* 21 73–130.

Kennedy, E. P. 1953. Energetics and metabolic function. *Biochem. Physiol. Nutr.* 2 197–229.

Lipmann, F. 1953. On the chemistry and function of coenzyme A. *Bacteriol. Rev.* 17 1–16.

McElroy, W. D., and Glass, B. 1951. *Phosphorus Metabolism* (2 vols.). Johns Hopkins Press, Baltimore, Md.

Ochoa, S. 1951. Biological mechanisms of carboxylation and decarboxylation. *Physiol. Rev.* 31 56–106.

Ogston, A. G., and Smithies, O. 1948. Some thermodynamic and kinetic aspects of metabolic phosphorylation. *Physiol. Rev.* 28 283–303.

Pardee, A. B. 1954. Free energy and metabolism. *Chem. Path. Metab.* 1 1–25.

Reed, L. J. 1957. The chemistry and function of lipoic acid. *Adv. Enzymol.* **18** 319–347.

Slater, E. C. 1958. The constitution of the respiratory chain in animal tissues. *Adv. Enzymol.* **20** 147–199.

Szent-Györgyi, A. 1957. *Bioenergetics.* Academic Press, New York.

Synthesis

Brachet, J. 1960. Ribonucleic acid and the synthesis of cellular proteins. *Nature* **186** 194–199.

Brenner, S. 1962. RNA, ribosomes, and protein synthesis. *Cold Spring Harbor Symp. Quant. Biol.* **26** 101–110.

Borsook, H. 1954. Enzymatic synthesis of peptide bonds. *Chem. Path. Metab.* **2** 173–222.

Campbell, P. N., and Work, T. S. 1953. Biosynthesis of proteins. *Nature* **171** 997–1001.

Harris, R. J. C. (ed.) 1961. *Protein Biosynthesis.* Academic Press, New York.

Hollaender, A. (ed.) 1956. Symposium on the structure of enzymes and proteins. *J. Cell. Comp. Physiol.* **47** Suppl. 1.

Kalckar, H. M. 1947. Aspects of the biological function of phosphate in enzymatic syntheses. *Nature* **160** 143–147.

Lipmann, F. 1949. Mechanism of peptide bond formation. *Fed. Proc.* **8** 597–602.

Lipmann, F. 1955. Coenzyme A and biosynthesis. *Am. Scientist* **43** 37–47.

Lipmann, F. (ed.) 1958. Symposium on amino acid activation. *Proc. Nat. Acad. Sci. U.S.A.* **44** 67–97.

Raacke, I. D. 1958. Chemical aspects of recent hypotheses on protein synthesis. *Quart. Rev. Biol.* **33** 245–261.

Simkin, J. L., and Work, T. S. 1957. Biochemical approaches to the problem of protein synthesis. *Nature* **179** 1214–1219.

3 Cell structure and metabolic localization

The emergence of the cell theory in the first quarter of the nineteenth century led to enormous advancement in studies of the microscopic organization of the cell. Elaborate and useful techniques of fixation and staining were developed as a first step. These techniques were then used to work out the whole classical science of cytology, with its careful description of the structures of the cell and their behavior in varied cellular activities. The results of these classical studies were later brought under severe critical scrutiny by a new kind of biologist trained in chemistry and physics, and skeptical of conclusions based only on microscopic observation. At the end of the nineteenth century the structure of a typical cell could be described minutely in terms of a universal protoplasm enclosed in a membrane and

enclosing in turn a great variety of structures, chief among which was the nucleus (Figure 3.1). By the middle of the present century the physical reality of everything but the membrane and the nucleus had been questioned; two generations of practicing physiologists were accustomed to think of the cell as a colloidal system of enzymes enclosed in a semi-permeable envelope and enclosing a nucleus.

The invention of the electron microscope in the early 1930's has brought us back to a position somewhere between these extremes. After some twenty years of learning how to use their instrument, electron microscopists began to obtain pictures which corresponded in general to the pictures obtainable with light microscopy but showing much more fine detail. At the same time biochemists were learning

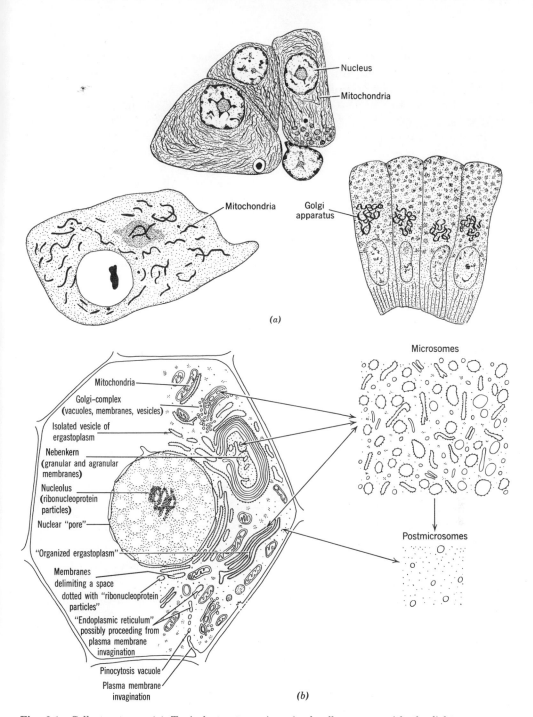

Labels in figure (a):
Nucleus
Mitochondria
Mitochondria
Golgi apparatus

(a)

Labels in figure (b):
Mitochondria
Golgi-complex (vacuoles, membranes, vesicles)
Isolated vesicle of ergastoplasm
Nebenkern (granular and agranular membranes)
Nucleolus (ribonucleoprotein particles)
Nuclear "pore"
"Organized ergastoplasm"
Membranes delimiting a space dotted with "ribonucleoprotein particles"
"Endoplasmic reticulum" possibly proceeding from plasma membrane invagination
Pinocytosis vacuole
Plasma membrane invagination

Microsomes

Postmicrosomes

(b)

Fig. 3.1 Cell structure. (a) Typical structures in animal cells as seen with the light microscope (redrawn from Wilson, *The Cell,* Macmillan, New York, 1925). (b) A diagrammatic representation of the structures visible in a "typical" cell with the electron microscope. (From Haguenau, F., 1958, *Int. Rev. Cytol.* **7** 461, Academic Press, New York.)

how to take cells apart without damaging the parts and were learning that the enzymes of the cell are, most of them, associated with definite structures. The picture of the cell as a relatively unorganized colloidal protoplasm which dominated the first half of this century has now been replaced by the concept of an organized structure in the cytoplasm close to, but more thoroughly authenticated than, the old picture drawn by the classical cytologist. If in the process we have lost "protoplasm," we can confidently feel that we now know much more about cells. It is this new picture which will be presented here; for most of it we can only sketch lightly the evidence on which the picture rests.

Membrane and Permeability

The cell membrane remains the most poorly understood of all the parts of the cell. Our knowledge of its composition is based largely on indirect evidence, since until very recently there was no method by which it could be readily separated from the rest of the cell. There is one exception—the erythrocyte. Exposure of red blood cells to dilute salt solutions or distilled water results in osmotic damage to the cell membrane, such that the hemoglobin and other cell constituents leak out, leaving behind a "ghost" which includes the cell membrane and some of the internal cell structure as well. These ghosts contain all the lipid of the cell, which includes a substantial amount of phospholipid and cholesterol as well as smaller amounts of triglyceride. If this cell lipid is spread as a monomolecular layer on water it occupies an area which is equal to about twice the surface area of the cells from which it was extracted. This observation and others to be noted

below have led to the general conclusion that cell membranes contain a layer of lipid two molecules thick (Figure 3.2).

The idea of the presence of lipid in the cell membrane is a relatively old one, going back to the observations of Overton about 1900 on the permeability of plant cell membranes. He found a general correlation between solubility in oils, or fat solvents such as chloroform or ether, and the readiness with which substances penetrate the membrane. This correlation has been extensively explored since, and in plant and animal cells such as erythrocytes and invertebrate eggs the relation holds very well as long as the molecules are above a certain size (diameter above 10 Å). For such large molecules penetration is directly related to solubility in nonpolar solvents. The concept of a double layer of lipid fits reasonably well also with the measurements of the thickness of the cell membrane. Indirect measurements on erythrocyte ghosts gave values of 30 to 120 Å. A lipid double layer would be about 30 Å thick. The outer boundary of cells as seen in the electron microscope appears as a single membrane about 25 Å thick separated from a second membrane of similar appearance by a space also about 25 Å wide. The most widely used fixative and stain for electron microscopy is osmic acid, which combines with unsaturated fatty acid molecules, and so one may suppose that the cell membrane seen in electron micrographs is primarily a lipid membrane.

There is some additional evidence, however, suggesting that the membrane has more to it than this. The permeability relation to fat solubility breaks down with small molecules. These in general penetrate in relation to molecular size rather than to polar

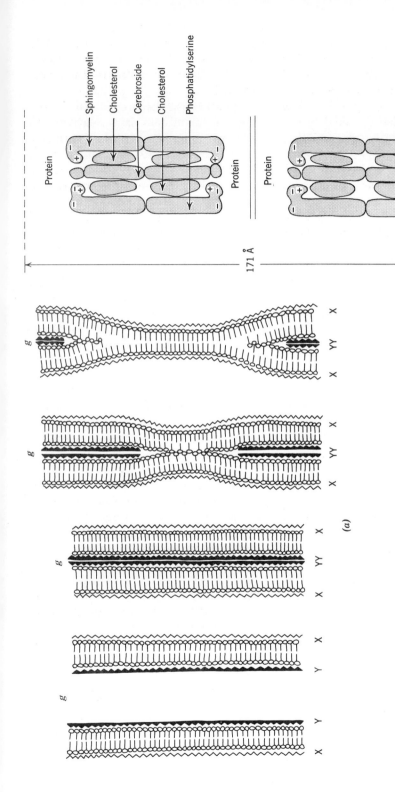

Fig. 3.2 The cell membrane. (*a*) Hypothetical arrangement of the lipid layers of the membranes of two adjacent cells, with varying degrees of intimacy of contact. (Robertson, 1961, *Ann. N.Y. Acad. Sci.* **94** 386). (*b*) A suggested arrangement for the lipid constituents of myelin, the insulating material surrounding many nerve axons; in the electron microscope, the "unit membrane" of myelin appears much the same as the cell membrane, with respect to dimensions and general arrangement. The details shown here are, of course, below the limit of resolution of the electron microscope. (After Finean, 1954, *Nature* **173** 549.)

character. This fact suggests that the membrane is to some degree porous. By studying the rates at which substances enter the cell across the membrane one can estimate the average diameter of the pores, if pores are present. This comes out to be between 5 and 10 Å. Such a figure is of course a statistical average, and there may be a considerable range of pore sizes. Such pores are too small to be resolved by the electron microscope and there is no independent means of verifying their existence, but most cell physiologists are willing to accept the pore hypothesis as the most likely one at present. In addition surfaces of most cells are charged electrically and are wetted by water rather than oil, suggesting the presence of a protein or mucopolysaccharide layer outside the lipid layer. This layer probably provides for some 70 Å of a total membrane thickness of about 100 Å in the erythrocyte.

We should not in any case think of the cell membrane as an inert, unchanging envelope of lipid and protein with pores. By combining the ordinary light microscope with time-lapse photography, cytologists have been able to show vigorous activity in the cell membrane. It forms blisters and retracts them, and in some cells takes in surrounding fluid by pinocytosis, a process which resembles on a very small scale the ingestion of food by an amoeboid protozoan. Microdissection of living cells also shows that the membrane can be stretched and can be reconstituted after rupture.

Ergastoplasm, Ribosomes, and Protein Synthesis

Our concepts of what lies inside the cell membrane have been greatly modi-

fied by electron microscopy. The microscopists described various networks in the cytoplasm on the basis of observations of fixed cells. The colloidally oriented physiologists dismissed these as artifacts of fixation. The electron microscope again reveals a highly organized network which cannot be dismissed as entirely an artifact since parts of it can be separated from the cell and identified by means other than electron microscopy. What the electron microscope sees is a more or less elaborate and oriented system of double membranes, often concentrically arranged (Figure 3.3). These membranes appear as paired dense lines about 40 Å thick separated by a space 100 to 150 Å wide. Between each pair of double membranes is a space 150 to 450 Å in width, in which small granules appear attached to the membrane or free. The whole structure is called the endoplasmic reticulum or ergastoplasm.

When cells are broken up by grinding with a ground glass pestle, in the process called homogenization, and the heavier particles (cell debris, nuclei, mitochondria) are centrifuged out, prolonged further centrifugation at high forces brings down a deposit of small particles about 500 Å in diameter. These are sometimes called microsomes. When these particles are examined in the electron microscope they resemble fragments of the endoplasmic reticulum. They have the same appearance of a membrane 40 Å thick with granules 100 to 150 Å in diameter attached. By still more prolonged centrifugation it is possible to separate out these latter small (100 Å) granules, which are also called microsomes by some investigators. Chemical analysis of the two microsome fractions shows that the 500 Å particles contain ribo-

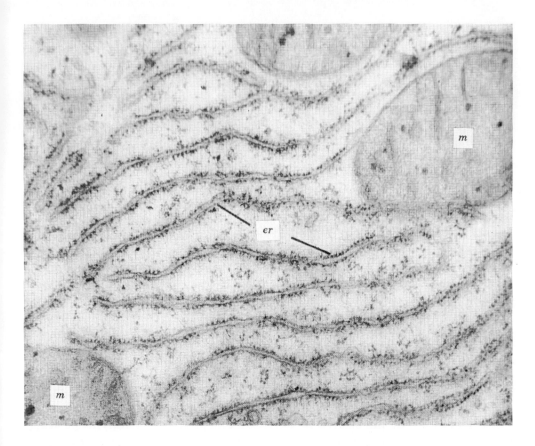

Fig. 3.3 Ergastoplasm or Endoplasmic Reticulum (*er*); Note the double character of the structure, and the presence of small dark granules (microsomes or ribosomes) along the outer sides of the double membrane. Portions of three mitochondria (*m*) are also seen. (From Porter, K. R., 1961, *The Cell,* **2** 628; ed. J. Brachet and A. E. Mirsky, Academic Press, New York.)

nucleic acid (RNA) and lipid. Practically all of the RNA of the cell appears in this fraction. The lipid consists largely of cholesterol and phospholipid. When the small (100 Å) granules are isolated they are found to contain all the RNA with little lipid. From this kind of evidence the view has gained general acceptance that the endoplasmic reticulum is made up primarily of lipid membranes associated with small RNA granules, which are now often called ribosomes. We must still use caution, however, in interpreting the electron micrographs as completely reliable pictures of the structure of living cytoplasm. The cells, when being prepared for the electron microscope, receive a rather severe treatment. We do not yet know to what extent this treatment induces alterations or artifacts in the structure, but we do know that living cells are capable of very extensive cytoplasmic movements incompatible with any permanent, rigid structure in the cytoplasm.

A biochemical study of the particles obtained by cell disintegration and centrifugation has also established some clear functional distinctions within the cytoplasm. The supernatant fluid which remains after all the particles have been centrifuged out is primarily a solution of proteins. More than 50% of the protein of the cell is found in this fraction. This fraction contains the enzymes of glycolysis, and these are not found to any extent in the particulate portion of the cell contents. The microsome fraction, on the other hand, and the small RNA granules (ribosomes) of this fraction in particular are the sites of protein synthesis in the cell. The incorporation of amino acids into proteins occurs primarily in this fraction. Since there is clear indication that RNA is the controlling factor in protein synthesis, the occurrence of most of the cellular RNA in these granules is further evidence of their role. The whole microsome fraction also contains hydrolytic enzymes and may be involved in breakdown and formation, though not in the oxidation, of lipids in the cell.

A cytoplasmic structure which in the past has been the subject of much controversy is the Golgi apparatus. The existence of this structure in animal cells generally now seems fairly well established; it has been seen not only in fixed cells stained by the original Golgi method and examined by light microscopy, but also in electron micrographs and in living cells examined by phase contrast microscopy. In electron micrographs the Golgi body appears as a rather dense arrangement of paired membranes and associated vesicles lacking the RNA granules of the rest of the reticulum. Its function has long been associated with secretion in certain cells, but its occurrence in nonsecreting cells as well suggests that this is not the only function. One recent reviewer thinks of the Golgi apparatus as a "gate" through which materials may be taken into or eliminated from the cell, but the evidence for or against this view is still quite limited.

Mitochondria and Oxidation

Among the best known of the larger structures of the cytoplasm are the mitochondria or chondriosomes. These were observed and rather carefully studied by classical cytological and cytochemical techniques as rods or filaments, most often about 1 micron long, with characteristic staining properties. These observations led to the hypothesis that the mitochondria have something to do with cellular respiration. The hypothesis was based largely on their reactions with oxidation-reduction indicator dyes. The recent studies of cell chemistry have confirmed and amplified this view, and electron microscopy has given us a clear picture of mitochondrial structure. The cellular fraction which contains the Krebs cycle enzymes when isolated by centrifugation from homogenates has the structural and chemical properties of the mitochondria. The mitochondria also contain the enzymes for oxidation of fatty acids to acetyl coenzyme A, which then enters the Krebs cycle. In other words the whole machinery for oxidation of foodstuffs and for oxidative phosphorylation (except for glycolysis and the initial stages of amino acid catabolism) seems to be in the mitochondria. The structure of these bodies then takes on great interest. In electron micrographs of cell sections they often appear in longitudinal section as bean-shaped objects with more or less regular cross bands at frequent intervals.

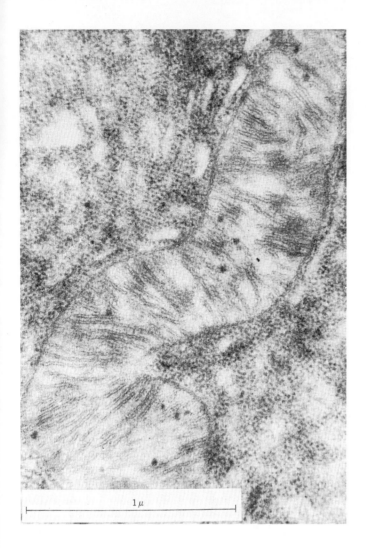

Fig. 3.4 A mitochondrion, seen in longitudinal section with the electron microscope. (From Sjöstrand, 1956, *Int. Rev. Cytol.* **5** 469, Academic Press, New York.)

Closer examination shows that the whole structure is enclosed in a thin membrane, double like those in the reticulum, but thinner, and lacking the RNA granules. The inner layer of the double membrane appears to be thrown into folds which extend all or part of the way across the central cavity of the mitochondrion, forming double partitions or cristae which divide the central cavity into small chambers. (Figures 3.4, 3.5). This rather complex structure appears to have some functional significance, since minor damage to the mitochondria will destroy the ability to carry out the complete Krebs cycle oxidations, whereas anything which destroys the double membrane arrangement prevents synthesis of ATP during oxidation. This fact has suggested to many that oxidative phosphorylation must depend on some specific spatial relation of the enzymes concerned, and hence will be disrupted if the structure of the mitochondrion is altered. Chem-

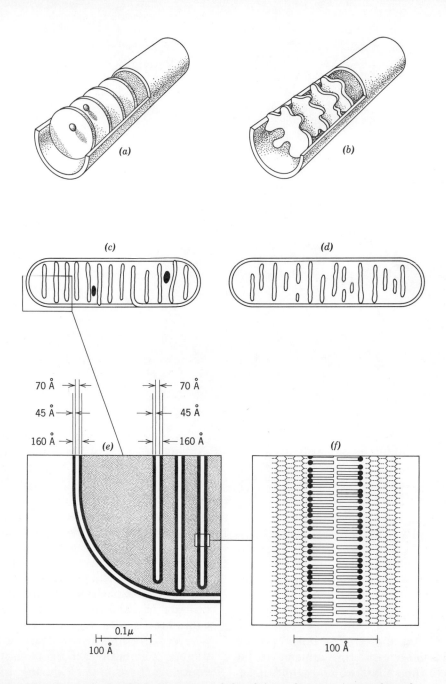

Fig. 3.5 Details of mitochondrial structure as deduced from electron micrographs and biochemical evidence. (*a*), (*b*) Three-dimensional reconstructions of two types of mitochondrion, based on electron micrographs; (*c*), (*d*) Idealized cross sections of (*a*) and (*b*). (*e*) Enlargement of part of (*c*) to show dimensions of the membrane structure. (*f*) Further enlargement of (*e*) on the assumption that the mitochondrial membranes, like the cell membrane, consist of lipid double layers coated with protein; note similarity to Figure 3.2 (*a*) and (*b*). (From Sjöstrand, 1956, *Int. Rev. Cytol.* **5** 467, Academic Press, New York).

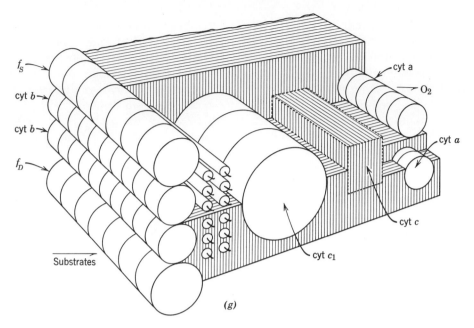

f_S

cyt b

cyt b

f_D

Substrates

cyt a

O_2

cyt a

cyt c

cyt c_1

(g)

(g) Hypothetical arrangement, in the mitochondrial membrane, of the electron transport system (Figure 1.12). (From Green and Lester, 1959, *Fed. Proc.* **18** 998.)

ically the mitochondria contain considerable amounts of both lipid and protein and relatively little RNA. Their membranes appear to be semipermeable, in that the mitochondria swell or shrink when placed in solutions more dilute or more concentrated than the cytoplasm. They also accumulate certain ions, notably K^+, in relatively high concentrations.

Nucleus and Control of Protein Synthesis

We may now turn briefly, more briefly than it deserves perhaps, to the nucleus. Classical cytology was far more interested in the nucleus than in the cytoplasm, and one of the great triumphs of this science during the last half of the nineteenth century was the working out of the details of mitosis and meiosis, which are now familiar to all biology students. In the first quarter of the present century this work was complemented by the experimental proof that the chromosomes are the bearers of the hereditary factors first postulated by Mendel and now known as genes. The nucleus thus takes on a great interest for students of reproduction and heredity. Here, however, we shall be concerned primarily with its role in the everyday life of nonreproducing cells.

Structure of the Nucleus

Structurally, the three obvious features of the nucleus are (1) its limiting membrane, surrounding (2) a mass of chromatin, which includes (3) a small spherical nucleolus. Electron microscopy has added little but detail to this picture. The nuclear membrane in electron micrographs appears as a double membrane much like those in the cytoplasmic reticulum (Figure 3.6). Indeed an increasing number of students of the cell consider that the nuclear membrane is continuous with the double membrane of the reticulum, and some consider that these in turn may at times be continuous with the plasma membrane and the membranes of the mitochondria. At any rate the membranes all look much alike in electron micrographs, and continuities have been observed in many instances. The nuclear membrane appears quite porous. It offers no osmotic barrier to the movement of small molecules, and proteins can move in and out with relative freedom through pores as large as 400 Å in diameter, yet in one instance an electric potential difference has been recorded across the membrane. This observation suggests low permeability to ions.

The chromatin has proved resistant to the techniques of electron microscopy, which reveals little detail in this

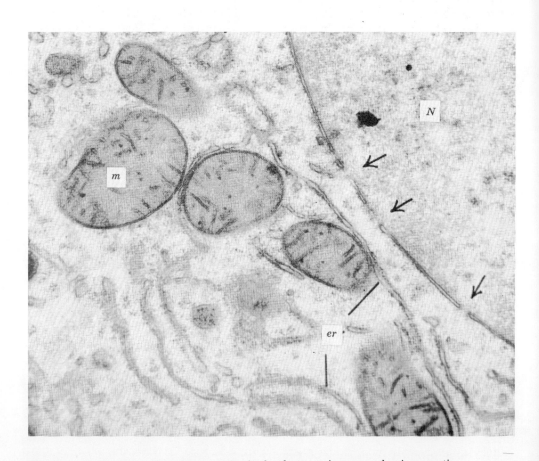

Fig. 3.6 A portion of a cell as seen in section in the electron microscope, showing a portion of the nucleus (*N*) with its membrane, as well as several mitochondria (*m*) and portions of the ergastoplasm (*er*) Arrows indicate pores. (From Porter, 1961, *The Cell* **2** 628; ed. J. Brachet and A. E. Mirsky, Academic Press, New York.)

part of the nucleus. Chemical separations of chromatin material have been effective, however, and we know it to be made of deoxyribonucleic acid (DNA), ribonucleic acid (RNA) and proteins, including the highly alkaline histones. DNA and the histones are confined to the nucleus and are now generally held to be the significant components of the chromosome. DNA in particular is considered to be the carrier of the hereditary information, since only DNA is transferred from gamete to zygote in sexual reproduction. The continuity of chromosome structure from one mitotic cycle to the next is also well established, even though the interphase chromatin shows little detectable structure.

The nucleolus, usually appearing as a spherical structure, is seen both in electron micrographs and in the light microscope as a filamentous network surrounding vacuoles. There is much RNA in the nucleolus and some protein, but the presence of DNA is disputed. The nucleolar RNA is highly active metabolically, being broken down and resynthesized rapidly as shown by the rate of incorporation of labeled molecules.

Role of the Nucleus: Genes

The role of the nucleus in the resting cell was a subject of speculation for many years. The present views on the problem, unlike the earlier ones, are reasonably firmly based on observation and experiment. In the following account we shall try to outline the observations and conclusions both very briefly.

The first problem was that of the mechanism of gene action. The work of the Morgan school of geneticists demonstrated that chromosomes contain entities which are called genes, each of which is responsible for the hereditary transmission of a specific character or set of characters from parent to offspring. Examples are eye color or the length or shape of bristles or wings in the fly *Drosophila.* The gene was a theoretical postulate which could be demonstrated only by its effects; these could be shown to be associated with a specific region or locus in the chromosome, which was able, like the chromosome of which it was a part, to duplicate itself exactly at each cell division.

The mechanism of action of genes was studied by Ephrussi and Beadle, first in *Drosophila,* in relation to the inheritance of eye color, and then by Beadle and Tatum in the mold *Neurospora* in relation to the inheritance of the ability to synthesize specific compounds such as amino acids or vitamins. The eye color work of Beadle and Ephrussi rested on the fact that the eyes of *Drosophila* contain two pigments, one red and the other brown. In one series of mutants—flies in which one or the other gene controlling eye color has become lost or modified—the ability to make brown pigment is lost and the eyes are red. In another series red pigment cannot be formed and the eyes are brown. When both conditions exist together the eyes are white. Experiments in which embryonic eye discs were transplanted between flies of different genetic constitution showed that synthesis of the red pigment involves a definite set of stepwise chemical reactions and that each step depends on a specific gene. Deficiency in any step prevents synthesis of the pigment.

From these studies the "one gene–one enzyme" hypothesis was proposed: each gene is considered to be responsible for the synthesis of a specific enzyme. This hypothesis was abundantly confirmed in the *Neurospora* studies of Beadle, Tatum, and collaborators. This mold can normally synthesize from simpler substances all the amino acids and most of the vitamins that it needs. But under treatment with ultraviolet light or X-rays gene mutations may occur which cause the mold to lose the ability to synthesize one or another compound. In every case analyzed a single gene mutation was associated with a particular chemical reaction. By inference loss of the gene meant loss of the ability to synthesize a specific enzyme. Extensions of this approach to other situations have widened the picture to include proteins other than enzymes. The synthesis of specific forms of the blood pigment hemoglobin, for example, depends on specific genes, and we may now state with great confidence that the major function of genes demonstrated thus far is to control the synthesis of proteins; the synthesis of each specific protein is controlled by a specific gene.

DNA and Protein Synthesis

The next question was that of the chemical nature of the gene. The chromosome was shown by cytochemical methods, enzymic methods, and direct chemical analysis of isolated chromatin to consist of DNA, histone, and residual nonhistone protein. Studies of viruses, some of which consist only of DNA, show that these particles are able to reproduce themselves within cells and that they control protein synthesis within the infected cells. No known histone or other protein can do this. Chemical studies on DNA show that the DNA molecule is large

and complex in structure. The spiral pattern of the molecule, the possibility of a "coding" of genetic information in the pattern of successive nucleotide units, and the evidence that spirals of DNA are complementary and thus could be self-duplicating, all mean that DNA fills all the requisites of a hereditary transmitter (Figure 3.7). It has become evident that of the three constituents of chromosomes only DNA has these properties.

How, then, does DNA exert its control over protein synthesis? Protein synthesis occurs mostly in the microsomes of the cytoplasm, and there is no DNA in the microsomes or anywhere

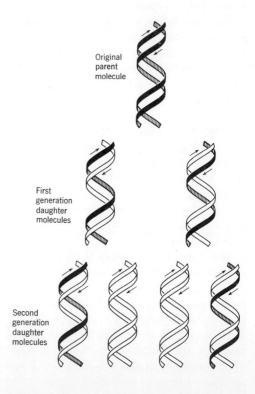

Original parent molecule

First generation daughter molecules

Second generation daughter molecules

Fig. 3.7 The replication of DNA; each strand of the molecule serves as a pattern or template for the synthesis of a duplicate daughter strand. (From Meselson and Stahl, 1958, *Cold Spring Harbor Symposium* **23** 10.)

else in the cytoplasm. There is RNA, and the association of RNA and protein synthesis is universal and quantitative. Protein synthesis occurs only in presence of RNA, and the amount of protein synthesis in any cell or tissue is directly related to the amount of RNA. When RNA is removed by enzyme action protein synthesis stops. On the other hand when the nucleus is removed from those few cells on which this operation can be performed (e.g., amoeba or the large unicellular alga *Acetabularia*) protein synthesis may continue for some time, though it ultimately stops. Many viruses consist largely of RNA. These viruses, like their DNA counterparts, also control protein synthesis in their host cells. RNA has the same complexity and the same ability to duplicate itself that DNA has, so that it seems entirely probable that protein synthesis in the cytoplasm is controlled by RNA.

Thus by a combination of classical genetic studies on animals, combined genetical and biochemical studies with *Neurospora,* and the chemical studies on cells and viruses, geneticists came to a concept of genetic control that can be summarized in the aphorism: "DNA makes RNA, and RNA makes protein." The elaboration of this concept and its development into the current and still rapidly developing picture of protein synthesis has in recent years been the work of a new school of biological research known as molecular biology. Molecular biology uses, to a greater extent than classical biology did, the abstract reasoning characteristic of the physical sciences and has hence attracted a number of investigators trained originally in physics or theoretical chemistry. Most of the experimental work is done with microorganisms and viruses which,

because of their rapid reproduction and, in the case of the viruses, their relative simplicity of structure, offer special opportunities in experimental design. The starting point of these studies was the discovery that processes resembling the sexual union of cells in higher animals can also occur in bacteria and even in viruses. This fact makes possible experiments in which genetic material from different strains can be combined. Such experiments duplicate in principle the breeding experiments of the animal or plant geneticist.

The principal problems proposed by the concept DNA $\longrightarrow$ RNA $\longrightarrow$ protein are: (1) The coding problem; what features of the chemical structure of the DNA molecule in the gene correspond to features in the protein molecule whose synthesis that gene controls? (2) The transmission problem; how is the information contained in the gene structure transmitted from the nucleus to the sites of protein synthesis (microsomes or ribosomes) in the cytoplasm? Both of these problems have been solved in essence in the last two years, though many details remain to be worked out. In particular, from our point of view, the application to animal cells and to the problems of animal development and differentiation remains to be made.

One approach to these two problems was through chemical analyses and comparison of base composition in DNA and RNA. The results of this approach were disappointing because, in overall composition, there is no correspondence between the composition of the two kinds of nucleic acid as isolated in bulk from cells, beyond their general structural similarity. Moreover in bacterial cells it turned out that there was a remarkable uniformity in the composition of the RNA. The molecules fall, in many cases, into only two major size groups with rather uniform composition, and these two size groups correspond with two sizes of ribosomes. Moreover when isotopic labeling was used to measure the turnover of ribosomal RNA, this turnover was found to be very small, much too small to account for any protein synthesis in which the RNA was broken down and reformed.

The clue to the answer came, as is so often the case in science, from another and apparently unrelated kind of study in bacterial genetics. One of the advantages bacteria offer for genetic study is the existence of inducible enzyme systems. Certain bacteria, for instance, when grown in a medium of sucrose as a carbon and energy source, will not have the enzymes necessary to utilize lactose. If, however, lactose is added to the medium, the enzymes for lactose metabolism soon appear in the bacterial cells; they are induced to form by the presence of the substrate. Not all strains of bacteria have the ability to respond this way, and the ability to form induced enzymes is inherited.

Jacob and Monod, studying the inheritance of these induced enzyme systems, found evidence of two kinds of genes. Some of the genes were classical structural genes, each responsible for synthesis of a specific enzyme. Thus, *Escherichia coli* has genes specific, respectively, for the enzymes galactosidase (z) and galactoside permease (y) (Table 3.1). Galactoside permease is necessary for penetration

TABLE 3.1

Relation of genotype to enzyme constitution in the bacterium *Escherichia coli*

	Enzyme Activity (relative units)			
	Noninduced		Induced	
Genotype	Galactosidase	Permease	Galactosidase	Permease
$i^+z^+y^+$	0	0	100	100
$i^-z^+y^+$	120	120	120	120
$i^+z^-y^+/i^-z^+y^+$	2	2	200	200
$i^-z^-y^+/i^+z^+y^-$	2	2	250	120
$i^-z^-y^+/i^-z^+y^+$	250	250	200	250
$i^+o^+z^+y^+$	0	0	100	100
$i^+o^cz^+y^+$	25	25	100	100
$i^+o^+z^+y^+$	0	0	100	100
$i^+o^0z^+y^+$	0	0	0	0
$i^+o^0z^+y^+/i^+o^+z^+y^+$	0	0	250	250
$i^+o^0z^+y^+/i^+o^+z^-y^+$	0	0	0	250
$i^+o^0z^+y^+/i^+o^cz^+y^+$	75	75	250	250
$i^+o^0z^+y^+/i^-o^+z^+y^+$	1	1	250	250

i is the regulator gene for the lactose system, i^+ the allele for the inducible system, i^- the allele for the constitutive system. z^+ is the structural gene for galactosidase, z^- its negative allele. y^+ is the structural gene for galactoside permease, y^- its negative allele. o^+ is the operator gene, o^c its constitutive allele, o^0 its negative allele. Note that bacterial forms with either two sets or one set of genes can occur. Noninduced cultures are grown without lactose; induced cultures are grown with lactose in the medium. Data from Jacob and Monod, 1962, *Cold Spring Harbor Symp. Quant. Biol.* **26** 193.

of lactose into the cell, and galactosidase is necessary for hydrolysis of lactose preparatory to metabolism. In addition to these two structural genes, a third gene (i) can be identified that is essential for formation of both enzymes. Monod has called the third type of gene a "regulator" gene, since it controls a whole system of genes and their associated enzymes. A number of other instances of regulator genes has been observed.

By techniques normally considered in courses in genetics, which we have no time to discuss here, it is possible to determine the relative position of genes in a linear order on a chromosome, or on the corresponding structure in a bacterium or virus. The two structural genes for the galactose enzymes are found to be adjacent, while the regulator gene is located at some distance from the others. Further study then reveals a fourth gene (o), closely associated with the regulator gene and responsible for the inducible character of the enzyme system for lactose utilization. Thus, when one allele of this gene (o^o) is present, the enzyme system is not formed under any conditions. With another allele (o^+), the enzyme system is formed only when lactose is present. With a third allele (o^c) the system is formed whether lactose is present or not, as long as i^+ is also present.

The existence of regulator genes of this sort has important consequences that have not yet been fully explored in the genetic control of cellular processes. For our present purposes however, the importance of the concept of regulator genes is that, to interpret their action in relation to enzyme induction and related phenomena, it became necessary to postulate the existence of a "messenger" in the cytoplasm which would carry information

from the regulator genes to the structural genes. Inducers would then act by controlling synthesis of this messenger (Figure 3.8). Demonstration that the messenger is in fact able to carry genetic information came from studies with the bacteriophage. The phage is a DNA virus which, on entering the bacterial cell, diverts the activities of the cell to the synthesis of phage DNA and of the specific phage protein. Cells infected with a specific phage can be shown to develop a specific soluble RNA which corresponds closely in its base ratios to the phage of DNA, which combines readily and specifically with the phage DNA and is found associated with it in the cell, and which turns over rapidly. When the composition of the soluble

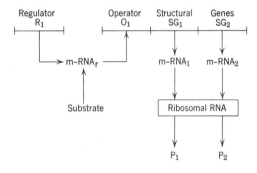

Fig. 3.8 A hypothetical scheme for the control of protein synthesis by genetic systems. Specific proteins (enzymes) P_1 and P_2 are synthesized in the ribosomes. The sequence of amino acids in the peptide chain is determined by the sequence of nitrogenous bases in the specific messenger ribonucleic acids RNA_1 and RNA_2. The sequence of bases in the messenger RNA is determined by the sequence of bases in the DNA chain of the chromosomes corresponding to the structural genes SG_1 and SG_2. The synthesis of messenger RNA by SG_1 and SG_2 depends on the activity of the operator gene O_1 which, in the absence of the substrate for P_1 and P_2, is prevented from acting by the regulator gene R_1. In the presence of the substrate, the repressor RNA (m–RNA_r) formed by R_1 is ineffective, and the proteins P_1 and P_2 are formed. See also Figure 3.9 and Table 3.1.

RNA is altered by supplying the cell with a nitrogenous base, differing slightly in structure from those normally found in RNA, the protein synthesized by the cell is also altered in composition. From these observations it became evident that the soluble RNA includes the messenger required by the Jacob and Monod theory.

It then became important to identify the messenger specifically. We mentioned briefly earlier that protein synthesis involves the soluble fraction of cellular RNA, not associated with the ribosomes. Most hypotheses as to its function centered around a possible role in activating amino acids prior to their incorporation into protein by peptide-bond formation. The soluble fraction, moreover, unlike the RNA of the ribosomes, undergoes rapid synthesis and breakdown in the cell, as shown by the rapid turnover in the labeling experiments. The bulk of the soluble RNA can be distinguished from another RNA fraction, also with a very high turnover rate, in which the base composition is similar to that of DNA and which reflects in its base composition changes occurring by mutation in the DNA. Very recently, enzyme systems have been isolated from bacterial cells that will, in the presence of purified DNA and ribonucleotide triphosphates, synthesize RNA with a base composition complementary to that of the DNA. We thus have at least three kinds of RNA: the messenger RNA, which is synthesized in association with the DNA, has a complementary base composition to the parent DNA and carries the specific information of protein synthesis from gene to microsome; the soluble RNA, which activates the amino acids in preparation for incorporation into proteins; and the ribosomal RNA in the microsomes which

is concerned in the final assembly of the amino acid in the protein molecules in some still undetermined way.

The aphorism with which we began must now be restated: "DNA makes messenger RNA, messenger RNA carries the information required for protein synthesis to the ribosomes." This is not as good an aphorism, but it is better biology. The problem of coding (the language of genetic information) remained, and its essential solution has come during the last year. It was clear from the beginning that the most probable code is one in which the sequence of bases in the nucleic-acid molecule represent a specific amino acid, and the order of base sequences determines the order in which the amino acids are incorporated into the protein molecule. Logical arguments suggested that the simplest code would be one in which a set of three bases in the DNA molecule represent each particular amino acid.

Proof that the code takes this form and evidence of its nature came from studies on cell-free systems capable of synthesizing proteins. It is possible to prepare ribosomes free of other cellular constituents and provide them with nucleotide phosphates and amino acids. Addition of specific RNA to this system will then induce synthesis of specific proteins. When synthetic polynucleotides are added to the system in place of RNA, the rate of incorporation of individual amino acids depends on the composition of the added nucleotide. Thus, a synthetic nucleotide made up entirely of uridine units causes incorporation of phenylalanine. The simplest interpretation of the results available at present is that the code is a triplet code; that is, each amino acid is represented by a specific sequence of three bases. The question of the universality of the code—that is, the question of whether all species have the same code—requires much more study. The code appears to be a degenerate one, in that a particular amino acid may be represented by more than one base sequence. As this is written, work is very active in this field and the interested student should consult the recent original literature for further developments.

The general pattern of control of protein synthesis, as we understand it at present, is shown in Figure 3.9. Much of this is deduced from studies with bacteria and viruses, and detailed verification for animal cells has not been possible. However, the scheme coincides in major outlines with the picture developed earlier on morphological, genetic, and other evidence in animal cells. Caspersson, using the ultraviolet microscope, showed an accumulation of RNA around the cell nucleus, especially in the region of the nucleolus during periods of intensive protein synthesis (Figure 3.10). The rapid turnover of the RNA in the nucleolus suggests that RNA is synthesized in association with the latter,

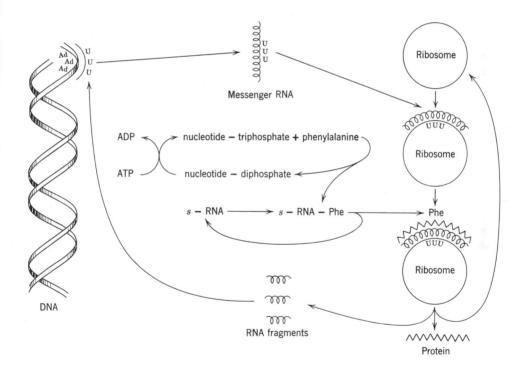

Fig. 3.9 Diagram of a current hypothesis for the control of protein synthesis. The double-stranded DNA chain of the chromosome forms messenger RNA. A small portion of the DNA chain, made up of 3 adenine units, is shown forming RNA with 3 uridine units. The messenger RNA moves to the cytoplasm and to the ribosome. The sequence in which amino acids are incorporated into a peptide chain in the ribosome is determined by the sequence of nitrogenous bases in the m-RNA; U-U-U is the "code word" for phenylalanine. The amino acids are activated by combination with soluble RNA (s-RNA), and then transferred into the peptide chain. The completed protein molecule is then set free from the ribosome, and the m-RNA is broken down.

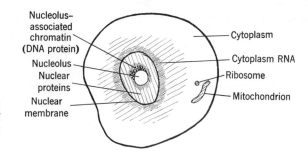

Nucleolus-associated chromatin (DNA protein)

Nucleolus

Nuclear proteins

Nuclear membrane

Cytoplasm

Cytoplasm RNA

Ribosome

Mitochondrion

Fig. 3.10   A cell in the process of protein synthesis. (After Caspersson, 1950, *Cell Growth and Cell Function,* Norton, New York.)

and passes into the cytoplasm. Recent work has traced the movement of labeled RNA from nucleolus to cytoplasm, and a current hypothesis proposes that the nucleolus "amplifies" the synthesis of RNA initiated by the chromosomes.

References

Cell Structure and Composition, General

Brachet, J. 1957. *Biochemical Cytology.* Academic Press, New York.

Bradfield, J. R. G. 1950. The localization of enzymes in cells. *Biol. Rev.* **25** 113–157.

Butler, J. A. V. 1959. *Inside the Living Cell.* Allen and Unwin, London.

Cori, C. F. 1956. Problems of cellular biochemistry. *Curr. Biochem. Res. 1956.* 198–214.

Danielli, J. F. 1953. *Cytochemistry.* Wiley, New York.

Sjöstrand, F. S. 1956. The ultrastructure of cells as revealed by the electron microscope. *Int. Rev. Cytol.* **5** 456–533.

Cell Membrane

Davson, H., and Danielli, J. F. 1952. *The Permeability of Natural Membranes* (2nd ed.) Univ. Press, Cambridge, England.

Klenk, E. 1953. Die Lipoide in chemischen Aufbau des Nervensystems. *Naturwiss.* **40** 449–452.

Parpart, A. K. and Ballentine, R. 1952. Molecular anatomy of the red cell plasma membrane. *Mod. Trends Physiol. Bioch.* 135–148.

Robertson, J. D. 1960. The molecular structure and contact relationships of cell membranes. *Progr. Biophys.* **10** 343–418.

Willmer, E. N. 1961. Steroids and cell surfaces. *Biol. Rev.* **36** 368–398.

Cytoplasm

Boxer, G. E., and Devlin, T. M. 1961. Pathways of intracellular hydrogen transport. *Science* **134** 1495–1501.

Brenner, S. 1962. RNA, ribosomes, and protein synthesis. *Cold Spring Harbor Symp. Quant. Biol.* **26** 101–110.

Campbell, P. N. 1960. The synthesis of proteins by the cytoplasmic components of animal cells. *Biol. Rev.* **35** 413–458.

Campbell, P. N. 1961. The role of the cytoplasmic components of the cell in protein synthesis. *Cell. Mech. Hormone Prod. Act.* 55–59.

Claude, A. 1954. Cell morphology and the organization of enzymatic systems in cytoplasm. *Proc. Roy. Soc. London. B* **142** 177–186.

Green, D. E. 1959. Mitochondrial structure and function. *Subcellular Particles* (T. Hayashi ed.) Ronald Press, New York.

Green, D. E., and Hatefi, Y. 1961. The mitochondrion and biochemical machines. *Science* **133** 13–19.

Green, D. E., and Järnefelt, J. 1958. Enzymes and biological organization. *Perspectives in Biol. and Med.* **2** 163–184.

Haguenau, F. 1958. The ergastoplasm. *Int. Rev. Cytol.* **7** 425–534.

Holter, H. 1952. Localization of enzymes in cytoplasm. *Adv. Enzymol.* **13** 1–20.

Jackson, S. F. 1961. Aspects of cell structure in relation to synthesis and secretion. *Cell. Mech. Hormone Prod. Act.* 3–22.

Kirkland, R. J. A. 1958. Particles in plant and animal cells. *Adv. of Sci.* **14** 353–364.

Lehninger, A. L. 1960. Oxidative phosphorylation in submitochondrial systems. *Fed. Proc.* **19** 952–962.

Marshall, A. J. 1952. The structure of the so-called Golgi body. *Sci. Progr.* **40** 71–77.

Nath, V. 1957. The Golgi controversy. *Nature* **180** 967–969.

Oberling, C. 1959. The structure of cytoplasm. *Int. Rev. Cytol.* **8** 1–32.

Porter, K. R. et al. (eds.) 1961. The sarcoplasmic reticulum. *J. Biophys. Biochem. Cytol.* **10** suppl.

Rendi, R., and Warner, R. C. 1960. Intracellular sites for amino acid incorporation into proteins. *Annals N.Y. Acad. Sci.* **88** 741–744.

Roberts, R. B. 1960. Synthetic aspects of ribosomes. *Annals N.Y. Acad. Sci.* **88** 752–769.

Runnström, J. 1952. The cytoplasm, its structure and role in metabolism, growth, and differentiation. *Mod. Trends Physiol. Biochem.* 47–76.

Schneider, W. C. 1959. Mitochondrial metabolism. *Adv. Enzymol.* **21** 1–72.

The Nucleus

Allfrey, J. G. A., Mirsky, A. E., and Stern, H. 1955. The chemistry of the cell nucleus. *Adv. Enzymol.* **16** 411–500.

Bowen, V. T. (ed.) 1952. *The Chemistry and Physiology of the Nucleus.* Academic Press, New York.

Mazia, D. 1952. Physiology of the cell nucleus. *Mod. Trends Physiol. Biochem.* 77–122.

Mitchell, J. S. (ed.) 1960. *The Cell Nucleus.* Academic Press, New York.

Sirlin, J. L. 1961. The nucleolus of the cell nucleus. *Endeavour* **20** 146–153.

Sirlin, J. L., and Jacob, J. 1962. Function, development and evolution of the nucleolus. *Nature* **195** 114–117.

Stich, H. 1956. Bau und Funktion der Nukleolen. *Experientia* **12** 7–14.

White, M. J. D. 1961. *The Chromosomes.* (3rd edn.) Wiley, New York.

Wischnitzer, S. 1960. The ultrastructure of the nucleus and nucleocytoplasmic relations. *Int. Rev. Cytol.* **10** 132–162.

Genetic Control of Cell Function

Beadle, G. W. 1945. Genetics and metabolism in Neurospora. *Physiol. Rev.* **25** 643–663.

Beadle, G. W. 1946. The gene and biochemistry. *Curr. Biochem. Res.* 1–12.

Brachet, J. 1960. Ribonucleic acids and the synthesis of cellular proteins. *Nature* **186** 194–199.

Brenner, S. 1962. RNA, ribosomes, and protein synthesis. *Cold Spring Harbor Symp. Quant. Biol.* **26** 101–110.

Caspersson, T. O. 1950. *Cell Growth and Cell Function.* Norton, New York.

Crick, F. H. C., Barnett, L., Brenner, S., and Watts-Tobin, R. J. 1961. General nature of the genetic code for proteins. *Nature* **192** 1227–1232.

Davis, B. D. 1962. The teleonomic significance of biosynthetic control mechanisms. *Cold Spring Harbor Symp. Quant. Biol.* **26** 1–10.

Drysdale, R. B., and Peacocke, A. R. 1961. The molecular basis of heredity. *Biol. Rev.* **36** 537–598.

Gros, F., Gilbert, W., Hiatt, H. H., Attardi, G., Spahr, P. F., and Watson, J. D. 1962. Molecular and biological characterization of messenger RNA. *Cold Spring Harbor Symp. Quant. Biol.* **26** 111–132.

Harris, R. J. C. (ed.) 1959. *The Relationship between Nucleus and Cytoplasm.* Academic Press, New York.

Holley, R. W., Apgar, J., and Doctor, B. P. 1960. Separation of amino acid-specific "soluble"-fraction ribonucleic acids. *Annals N.Y. Acad. Sci.* **88** 745–751.

Monod, J., and Jacob, F. 1962. Teleonomic mechanisms in cellular metabolism, growth, and differentiation. *Cold Spring Harbor Symp. Quant. Biol.* **26** 389–401.

Raacke, I. D. 1958. Chemical aspects of recent hypotheses on protein synthesis. *Quart. Rev. Biol.* **33** 245–261.

Spiegelman, S. 1962. The relation of informational RNA to DNA. *Cold Spring Harbor Symp. Quant. Biol.* **26** 75–90.

Taylor, J. H. 1960. Chromosome reproduction and the problem of coding and transmitting of the genetic heritage. *Am. Scientist* **48** 365–382.

4 Functions of the cell boundary

The visible boundary of the cell is clearly identifiable, whether it is seen with the light microscope as the margin of the cytoplasm without resolvable structure or with the electron microscope in sections of cells as a membrane about 25 Å thick. There is also a functional boundary of the cell known from osmotic and electrical properties.

Osmosis

When a cell is exposed to external aqueous media of varying concentrations it undergoes typical changes in volume, swelling in solutions of low solute concentration and shrinking in solutions of high solute concentration. We can simulate this behavior with various artificial membranes or with dead animal membranes. If an inert membrane is used to separate two chambers, I and II, in which are placed two aqueous solutions containing a solute which does not penetrate the membrane, at solute concentrations C^I and C^{II}, then water will flow from I to II when $C^I < C^{II}$. The simplest qualitative interpretation is that in I the concentration of water particles is greater than in II, hence the probability that a water molecule will move from I to II is greater than the probability of movement in the opposite direction. In other words, the movement of water occurs by diffusion, and diffusion is a consequence of the random motion of the particles of a fluid and of a difference in concentration of those particles. There has been a considerable amount of theoretical and experimental study of osmosis or the diffusion of water in artificial membrane systems, and some of the concepts developed have been useful in such matters, for example, as the determination of molecular weights of large molecules.

There has also been a large amount of work done on the osmotic behavior of cells. This work has in general assumed that, since osmotic swelling and shrinkage occurs, the cell is surrounded by a semi-permeable membrane with properties much like those of the artificial membranes used in physicochemical studies. For some purposes this assumption is valid, if only approximate results are required. For other purposes, as we shall see, it is not reliable.

Permeability

The most widely used relation in the study of diffusion is Fick's law, which in essence states that the time rate of diffusion is proportional to the concentration gradient. In the simple case of two homogeneous solutions of a solute i at concentrations C_i^I and C_i^{II}, separated by a membrane which we shall assume to be permeable to the solute, the rate of diffusion of i, J_i, in moles per liter per second, across the membrane from I to II will be given by

$$J_i = P_i A (C_i^I - C_i^{II}).$$

Here A is the area of the membrane in square centimeters and P_i is a constant known as the permeability constant. The principal virtue of this equation is its simplicity. This is not the place for a detailed criticism of the equation, but the assumptions on which it rests include the following, none of which is strictly valid in biological situations: (1) The diffusion of any substance i must be independent of the diffusion of all other substances in the system.

(2) The concentrations C_i^I and C_i^{II} must be the physicochemical activities, not simply the chemical concentrations; in other words, the diffusing substances must not be associated with any other substances chemically. (3) P_i should be independent of concentration. (4) The rate of diffusion or mixing in the two solutions I and II must be much greater than that across the membrane itself since the solutions are assumed always to be homogeneous. (5) The membrane is assumed to be homogeneous, not porous.

In spite of its limitations the permeability equation has proved useful. Permeability coefficients have been measured for a great variety of substances, and by correlation of values of the coefficients with known properties of the substances it is possible to deduce the properties of a model membrane to which the coefficients would apply. The most general relation, as noted earlier, is that between permeability and solubility in lipids and other nonpolar organic solvents. This relation is apparent in Table 4.1. Substances which are readily soluble in nonpolar solvents have permeability coefficients with relatively high values. Substances insoluble in nonpolar solvents have small permeability coefficients. As we noted earlier these observations led to the suggestion that the permeability barrier of the cell is a lipid membrane, and there is independent evidence that the visible cell boundary is a lipid membrane. This line of evidence therefore supports the assumption that the permeability or osmotic barrier and the visible boundary are the same.

The permeability-solubility relation breaks down with small molecules. When permeability coefficients are determined for very small molecules

TABLE 4.1

The Relation of Permeability Constants (P) to Molecular Size and Solubility in Lipids

Substance	Molecular Weight	Molecular Diameter (Å)	Oil/Water Partition Coefficient (log 1/C)	Calculated Permeability of 5-μ Layer of Oil (log 1/P)	Permeability Coefficient (log 1/P) for			
					Beggiatoa	Chara Cell	Arbacia Egg	Ox Erythrocyte
Propionamide	73	–	1.4	4.5	–	4.5	4.6	–
α, β-dioxypropane	76	–	2.3	4.6	–	4.6	4.9	5.4
Acetamide	59	–	1.1	5.1	–	4.8	5.0	–
Ethylene Glycol	62	–	3.3	5.1	4.9	4.9	5.1	5.7
Urea	60	1.8	3.8	6.7	4.8	6.0	–	4.1
Glycerol	92	3.1	4.2	7.3	5.0	6.7	7.3	7.8
Erythritol	122	3.5	4.5	9.2	7.3	7.9	–	–
Sucrose	342	5.2	4.5	–	5.9	8.1	–	–

Beggiatoa is a large bacterium, *Chara* an alga with large cells, *Arbacia* a sea urchin. *P* in cm per sec. (Recalculated from Davson and Danielli, 1943, *Permeability of Natural Membranes*, Cambridge University Press. Data on molecular diameters from Schultz and Solomon, 1961, *J. Gen. Physiol.* **44** 1189–1199).

they are more closely related to molecular size than to lipid solubility. As we noted earlier this suggests that there are pores in the membrane with a mean diameter of about 5 Å. The existence of such pores has not yet been verified independently. However, recent studies of the permeability of membranes to water and inorganic ions show much better quantitative agreement with the equations derived on the assumption of a porous membrane than they do with simple Fick's law equations.

The permeability-solubility relation also breaks down for certain molecules such as glucose and glycerol, both of which have relatively large molecules, are quite insoluble in nonpolar solvents, and yet penetrate most cells with relative ease. In the case of glucose the kinetics of permeation and the fact that glucose appears to compete for specific entry sites with other closely related monosaccharides suggest that glucose penetrates the cell membrane by combining with a specific component of the membrane. The same mechanism has been proposed for glycerol and several other substances. The classical permeability equation is not applicable to this situation.

The study of the permeability of membranes to water and ions is complicated by many factors. For water and for ions at higher concentrations, and possibly at lower concentrations in the presence of certain substances which bind ions, the concentrations determined by chemical analysis are not equal to the chemical activities but are generally greater. Water molecules are associated into complexes of various size, and ions are held by electrostatic forces in the neighborhood of protein molecules. Moreover, as we shall see shortly, the membranes of all cells examined, and probably of all living cells, exhibit a difference of electrical potential which will influence strongly the movements of ions across the membrane. There is evidence for some cells that certain ions can be "pumped" into or out of the cell across the membrane by a process that involves the performance of work and the expenditure of energy. Even if these factors were not operative there is experimental evidence that in simple diffusion the movements of ions may be influenced by the simultaneous movements of other ions or of water. One must conclude then that the classical permeability equation is in general reliable only for substances which are not concerned in vital processes, and even for these only as an approximate relation.

Ion Transport and Bioelectricity

Membrane Potentials

At the beginning of this chapter we mentioned that the functional cell boundary can be identified by electrical as well as by osmotic properties. If a piece of glass tubing is drawn out to an extremely fine point with a diameter about 1 μ or less, the resulting capillary may be filled with an electrolyte solution (for example a KCl solution) and connected to a potentiometer circuit through a silver wire which is plated with silver chloride. If now a second electrode of the same composition, but not necessarily with a capillary tip, is prepared and both electrodes, connected to a potentiometer, are placed in the medium bathing a living cell, there should be little or no difference of potential recorded. If the capillary electrode is now slowly moved into the cell there will at some point be a sharp change of potential. Usually the cell interior is electrically negative to the medium, at least in nerve and muscle cells, to the extent of 50 to 100 mV. In the few other cases which have been studied the difference is smaller. The exact location of this potential change has not been established, but its sudden character suggests that a single thin barrier is the site and the visible cell boundary has all the requisite properties.

The cause of this potential difference has been much discussed, often with reference to simple electrochemical systems which are known to develop potential differences. Such systems are of three types. (1) In concentration cells, two solutions of different concentrations are in electrical contact, but in such a way that no exchange of materials between the two solutions is possible. The potential difference in this situation is directly related to the logarithm of the concentration difference. (2) Concentration cells with transference are similar to the above, but the two solutions are connected by a membrane such that some exchange of materials is possible. The potential difference is then a function both of the concentration differences and of the rate of movement across the membrane of the various ions making up the solution. (3) In galvanic cells chemical reactions normally involving oxidation and reduction occur at the electrodes. The potential difference is a function of the rates and the free energy changes of the reactions. There is no reason to present the theory of these cells here because it will appear in what follows that no one of the classical electrochemical situations is strictly applicable to the cell membrane.

Ion Concentrations in Cells

Instead let us first look at the possible sources of electrical phenomena in the region of the membrane. When the contents of living cells are analyzed it invariably turns out that the concentrations of ions in the cell interior are quite different from those in the external medium. For most cells the exact interpretation of this fact with respect to the cell membrane is questionable, since the cell contents are morphologically heterogeneous and we know that some cell structures such as the mitochondria have proportions of ions quite different from those of the surrounding cytoplasm. Moreover, there is always the possibility that some ions are bound by cell components, so that a simple determination of potassium content, for example, will not necessarily give a true picture of the activity of the potassium ion in the cell contents in contact with the cell membrane.

In two types of living cells, however, we may suppose that these qualifications are less serious. The erythrocyte has little internal structure and no mitochondria, hence its composition may more fairly reflect the ionic composition of the cell contents. The nerve axon has more internal structure, but in the case of the giant axon of the squid the axoplasm can be extruded and analyzed much more completely and accurately than is the case for most cells.

Erythrocytes in general—with some exceptions—and human erythrocytes in particular, normally have higher K^+ and lower Na^+ concentrations than the plasma in which they are suspended. Such a situation might conceivably arise if the membrane were completely impermeable to one of the two ions, but there is abundant evidence that this is not the case. In the course of studies of blood preservation it was noticed that when blood is stored in the cold (5°C) the erythrocytes lose K^+ and take up Na^+. If the blood, containing normal amounts of glucose, is returned to body temperature (38°C) the Na^+ leaves the cells and the K^+ enters, with eventual restoration of the original concentration levels. The same exchanges can be brought about by poisoning the energy-yielding systems of the cell with metabolic poisons and then washing out the poisons. Clearly the membrane is permeable to both Na and K ions, and hence the normal distribution cannot represent an equilibrium; clearly also

the normal distribution depends on the expenditure of metabolic energy for its maintenance.

In the axon of the giant motor neurons of the mantle of the squid the same relations are seen. Table 4.2 gives relative concentration figures for ions in the axoplasm and in sea water. Again the K^+ concentration is much higher, and the Na^+ lower in the axoplasm than in the medium. Moreover, if the axon is electrically stimulated by repeated shocks at high frequency for long periods there is a loss of K^+ and a parallel increase in the Na^+ of the axoplasm. When the axon is allowed to recover, K^+ enters and Na^+ leaves the axoplasm. Similar phenomena have been noted in muscle cells, and in both cases the recovery of

TABLE 4.2
The Ion Composition of the Cytoplasm of the Giant Axon of the Squid, Compared with That of Sea Water

| Ion | Concentration, mM per liter | | Activity Axoplasm | Concentration Ratio, c_o/c_i | Equilibrium Potential, mV (inside negative) |
	Sea Water	Axoplasm			
K^+	9.9	298	203	0.0333	-86
Na^+	465	59.1	37	7.86	$+52$
Ca^{2+}	10.2	2.7			
Mg^{2+}	53.0	7.6			
Arginine$^+$	—	3.1			
Lysine$^+$	—	0.2			
Ornithine$^+$	—	0.2			
Cl^-	542	109		4.97	-29
HCO_3^-	—	11.5			
SO_4^{2-}	35	5.5			
HPO_4^{2-}	—	5.4			
$H_2PO_4^-$	—	6.7			
5'Adenosine mono-phosphate^{2-}	—	0.7			
Isethionate$^-$	—	120.5			
Aspartate$^-$	—	81			
Glutamate$^-$	—	20.1			

Data from Koechlin, 1955, *J. Biophys. Biochem. Cytol.* **1** 511, and Hinke, 1961, *J. Physiol.* **156** 314–335.

normal concentration levels has been shown to depend upon energy arising from metabolic processes.

Ion Transport

It should be clear from the foregoing example that at least one of the ions, either Na^+ or K^+, must at times be moved in a direction opposite to that in which it would move passively, and that it is this movement which constitutes the performance of work and requires the expenditure of energy. However, the situation is complicated by the existence across the membrane of the axon or muscle cell of a difference of electrical potential, which will exert a force on the ion in addition to the forces of chemical concentration that are normally involved in diffusion.

To analyze these factors further we may turn to a tissue which has become a classic material for the study of ion transport and bioelectric potential—the skin of the frog. If the skin is removed from a frog and a piece of it is used as a membrane to separate two solutions containing Na^+ and K^+ ions, there will in general be a measurable difference in potential between the two solutions. If these solutions are made identical in composition, to eliminate concentration potentials, there will still be a measurable potential difference, indicating that the origin of the potential is in the skin, not in the solutions. The potential will persist for hours, and if the two solutions are connected through an external circuit a small current will flow for hours, showing that the skin is capable of performing electrical work. If the composition of the solutions bathing the skin is initially identical, it will be found after some time that a small amount of Na^+ has been transferred from the solution bathing the outside or epidermal surface of the skin to the solution bathing the inside or dermal surface. The same transfer can be demonstrated by the use of the radioactive isotopes of Na^+. The isotope will move from outside inward ten to twenty times as rapidly as it moves in the opposite direction.

The experiment which demonstrated most clearly the activity of the skin is that performed by Ussing and Zerahn (Figure 4.1 and Table 4.3). They arranged an experimental chamber with the skin as a membrane separating identical NaCl-KCl solutions, with two sets of electrodes on each side of the skin. One electrode on each side was connected to a potentiometer which served to record the potential difference between the two chambers. The second electrode on each side was connected to an external circuit including an ammeter and a variable electromotive force. By adjusting the external EMF until it exactly equaled and opposed the EMF of the skin the potential difference between the two solutions bathing the skin could be brought to zero. Under these circumstances a small current flows through the external circuit. Measurement of the net Na^+ flux with isotopes during the period in which the skin potential is maintained at zero shows that the external current at zero potential (short circuit current) exactly equals the current carried across the skin by Na^+. In other words, the only ion moving across the skin when there is no chemical concentration gradient and no difference of electrical potential is Na^+.

We may therefore conclude that the skin is able to pump or transport Na^+ by the expenditure of metabolic energy. The pump must then be re-

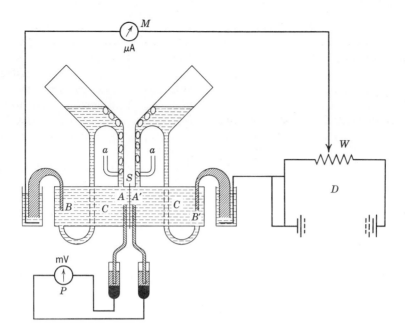

Fig. 4.1 Apparatus for measuring the current flux across a membrane at zero potential (short-circuit current). A and A' are calomel electrodes connected to a potentiometer P reading in millivolts; B and B' are salt bridges connected to Ag-AgCl electrodes, which in turn form part of a circuit including a variable source of electromotive force D, a microammeter M, the two chambers C containing identical saline solutions, and the membrane S. The solutions in the chambers C are circulated and aerated by air lifts supplied through a. (From Ussing and Zerahn, 1957, *Acta Physiol. Scand.* **23** 110.)

TABLE 4.3

The Relation of Sodium Influx across the Isolated Skin of a Frog to the Electric Current Flux Measured Simultaneously

Hours	Na Influx, μmole per sq cm per hr	Na Current, coulombs per sq cm per hr $\times 10^3$	Current Flux, coulombs per sq cm per hr $\times 10^3$
1	1.85	178	174
2	1.85	178	162
3	0.88	85	0
4	0.62	60	0
5	1.28	123	123

Data from Ussing and Zerahn, 1951, *Acta Physiol. Scand.* **23** 110–127. The apparatus used is diagrammed in Figure 4.1. Sodium influx was measured by adding ^{24}Na to the solution on the outside of the skin at the beginning of the experiment, and measuring the radioactivity of the solution on the inside of the skin at hourly intervals. During the third and fourth hours no external emf was applied, hence there was no net current flux, and the skin potential was at the "resting" level; during the first, second, and fifth hours, the skin potential was held to zero by connecting the skin in series with an external emf so that a current flowed through the circuit.

garded as the electromotive force of the skin, which is primarily responsible for the skin potential. Its mechanism remains unknown, though a number of hypotheses have been proposed and are currently being tested. No other ion is transported actively. When the skin is allowed to develop its resting potential (i.e., when no current flows between the chambers) the inside is positive to the outside and Na^+ must move against a potential gradient. When the skin is in place on the frog and the frog is in tap water with an Na^+ concentration of 1 mM or less, as compared to the Na^+ concentration of 100 to 150 mM in the blood, there is a large concentration gradient as well; yet Krogh showed years ago that NaCl is taken up against this gradient. We now know that the Na^+ is taken up actively while Cl^- enters passively along the potential gradient.

In the case of the squid axon and the muscle cell the interior of the cell is normally negative to the exterior. It is therefore evident that when Na^+ moves outward during recovery after prolonged stimulation it must be transported actively. In the human erythrocyte the electrical potential difference across the membrane is thought to be such that the K^+ movement is active.

Origin of the Resting Potential

The problem of the ion distribution across the membrane of the nerve axon, and its relation to the electrical and permeability properties of the membrane, is of especial importance in the excitation of nerve cells, and hence deserves special attention. We may begin by supposing that, as in frog skin, the primary electromotive force in the axon membrane is a Na^+ pump, which by separating Na^+ from other ions sets up a potential difference. This difference will result in further movements of ions across the membrane in consequence of electrical forces. For any ion i, the relation of the concentration C_i^I on one side of a membrane to the concentration C_i^{II} on the other side at equilibrium when the potential difference is E, is given by

$$E_i = \mu_i^I - \mu_i^{II} = \frac{RT}{z_i F} \ln \frac{C_i^I}{C_i^{II}}$$

Here μ_i^I is the chemical potential of i in I, z_i is the electrochemical valence of i, F is the faraday (a conversion factor between concentration units and electrical units), R is the gas constant, and T the absolute temperature. The first of the two equations, relating E to μ, is generally valid for equilibrium. The second equation, relating E to C, is an approximation which may be reliable in the biological concentration range if the ion in question is not bound or adsorbed. Equilibrium potentials for the three major ions of biological fluids (Na^+, K^+, Cl^-) are calculated in Table 4.2 from concentration values for squid axoplasm, and it is clear that none of the ions is in chemical diffusion equilibrium, although K^+ is nearly so. We know from isotope studies and from studies of ion movements following nerve stimulation that the membrane is permeable to the three major ions, but probably is not permeable to any of the other ions of the medium or the axoplasm. The permeability of the membranes to the three ions differs; Hodgkin and Katz have calculated relative values of $1:0.04:0.45$ for $K^+:Na^+:Cl^-$ in the resting membrane. We may then analyze the situation in the resting axon as follows, assuming that the concentrations of the ions represent their chemical potentials. Na$^+$ is far from its equilibrium value. This distribution is the result of the activity of the Na$^+$ pump which removes Na$^+$ as rapidly as it diffuses inward. The Na$^+$ distribution represents the balance between the force exerted by the pump moving Na$^+$ outward and the electrical and diffusion forces tending to move Na$^+$ inward. The rate of inward diffusion of Na$^+$ is slow because of a low permeability to Na$^+$. K$^+$ ion is near its equilibrium value. Its distribution represents a balance between the diffusion force which tends to move K$^+$ outward and the electrical force tending to move it inward. Chloride ion is subject to the same forces but the membrane permeability to Cl$^-$ is somewhat lower than that for K$^+$. Moreover, the axoplasm contains large amounts of nondiffusible anions, of which the major one is isethionate. This means that the internal chloride concentration must remain low to insure the electrical neutrality of the axoplasm. The sum of the ionic charges within the axoplasm is close to electrical neutrality; this fact is evidence that none of the ions is bound in such a way as to alter its electrical charge.

The balance of these forces across the membrane can be expressed in quantitative terms by the following equation for the resting potential E_R of the axon membrane:

$$E_R = g_{Na}E_{Na} + g_K E_K + g_{Cl}E_{Cl} - \frac{I_{Na}}{g}$$

Here g_{Na}, g_K, g_{Cl} are the ionic conductances or the contribution made by each ion to the total membrane conductance g. It is assumed that $g = g_{Na} + g_K + g_{Cl}$, or in other words that no other ions contribute to the conductance. These assumptions still require careful verification. The ionic potentials E_{Na}, E_K, E_{Cl} are the values of the membrane potential at which the measured concentration ratios across the membrane would represent equilibrium; in other words the difference between E_R and E_{Na} represents the deviation of the resting potential from the equilibrium potential for Na$^+$. The last term I_{Na} represents the current produced by the sodium pump. The importance of this term is questioned. The suggestion has been made that the pump exchanges Na$^+$ for K$^+$ on a $1:1$ basis. In this case the transport of K$^+$ would be active also, and a term I_K/g, equal in magnitude but opposite in sign to the term I_{Na}/g, would be added to the equation. Such a pump would be "nonelectrogenic." The entire ion distribution pattern and the potential represent a dynamic study state in which none of the components is at equilibrium, but all are maintained at constant concentration levels by the continuous expenditure of metabolic energy through the sodium pump.

The picture which has just been presented is still to a degree controversial and in any case applies strictly only to the giant axon of the squid. When axons are deprived of oxygen or poisoned with cyanide (blocking the cytochrome system) or dinitrophenol (blocking oxidative phosphorylation) the membrane potential remains unchanged for some time in spite of the fact that the sodium pump is inhibited almost immediately by these treatments. Likewise the injection of ATP and certain other phosphate donors into axoplasm, which stimulates the sodium pump, does not alter the membrane potential. These results favor the nonelectrogenic hypothesis for the pump. Injection of KCl into the axoplasm in amounts sufficient to change the internal KCl concentration considerably does not change the membrane potential, although alterations in the KCl concentration of the external medium bring about such changes almost exactly as predicted by the membrane potential equation. Muscle fibers, which in their electrical properties resemble axons very closely, can be soaked in potassium-free solutions until their internal K^+ concentration falls to 20% of normal values and the resting potential on return to the normal medium is essentially unchanged. These results are inconsistent with the view that the resting potential is a sum of equilibrium potentials. We are therefore led to reserve our judgment concerning the interpretation of the membrane potential in relation to ion permeability and the Na pump.

Summary

In thus concluding this chapter we may appear to suggest that studies of the properties of the cell membrane are hopelessly complex and confused. It appears desirable to summarize our positive knowledge of these properties. (1) Structurally the membrane appears to be a thin lipoprotein film not greatly different from, and possibly continuous with, the membranes of the endoplasmic reticulum. (2) Functionally the membrane constitutes a definite boundary, identifiable in terms of its electrical and permeability properties. (3) Some of the permeability properties are understandable in terms of the lipoid nature of the membrane material; others require the assumption of a porous structure. (4) Some substances are selectively absorbed across the membrane at rates and in manners clearly related to their chemical structures, rather than to some more general property such as molecular size or solubility. These phenomena are properly best explained in terms of some specific combination between the absorbed substance and the membrane constituent. (5) Certain ions and other substances are moved across cell membranes against gradients of chemical concentration or electrical potential or both by processes which involve performance of work by the expenditure of metabolic energy. Such processes are called active transport. (6) In the normal resting distribution of substances across the cell membrane and in the net movement of substances across the membrane when this occurs, a complete interpretation must take into account the forces arising from chemical concentration differences, from electrical potential differences, and from active transport processes. (7) There is, in those cells studied so far, always an electrical potential difference across the membrane. This difference may be considered to arise from two possible sources: an equilibrium potential representing the net effects of the chemical concentration and passive electrical forces, and an active transport potential arising from active transport processes. Serious questions remain concerning the existence and importance of other factors in these phenomena.

References

Christensen, H. N. Active transport, with special reference to the amino acids. *Perspectives in Biol. and Med.* 2 228–242.
Danielli, J. F. 1954. Phosphatases and other enzymes considered in relation to active transport and the functions of fibrous protein structures. *Proc. Royal Soc. London B* 142 146–154.

Davson, H., and Danielli, J. F. 1952. *The Permeability of Natural Membranes* (2nd edn.) Univ. Press, Cambridge, England.

Deysson, G. 1952. Sur les methodes d'étude de la perméabilité cellulaire. *Rev. Gén. des Sciences* **49** 215–228.

Durbin, R. P., Curran, P. E., and Solomon, A. K. 1958. Ion and water transport in stomach and intestine. *Adv. Biol. Med. Phys.* **6** 1–36.

Glynn, I. M. 1961. The movements of water and salt through natural membranes. *Symp. Water Electrolyte Metab.* 3–13.

Grundfest, H. 1952. Mechanism and properties of bioelectric potentials. *Mod. Trends. Physiol. Biochem.* 193–229.

Harris, E. J. 1960. *Transport and Accumulation in Biological Systems.* (2nd. edn.) Butterworths, London.

Hodgkin, A. L. 1951. The ionic basis of electrical activity in nerve and muscle. *Biol. Rev.* **26** 339–409.

Johnson, P. A., and Babb, A. L. 1956. Liquid diffusion of non-electrolytes. *Chem. Rev.* **56** 387–453.

LeFevre, P. G. 1955. *Active Transport through Animal Cell Membranes.* Springer Verlag, Vienna.

Manery, J. F. 1955. General principles and problems of electrolyte research. *Canadian J. Biochem. Physiol.* **33** 453–461.

Murphy, Q. R. (ed.) 1957. *Metabolic Aspects of Transport across Cell Membranes.* Univ. Wisconsin Press, Madison, Wisc.

Pappenheimer, J. R. 1953. Passage of molecules through capillary walls. *Physiol. Rev.* **33** 387–423.

Robinson, J. R. 1953. The active transport of water in living systems. *Biol. Rev.* **28** 158–194.

Sols, A. 1957. Phosphorylation et transport actif des sucres. *Bull. Soc. Chim. Biol.* **39** Suppl. 2, 3–15

Ussing, H. H. 1949. Transport of ions across cellular membranes. *Physiol. Rev.* **29** 127–155.

part II
Irritability

5 Excitation of animal cells

Irritability has long been considered one of the fundamental characteristics which distinguish living from nonliving things. In general any of a great variety of changes in the physical environment of the organism will be followed by changes in the activities of the organism which differ from those we expect to find in an inanimate system. We may speak of the environmental change as a stimulus and of the change in the activities of the organism as a response. Responses, in the sense used here, are usually disproportionate to the stimuli which elicit them and are adaptive, in that they can usually be interpreted as tending to preserve the life of the individual or species. If one pursues this general concept of irritability to philosophical extremes one encounters many difficulties, the discussion of which would be out of place here. Moreover, there is not now and probably never will be a general physiological theory of irritability which will cover all or most instances. We shall therefore confine our considerations here to one set of structures, comprising the neuromuscular system of animals. This system is clearly specialized in the direction of irritability, and the mechanisms of action are fairly well understood. Some of these mechanisms may also be applicable to other irritable systems; some clearly are not.

Neuromuscular System

The neuromuscular system of animals is remarkably uniform in its structural essentials and as far as we know in its functional mechanisms as well. It is also a remarkably complex system in its total organization and as such exhibits an enormous variety in various animal species. Structural units of the system may be grouped into two categories, neurons (or nerve cells) and muscle cells. Each of these units occurs in a great many forms, but each of the many forms has certain properties in common.

Neurons are cells with one or more elongate cytoplasmic projections extending from the cell body. The cell body contains the nucleus, and the projections (known as axons if they are long and single and dendrites if they are short and branched) are usually much smaller in cross-sectional area than is the cell body. Neurons usually have characteristic staining properties, particularly with respect to their ability to reduce silver in fixed preparations and their affinity for methylene blue in living preparations. Functionally, neurons are characterized by highly developed irritability and the ability to conduct a state of excitation from the point of stimulus to the termini of the axons and dendrites. This last statement is not strictly an operational one. Neither the excitation nor the conduction can be observed in the neuron itself without the aid of very sophisticated electrical apparatus. Both can be observed indirectly, however, since the stimulation of a nerve which is attached to a muscle will cause a contraction in the muscle. Obviously something has been caused to happen in the nerve, and the state of excitation thus produced has been somehow transmitted to the muscle at a distance.

Muscle cells are also quite heterogeneous in structure. They have in common the structural property of an elongate shape—the length being generally greater than the diameter—and

the functional property of contractility. When a muscle cell or a tissue composed of such cells is stimulated by some appropriate means the cell or tissue shortens and becomes thicker. If the cell or tissue is arranged so that its contraction is opposed by a force, such as is exerted by a weight, the contraction will do work. Consequently, a contraction must involve liberation of energy. The distribution of nerve and muscle cells in animals is almost but not quite universal. Among Protozoans there are contractile structures, such as the stalk of *Vorticella* and related forms, and conducting structures, such as the "neuromotor" system of certain Ciliates, but these we shall not examine in detail. Among the Porifera we find muscle cells without associated nerve cells; structures resembling nerve cells have been described in this group by some zoologists, but physiological studies provide no evidence of nerve function. In the Coelenterates and all higher animals, nerve and muscle cells occur together and in definite association. In the Coelenterates the patterns are quite varied, and clearly differentiated nervous and muscular tissues are not usually present.

Most of our knowledge of nerve and muscle comes from higher animals and specifically from members of the phyla Mollusca, Arthropoda, and Chordata. In all these groups there are well-developed and clearly defined muscles, which are organs composed predominantly of muscle cells and so arranged as to be conveniently accessible to physiological study. Likewise all of these groups have a well-defined nervous system, consisting of a central or ganglionic portion made up of nerve cells and their processes, and a peripheral portion including well-defined nerves or bundles of axons extending from the central portion to muscles or other organs. Most of our discussion in this chapter is based on studies of nerves, axons isolated from them, muscles, and preparations of a muscle with its attached nerve.

Nerve-muscle Preparation

Let us begin with the nerve-muscle preparation. The most familiar and widely used preparation of this sort is that comprising the sciatic nerve and gastrocnemius muscle of the frog. This type of preparation has been in use at least since the early eighteenth century; Swammerdam used it in work published in 1738. It offers us an opportunity to give an operational basis for the terms we have used earlier in this chapter. The preparation is made by freeing the sciatic nerve from the adjacent tissues between its origin at the spinal cord and its termination in the gastrocnemius muscle. This muscle is left attached to the femur, which is cut and freed of other muscles. The Achilles' tendon is cut and the gastrocnemius is freed from the other muscles of the leg, which is then cut off below the knee. The final preparation consists only of the sciatic nerve, the femur for convenience of handling, and the gastrocnemius.

Excitation

If we now stimulate any part of the sciatic nerve by any of a variety of means—cutting, pinching, chemical treatments, electrical shock, heating— the muscle will contract. Many of these stimuli produce no visible change in the nerve, but the fact that the muscle responds suggests, first, that some change (excitation) has occurred

in the nerve and, second, that this change has been communicated or conducted to the muscle. Some of the stimuli listed above—or any of them if too strong—will damage the nerve so that it no longer responds. Of them all the most readily controlled and the least likely to damage the cell is the electrical shock.

In the early days of physiology direct currents from a galvanic cell were used for stimulation. With the discovery of electromagnetic induction by Faraday the induction coil was brought into use, especially by Du Bois-Reymond before the middle of the nineteenth century. In the present century electronic stimulators have come into general use. The electronic stimulators permit the most exact control over the strength, duration, frequency, and time course of stimuli. Regardless of the source of stimulating current, it is applied to the nerve through a pair of electrodes, usually of platinum or silver wire.

Conduction

Before 1850 the German physiologist von Helmholtz devised methods to determine the time required for the state of excitation to pass from the point of stimulus to the muscle. He used an induction coil as his source of stimulus. When the current is caused to flow in the primary coil of this system by closing a switch ("make" of the primary circuit) a transient current is momentarily induced in the secondary coil. The magnitude of the secondary current depends on the ratio of the number of turns in the primary coil to the number in the secondary, on the distance between the two coils, and on their relative geometrical positions. A similar and somewhat larger transient current is also induced in the secondary when the primary circuit is opened ("break" of the primary circuit). In one system used by von Helmholtz the primary circuit had two switches. One was operated by the experimenter while the second, initially closed, was attached to the muscle of the nerve-muscle preparation in such a way that when the muscle contracted the switch was opened. Thus by measuring the time between the closing of the first switch and the opening of the second von Helmholtz could estimate the time between stimulation of the nerve and contraction of the muscle. This time, now known as the latent period, he found to be appreciably shorter when the stimulating electrodes are placed on the nerve close to the muscle than when the electrodes are placed far from the muscle. By careful measurements of time and distance in such experiments he was able to calculate the rate of conduction of the state of excitation along the nerve at about 30 meters per second. From this experiment, which has been abundantly confirmed by a variety of methods, it became clear that something which we shall henceforth call the nerve impulse travels along the nerve from the point of stimulation to the muscle at a rate which is, for electrical phenomena, relatively slow.

Excitation of Axons

From the early part of the eighteenth century, at least, suggestions had been made that the phenomena of excitation might somehow involve electricity, but this suggestion could not be tested until means of measuring or at least identifying very small electrical currents became available. In the period around 1840 the Italian physiologist

Matteucci showed that muscles produce small electrical currents when injured or stimulated, and shortly afterward Du Bois-Reymond demonstrated the same phenomena in nerves. By 1868 Reymond's student Bernstein had demonstrated that the properties of the electrical changes in nerve coincide in all measurable respects with the nerve impulse. He had also begun to develop a model of the axon and its electrical behavior, which can serve with minor but significant modifications even today. It is of considerable interest that this physiological theory was largely worked out over twenty years before the structure of the nervous system, as composed of distinct nerve cells or neurons, was fully understood.

The Axon Model

The present model of the axon is that of a cylinder filled with axoplasm (nerve cell cytoplasm) surrounded by a thin plasma membrane. The electrical resistance of the axoplasm is low (40 ohm cm for the giant axon of the squid) as is that of the external medium (20 ohm cm for sea water), but the resistance of the axon is quite high (1 to 2.5×10^3 ohm cm^2 for the squid giant axon). The axon membrane is polarized, with the inner surface negative to the exterior by 50 to 100 mV, as was pointed out in the last chapter. When the axon is stimulated this polarization is momentarily reversed in the stimulated region by a mechanism we shall describe later. As a result of this momentary and local reversal of polarity currents carried by ions are caused to flow in the axoplasm and medium. In electrical terminology the excited region serves as a "sink" for currents flowing from sources in the normally polarized adjacent regions of the axon membrane (Figure 5.1). The result of this current flow is a partial depolarization of the adjacent regions of the membrane, and this is followed by excitation and the reversal of polarity in those regions. Meanwhile the initial point of excitation regains its normal polarity, and the newly excited adjacent regions now serve as sinks for regions farther along the axon membrane. Thus the state of excitation is propagated from point to point along the membrane much as combustion is propagated along a fuse filled with gun powder. Once the powder is ignited at one point the heat of its combustion is conducted to adjacent regions igniting these. The amount of heat generated in the fuse and the magnitude of the electrical changes in the axon are determined by the amount of energy stored in the gun powder or in the axon membrane, and not by the strength of the original stimulus. Likewise the rate of conduction is slow, since time is re-

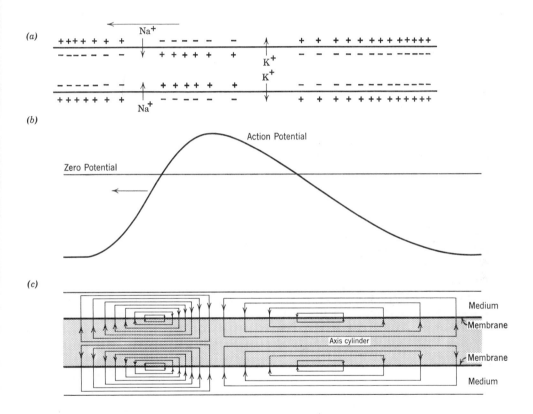

Fig. 5.1 Conduction of a nerve impulse along an axon. (*a*) The distribution of charge and the movement of ions along an axon and across the membrane during conduction of an impulse in the direction of the arrow. The influx of Na$^+$ is initiated by a partial depolarization. As a consequence of Na$^+$ influx, the membrane potential is reversed, as in (*b*). This reversal in turn causes outflux of K$^+$, which returns the membrane to its original state of polarization. The currents that flow across the axon membrane and in the medium and axoplasm are shown in (*c*). (From J. C. Eccles, 1960, in *Handbook of Neurophysiology: section 1, Neurophysiology,* **1** 64, J. Field Ed., Am. Physiol. Soc., Washington.)

quired for the successive events in propagation.

The foregoing picture is essentially Bernstein's theory with one exception. In the eventual development of Bernstein's thought he proposed that the axon membrane is selectively permeable to potassium ions and impermeable to all other ions and that the principal phenomenon in excitation is a sudden breakdown of this impermeability. This picture is now known to be oversimplified and has been replaced by a more complex one, which better fits the evidence now available.

Excitation

Before we develop the modern view, however, we must examine some of the experimentally observable properties of excitation. The first of these is the phenomenon of threshold. When a series of electrical shocks, carefully graded as to intensity (potential) but with the same time course, is administered to a nerve, weak shocks fail to arouse a propagated nerve impulse or to cause contraction in the muscle of the nerve-muscle preparation. If the intensity is increased, a value will be found which is just sufficient to cause a nerve impulse or a contraction, whichever is being measured. This value is known as the liminal or threshold intensity or strength of stimulus. Further increase in intensity in a nerve-muscle preparation will cause increases in the observed response, but in a single axon the liminal intensity produces the full response of which the axon is capable. Further increases in intensity will cause no further increase in response. The same phenomenon can be demonstrated in muscle. It was first noted by the Italian Fontana in 1767, rediscovered but not fully appre-

ciated by the American Bowditch in 1871, and elaborated into a general principle by the Englishman Adrian between 1914 and 1922. Adrian first used the expression "all or none," later corrected to "all or nothing," to describe the principle that an excitable cell responds to a stimulus with its maximum response if it responds at all. This principle arises from a prime characteristic of biological responses, which is that responses depend on stored energy in an unstable system, and their magnitude depends on the amount of energy stored, not on the releasing stimulus. This property is shared by many inanimate systems, from weapons to water closets.

If we now vary the time course of the electrical stimulus as well as its intensity, we at once enter into more complex fields which are not yet fully explored. There are, however, three important concepts which we shall mention. The first is the general relation between intensity and duration of stimulus. In the ideal case this relation should be studied with square wave stimuli: that is, stimuli in which the maximum intensity is reached instantaneously, is maintained for a definite period, and then returns to zero instantaneously. With such stimulation the curve relating liminal intensity to liminal duration is approximately parabolic in shape (Figure 5.2). Weak stimuli must act for very long times to produce a response, while strong stimuli are effective within a very short time. There is, however, a limiting duration of action required for the strongest of stimuli and a limiting intensity (known as the rheobase) below which excitation will not occur with any duration. The empirical equation describing the strength-duration curve is

$$S = b\left(1 + \frac{\sigma}{t}\right)$$

where S is the threshold strength or intensity which will just excite when it acts for the time t, and b and σ are constants, σ being known as the chronaxie and b as the rheobase. This equation has not yet been derived from any theory.

The second concept is that of accommodation. If, instead of using a square wave for stimulation, we use a stimulus for which the intensity increases almost linearly with time, then the intensity which causes a response is a function of the slope of the intensity-time curve. In other words, if the intensity increases slowly, the liminal value at which a response occurs is higher than it is when the intensity increases rapidly (Figure 5.3). This phenomenon has been interpreted in

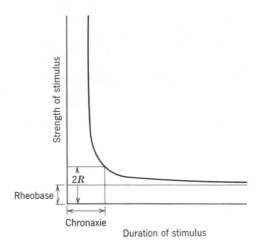

Fig. 5.2 The relation of minimum effective strength of a stimulus to its minimum effective duration.

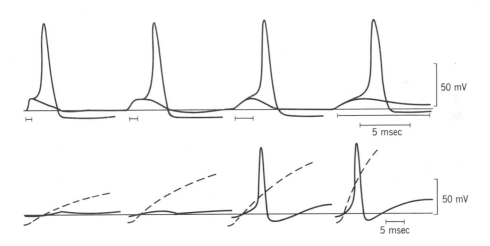

Fig. 5.3 Excitation and accommodation in an isolated axon. In the upper row, square-wave stimuli of the duration shown by the line under the experimental record were applied at strengths just below and just above threshold. The local potential is shown, with the spike superimposed; the origin of the spike is seen to occur later, and at a higher level of depolarization as the duration of the stimulus increases. In the lower row, stimuli of slowly increasing magnitude, along the time course shown by the dotted line, were used. With very slow rates of rise, the strength can be increased well above the level required to stimulate at more rapid rates of rise. (From Tasaki, after Hagiwara, in *Handbook of Physiology: Neurophysiology*, J. Field ed., Am. Physiol. Soc., Washington, 1960.)

terms of two competing processes in the membrane: One leads to a response; this we may call the excitation process. The other opposes the response; this second process is called accommodation.

The third concept is that of the refractory period. If we stimulate with a very brief shock and then repeat the stimulation with a second identical shock at varying periods of time thereafter, we find that when the shocks are far apart in time (15 to 20 millisecond or msec) each shock produces a full response. If they are very close together in time (2 msec or less) the second shock produces no response at all. Between these limits there is a period in which the response to the second shock is less than that to the first. If we do the experiment differently and determine the liminal intensity for the second shock, we find that there may be a period in which no second response can be obtained, with any intensity. This has been called the absolute refractory period. Following this there is a period in which the value of the liminal intensity is higher than in the resting cell and approaches the resting value as the time between shocks increases. This period is known as the relative refractory period.

Electrical and Ionic Changes in Excitation

These properties of the excitation process must now be interpreted in terms of the electrical properties of the axon, of the changes in these properties in excitation, and of the ionic and metabolic exchanges which underlie the electrical phenomena. The major advances in our understanding of excitation have come about during the last forty years. The electrical instruments available to Bernstein had two defects;

they were insensitive and hence unable to measure accurately the small currents and potentials in nerves, and they had considerable inertia, hence could not give a true representation of the time course of these changes. The major improvement came in the early 1920's with the development of electronic instruments and particularly of the cathode-ray oscilloscope (Figure 5.4). This instrument, in which the responsive mechanism is a beam of electrons moving through an electrostatic field, has virtually zero inertia and gives an exact record of the time course of the actuating event. With the aid of suitable amplifiers it can be made as sensitive as desired and easily covers the range of electrical events in nerve excitation. In 1922 Gasser and Erlanger published the first results using these instruments, and the technique has since become standard in physiology.

Action Potentials

We may first examine the potential changes accompanying excitation. These are commonly measured in two ways. In the older and more generally applicable method one electrode (either a silver wire coated with AgCl, which may be enclosed in a glass pipette filled with KCl solution, or an $Hg-HgCl_2$ electrode connected with a KCl bridge) is placed on or near the surface of the nerve or axon; the other electrode, of identical composition, is placed on a dead, injured, or narcotized portion of the nerve or axon. In the second method—readily applicable only to the giant axons of certain invertebrates (notably the squid) or to muscle fibers and neuron cell bodies—one of the electrodes, which must be very small in diameter, is inserted directly into

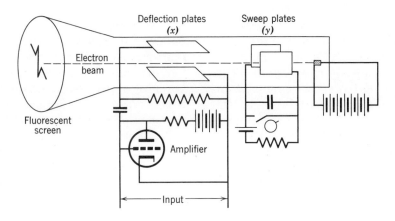

Fig. 5.4 Diagram of a cathode-ray oscilloscope. The cathode, at the far right, emits a beam of electrons within the evacuated tube. The beam strikes the screen on the left, where it causes emission of light by the fluorescent material of the screen. The beam is caused to move horizontally across the screen at a constant rate, and then return to the starting point at a much more rapid rate, by a potential applied to the "sweep plates." An input potential, applied to the "deflection plates," will then cause a vertical deflection of the beam in proportion to the input potential change, faithfully reflecting the time course of that change.

the cell either through the cut end of an axon or through the membrane. The other electrode is then placed in the medium outside the cell. The results of the two methods differ only quantitatively and slightly. In either case the dead or injured end of the nerve, or the axoplasm, is electrically negative to the medium. When the nerve or axon is stimulated at some distance from the recording electrodes there occurs at those electrodes, a short time later, a sudden reversal of the membrane potential so that the axoplasm becomes for a very short time positive to the medium with internal recording, or the active region becomes negative with respect to the injured region. The time course of this change is shown in Figure 5.5. The sharp peak is referred to in physiological jargon as a "spike," and the pattern of potential change is known as the action potential. The magnitude of the action potential is taken as the magnitude in

millivolts of the change from the resting potential to the peak of the spike.

If we place our recording electrodes in the region of a single axon at which the stimulus is applied we can obtain further information about the potential changes and in particular about the changes which occur after subliminal stimuli. We noted earlier that an all or nothing pattern of response is characteristic of single excitable cells. If we examine potential changes at the site of stimulation, however, we find that every stimulus, no matter how small, produces some change at the point of application (Figure 5.6). The all or nothing character applies only to the propagated action potential. When subliminal shocks of very short duration are applied, and potential changes are observed at both the anode and cathode of the stimulating electrode, it is found that the decrease in membrane potential at the cathode is somewhat greater than the increase at

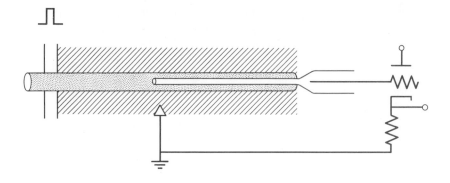

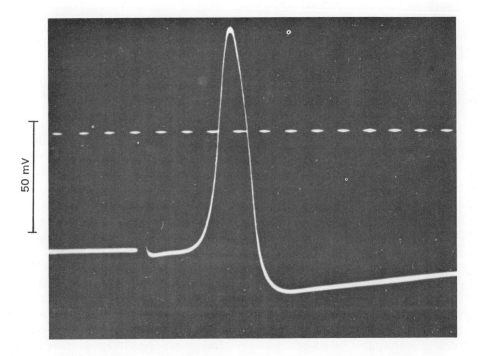

Fig. 5.5 The resting and action potentials of the giant axon of a squid. The drawing at the top shows the arrangement of electrodes used in recording the potentials. The stimulus was applied through the pair of Ag-AgCl electrodes shown as dark vertical lines at the left. The axon was impaled on a glass microelectrode inserted from one end, as shown on the right; this electrode was filled with a KCl solution, and a Ag-AgCl electrode was inserted into the solution. An indifferent electrode, of the same composition, was placed outside the membrane, and grounded. The broken line shows the potential difference between the two electrodes before the microelectrode was inserted into the axon, and serves as a zero line; it is broken at intervals of 0.5 msec. The solid line is the record obtained when the nerve was stimulated. The first (level) part of the line is the resting membrane potential; the break in the line is an artifact caused by the stimulus. (From Tasaki, 1960, *Handbook of Physiology; Neurophysiology,* 1 84, ed. J. Field, Am. Physiol. Soc., Washington.)

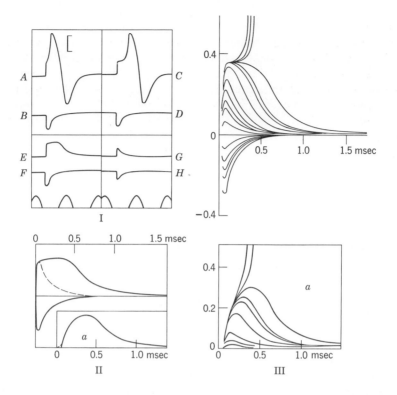

Fig. 5.6 Local potentials. I. The electrical changes at the stimulating electrode produced by shocks of relative strengths. *A.* 1.05, *B.* −1.05, *C.* 1.00, *D.* −1.00, *E.* 1.00, *F.* −1.00, *G.* 0.61, *H.* −0.61. Scale 15 mV. Time 1 msec. II. Cathodal and anodal potentials traced from I*E* and *F*. The cathodal potential is analyzed into the polarization potential (broken line) and the local response (insert *a*). III. Upper curves, electrical changes at the stimulating electrode produced by a series of shocks of progressively decreasing strength. Lower curves (*a*) obtained by subtracting the anodal from the cathodal curves. (From Hodgkin, *Proc. Roy. Soc. B* **126** 87–121, 1938.)

the anode and that this difference is greater as the intensity of the stimulus increases. If square wave stimuli are used the membrane potential at the cathode decreases, sharply at first and then more slowly. If the stimulating period is of long duration (5 msec or more) the membrane potential begins to return towards its resting value before the current is turned off. If a slowly rising current is used as a stimulus the membrane may show little or no depolarization with a potential change which, in a square wave, would

elicit an action potential. Intermediate rates of rise in the stimulus produce depolarizations which are larger as the rate of rise increases. Regardless of the mode of stimulation, when the axon membrane is depolarized to a critical extent (e.g., 15 mV), an action potential invariably develops. If the membrane begins to regain its original resting polarization before it has been depolarized to this extent, no action potential develops, no matter how long the stimulus continues to act.

These observations give us a fuller

understanding of the opposing processes of excitation and accommodation. Excitation involves progressive membrane depolarization. When this reaches the critical level an action potential follows. Excitation is opposed by a process tending to restore the membrane to its resting level of polarization. If this process is able to overtake and reverse the depolarizing process, no excitation occurs. If, as we suggested in the last chapter, the normal resting polarization depends on a sodium pump acting in a selectively permeable membrane, we must seek an explanation for the potential changes in variations of the activity of the pump or of the selective permeability of the membrane. The subthreshold phenomena have been little explored from this point of view, but recent studies on lobster axons suggest that changes in sodium movements, probably passive, are the primary factors in the subthreshold phenomena of these cells.

The phenomena which occur during the spike of the action potential have been explored much more fully. In addition to the potential measurements noted earlier, studies of the resistance of the axon membrane and of the current-voltage relations across the membrane have proved to be very informative. The resistance has been measured in studies of the alternating current impedance of the membrane during the action current. The a-c impedance is made up of the capacitance (10^{-6} farad per cm^2) and the resistance ($1 - 2.5 \times 10^3$ ohm cm^2) of the membrane. During the development of an action potential the impedance decreases sharply, reaching a minimum at the peak of the spike and returning rapidly to normal. Analysis of the changes shows them to be entirely due to a decrease in membrane resistance, with little change in capacitance. The membrane resistance is, from the nature of the system, primarily related to the permeability of the membrane to ions, and a decrease in resistance means an increase in permeability. It will be recalled that for the three major ions in biological media the membrane appears to be least permeable to Na$^+$ and most permeable to K$^+$, with Cl$^-$ occupying an intermediate position.

Current-voltage Relations in the Spike

The most elaborate, well-designed, and informative experiments thus far performed with the squid axon were carried out about 10 years ago by Hodgkin, Huxley, and Katz in England. They used a complex electrical circuit involving two electrodes inserted into the axon, and a set of external electrodes (Figure 5.7). One of the internal electrodes, paired with one of the external electrodes, led to a feedback amplifier system which could be set to change the membrane potential to any predetermined extent in square wave pattern and hold it at the predetermined level by feeding current into the second internal electrode. This system is referred to as a "voltage clamp." The other external electrode was connected to an oscilloscope to record the current flowing across the membrane. With this machinery it was possible to determine the steady state current-voltage relations across the membrane and to study the time course of current flow during the establishment of the steady state. The steady state current-voltage curve has three parts. If we assume a resting membrane potential of about 75 mV,

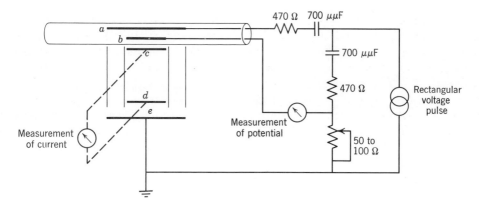

Fig. 5.7 The experimental arrangement for the voltage clamp experiment of Hodgkin et al. The giant axon of the squid is represented by a cylinder. Into the axoplasm are inserted two electrodes, *a* and *b;* both are thin wires insulated over their entire lengths except for the portion shown as thick in the diagram. The region of the axon containing the electrodes is insulated from the rest of the axon and lies in a pool of salt solution in which are placed three other electrodes *c*, *d,* and *e.* The external circuit, only part of which is shown, is arranged so that a rectangular voltage pulse can be applied between *a* and *e*, and the resulting membrane potential change recorded between *b* and *e.* The dimensions of *a* and *e* are closely similar, hence a measurement of the potential drop between *c* and *d,* which in turn have the same dimensions as *b*, gives a measure of the current flux across the axon membrane (that is, from *a* to *e*). In the voltage clamp experiment, the system shown is coupled to a feedback amplifier system so arranged that the rectangular voltage pulse can be preset to bring the membrane potential to any desired level, and hold it there. (Hodgkin, Huxley & Katz, 1952, *J. Physiol.* **116** 424.)

with a steady state current of zero at this level, we find that increasing the polarization beyond this point results in an inward current flow which increases only slightly with increasing potential difference, suggesting a high resistance. When the potential difference is decreased below the resting level we enter a region in which the *E/I* relation is no longer linear in the steady state. This is also the region in which the phenomena of excitation occur. Finally, in the neighborhood of zero membrane potential and beyond to reversed polarity, the relation becomes linear again but with a steeper slope indicating greatly decreased resistance. This agrees with the impedance measurements showing decreased resistance at the peak of the spike.

The most revealing aspect of the observations is that involving the transient changes in current flow across the membrane (Figure 5.8). It will be recalled that the electronic feedback system was arranged so that current is fed into the axon or drawn from it in amounts sufficient to hold the membrane potential constant at a predetermined level. When this level involves an increase in the membrane potential (hyperpolarization) the current flow across the membrane increases sharply from zero as the new potential level is imposed and then remains constant at the new level. The current flow in the hyperpolarized membrane is inward; that is, positive ions are moving into the axon or negative ions are moving out. When the new potential level involves a decrease in the membrane

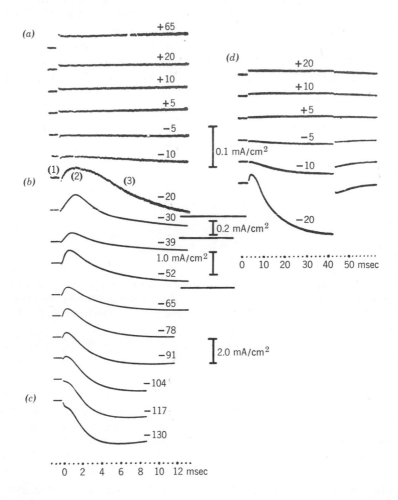

Fig. 5.8 Results of the voltage clamp experiment. The records show the current changes when the membrane potential is increased (+) or decreased (−) by the number of millivolts shown above each record. In the series on the left there are three types of curves. (*a*) In the range of −10 to +65 mV the change in membrane potential merely causes a small change in current flux, which is directly proportional to the potential change. (*b*) With depolarizations greater than 10 mV, the curve is complex and has three parts: (1) a brief surge of outward current too rapid for recording here, but similar to that seen in the upper curves and attributable to a discharge of the membrane capacitance. (2) an inward current which slowly rises to a maximum in 1-2 msec, and then returns to zero; the magnitude of the maximum inward current varies with the extent of depolarization and falls to zero beyond −104 mV. (3) a prolonged outward current, which ultimately reaches a steady state proportional to the extent of depolarization. (*c*) In the third type of curve, with depolarizations of 117 and 130 mV, only this last phase is seen. (*d*) In the curves on the right, the membrane is returned to its normal level of polarization after 40 msec. (From Hodgkin et al., 1952, *J. Physiol.* **116** 424.)

potential (depolarization) the current flow again increases sharply to a new level and then holds steady as long as the depolarization is less than 15 mV. Now, however, the direction of the current flow is outward. Both of these changes are those expected from a passive system.

When a depolarization greater than 15 mV is produced the current flow varies in a complex fashion. First, there is a very brief outward surge as the membrane capacitance is discharged; then the current rapidly shifts to a large inward value, a change which would not be expected in a simple passive membrane. Finally, the current gradually returns to an outward direction which is maintained as long as the depolarization continues. The most remarkable feature in these observations is the inward current which follows the initial capacity surge. This is greatest in magnitude for depolarizations of about 30 mV and decreases with large depolarizations until at about 100 mV it disappears altogether. At and above 100 mV depolarization, when the membrane potential is reversed, the initial capacity surge is followed by a slowly increasing outward current which finally reaches a level maintained as long as the depolarization lasts. The level of 100 mV is approximately the level of the action potential and hence represents the level from which the membrane potential begins its return to normal in the spike. Hodgkin and his associates also consider this to be approximately the level of the equilibrium potential for sodium ion.

The Effects of Ions

Hodgkin and Huxley then went on to examine the effects of variation in sodium ion concentration on the current changes. They had observed earlier that the magnitude of the action potential is directly related to the logarithm of the external sodium ion concentration. They now found that the level at which the inward current disappears is also directly related to the logarithm of the sodium concentration and in the same way as the action potential. They therefore concluded that the inward current is carried by sodium ion flowing into the axon along its electrochemical diffusion gradient and that this flow stops when the diffusion gradient reaches zero. In the normal axon, they reason, excitation produces a change in membrane properties which allows sodium ion to enter. They assume this change to be a sudden increase in permeability to Na^+. As the Na^+ enters, the movement of positive charge inward causes depolarization and reversal of the membrane potential. The process continues until the membrane potential reaches the equilibrium potential for Na^+, at which point there is no net force acting on the Na^+ and its movement stops. Meanwhile the change in membrane potential has unbalanced the forces previously in equilibrium acting on the potassium ion, and as the depolarization continues K^+ begins to move outward. By the time the Na^+ movement stops, K^+ is rapidly flowing out, and this initiates a repolarization as the positive charge brought in by Na^+ moves out again with K^+. The actual amount of ions which cross unit area of nerve surface is small, as the student can calculate for himself with the aid of Avogadro's number, the faraday, and simple electrical principles. Consequently a single impulse produces only a small change in the ion distribution across the membrane, and this is quickly repaired by the sodium pump in the recovery period.

A large number of studies using the voltage clamp technique have now been made on a variety of types of cells. The results have been in general similar to the original results of Hodgkin's group, with only minor qualitative variations. The general concept therefore appears to be well established. There are questions of detail, such as the roles of calcium and chloride ion, which remain to be studied. There are also some broader questions of theoretical principle. Thus we noted in the last chapter that the nature of the resting membrane potential is still not entirely clear. Moreover the elaborate mathematical theory which Hodgkin and associates developed from their observations still requires more testing. It fits most but not all the available experimental data at present.

The Nature of Excitation

Nevertheless we can be reasonably confident that the following picture of the phenomena of excitation is reliable for nerve. The question of its applicability to muscle must remain open at present. The resting membrane potential represents a balance of forces involving (1) a metabolically driven sodium pump and (2) asymmetrical ion distributions in which the major factor is the electrochemical imbalance of sodium ion, maintained by the sodium pump and a low permeability to sodium ion. Excitation produces some change in the membrane which allows Na^+ to move in more freely, and this movement initiates depolarization. Accommodation represents some process tending to restore the original membrane properties. When the depo-

larization reaches a critical level the change in membrane properties is complete and Na^+ rushes in, causing a reversal of the membrane polarity to a point where the forces acting on Na^+ are in equilibrium. The forces acting on K^+ are now no longer in equilibrium, and this ion moves rapidly outward, restoring the membrane to its original polarity. During the recovery period the Na^+ is pumped out and K^+ moves in simultaneously to restore the system completely.

Recently Caldwell has examined the energization of this system and has shown that the sodium pump is energized by ATP and related substances such as creatine phosphate but that these compounds have no influence on the ion movements during the spike process. The compounds are effective in increasing the rate of sodium pumping only when injected into the axoplasm.

References

Adrian, E. D. 1932. *The Mechanism of Nervous Action.* Univ. Pennsylvania Press, Philadelphia.

Bishop, G. H. 1956. The natural history of the nerve impulse. *Physiol. Rev.* **36** 376–399.

Bonhoeffer, K. F. 1953. Modelle der Nervenerregung. *Naturwiss.* **40** 301–311.

Bonhoeffer, K. F. 1954. Modéles physicochimiques de l'excitation nerveuse. *J. Chim. Phys.* **51** 521–529.

Brazier, M. A. B. 1960. *The Electrical Activity of the Nervous System.* (2nd edn.), Macmillan, New York.

Eccles, J. C. 1957. *The Physiology of Nerve Cells.* Johns Hopkins Press, Baltimore, Md.

Eccles, J. C. 1959. Neuron Physiology. *Hdbk. Physiol. I Neurophysiol.* **1** 59–74.

Grundfest, H. 1952. Mechanism and properties of bioelectric potentials. *Mod. Trends Physiol. Biochem.* 193–229.

Hill, D. K. 1950. Advances in the physiology of the peripheral nerve. *J. Mar. Biol. Assoc. U.K.* **29** 241–246.

Hodgkin, A. L. 1951. The ionic basis of electrical activity in nerve and muscle. *Biol. Rev.* **26** 339–409.

Hodgkin, A. L. 1958. Ionic movements and electrical activity in giant nerve fibres. *Proc. Royal Soc. London B* **148** 1–37.

Huxley, A. F. 1959. Ion movements during nerve activity. *Annals N.Y. Acad. Sci.* **81** 221–246.

Hydén, H. 1960. The neuron. *The Cell* 4 215–324.

Lucas, K. 1917. *The Conduction of the Nervous Impulse.* Longmans, Green, London.

Nachmansohn, D. 1961. Chemical factors controlling nerve activity. *Science* **134** 1962–1968.

Shedlovsky, T. (ed.) 1955. *Electrochemistry in Biology and Medicine.* Wiley, New York.

Stämpfli, R. 1954. Saltatory conduction in nerve. *Physiol. Rev.* **34** 101–112.

Steinbach, H. B. 1952. The sodium and potassium balance of muscle and nerve. *Mod. Trends Physiol. Biochem.* 173–192.

Tasaki, I. 1959. Conduction of the nerve impulse. *Hbdk. Physiol. I Neurophysiol.* **1** 75–121.

6 Contraction of muscle

Perhaps the most dramatic of physiological phenomena is the sudden rapid shortening of a vertebrate striated muscle on stimulation. The shortening is, moreover, the basis of all animal movements and hence important as well as dramatic. The study of its mechanism has engaged the best efforts of many generations of physiologists and has utilized techniques drawn from morphology, chemistry, and physics. Observations on muscle have in turn led to the discovery of many principles and phenomena of more general significance, from the law of conservation of energy to the elaborate biochemical mechanisms of glycolysis and cellular respiration.

The first problem considered was the nature of the contraction itself. In the Greek philosophical synthesis of ancient times all physiological phenomena were interpreted in terms of the movements of fluids or humors. Contraction of muscle was thought to be caused by the movement of "animal spirits" distilled in the brain from materials derived from food and flowing along the tubular nerves to inflate the muscles, much as a balloon can be inflated with air. The early biophysicists of the eighteenth century were able to disprove this theory by demonstrating that when a muscle contracts its volume does not change to any large extent; shortening is accompanied by thickening.

The Source of Energy

During the nineteenth century the extensive development of power machinery and particularly the steam engine led to theoretical considerations of the relations between various forms of energy. Of particular note is the concept of the conservation of energy (now embodied as the first law of thermodynamics) which was developed before the middle of the nineteenth century, and biological observations had a part in this development. von Helmholtz, who has been mentioned earlier in connection with studies of the nerve impulse, began his scientific work with the study of muscular contraction. By 1845 he had developed the idea that in the liberation of energy in the form of mechanical work as it occurs in muscle the energy must come from some pre-existing energy. The only possible source in muscle was a chemical reaction. von Helmholtz went on from this to develop the general idea that energy cannot be created or destroyed but only transformed from one form to another.

The search for the chemical reaction which is the source of the energy liberated in muscular contraction had to await the development of adequate biochemical knowledge. The first major step forward was made in 1907, when Fletcher and Hopkins, in England, published their demonstration that during the anaerobic contraction of vertebrate muscle lactic acid is formed. A few years later Parnas showed that the lactic acid originates from glycogen. This discovery led to an enormous surge of activity, both biophysical and biochemical. On the biophysical side A. V. Hill, again in England, began his studies of the energetics of muscular contraction which have continued to the time of the present writing. On the biochemical side Otto Meyerhof, in Germany, began the studies of glycolysis, which ultimately led to our present rather complete understanding of this complex and important process. Hill

and Meyerhof, approaching the problem from completely different viewpoints, developed a collaboration which survived the First World War and from which came the first general hypothesis of muscular contraction.

Heat Production

Hill utilized the fact that a junction of dissimilar metals (thermocouple) will produce a small electric current which is proportional to the temperature. A large number of thermocouples joined together in series to form a thermopile will be extremely sensitive to small changes in temperature. If a muscle is caused to contract in close contact with such a thermopile the change in current flux will give an accurate picture of the changes in muscle temperature and hence provide a means for measuring the heat produced by the muscle.

When a vertebrate striated muscle is stimulated directly by a brief electrical shock it shortens rapidly and briefly; if it is prevented from shortening it develops tension for a brief period and then relaxes. These changes are known as contraction, and a single rapid contraction is called a twitch. Hill's initial apparatus was not sufficiently sensitive to detect the temperature change in a twitch and he used instead a brief tetanus. Tetanus is a type of contraction caused by repeated brief stimuli at a frequency such that each successive stimulus comes after the refractory period of the preceding one. In a tetanus lasting 0.2 second the heat production occurs in three successive waves (Figure 6.1). The first begins very close to the beginning of stimulation, with steadily increasing heat production while stimulation continues. With cessation of stimulation the heat

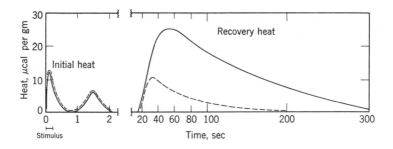

Fig. 6.1 Heat production of muscle in tetanus. Solid curves in O_2; dotted curves in N_2; 0.2 sec tetanus at 0°C. (Data from Hill and Hartree, *J. Physiol.* **54** 84–128, 1920, and Hartree and Hill, *J. Physiol.* **56** 367–381, 1922.)

production falls off to zero in less than 1 second. This initial heat is followed by a delayed heat production of about the same amount during a subsequent period of about 1 second. These two phases of the heat production are the same whether the muscle contracts in an atmosphere of O_2 or in one of N_2. Beginning roughly 10 seconds after the stimulation, and continuing for as long as 5 minutes, there is a second delayed heat production when the muscle is in the presence of O_2. In the absence of O_2 this second delayed heat production is much reduced in quantity and lasts for a shorter period.

Glycolysis

While these experiments were in progress, between 1910 and 1920, Meyerhof was engaged in a study of the energetics of glycolysis. He made accurate measurements of the heat produced by the combustion of glycogen and of lactic acid and from these (using the principle of conservation of energy) could compute the amount of heat which would be produced by conversion of glycogen to lactic acid. He could then measure chemically the amount of glycogen broken down and the amount of lactic acid formed in a

brief tetanus, calculate the amount of energy which would be liberated by this chemical change, and compare this amount with the actual amount of heat produced by the muscle when its contraction was brought about isometrically (that is, in such a way that no shortening could occur, and hence no mechanical work could be done). The figures for heat production derived from these calculations were in remarkable agreement with Hill's direct observations of heat production. During anaerobic contraction of a frog muscle lactic acid accumulates in exact equivalence to the amount of glycogen destroyed. However, if oxygen is now admitted to the system roughly one-fourth of the lactic acid is oxidized, while the remaining three-fourths is resynthesized to glycogen. The energy liberated by oxidation of part of the lactic acid is quite adequate to provide energy for the resynthesis of glycogen from the remainder and to account as well for the aerobic portion of the second delayed heat.

The picture of muscle contraction which emerged from these studies was beautifully simple and adequately answered the question which von Helmholtz had asked 75 years earlier. The source of the energy for anaerobic contraction of frog muscle is the reaction of glycolysis, in which glycogen is converted to lactic acid; this accounts for the initial heat production in the recovery period. Following a contraction, and in presence of O_2, the lactic acid is removed by oxidation and resynthesis to glycogen. These reactions account for the delayed heat.

The major remaining question in 1920 appeared to be that of the link between glycolysis and the mechanical changes involved in contraction. In that period the study of the chemistry of colloids was very active, and considerable information of a qualitative nature about the effects of acids and alkalies on the properties of proteins and other colloids had been accumulated. Consequently many hypotheses were formulated in which the lactic acid somehow changed the mechanical properties of muscle proteins. As are nearly all beautifully simple biological concepts however, this one was doomed. Its downfall came with dramatic suddenness as the result of studies arising from Meyerhof's observations on glycolysis.

The First Revolution in Muscle Chemistry

Among these observations it was discovered that iodoacetic acid somehow interferes with glycolysis. We know now that it inactivates glyceraldehyde phosphate dehydrogenase. Lundsgaard, a Dane, performed in 1928 the experiment of poisoning muscles with iodoacetic acid. He found, quite contrary to expectation, that "poisoned" muscles continue to contract for long periods in spite of the fact that no lactic acid is produced in such muscles. This observation at one stroke destroyed all the hypotheses of con-

traction in which lactic acid played an essential role. Lundsgaard was able, however, to offer an alternative hypothesis and to establish its adequacy experimentally. During the heyday of the lactic acid theories more patient biochemists had continued to investigate other chemical changes during muscle contraction. The Eggletons in England had demonstrated the presence in muscle of substances they called phosphagens, which break down during contraction to liberate inorganic phosphate in substantial quantities. In vertebrate muscles the major phosphagen was identified as creatine phosphate, while in arthropods and mollusks the phosphagen is arginine phosphate. Annelids are unique in having a considerable array of phosphagens, as indicated in Table 6.1. Some point has been made of the presence, in echinoderms and protochordates, of both creatine and arginine phosphates, as evidence for a presumed evolutionary relationship between echinoderms and chordates.

ATP as Energy Source

To return to our story, Lundsgaard suggested that the breakdown of creatine phosphate and of ATP might supply the energy for contraction in muscles poisoned with iodoacetate and the nonpoisoned muscles as well. He was able to show experimentally that these substances are hydrolyzed in the course of muscular contraction in poisoned muscles, and in unpoisoned muscles that hydrolysis of phosphagens occurs before the conversion of glycogen to lactic acid; the latter is merely a recovery process (Figure 6.2 and Table 6.2). From later studies it was concluded that the closest identifiable source of energy for muscular contrac-

TABLE 6.1
The Phosphagens

Name:	Phosphorylarginine	Phosphorylcreatine	Phosphorylglycocyamine	Phosphoryltaurocyamine	Phosphoryl Lumbricine
Formula:	COOH | H—C—NH$_2$ | CH$_2$ | CH$_2$ | CH$_2$ | NH | C=NH | NH | H$_2$PO$_3$	COOH | CH$_2$ | N·CH$_3$ | C=NH | NH | H$_2$PO$_3$	COOH | CH$_2$ | NH | C=NH | NH | H$_2$PO$_3$	SO$_3$H | CH$_2$ | CH$_2$ | NH | C=NH | NH | H$_2$PO$_3$	COOH | H—C—NH$_2$ | CH$_2$ | O | HO—P=O | O | CH$_2$ | CH$_2$ | NH | C=NH | NH | H$_2$PO$_3$

Occurrence:	Coelenterates
	Nemerteans
	Sipunculids
	Mollusks
	Arthropods
	Annelids:
	  Spirographis
	  spallanzanii
	Echinoderms:
	  Asteroids
	  Holothurians
	  Echinoids
	Chordates:
	  Hemichordates
	  Some ascidians
		Annelids:
		  Many polychaetes
		  Glycera convoluta
		  G. gigantea
		Echinoderms:
		  Some echinoids
		  Ophiuroids
		Chordates:
		  Hemichordates
		  Some ascidians
		  Cephalochordates
		  Vertebrates
			Annelids:
			  Nereis
			  diversicolor
				Annelids:
				  Arenicola
				  G. gigantea
					Annelids:
					  Lumbricus

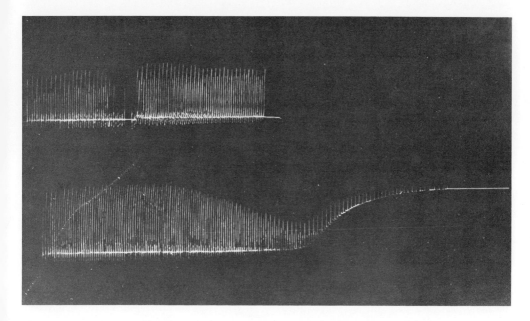

Fig. 6.2 The effect of iodoacetic acid on muscle contraction. Frog muscles were stimulated to contract at regular intervals; the upper record shows part of the contractions of the normal muscle (the break is an artifact of recording). The lower record shows the contractions of the poisoned muscle, with development of fatigue and contracture. Information on the chemical changes in these two muscles is presented in Table 6.2. (From E. Lundsgaard, 1930, *Biochem. Zeitschr.* **217** 164.)

tion is the hydrolysis of ATP. This is the earliest chemical reaction which has yet been observed to follow stimulation of muscle. ATP is in equilibrium with the phosphagen, whatever it may be; thus in vertebrate muscle, if C represents creatine and CP its phosphate

$$ATP + C \rightleftharpoons CP + ADP$$

and the amount of creatine phosphate present is normally considerably greater than the amount of ATP. The phosphagen thus serves as a reserve of energy which can be transferred rapidly

TABLE 6.2

Content of Lactic Acid, Phosphate, and Phosphagen in Muscles Poisoned with Iodacetic Acid Compared with Unpoisoned Muscle

Muscle Treatment	Relative Content of		
	Lactic Acid	Inorganic Phosphate	Phosphagen
Normal, resting	25	21	61
Normal, fatigued	84	29	46
Poisoned, resting	16	29	57
Poisoned, fatigued	15	28	0

From Lundsgaard, 1930, *Biochem. Zeitschr.* **217** 164 (see Figure 6.2).

to ATP following stimulation of the muscle. The original source of ATP and hence of CP as well lies in reactions such as glycolysis which can synthesize ATP. The predominance of glycolysis as a source of energy, first observed in frog muscle, is by no means universal. It is, rather, confined to muscles which must execute rapid contractions under partially or wholly anaerobic conditions—that is, muscles involved in vigorous running, jumping, or swimming or muscles of animals living under conditions of limited oxygen supply. Other muscles rely largely on oxidation for ATP synthesis, and carbohydrates, fats, or even amino acids may be used as substrates for the oxidation. The resynthesis of glycogen from lactic acid which was observed in frog muscle may not be common, and the lactic acid which is formed during anaerobic contractions in mammalian muscle is carried to the liver by the blood and there converted into glycogen. The glycogen supply in muscles is reformed from glucose taken from the blood.

The question of the immediacy of ATP as the source of energy for contraction has been called into question in recent years in studies designed to measure the rate at which this compound is "turned over"—that is, broken down and resynthesized—in muscle. These studies have usually used the radioactive isotope of phosphorus P^{32} or the heavy isotope of oxygen O^{18}. Chemical studies in which the muscle is frozen in liquid air immediately after stimulation have also shown that muscular contraction can occur without breakdown of ATP or CP. When the rate of incorporation of inorganic phosphate into ATP is studied by labeling the phosphate with P^{32} or O^{18} the rate does not increase from resting levels during contraction but only during recovery following contraction. There is some evidence that some other as yet unknown phosphorus compound is the actual immediate energizer of contraction.

The Contractile Substance: Proteins

Whatever the immediate source of the energy the question of the actual mechanism of shortening of muscle still has to be considered. For at least the last 50 years it has been clear that the mechanism must somehow involve proteins of the muscle; these are its most abundant constituents (20%) after water (75%). For a long time the methods of protein purification and the knowledge of protein structure were so poorly developed that efforts to learn something about muscle contraction from protein studies were largely futile. The first muscle protein to be isolated about 1910 was called myosin. About 1935 it became possible to prepare reasonably native—that is, not denatured—myosin, and it also became clear that myosin is rather odd in its properties. If a muscle is minced and the mince is extracted in the cold for about 24 hours with dilute ($0.5N$) solutions of salts such as KCl, a solution of myosin is obtained which has a very high viscosity. If this solution is stirred the viscosity decreases, and the phenomenon of flow birefringence is observed. The term birefringence refers to the phenomenon whereby the velocity of light traveling in one direction (called the optic axis) through a solid or solution is different from that of light traveling in another direction at right angles to the optic axis. If light enters a system with this property at an angle to the optic axis it is split into two polarized beams of light. Birefringence may result from the pres-

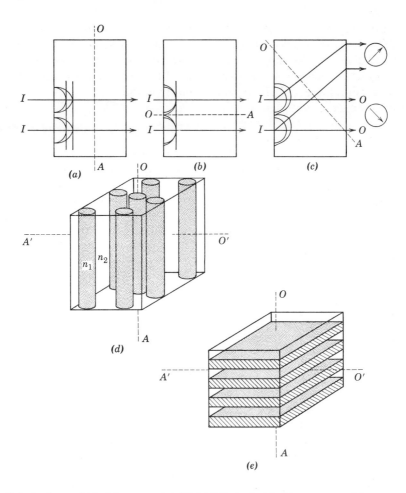

Fig. 6.3 Polarization and birefringence. (*a*) (*b*) (*c*) Effect of a birefringent material on an incident beam *I*. In (*a*) the beam is perpendicular to the optic axis *OA,* and no change occurs. In (*b*) the beam is parallel to the axis, and again no change occurs. In (*c*) the beam enters at an angle of 45° to the optic axis, and as a result is split into an ordinary beam *IO,* polarized in the direction of the axis, and an extraordinary beam *IE,* polarized at 90° to the plane of the axis. In (*d*) and (*e*) two kinds of structures which exhibit birefringence are diagrammed.

ence in the medium of elongated or flattened oriented particles (Figure 6.3). In muscle extracts, where the birefringence is observed only when the solution is flowing, it is caused by the alignment of elongated protein molecules, much as logs might become aligned when moving in a rapidly flowing stream. The change in viscosity has the same explanation: in the solution at rest the elongated protein particles are present in a random arrangement, and hence the viscosity is high, but if the solution is caused to flow the particles become aligned and the viscosity falls.

In 1937 D. M. Needham suggested that the key to muscular contraction would be found in the relation between ATP and myosin. The succeeding years saw apparent confirmation of this suggestion in two ways. First, the

Russian biochemists Engelhardt and Ljubimova and the English biochemist Bailey showed that myosin as usually prepared also contains most of the adenosinetriphosphatase activity of the muscle. Subsequent studies have shown this to be true even of crystalline myosin, though the preparations used by the earlier investigators were not pure. Second, the Needhams and collaborators in England showed that the addition of ATP to crude myosin solution causes an immediate decrease in the viscosity and birefringence of the solution, indicating that the myosin particles have become shorter and thicker. The change is reversible, and the solutions slowly regain their original properties. The rate of reversal is parallel to the rate of hydrolysis of ATP.

These observations, made just before the beginning of the Second World War, appeared to have brought the problem of muscle contraction very close to a solution. The war seriously interrupted but did not stop the work, and as soon as normal scientific activity became possible again there was a tremendous burst in activity in two directions. The first was in the construction of muscle models out of muscle proteins and by various treatments of muscle fibers. The second was in the purification of the muscle proteins and the study of their properties. Among the leaders in this work were the German biochemist H. H. Weber and the Hungarian biochemist Szent-Györgyi, who later came to the United States. Szent-Györgyi, mentioned earlier for his work in tissue respiration, has provided us with a series of charming and stimulating accounts of his studies in book form as well as some very solid scientific papers. He and Weber utilized, on the one hand, gels prepared of myosin, which will contract vigorously when treated with ATP in a suitable salt solution. On the other hand, they utilized muscle preparations made by extracting muscles in the cold with glycerin, a process which removes ATP and inorganic salts. Such preparations also contract when treated with suitable concentrations of ATP and salts. Szent-Györgyi's work has emphasized in particular that the interaction of myosin with ATP depends very strongly on salt concentration and that myosin is not a simple protein but a very complex one.

Specifically, crude myosin as extracted from muscle can be separated into two fractions, one of which is called myosin and the other actin. Pure myosin occurs in the form of rod-shaped molecules 1650 Å long and 26 Å thick, with a molecular weight of about 420,000. By treatment of pure myosin with trypsin it is possible to obtain two fragments—one, called H meromyosin, is a large unit of molecular weight 230,000, length 435 Å, thickness 29 Å and contains the adenosinetriphosphatase activity of the molecule. The other fragment, called L meromyosin, is a smaller unit of molecular weight 96,000, length 550 Å, thickness 16 Å. Two L units combine with one H unit to form a single myosin molecule.

Actin is a protein of relatively low molecular weight (70,000) which contains ATP as a prosthetic group and forms, by end-to-end attachment of two molecules in the presence of Mg^{2+}, Ca^{2+}, and ATP, a dimer of molecular weight 140,000. This dimer is readily polymerized, with hydrolysis of the ATP, to a long fibrous particle, F-actin. F-actin will in turn combine with the H fraction of myosin in solution to form a complex called actomyosin.

This complex is the material present in crude myosin solutions as extracted from muscle and is the one whose properties are changed so dramatically by ATP. It now appears, however, that actomyosin does not exist as a single protein unit in muscle, but rather that actin and myosin are arranged in a pattern which is intimately related to the submicroscopic structure of the muscle fiber.

The Contractile Mechanism: Structure

The current picture of muscle contraction began to emerge about 1950. It is still not complete, but it has many advantages over the previous pictures and is able to account for most of the evidence presently available. The intensive biochemical work on the muscle proteins, which at first promised so much, led ultimately to some confusion, since it proved impossible to determine from the behavior of the pure proteins, alone, anything about the behavior of the intact muscle. Consequently many students of muscle, notably H. E. Huxley and his collaborators, turned to the problem of muscle structure. The general structure of a vertebrate striated muscle has been known to histologists for a long time, but the information was neglected by the biochemists in their pursuit of acids, proteins, and enzymes and by the biophysicists in their studies of potentials and heat production.

A striated muscle fiber is a single large cell made up of large numbers of fibrils which extend the entire length of the muscle fiber and are embedded in a more conventional cytoplasm called the sarcoplasm (Figure 6.4). The entire fiber is enclosed in a membrane, the sarcolemma. The sarcoplasm contains mitochondria and all the usual cytoplasmic apparatus, but the fibrils are unique in being made up of many fine filaments which are alternately light and dark in appearance in stained preparations and likewise show differences in optical properties when examined in polarized light or with a phase contrast optical system. This banded or striped appearance of the fibrils is responsible for the term "striated muscle." The optically distinct bands are characterized as the anisotropic or *A* and isotropic or *I* bands. The term anisotropic refers to the fact that the *A* bands are birefringent. In this case the birefringence arises from a permanent structural arrangement of rod-shaped material parallel to the long axis of the fibril. This material is also responsible for the staining properties which make the *A* bands look dark in stained preparations. It is absent from the *I* bands. Each *I* band has in its center a transverse membrane, the *Z* membrane; the unit extending from one *Z* membrane to the next is called a sarcomere. There is also a clear space, the hyaline or *H* zone, in the center of the *A* band and an apparent membrane (*M* membrane) is sometimes visible in the center of the *H* zone.

Proteins and Structure

It has recently become possible by use of serological techniques to establish the relation of the muscle proteins to the structure of the muscle. Antibodies specific to myosin can be prepared by injecting pure myosin into an animal such as a rabbit. These antibodies when mixed with myosin in solution will combine specifically with the myosin but not with, for example, actin. If the antibodies are isolated from the serum and "labeled" by con-

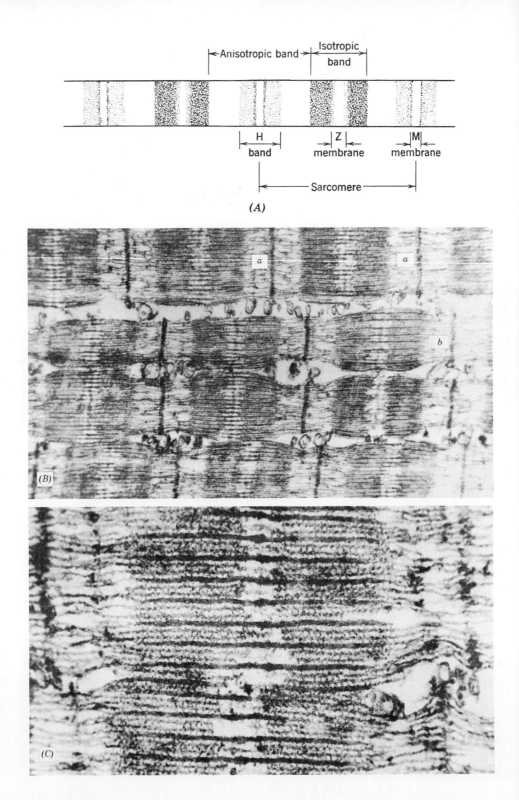

(A)

(B)

(C)

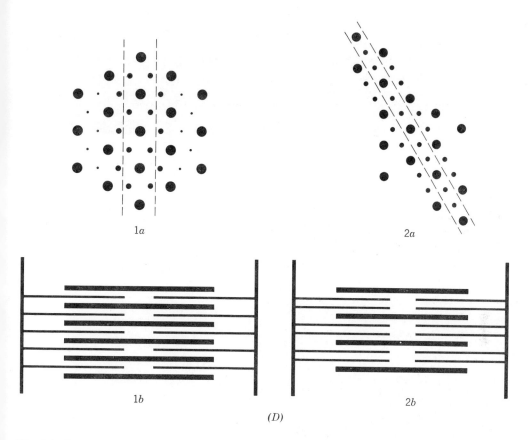

$1a$

$2a$

$1b$

$2b$

(D)

Fig. 6.4 Structure of vertebrate striated muscle. (A) Diagram of part of a muscle fibril, showing the parts of a sarcomere. (B) Electron micrograph of portions of several muscle fibrils, with small amounts of sarcoplasm between. (C) Electron micrograph of a single sarcomere at higher magnification. In B and C, the Z-membranes are the thin dark transverse bands; in B these appear to the right of the letter a, and in C at the left and right ends of the sarcomere. (D) Diagrams of the probable arrangement of the constituent materials of the sarcomere as they would appear in a cross section ($1a$, $2a$) and in longitudinal sections cut at different angles ($1b$, $2b$); the electron micrograph of D shows an arrangement similar to $1b$ in fibril a, and an arrangement similar to $2b$ in fibril b. In these diagrams, the heavy rods are supposed to represent myosin, and the thinner ones actin; the vertical lines at left and right of $1b$ and $2b$ are the Z membranes. (From H. E. Huxley, 1957, *J. Biophys. Biochem. Cytol.* **3** 631.)

jugating them with a fluorescent dye they can then be used to determine the localization of myosin in the muscle fiber. When a muscle fiber is immersed in a solution of fluorescent antibody, the antibody combines with myosin, and the region in which the myosin is present can be seen by its fluorescence. By this technique the myosin is seen to be localized entirely in the A bands. This agrees with evidence from extraction studies, which show that when myosin is selectively extracted from fibers the A bands disappear. Antibodies specific for the H and L fractions of myosin have also been prepared, and with these the *H* fraction is seen to be concentrated in the center of the *A* band, with the *L* fractions at the margins. The antibodies specific for actin, on the other hand, attach themselves to the entire sarcomere.

This information has been supplemented by electron microscopy (Figure 6.4). Electron micrographs of muscle fibrils in longitudinal section show two kinds of filaments: thin ones, which extend through the whole sarcomere from one *Z* membrane to the next, and thicker ones, lying between the thin ones and extending only the length of the *A* bands. In cross section there is a regular alternation of thin and thick filaments in the regions of the *A* band, but only the thin filaments appear in the *I* band. The thin filaments appear to be double in some sections; this is interpreted as a consequence of the hexagonal array of the two types of fibers as shown in Figure 6.4. The thin filaments almost certainly are made up largely or wholly of actin, while the thicker filaments of the *A* band must be myosin.

Changes in Contraction

It is now of the greatest interest to know what happens to these various structures when the muscle is stretched or caused to contract. When a muscle is stretched it develops tension. In a purely elastic body, according to Hooke's law, the tension would be proportional to the degree of stretch. In a resting muscle a moderate amount of stretch can be applied without changing the tension. Further stretching causes the tension to increase at first slowly, then more rapidly, finally

approaching the linear form characteristic of elastic bodies. The linear portion of the curve is generally interpreted as being due to the properties of the elastic elements (tendons, sarcolemma) in the muscle other than the muscle fibrils. When the muscle is stretched passively the *I* bands, and to a limited extent the *H* zone of the *A* band, extend, while the remainder of the *A* band remains unaltered.

When the muscle is stimulated its properties change markedly. In isometric contraction the muscle develops tension, which then passes off again, and there is no change in the length of either *A* or *I* bands. By applying a sudden very quick stretch to the muscle at various intervals of time after stimulation it can be shown that the muscle enters into an "active state" quite suddenly after a short latent period. The resistance to stretch suddenly increases to a maximum value and remains there for a definite period (25 msec in frog sartorius muscle at 0°C), after which the resistance to stretch rapidly falls off to resting values. If the muscle is arranged so that it can shorten against a constant force such as a weight, the contraction (isotonic) involves shortening primarily of the *I* bands. The length-tension curve of the stimulated muscle at the peak of its contraction is at a higher level than is the resting curve, but the two become identical at very large values of the resting length, where the muscle is stretched to an extent such that it can no longer shorten on stimulation (Figure 6.5). The difference between the resting-tension and the contracted-tension curves is known as the twitch tension. This increases up to the point at which the resting tension exceeds zero and then begins to decrease.

The Sliding-filament Hypothesis

The shape of the length-tension curves and of the curves relating tension to time in an isometric twitch, or length to time in an isotonic twitch, depends in part on the elastic properties of the tendons and sarcolemma. The true picture of events in the muscle fiber itself is best given by the development of the active state as seen in resistance to stretch. This is a sudden change in some internal property of the myofibril itself, and the prime task of muscle physiology is to explain its nature. The evidence that in isotonic twitches the *I* bands are shortened has suggested to Huxley and others the hypothesis that this shortening involves a sliding motion, in which the actin filaments are pulled inward toward the center of the *A* bands between the myosin filaments. This would give the appearance of shortening of the *I* bands and bring the *Z* membranes closer together, thus shortening the muscle. In an isometric contraction, on the other hand, the force which would otherwise cause the sliding of the fibrils is manifested only as an increased tension and a resistance to stretch.

Huxley and Hanson point to the existence of cross links between the actin and myosin filaments—about six for every 400 Å of filament length. They suggest that in the resting muscle these links are not fastened, so that the filaments can slide easily when stretch is applied. In the active state the links become firmly fastened; in the permanent contraction called rigor they are permanently and irreversibly fastened. However, the fastening of the links involves some movement of the filaments; either they slide

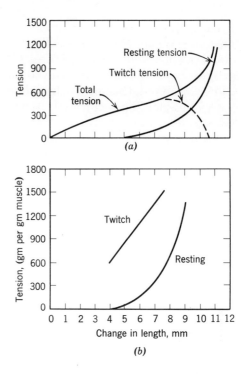

Fig. 6.5 The relation of muscle length to muscle tension in the triceps surae muscle of the rat. In (*a*) the muscle was stretched before contraction by the amounts indicated; the tension actually developed by the contractile substance of the muscle (broken line) is the difference between the resting tension and the total tension. In (*b*) a quick stretch of 4 mm was applied to the muscle at rest (lower curve) or in the early rising phase of a twitch (upper curve), after the muscle had been stretched to the extent indicated on the abscissa. (After Walker, *Am. J. Physiol.* **164** 238–247, 1951.)

inward as in isotonic contraction, or they are put under tension as in isometric contraction. In either case they resist stretching.

Weber, on the basis of studies with muscle fibers extracted with glycerol, carries this view somewhat farther. The extracted fibers, which contain no salt or ATP, are in a state of rigor. They cannot be stretched to any great extent without very marked increase in tension. When Mg^{2+} and ATP are added the fibers contract, and the ATP is hydrolyzed. If the hydrolysis of ATP is inhibited, the fibers behave like resting muscle. They can be stretched without developing tension. Weber's hypothesis is that ATP activates a site on the actin filament by transferring phosphate to it. This activated site then pulls an SH group on the myosin filament close to itself and forms a sulfide bond. The sulfide bond in turn pulls a phenolic (OH) group to itself and forms an oxygen bond. There is evidence that the actin-myosin interaction depends on SH groups while the adenosinetriphosphatase action does not. Weber and others have also given much attention to a relaxing factor, which is present in granules in muscle and inhibits ATP hydrolysis; hence it brings muscle fibrils into a resting position. This factor might act to terminate the active state. In this view the active state would be maintained as long as ATP could be fed into the system and be hydrolyzed. Relaxation would begin when ATP hydrolysis was stopped. The principal difficulty with this hypothesis is the evidence that ATP is hydrolyzed only during recovery.

Summary

We may by way of conclusion summarize the current picture of striated muscle contraction as follows: (1) Stimulation of muscle is followed, after a short latent period, by sudden development of an active state characterized by increased resistance to stretch and leading to development of tension or shortening. The active state persists with little change for a short period and then disappears, leading to relaxation. (2) The isotropic bands of striated myofibrils appear to be made up of actin filaments. These filaments continue into the anisotropic bands where they alternate with myosin filaments. (3) In isotonic contractions the *I* bands shorten, and in passive stretch the *I* bands lengthen. The *A* bands change only slightly in length in either case. (4) These structural relations suggest that isotonic contractions and passive stretch involve a sliding movement of the actin fibrils into and out of the *A* bands between the myosin filaments. (5) The essential feature of the active state is probably the formation of cross links between actin and myosin filaments in specific relation to their positions and movements in the fibril. (6) The formation of these links is energized by a substance of undetermined nature, which in turn receives its energy from glycolytic and oxidative processes in the sarcoplasm by way of ATP and phosphagen (e.g., creatine phosphate).

The problems for the current decade in muscle physiology are the elucidation of the details of the mechanism by which ATP energy is transferred to energize the actin-myosin interaction. Still farther ahead is the question of the way in which the excitation of the muscle fiber membrane and the development of the action potential is transmitted to the substance of the myofibril and there sets in motion the contractile machinery.

Smooth Muscle

We have presented here primarily the picture as it is seen in vertebrate striated muscle, which is specialized for rapid contraction. In vertebrates and invertebrates there are many smooth or nonstriated muscles. In general these contract slowly and maintain contraction for long periods. They usually show, to a considerable degree, the phenomenon of summation of contraction. In nearly any muscle a series of stimuli applied at a frequency such that each successive stimulus reaches the muscle before relaxation from the preceding contraction is complete will cause a final development of tension which is considerably greater than that in a single twitch. The contraction resulting from such repetitive stimulation is called a tetanus, and the tetanus tension for smooth muscle is usually many times the twitch tension.

The basis of the differences between smooth and striated muscle is not fully understood. The structure of the myofibril in the smooth muscle appears to involve the same alternate arrangement of actin and myosin filaments, but the array is not as regular in smooth muscle, so there is no striated appearance. The stretching and the contraction probably involve the same basic processes, but the myosin of smooth muscles in some cases shows different properties. Finally, the amount and the arrangement of elastic tissue vary greatly in different kinds of muscles and influences contraction properties.

References

Baldwin, E. H. F. 1933. Phosphagen. *Biol. Rev.* **8** 74–105.

Bourne, G. H. (ed.) 1960. *The Structure and Function of Muscle.* (3 vols.) Academic Press, New York.

Buchthal, F., and Sten-Knudsen, O. 1959. Impulse propagation in striated muscle fibers and the role of the internal currents of activation. *Annals N.Y. Acad. Sci.* **81** 422–445.

Buchthal, F., Svensmark, O., and Rosenfalck, P. 1956. Mechanism and chemical events in muscle contraction. *Physiol. Rev.* **36** 503–538.

Davies, R. E., Cain, D., and Delluva, A. M. 1959. The energy supply for muscular contraction. *Annals N.Y. Acad. Sci.* **81** 468–478.

Dubuisson, M. 1954. *Muscular Contraction.* Thomas; Springfield, Ill.

Eggleton, P. 1933. Recent progress in the chemistry of muscular contraction. *Biol. Rev.* **8** 46–73.

Engelhardt, V. A. 1946. Adenosinetriphosphatase properties of myosin *Adv. Enzymol.* **6** 147–191.

Ennor, A. H., and Morrison, J. F. 1958. Biochemistry of the phosphagens and related guanidines. *Physiol. Rev.* **38** 631–674.

Gergely, J. 1959. The relaxing factor of muscle. *Annals N.Y. Acad. Sci.* **81** 490–504.

Hill, A. V. 1932. The revolution in muscle physiology. *Physiol. Rev.* **12** 56–67.

Hill, A. V. 1950. A challenge to biochemists. *Biochim. Biophys. Acta.* **4** 4–11.

Hill, A. V. 1952. A discussion on the thermodynamics of elasticity in biological tissues. *Proc. Royal Soc. London B.* **139** 464–497.

Hill, A. V. 1960. Production and absorption of work by muscle. *Science* **131** 897–903.

Huxley, A. F. 1957. Muscle structure and theories of contraction. *Progr. Biophys.* **7** 257–318.

Huxley, A. F. 1959. Local activation of muscle. *Annals N.Y. Acad. Sci.* **81** 446–452.

Huxley, H. E. 1956. Muscular contraction. *Endeavour* **15** 177–188.

Huxley, H. E. 1960. Muscle cells. *The Cell* **4** 366–481.

Huxley, H. E., and Hanson, J. 1959. The structural basis of the contractile mechanism in striated muscle. *Annals N.Y. Acad. Sci.* **81** 403–408.

Mommaerts, W. F. H. M. 1950. A consideration of experimental facts pertaining to the primary reaction in muscular activity. *Biochim. Biophys. Acta.* **4** 50–57.

Mommaerts, W. F. H. M. 1952. Studies on the contractile protein system of muscle. *Mod. Trends Physiol. Biochem.* 396–404.

Morales, M. F., Botts, J., Blum, J. J., and Hill, T. L. 1955. Elementary processes in muscle action: an examination of current concepts. *Physiol. Rev.* **35** 475–505.

Muralt, A. von. 1950. The development of muscle chemistry, a lesson in neurophysiology. *Biochim. Biophys. Acta* **4** 126–129.

Needham, D. M. 1950. Myosin and adenosinetriphosphatase in relation to muscle contraction. *Biochim. Biophys. Acta* **4** 42–49.

Perry, S. V. 1956. Relation between chemical

and contractile function and structure of skeletal muscle cells. *Physiol. Rev.* **36** 1–76.

Sandow, A. 1952. Excitation-contraction coupling in muscular response. *Yale J. Biol. Med.* **25** 176–201.

Szent-Györgyi, A. 1950. Actomyosin and muscular contraction. *Biochim. Biophys. Acta* **4** 38–41.

Szent-Györgyi, A. 1953. *Chemical Physiology of Contraction in Body and Heart Muscle.* Academic Press, New York.

Szent-Györgyi, A. 1955. Structural and functional aspects of myosin. *Adv. Enzymol.* **16** 313–360.

Weber, H. H. 1950. Muskelproteine. *Biochim. Biophys. Acta* **4** 12–24.

Weber, H. H. 1959. The relaxation of the contracted actomyosin system. *Annals N.Y. Acad. Sci.* **81** 409–421.

7 Excitation of receptors

The systems we have examined in the two previous chapters—the axon and the muscle fiber—are excitable systems, but the mode of excitation which is used in the experimental study of these systems is not, strictly speaking, the normal mode of excitation. The phenomenon we call the nerve impulse is normally aroused either by excitation of a specific structure known as a receptor or by spontaneous activity in a central nervous system. The word spontaneous in this case simply means that we do not know the origin of the activity, but we do know it is not caused by an external stimulus. In this chapter we shall examine the nature of receptors and the way in which they originate nervous impulses.

General Principles

In general we may say that a receptor is an element of the nervous system which responds to a change in the energy flux in the environment of the receptor by initiating, in axons connected to the receptor, a pattern of nervous impulses. This rather careful technical definition can be made clear in operational terms by many examples. A change in the intensity, wavelength, or pattern of intensities and wavelengths of light striking the eye will set up nervous discharges in the optic nerve. Pressure applied to a Pacinian corpuscle in the skin or mesentery will arouse a pattern of sequential nervous discharges in the axon connected with the corpuscle. If a solution of salt is applied to the tongue a pattern of nerve impulses will be set up in nerve axons connected with certain taste buds. If a sugar solution is similarly applied nerve impulses will appear in other axons.

The study of receptors is rather more complex than is the study of nerve or muscle function. For nerve and muscle there is a very great similarity in structure and in activity in the entire animal kingdom, but receptors exhibit great variety in structure and a considerable range of functional activity within one class of animals; if we consider the entire animal kingdom the variety is still greater and of unknown extent. In such a situation we can effect some simplification in our analysis by classification. If we can establish categories of receptors with a set of significant common characteristics we can then direct our inquiries toward these common characteristics.

The most satisfactory basis for classification of receptors appears to be one based on types of energy flux to which they respond. This basis of classification was recognized in the early nineteenth century by Johannes Müller, probably the outstanding physiologist of his day. Müller developed the doctrine of "specific nerve energies." This doctrine was originally based on the observation that stimulation of a sensory nerve gives rise to the same sensation as does stimulation of the receptor to which that nerve is attached, and that stimulation of a particular receptor by any sort of stimulus likewise always arouses the sensation characteristic of that receptor, regardless of the nature of the stimulus. Müller's doctrine in its original form is no longer tenable. We would now say that each receptor has a low threshold for some specific form of energy and a high threshold for all other forms of energy. This specificity in turn is reflected by the higher nervous centers concerned with sensation so that the sensation aroused, whenever that receptor or its sensory nerve is stimulated, is the sensation appropriate to that form of energy to which the receptor is most

sensitive. Thus the sensation of light is produced when the eye is illuminated or when it is struck a blow or when the optic nerve is stimulated. The sensation of heat might be aroused by an increase in temperature in the neighborhood of a heat receptor in the skin or by electrical stimulation of its sensory nerve axon.

We can then classify receptors under five categories with respect to their sensitivity to various forms of energy. (1) Mechanoreceptors are sensitive to changes in pressure or tension. (2) Chemoreceptors are sensitive to changes in concentration of specific substances or classes of substances. (3) Thermoreceptors are sensitive to change in temperature or heat flux. (4) Photoreceptors are sensitive to changes in intensity or wavelength of light. (5) There are some receptors which have little specific sensitivity but respond to most changes in energy flux when they approach or exceed the level of tissue damage. As biological classifications go this is a very satisfactory one in that nearly all receptors can be fitted to it, and even the fifth category is not miscellaneous but has some specific properties. The classification probably owes its correspondence with fact to the necessity, not yet experimentally established, for quite distinct cellular mechanisms for the conversion of each form of energy flux into the same ultimate code, namely, a pattern of discharge of nerve impulses.

A second basis of classification is structural, and here the characteristic on which categories are based is complexity. The simplest receptors consist of single neurons, usually multipolar, with one axon, called afferent, extending to a junction or synapse with another neuron or neurons, or in a few cases with a muscle cell, at some distance. Such receptors are called primary sense cells. The second order of complexity finds the primary sense cells surrounded by or associated with other cells or structures constituting some sort of auxiliary apparatus. In some cases it is possible to infer from the nature of such auxiliary apparatus a possible function, and in some instances the function has been demonstrated experimentally. The lens of the eye is a familiar example which is known to function in increasing the light-gathering power of the eye and in forming a definite image on the retina, where are located the primary sense cells. The third order of complexity finds a number of primary sense cells, and possibly auxiliary structures as well, associated to form a sense organ. Finally, as in the vertebrate eye or ear, the sense organ may have, in addition to primary sense cells and auxiliary structures, secondary sense cells—neurons with which the axons of the primary cells synapse. In the retina of the vertebrate eye, for example, there are very complex synaptic connections between the primary sense cells (rods or cones) and several layers of secondary sense cells. The axons of the optic nerve arise in these secondary cells rather than in the primary sense cells.

From the definition of receptors we might anticipate a third basis for classification in the pattern of nerve impulses produced by the receptor. Such a basis exists, in fact, but before we examine it we must know more about the action of receptors in general. The study of receptor action has ramifications in psychology, and much of what we know about receptors is based on the study of sensation. To the animal physiologist, information of this latter sort has an undesirable subjective element. The discussion which follows will be based on objective observations of the results of stimulation of receptors. The range of phenomena which can be studied by such objective methods is limited, but the increased reliability of data obtained justifies our procedure.

Mechanoreceptors

Excitation

Most of the evidence presently available about the details of excitation of primary sense cells has been derived from studies of mechanoreceptors. This is partly because such receptors occur rather frequently in the vertebrates and arthropods as simple unicellular structures with only limited auxiliary apparatus. The structures best known are the muscle spindle and the Pacinian corpuscle of the vertebrates. The muscle spindle responds primarily to stretch of the muscle with which it is associated. The structure of the spindle and its relation to the muscle are shown in Figure 7.1.

When a muscle is stretched and records of activity in the afferent axon of a spindle are obtained, we find that an adequate stretch arouses, in the axon, a series of impulses which lasts as long as the stretch continues. The initial frequency of the impulses depends on the amount of stretch, being greater with larger amounts, but the increase in frequency is not linear with the increase in stimulus. The initial frequency is not maintained but falls off with time to a lower constant level, which is likewise directly but not linearly related to the amount of stretch. The decrease in frequency with time is called adaptation and is characteristic of many but not all sense cells. The

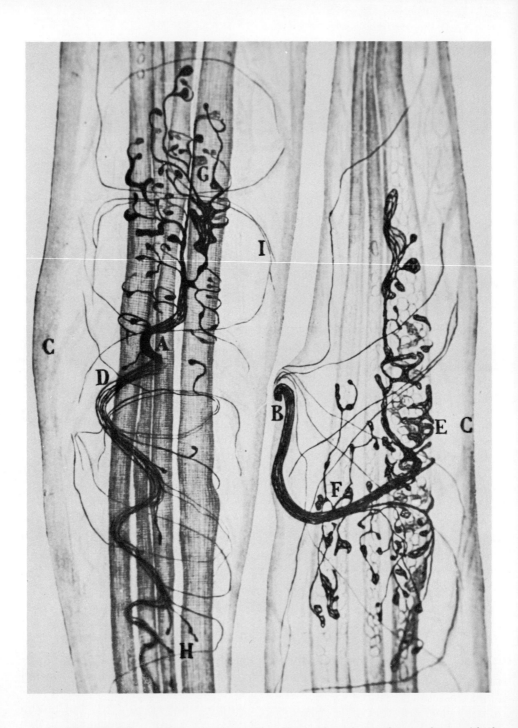

Fig. 7.1 The vertebrate muscle spindle. Two embryonic muscles are shown with the nerve bundles *A* and *B,* from which arise the terminations *E, F, G, H* surrounding the muscle fibers. (From Ramon-y-Cajal, *Histology,* English transl., 1933, Williams and Wilkins, Baltimore.)

receptors in the walls of the vertebrate artery, for example, which respond to stretch of the arterial wall, show little adaptation.

The rate and the extent of adaptation are important characteristics of receptors and are used as a basis for classification into (1) "tonic receptors," in which adaptation is slow and there is a continuing discharge as long as stimulation continues and (2) "phasic receptors," in which adaptation is rapid and ultimately complete, with no impulses discharged even though the stimulus continues to act (Figure 7.2). Primary sense cells vary from the extreme phasic type, which responds to any adequate stimulus by initiating a single nerve impulse only, no matter how long the stimulus continues, to the nearly perfect tonic type, in which a constant stimulus of long duration results in a constant frequency of discharge of impulses as long as the stimulus continues. There is a great variety of intermediate conditions. These patterns of response have been observed in all the major classes of receptors.

The origin of the discharge of nerve impulses in the afferent axon lies both in the properties of that axon and in those of the sense cell of which it is a part. The axons of crustaceans or vertebrates will, under certain experimental conditions, respond to stimulus from a constant direct current by discharge of a series of impulses at a frequency which is related to the strength of the current and may show the phenomenon of adaptation. When a recording electrode is applied to an axon close to the cathode of the stimulating electrode, and a direct current is caused to flow between the stimulating electrodes, currents of small intensity produce a local response which involves a very slow development of depolarization in the region of the cathode. We have seen earlier that this local response depends on the two opposing processes of excitation and accommodation. We have also seen that a conducted nerve impulse or spike is produced only when the excitation process leads to depolarization beyond a certain critical level before the accommodation process tending to repolarize the membrane overtakes it. As the magnitude of the stimulating current increases, the rate of depolarization also increases, and eventually a spike is initiated at the threshold. If the stimulating current continues to flow, however, depolarization begins again as soon as the membrane is repolarized at the end of the spike. Hence impulses are discharged at a regular frequency which depends on the rate of depolarization in the region of the stimulating cathode. This in turn depends on the intensity of the direct current used as a stimulus.

Generator Potentials

These experiments show that the behavior of any axon, with constant current as a stimulus, is similar to the behavior of an afferent axon from a sense cell stimulated by its appropriate stimulus. The question remains: How does a mechanical, chemical, photic, or thermal stimulus bring about this behavior? In 1942 Granit and associates in Sweden suggested that the adequate stimulus for any receptor causes a decrease in the membrane potential of the sense cell known as a generator potential. This depolarization in turn sets up a flow of direct current with the sense cell acting as a cathode or sink, and the direct current then arouses a repetitive discharge in the afferent axon (Figure 7.3). The exist-

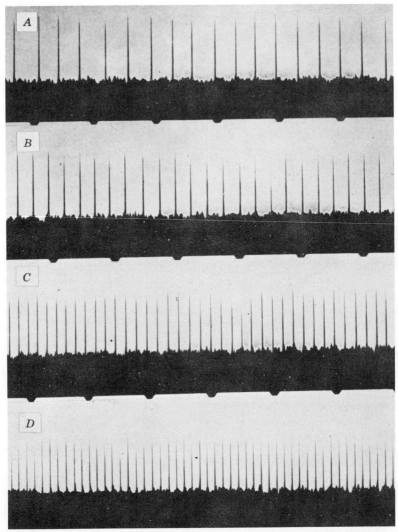

Fig. 7.2 I

ence of such generator potentials has been demonstrated in the muscle spindle of the frog (stretch receptor), a comparable stretch receptor in the crayfish, the Pacinian corpuscle (pressure receptor) in the cat, the ampullae of Lorenzini in the dogfish (mechanoreceptors), in the isolated ommatidium (photoreceptor) of the horseshoe crab *Limulus,* and in the olfactory receptors (chemoreceptors) of the frog among others.

The nature of the generator potential and its relation to excitation have been studied in considerable detail in the Pacinian corpuscle. This receptor consists of a single nonmyelinated nerve ending, surrounded by a concentric series of laminae separated by fluid (Figure 7.4). The laminae constitute the auxiliary apparatus. On emergence from the corpuscle the axon (continuous with the nerve ending) acquires a myelin sheath, with the

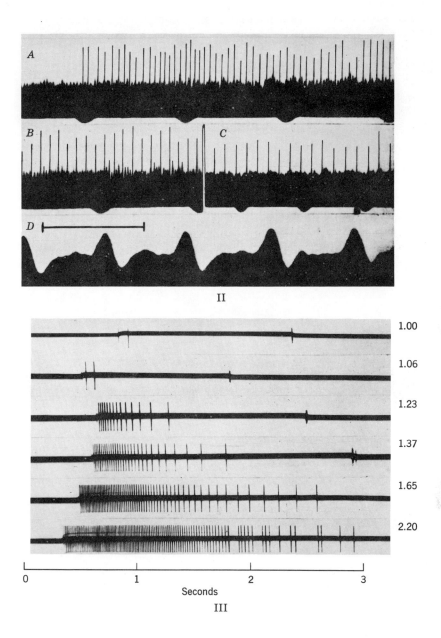

II

III

Fig. 7.2 Electric responses of receptors. I. Afferent impulses from a pressure receptor in the carotid sinus of a rabbit, stimulated by A0.40, B0.80, C0.140, D0.200 mm Hg. Time, $\frac{1}{5}$ sec. (From Bronk and Stella, *Am. J. Physiol.* **110** 708–714, 1935.) II. Response of a stretch receptor in the toe of a frog: A, immediately after stretching; B, 2 sec later; C, 5 sec later; D, record at high speed. Time, A, B, C, $\frac{1}{5}$ sec; D, 0.01 sec. (From Mathews, *J. Physiol.* **71,** 64–110, 1931.) III. Electric response of crab (*Carcinus*) axons resulting from sudden application of constant currents. The numbers give the relative current strength. Make and break indicated by small artifacts. (From Hodgkin, *J. Physiol.* **107** 165–181, 1948.)

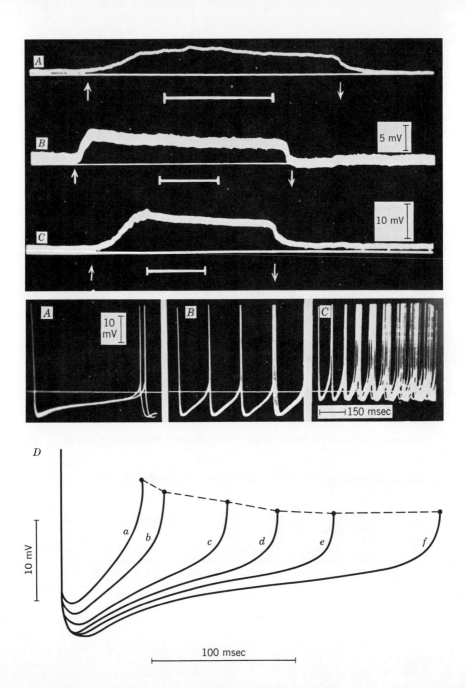

Fig. 7.3 Generator potentials in a stretch receptor in the abdomen of a crayfish. Upper portion, three recordings of pure generator potentials under different conditions; stretch was applied at the upward-pointing arrow, and released at the downward-pointing arrow; the bar under each recording indicates one second. Lower portion, *A, B, C* are recordings of generator and action potentials from the same cell at three levels of stimulus (stretch) strength. The spike appears as a reversal of potential because it is recorded from within the receptor; the initial effect of stretch is a depolarization of the receptor membrane, followed by a flow of current from the adjacent axon region. In *D,* the records from 6 increasing degrees of stretch, from *a* to *f,* are superimposed, with the threshold levels, at which spikes appear, connected by a dotted line. The frequency of discharge in the axons ranged from 4 (*a*) to 20 (*f*) per second. (From Eyzaguirre and Kuffler, 1955, *J. Gen. Physiol.* **39** 95.)

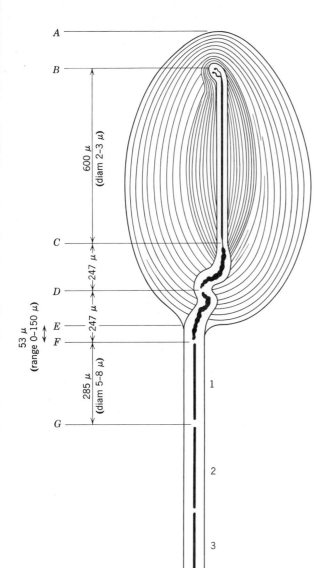

Fig. 7.4 The Pacinian corpuscle. The axon ending *BC* is enclosed in a capsule *AE;* only the region *BC* is sensitive to pressure. The action potential spikes arise first at *F,* the first node of Ranvier; the numerals indicate the successive internodes of the myelinated portion of the axon. (From Quilliam and Sato, 1955, *J. Physiol.* **129** 173.)

usual nodes of Ranvier at regular intervals. The generator potential in this receptor is aroused by pressure. When the nerve ending, either inside or outside the corpuscle, is subjected to increased pressure, the membrane potential in the region of the nerve ending is decreased. This change in potential depends on sodium ion. It is abolished reversibly within a relatively short period in sodium-free solutions. The magnitude and rate of change of the potential are both directly related to the sodium ion concentration. The magnitude and rate of rise are also directly related to the amount of pressure applied to the nerve ending.

The auxiliary structures (laminae with fluid between) are not involved as such in production of the potential, which can be evoked by pressure applied to the nerve ending after the laminae are stripped off. On the other hand, the free nerve ending shows less rapid adaptation than does the entire corpuscle, and it has been shown that a force suddenly applied causes considerable deformation of the laminae, which then by redistribution of pressures in the system return toward their initial positions, even though the compressing force continues to act. The rapid adaptation of this receptor may therefore be primarily a property of the auxiliary laminae, while the development of the generator potential itself depends on the nonmyelinated nerve ending.

The nerve ending is itself electrically inexcitable. Application of a direct current will cause a change in the membrane potential, and this change will add to the change produced by pressure, but a spike never appears in the nonmyelinated portion of the axon. The point nearest the corpuscle at which spikes can be elicited is the first

node of the myelinated portion. When the nonmyelinated portion is compressed spikes occur when the generator potential reaches a certain critical level. The critical level fluctuates from time to time; immediately after discharge of a spike the first node is in a relatively refractory period, and the critical level is quite high. This period is followed in turn by a supernormal period in which the critical level is lower than normal.

Summary

The picture of the receptor mechanism in the Pacinian corpuscle which emerges from these recent studies may be summarized thus: A nerve axon extending from the spinal cord to the corpuscle has two parts. The proximal afferent myelinated portion has the typical properties of axons; it is electrically excitable and capable of developing and conducting spike potentials. The terminal nonmyelinated portion responds to compression by a change in membrane properties comparable to that which occurs in the subthreshold or local response of the typical axon. There is an increase in the apparent permeability to sodium ion which allows increased entry of this ion, and hence partial depolarization, without a complete breakdown of the sodium barrier. The extent of the increase in sodium permeability is directly but not linearly related to the amount of compression. This in turn means that the amount of depolarization is directly related to the amount of compression. The depolarized terminal portion of the axon then becomes a sink for current flowing from the myelinated portion of the axon. This current flow leads to depolarization of the first node of the axon to an extent sufficient to arouse a spike. Following each spike a supernormal period occurs in which, as long as the depolarization of the ending continues, a second and subsequent spikes will be aroused. The rapid adaptation of the receptor is partly a consequence of the mechanical properties of the auxiliary corpuscle but may also depend in part on the properties of the membrane of the terminal portion of the axon.

No complete analysis has been made for other receptors as yet, but the evidence we have leads us to the belief that this picture may apply generally to receptors. The adequate stimulus causes a depolarization of the terminal portion of the receptor neuron. This in turn sets up a current flow from the adjacent excitable portion of the axon leading to excitation. The frequency of this excitation depends on the extent of depolarization which in turn depends on the magnitude of the original stimulus. The exact mechanism by which the adequate stimulus causes a change in the apparent sodium permeability, and hence depolarization, remains the basic problem in the interpretation of receptor mechanisms at the cellular level.

Photoreceptors

For a comparison with these relatively simple mechanoreceptors we shall now examine the visual mechanism of the vertebrate eye. Vertebrate eyes are among the most complex of all sense organs, but one may begin with the events in the type of primary sense cell known as a rod. These events may very well be typical in principle for all photoreceptors. They are typical in detail for the small number which have been carefully studied. The rods vary considerably in structure among the vertebrates, and completely adequate anatomical criteria for their recognition have not been developed. Rods are in general short and relatively thick neurons. For our present purpose their distinctive feature is the presence, in the terminal portion, of the pigment rhodopsin, formerly known as visual purple. In addition to the rods, the retina of most vertebrate eyes also contains other primary sense cells called cones. We shall discuss these later.

The Photochemical Basis of Excitation

When rhodopsin, either in the rod or in solution outside the eye, is illuminated with light of the appropriate wavelength it is converted to an orange intermediate, which then breaks down without further action of light into a yellow product. The most effective wavelength is 491 mμ in the blue-green portion of the spectrum (Figure 7.5). Rhodopsin is a conjugated protein. The orange intermediate formed by treatment with light is also a protein but is quite unstable and breaks down into a hydrocarbon aldehyde, derived from vitamin A and called trans-retinene, and a protein known as scotopsin. Rhodopsin is a compound of retinene and scotopsin. The spectral sensitivity curve for vision at low intensities, the spectral absorption curve for rhodopsin, and the curve relating wavelength to breakdown of rhodopsin all coincide exactly, and we can conclude that the breakdown of rhodopsin is the essential chemical reaction in stimulation of the rods by light.

The exact mechanism by which this chemical change is converted to an electrical change is still uncertain, but the following points are established.

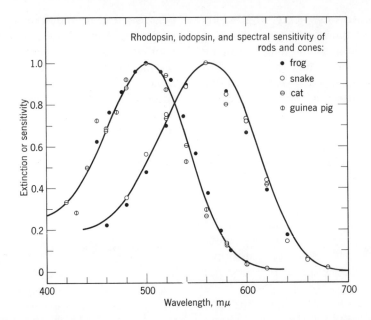

Fig. 7.5 The absorption and action spectra of visual pigments. The curves represent the absorption spectra of rhodopsin (left) and iodopsin (right), while the circles are measured values of spectral sensitivity in dim (left) and bright (right) light for the animals indicated. (From Wald 1955, *J. Gen. Physiol.* **38** 676.)

Rhodopsin makes up as much as 40% of the dry matter of the rod and is concentrated in the outer segment of the cell. Thin sections of this segment appear in the electron microscope as a dense arrangement of concentric layers which must be made up largely of rhodopsin. Similar arrangements are found in the primary sense cells of other receptors which have been studied. The bleaching of rhodopsin in solution, which liberates scotopsin, results in the appearance in the protein of active SH groups and a histidine group. Either of these changes could, in the proper medium, produce an electrical change, and artificial systems have been constructed in which such change occurs. The concentric layering of the rod material could well serve to multiply the effect of breakdown of rhodopsin molecules. However, it has been shown that a single light quantum is sufficient to excite a dark-adapted rod, and a single quantum will be absorbed by and cause breakdown of only a single molecule of rhodopsin.

Several photosensitive pigments other than rhodopsin have been discovered (Figure 7.6). These include in the vertebrates porphyropsin (520 mμ, rods of fresh water fishes, some amphibians), iodopsin (562 mμ, cones of chicken), and cyanopsin (620 mμ, cones of turtles). In addition pigments have been found in invertebrates: one absorbing at 463 mμ and occurring in euphausid crustaceans, one absorbing at 437 mμ from the housefly, and a third absorbing at 491 mμ and occurring in cephalopod mollusks, lobsters, and insects.

The study of the chemical nature of

the vertebrate pigments, largely carried out by George Wald and his students at Harvard University during the last 25 years, has established a number of interesting relationships. In general it appears that there are in the vertebrates two classes of visual proteins; one, called scotopsin, is characteristic of rods and involved in sensitivity to low light intensities, and the other, called photopsin, is characteristic

of cones and involved in sensitivity to higher light intensities. There are also two kinds of retinene: retinene₁ found in marine fishes and terrestrial vertebrates, and retinene₂ found in freshwater fishes and certain amphibians and reptiles. There is a general correlation but not a perfect one between the occurrence of retinene₂ and residence in fresh water. The four vertebrate visual pigments represent all the

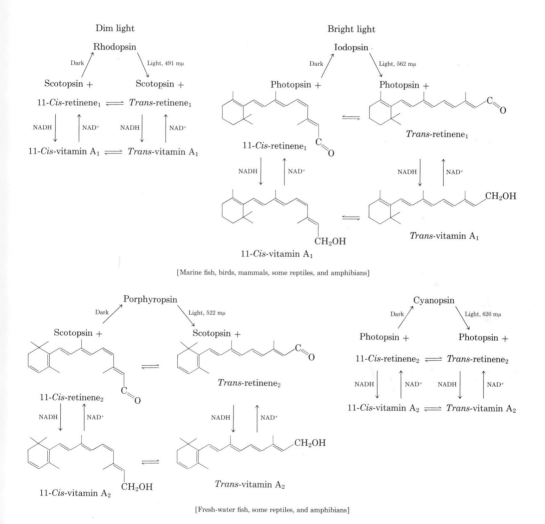

Fig. 7.6 The chemical changes in the visual pigments induced by light, and their relations to vitamin A. (After Hubbard and Kropf, *Ann. N.Y. Acad. Sci.* **81** 388.)

possible combinations of the two retinenes with the two proteins (Figure 7.6). The retinenes, which are aldehydes differing only in the position of a single methyl group on the ring, are readily reduced by NADH to the corresponding alcohols, which have long been known as vitamin A_1 and vitamin A_2. The reverse reaction can be brought about by the enzyme alcohol dehydrogenase, with NAD as hydrogen acceptor, forming retinene from vitamin A. Several of the invertebrate pigments absorbing at 491 mμ have been shown to contain retinene.

Each of the four vertebrate pigments has a different absorption maximum, as noted above. The absorption of visible light depends on the combination of retinene with opsin in the molecule. The opsin does not absorb visible light nor does retinene, but the combination does. When light is absorbed, each quantum breaks down a single molecule of pigment to its component opsin and the all-*trans* form of the retinene. The pigment cannot be reformed from these components. The retinene must first undergo an isomerization to the 11-*cis* isomer, which then combines with the protein to form the visual pigment. The overall interrelations are shown in Figure 7.6. In the squid eye rhodopsin does not break down to retinene and opsin but only undergoes the first step of the reaction, with conversion to an orange pigment. The rhodopsin is then reformed from this.

Late in the nineteenth century, the Czech Purkinje made a study of light and dark adaptation. When the eye is exposed to a bright light it loses its sensitivity to dim light and is said to be "light-adapted." After a period in the darkness the eye becomes more sensitive to bright light and also regains its sensitivity to dim light; it is then said to be "dark-adapted." Complete dark adaptation of the rods may require as much as 45 minutes, while the cones are completely adapted in 5 minutes. Purkinje studied the stimulus threshold for light of varying wavelengths in light-adapted and dark-adapted eyes and found that the maximum sensitivity in dark-adapted human eyes is in the blue-green region of the spectrum, while the maximum in bright light is shifted toward the red region. More careful studies in recent years have shown that the sensitivity curve in the dark-adapted eye corresponds exactly with the absorption curve of rhodopsin (or porphyropsin). In the light-adapted eye of some animals there is an exact correspondence between the sensitivity curve and the absorption curve for iodopsin (or cyanopsin). With the human eye the correspondence with iodopsin is not exact, suggesting the possibility that other pigments are involved in bright vision. This problem will be discussed again in connection with wavelength discrimination (color sensitivity).

The question of the universal occurrence of rhodopsin or porphyropsin in structures morphologically identifiable as rods and of iodopsin or cyanopsin in structures identifiable as cones is still not absolutely settled, since the structure of these elements varies greatly in different eyes. The occurrence of two types of sensitivity is widespread, and in general the eyes of nocturnal animals tend to be sensitive to dim light and have mostly rods, while the eyes of diurnal animals tend to be insensitive to dim light and have mostly cones. Most animals have both types of structures and both sensitivities in varying proportions.

The rods and cones of the vertebrate

eye are the primary photoreceptors in a very complex structure. In the animal kingdom as a whole, the variety of photosensitive structures is enormous, and it would be well beyond our scope to consider these in detail; however, it will be useful to examine some typical photoreceptors with the aim of understanding the principles of their operation. It is reasonable to assume that the photosensitive process itself depends in all photoreceptors on a photochemical reaction in which a molecule of a sensitive substance absorbs a quantum of light and is broken down to products which in some way produce a state of excitation in the primary sense cell. The nature of the excited state is entirely unknown, and the general statement requires further verification in a variety of animals and isolation of more pigments than we now have available.

Simple Photoreceptors

In the simplest photoreceptors the primary sense cell lacks any accessory structures whatever and is not associated with other sense cells to form a specific organ. This arrangement results simply in a general sensitivity to light and is found in representatives in most of the lower animal phyla, notably in echinoderms and some pelecypod mollusks. The simplest accessory structure is a layer of pigment which restricts the direction from which light can effectively stimulate the cell. Eye spots consisting of a receptor and associated pigment are common in worms, especially flatworms and some annelids. A further complication arises when sense cells with or without pigment are clustered together to form a compound eye spot. Experimental studies with animals having

these simple types of photoreceptors have shown that these animals can discriminate between intensities of light and to some extent between light coming from different directions (Figure 7.7).

Unicellular receptors have certain important properties in common with more complex photoreceptors. The siphon of certain pelecypod mollusks contains unicellular light receptors and is sensitive to light, retracting when illuminated. The threshold intensity is maximal when the animal has been in the dark for some time. Immediately after stimulation by a flash of light, the receptors are insensitive for a time; they recover slowly if kept in the dark (dark adaptation). Many years ago Hecht studied the kinetics of dark adaptation and the stimulus-response relations in these animals, and he concluded that the fundamental photoreceptor process is the photochemical breakdown of a single substance into two products. Dark adaptation involves the resynthesis from the products of the photosensitive substance. Clearly this is the type of process which has been described above for vertebrate eyes, and Wald's original chemical studies were suggested by Hecht's work.

Recently electrical recordings have been made in the nerve leading from these types of photoreceptors. The nerve shows a spontaneous discharge of impulses at constant frequency in the dark. On illumination with blue light this discharge is inhibited. When the light is turned off there is a discharge at high frequency which then returns to the normal dark level. Stimulation with red light on the other hand causes an increase in frequency, especially if it follows a period of stimulation with blue light. The dif-

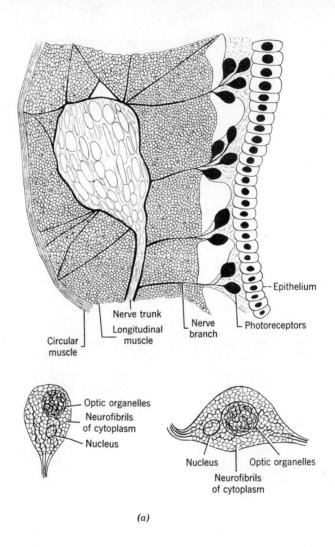

Nerve trunk

Circular
muscle

Longitudinal
muscle

Nerve
branch

Epithelium

Photoreceptors

Optic organelles

Neurofibrils
of cytoplasm

Nucleus

Nucleus   Optic organelles

Neurofibrils
of cytoplasm

(a)

Fig. 7.7 Photoreceptors. (*a*) Unicellular photoreceptors in the siphon of the clam, *Mya,* with
details of cell-body structure in unipolar and bipolar types. (From Light, 1930, *J. Morph.* **49**
25.) (*b*) A simple ocellus from a planarian flatworm; the rhabdomes are the presumed light-
sensitive portions of the receptor cells. (From
Taliaferro, 1920, *J. Exp. Zool.* **31** 59.)

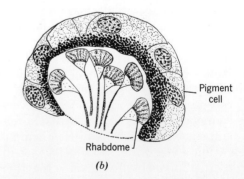

Pigment
cell

Rhabdome

(b)

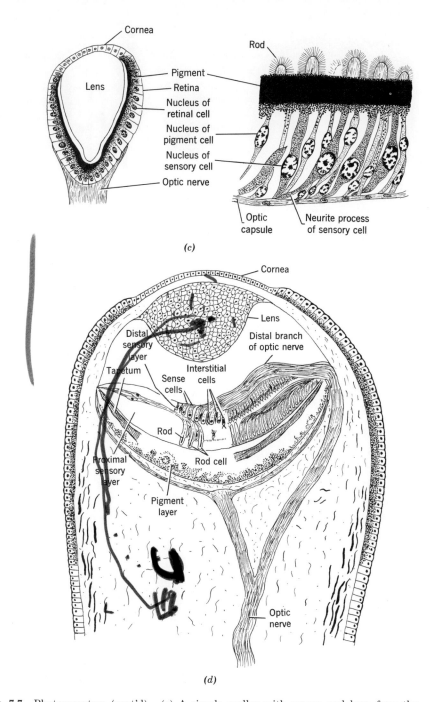

(c)

(d)

Fig. 7.7 Photoreceptors (cont'd). (c) A simple ocellus with cornea and lens, from the snail, *Planorbis,* with details of the retinal structure; note that the receptor cells ("rods") protrude through the pigment layer. (From Arey, 1916, *J. Comp. Neurol.* **26** 359.) (d) One of the eyes from the mantle rim of the scallop, *Pecten.* Note that there are two layers of sense cells; these are shown somewhat magnified on the left to show the structure, and form two superimposed inverted retinas. The responses of the two layers differ. (From Dakin, 1928, *Proc. Roy. Soc.,* London **103** 357.)

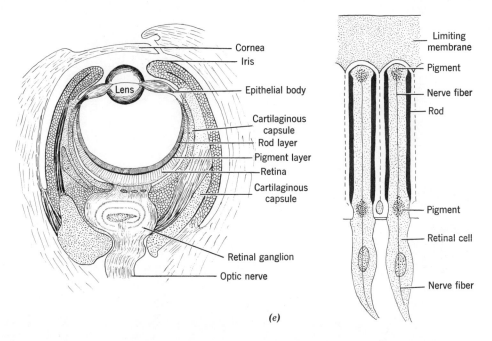

Fig. 7.7 Photoreceptors (cont'd). (*e*) The camera-type eye of a cephalopod, the cuttlefish, *Sepia;* a portion of the direct retina is shown at the right. (From Lang, *Lehrbuch der vergleichende Anatomie wirbellosen Thiere.*)

ferential response in the mollusks suggests that there are two different receptor pigments involved, one absorbing blue light and the other red. It is not clear whether these are in the same or different cells.

The Ocellus

When a group of sense cells is arranged in a cup-shaped structure and surrounded in part by a pigmented layer, we have a distinctive sense organ which we call an ocellus. Such structures are found in all the major groups of metazoan animals and have doubtless evolved independently many times. They show a great variety of arrangements. The simplest are cups with sense cells lining the cup and backed by pigment cells. Light coming through

the open end of the cup will stimulate the sense cells; light from other directions will not. The angular aperture of the open end of the cup—usually less than 180°—determines the field from which stimuli can reach the eye, and such eyes have often been shown to be involved in a directed response— as in orientation toward or away from a light source or in a parallel beam of light. This type of ocellus frequently has a lens in the mouth of the cup. The lens may serve to increase the light-gathering power of the organ or to modify the field of sensitivity; there is no evidence that it permits formation of an image or detection of form.

A significant modification of the ocellus of wide occurrence is the compound ocellus. In this structure individual eye spots consisting of a receptor

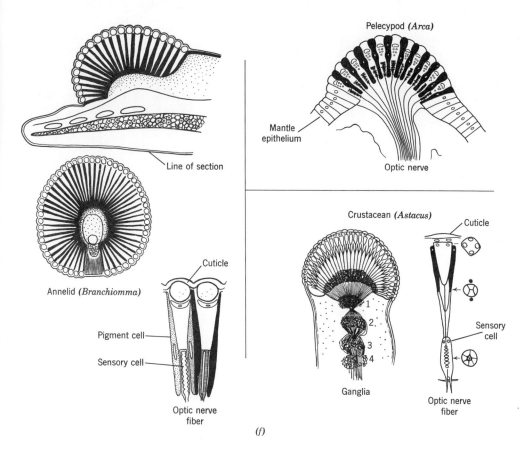

Fig. 7.7 Photoreceptors (cont'd). (*f*) Three types of compound eye from three animal phyla, with details of structure of the ommatidia of two. (From Milne and Milne, 1955, *Radiation Biology* **3** 633, ed. A. Hollaender, McGraw Hill, New York.)

cell with associated lens are grouped in a more or less radial arrangement so that the total receptor field is considerably greater than the field of any unit, and the total amount of light received is multiplied. This pattern has reached its maximum development in the compound eyes of the arthropods (Figure 7.7*f, g, h*).

The Compound Eye

The unit of the compound eye is the ommatidium, essentially a cylinder with sense cells at its base and pigment in its walls. There are always several sense cells in each ommatidium arranged in a ring (occasionally two rings) and usually surrounding a central rod or rhabdome secreted by the sense cells. A distal portion of the ommatidium is filled by a crystalline cone, typically secreted by a ring of cells in the wall. The distal end of the ommatidium is covered by a transparent cornea. The walls contain pigment cells, usually in two groups; the proximal pigment cells surround the sense cells, and the distal pigment cells surround the cone and the space between

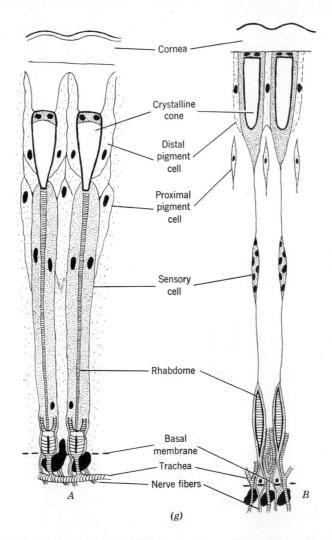

Cornea

Crystalline
cone

Distal
pigment
cell

Proximal
pigment
cell

Sensory
cell

Rhabdome

Basal
membrane

Trachea

Nerve fibers

A

B

(g)

Fig. 7.7 Photoreceptors (cont'd). (g,h) Ommatidia from apposition (top left) and superposition (top right) eyes of insects; the diagrams on facing page show the mechanism of image formation in the two types of eye. The receptor process occurs in the portion of the sense cell surrounding the rhabdome. (After Novikoff, 1931, *Z. wissenschaftl. Zool.* **138** and Wigglesworth, 1939, *Principles of Insect Physiology*, Dutton, New York.)

the cone and the sense cell. The compound eye is made up of large numbers of ommatidia arranged more or less as radii of a sphere.

The ommatidia function in two ways. In the apposition eye each ommatidium receives light from a restricted portion of the visual field determined by the orientation of the ommatidial axis and the refractive properties of the cornea and crystalline cone. The pigment in the wall of the ommatidium prevents light which enters the ommatidium from striking sense cells of adjacent ommatidia. Such an eye will permit the nervous mechanism to syn-

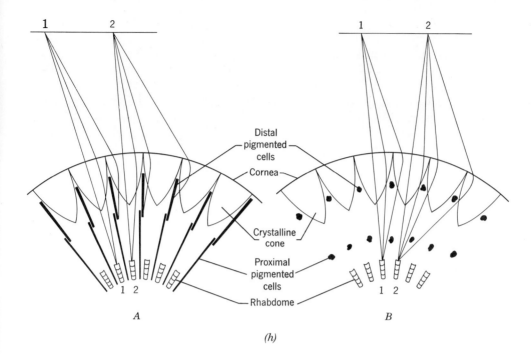

Distal pigmented cells
Cornea
Crystalline cone
Proximal pigmented cells
Rhabdome

A

B

(h)

thesize an image of the visual field by integration of the pattern of the intensities in the individual ommatidia. The visual acuity—that is, the minimum angular separation of objects which can be discriminated—will be determined by the angular distance between ommatidial axes, if there is no overlap in the individual ommatidial fields. This appears to be the mechanism of operation of the compound eye in many diurnal arthropods. Experiments have shown this type of eye to be especially effective in detecting movement in the visual field, much less so than in distinguishing form in stationary pattern. In many cases the distal pigment undergoes migration during dark adaptation so that light can penetrate the walls of the ommatidia.

In nocturnal arthropods or in dark-adapted eyes, the eye appears to function differently. The distal pigment cells are either contracted or poorly developed, and there is much straying of light between ommatidia. The refractive system of the crystalline cones is such that light entering the eye from a certain portion of the visual field is brought to a focus on a corresponding group of sense cells regardless of the ommatidia through which light enters the eye. This method of image formation is called superposition. Its effectiveness in living arthropods has been little studied, and the nocturnal arthropod eye may be largely a light-gathering organ. The arthropod eye is also sensitive to the plane of polarization of light, and this sensitivity is used by insects such as ants and bees in orientation to the position of the sun even when the sun is obscured by clouds. The suggestion has been made that the individual cells of the ring of sense cells in each ommatidium are the basis of this sensitivity.

The compound eye of the horseshoe crab *Limulus* has proved to be very useful in the analysis of the relation between stimulation by light and the electrical discharge in the axons leading from the eye. The eye in this animal is relatively simple and impulses can be recorded from single axons in the optic nerve. Stimulation of a single ommatidium with light of low intensity causes an initial discharge of nerve impulses at high frequency after a long latent period (0.8 sec in one experiment). The system adapts rapidly to a steady lower frequency (3 per sec) which continues as long as the stimulus continues. If the stimulating intensity is increased a hundredfold the latent period decreases (to 0.2 sec) and the steady frequency increases (to 15 per sec). A further hundredfold increase in stimulus further decreases the latent period (0.1 sec) and increases the frequency (40 per sec). This pattern is quite similar to that in many other types of receptors except for the long latent period, which may in part be due to a slow chemical reaction in the receptor.

It has not been possible as yet to obtain electrical records from the sense cells themselves, but when a microelectrode is inserted into the ommatidium among the sense cells there is a spike response on illumination, superimposed on a maintained negative potential. The spike response is first positive, then negative—the reverse of the axon spike. It appears that one or more of the sense cells is depolarized by light, and this depolarization arouses impulses in the axon as in other receptors. The spike observed in the ommatidium may not be an electrical response of the sense cell, but rather a reflection of the axon spike. Similar results have been obtained in the more elaborate eyes of insects such as the blowfly and the honeybee. Stimula-tion by light results in a sustained depolarization of the individual receptor cells. In the dark-adapted eye of the honeybee the maximum sensitivity is at 535 mμ, but the light-adapted eye is sensitive to the whole spectrum. There is also a sensitivity to ultraviolet light with a maximum at 345 mμ in many insects. The blowfly has three types of cells with sensitivity maxima at 524 mμ, 490 mμ (rhodopsin) and 524 mμ. All of the cells are also sensitive to ultraviolet light.

There is also evidence in the compound eye of interactions between adjacent ommatidia. If two ommatidia of the *Limulus* eye are illuminated, the frequency response from either is less than when just one is illuminated with the same intensity. In the blowfly the receptor potential in one ommatidium disappears if adjacent ommatidia are illuminated. These interactions are probably brought about through nervous connections in the nerve plexus at the bases of the ommatidia.

The Camera Eye

We may suppose that the compound eye of the arthropods represents the culmination of one line of evolution from the simple ocellus, in which the first step is the segregation of pigment cells in cylindrical tubes to form a compound ocellus. The other line of evolution has led to the camera-type eye. This type of eye has evolved independently several times in several groups of mollusks, a few annelids and crustaceans, and in the vertebrates. It reaches its full development in two groups, the cephalopod mollusks and the vertebrates, and its function has been most extensively studied in the latter group. Our account will be devoted largely to the eye of mammals

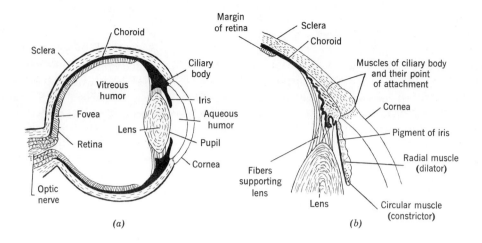

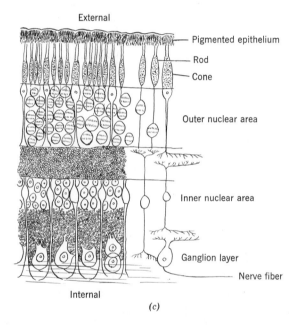

Fig. 7.8 The camera-type eye of a vertebrate. (*a*) A cross section of the eye. (*b*) The accommodation mechanism. (*c*) The retina (cf. Figure 7.11). (From Scheer, 1943, *Comparative Physiology,* Wiley, New York.)

with some notes on other vertebrates and on the cephalopods.

The mechanism by which the camera-eye forms an image has been known for over a century, and it was summarized by von Helmholtz in his great treatise on physiological optics. The camera-eye is essentially a sphere (Figure 7.8). Over most of its surface it is covered by the tough sclera, but this is interrupted in a circular area on the anterior surface, covered by the transparent cornea. The cornea has a spherical surface of smaller radius of curvature than the eye as a whole and hence forms a bulge on the anterior surface of the eye. Behind the cornea lies a body of aqueous saline fluid (the aqueous humor) which is separated from the main chamber of the eye by the lens and its suspensory apparatus and iris. The lens is a firm transparent gelatinous body made up of many concentric layers. The curvature of the anterior surface is considerably less than that of the posterior surface, but both are convex. The main chamber of the eye is filled with the vitreous humor, a transparent soft gelatinous body. The inner surface of the posterior half of the eye is lined by the retina which contains the photoreceptor cells (rods and cones) and their nervous connections.

The refractive system of the eye consists of the cornea and lens. This system acts like a simple lens to form an inverted image of an object in front of the eye in a focal plane behind the lens. Since the field of vision has depth, and objects in the field are at various distances from the eye, the plane at which one object is in focus will not be the same as that for another object closer to or farther away from the eye. In a photographic camera the optical system is adjusted to bring the desired portion of the field into focus on the sensitive film or plate by moving the lens closer to or farther from the surface of the photosensitive film or plate. This focusing mechanism is also used by cephalopod mollusks and the lower vertebrates, including snakes, but not by birds, mammals, or reptiles other than snakes. The process of focusing is known as accommodation. In the lampreys and teleost fishes the eyes are normally focused at rest for near vision and accommodation is required for distant objects. In the other vertebrates the resting eye is focused at some distance and accommodation is required for near vision. Accommodation in birds, mammals, and nonophidian reptiles involves a change in shape rather than position of the lens. The lens is normally under elastic tension from the suspensory ligaments which hold it in place and stretch it to a flattened shape. In accommodation the ciliary muscle, a ring of radially oriented fibers surrounding the lens, contracts. This contraction slightly reduces the diameter of the ciliary margin around the lens, and the lens can thus assume a more nearly spherical shape. The anterior surface in particular assumes a greater curvature.

In front of the lens lies a pigmented circular iris with a central opening, the pupil. The shape of the pupil varies considerably in different animals. The most common forms are that of a circle in diurnal animals, and that of a slit in nocturnal animals. The slit pupil can be closed more tightly than the circular and hence can preserve the sensitivity to dim light when the animal is in bright light. The size of the pupil is varied by muscles in the iris; radial muscles open the pupil and circular muscles close it. The pupil serves to regulate the amount of light entering the eye in relation to the intensity. It also serves to sharpen the image on the retina in bright light by cutting off stray light. The smaller the pupil opening the smaller will be the amount of stray light and hence blurring of the image.

Electrical Responses in the Retina

The accommodated eye forms on the surface of the retina a more or less sharp image of objects in a certain range of distance from the eye. The function of the retina is to translate into a pattern of nervous impulses in the optic nerve as many of the features of this image as possible. The features to be discriminated are intensity, wavelength, and the pattern of both. The individual photoreceptors (rods and cones) are presumably capable of responding to variations in intensity by variations in a generator potential; however, no recordings of potentials which can definitely be assigned to a sense cell or its axon have been obtained. Two types of measurements have been made frequently: the electroretinogram (ERG), in which potential differences between the front and back surface of the retina are meas-ured, and recordings of discharges in the optic nerve. The ERG can be restricted to a small area of the retina by use of microelectrodes, and the optic nerve measurements can be made on a single fiber by patient isolation of fibers.

In the optic nerve of the vertebrates, one type of fiber responds to illumination by a burst of impulses, adapting rapidly to a steady frequency which persists while the illumination continues. In the mammal, however, the fibers show a continuous discharge at low frequencies in the absence of illumination, and three types of single fiber response have been observed (Figure 7.9). In one type, illumination causes a sudden increase in frequency,

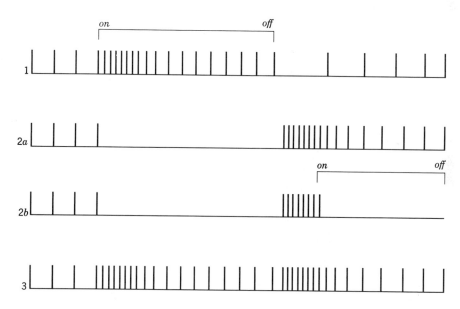

Fig. 7.9 Responses of single fibers in the optic nerve of a vertebrate to illumination. All fibers discharge spontaneously at a low frequency in the dark. Fiber *1* responds to illumination (*on*) by an increase in frequency, which rapidly falls off to a steady level higher than the spontaneous level. When illumination ceases (*off*), the fiber returns to its spontaneous frequency after a brief quiet period. Fiber *2* is completely inhibited by illumination, but the frequency of discharge is higher than the dark level for a brief period after cessation of illumination. Fiber *3* is the most common type and responds both to *on* and *off*; illumination during the *off* response of such a fiber has an inhibitory effect similar to that shown in *2b*. (From Granit, 1960, *Hdbk. Physiol. 1: Neurophysiol.* **1** 704.)

followed by adaptation to a steady level at a higher frequency than in absence of illumination. When the stimulus ceases there is a brief silent period, followed by a resumption of the low frequency pattern. The second type of fiber responds to illumination by complete cessation of activity. When the light is turned off there is a sudden burst of activity at high frequency followed by return to normal dark levels. If the light is turned on again during the high frequency response this too is inhibited. Finally single fibers may show both responses, with an increase in frequency when the eye is illuminated, a steady lower frequency while the illumination continues, and a second increase when the illumination ceases.

These phenomena are reflected in the ERG, which represents the potential change of the whole retina as measured typically between the surface of the cornea and some indifferent point on the body. When the eye is illuminated with high intensity the mammalian cornea becomes first negative (a wave), then strongly positive (b wave), and then the potential slowly falls to zero (Figure 7.10). If the intensity is sufficient and illumination continues a second positive deflection (c wave) appears in some cases; in others the c wave is negative. On cessation of illumination there is a sharp positive deflection (d wave). In mammalian eyes, which have no rods, only cones, there is no c wave. In pure rod eyes the c wave occurs, but the d wave is absent or much reduced. More detailed analysis suggests that the ERG is a composite of at least three component responses. In the eye of the cat, which has few cones, there appears to be a slowly rising component I largely responsible for the c wave, a component II with a sharp a wave falling to a plateau, and a component III which becomes negative on illumination.

Retinal Structure

Ultimately it should be possible to analyze both the single fiber discharges in the optic nerve and the electroretinograms in terms of the responses of the receptors and their nervous connections. The studies with microelectrodes in which this has been attempted have yielded conflicting results which it is not possible at present to interpret satisfactorily. This difficulty arises primarily out of the enormous complexity of the vertebrate retina. Histologists can distinguish as many as ten distinct layers in the mammalian retina (Figures 7.8, 7.11).

We shall begin the description of these at the outer or scleral surface of the retina. (a) A *pigmented layer* serves to prevent entrance of light from behind the eye and to absorb reflected or scattered light. In nocturnal animals, however, the layer may contain crystals of the purine, guanine, which reflect light that has passed through the receptors so that it passes through them again. This arrangement presumably sacrifices visual acuity to sensitivity in dim light. (b) The *receptor layer* contains the rods and the cones. (c) The rods and cones extend through the *outer limiting membrane;* the outer segments containing the visual pigments lie behind the membrane, and the essential nervous elements of the retina lie in front of it. (d) The *outer nuclear layer* contains the nuclei of the rods and cones. (e) The *outer plexiform layer* is made up of axons and synapses connecting the rods and cones with other nerve cells in a plexus. (f) The *inner nuclear layer* consists of

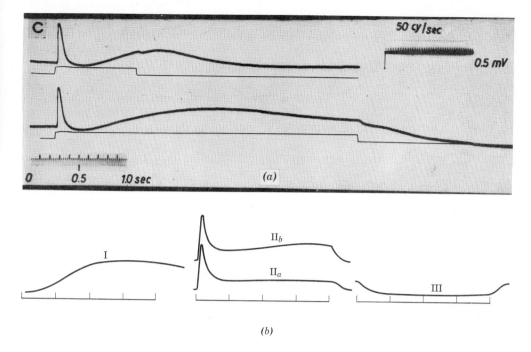

Fig. 7.10 Electroretinograms. (*a*) The electroretinogram of the eye of a cat, dark-adapted, exposed to two flashes of light. There is a very small *a*-wave seen as a slight dip in the curve, followed by a marked *b*-wave rising sharply to a peak and falling off more slowly to, or slightly below, the base line. The *c*-wave is a long, slow rise, followed by a still slower decline. In the upper curve, the illumination, as indicated by the faint line below the record of the potential, was discontinued during the rising phase of the *c*-wave; in the lower curve, the illumination was discontinued in the falling phase of the *c*-wave. In both cases, there is a small *off* effect or *d*-wave. (From R. Granit, 1955, *Receptors and Sensory Perception,* Yale Univ. Press, New Haven.) (*b*) Analysis of the cat retinogram into its components. I is a slow component, with the cornea positive to the retina and is primarily responsible for the *c*-wave. II is the component responsible for the *b*-wave and for part of the *c*-wave as well; two possible alternative forms are shown. III is a negative component responsible for the *a*-wave and usually submerged later in the *c*-wave. (From R. Granit, 1933, *J. Physiol.* **77** 207.)

the cell bodies of second-order neurons. These neurons are of two types: (1) multipolar cells which are connected laterally in such a way that impulses arising in one rod or cone are transmitted to adjacent rods or cones and (2) bipolar cells which are connected to the rods or cones at one end and to other nerve cells in the ganglion layer (*h*) at the other. (*g*) The *inner plexiform layer* is an elaborate plexus of fibers and synapses connecting the cells of the inner nuclear layer with the ganglion cells. (*h*) The *ganglion cell layer* is made up of large cell bodies, with dendrites at the outer ends having connections in the inner plexiform layer and a single long axon at the inner end. These long axons are the fibers of the optic nerve and extend without interruption to the brain. The axons of the optic nerve run over the inner surface of the retina to the area at which the optic nerve leaves

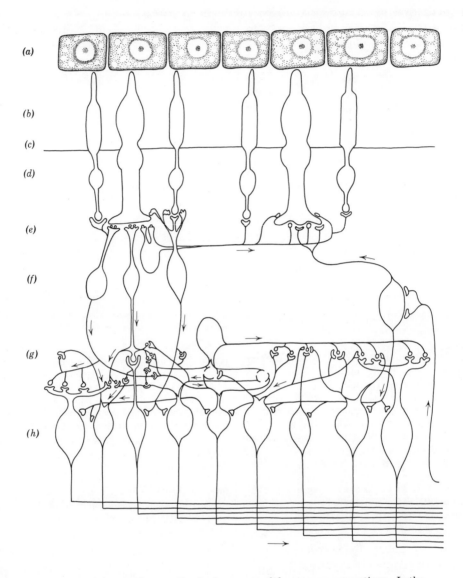

Fig. 7.11 Diagram of the vertebrate retina to show some of the nervous connections. In the diagram, we assume that the receptor cells on the left have been stimulated; the impulses aroused in the neurons of the inner nuclear layer are conducted along the axons to the inner plexiform layer, laterally to other receptor cells, or directly to cells in the ganglion cell layer. The synapses of the inner plexiform layer are very complex and result in spread of the impulses arising in a small group of receptor cells to a much larger group of ganglion cells. The axons from the ganglion cells go directly to the brain, running across the inner surface of the retina until they join to form the optic nerve, which leaves the eye from its posterior (outer) surface. There are also feedback circuits from the brain to the outer nuclear layer, with connection both to the receptor cells and to the cells of the ganglion layer. (After Polyak, 1941, *The Retina,* Univ. Chicago Press, Chicago.)

the eye, forming the *nerve fiber layer.* The *inner limiting membrane* covers the nerve fiber layer and separates it from the vitreous body.

The light entering the vertebrate eye must pass through all of the nerve cell and plexiform layers to reach the receptor cells. This situation (inverted retina) is found in many photoreceptors in most animal groups. The opposite situation (direct retina), with the nerve fibers arranged so that light strikes the receptor cells before it reaches the nerve fibers, is more common in the sense that it occurs more widely through the animal kingdom. The cephalopod eye, for example, has a direct retina. There seems to be no special advantage for one over the other arrangement.

Retinal Integration

It is clear, from examination of retinal structure, that whatever the nature of the state of excitation aroused by light in the receptor cells or their axons the excitation may be subject to extensive modification before emerging as a pattern of impulses in the axons of the optic nerve. There is a simple direct path with two synapses from the receptor to the bipolar cell to the ganglion cell. For the cones this may be a one-to-one correspondence, with a single cone connected through a single bipolar to a single ganglion cell. However, the bipolar will in general synapse with dendrites from other ganglion cells as well, and the cone will synapse with multipolar cells in the outer nuclear layer having connections with other receptors or with other ganglion cells. The rods frequently show convergence, in that several rods synapse with a single bipolar, which in turn leads to a single ganglion cell. Again

there are cross connections at the inner nuclear layer both with other rods and with other ganglion cells. Finally there are fibers which appear to have their cell bodies outside the retina, presumably in the brain. These fibers enter the retina with the optic nerve and synapse with cells in the outer nuclear layer.

Morphologically we can regard the cells of the inner nuclear layer, with their complex connections in the outer and inner plexiform layers, as serving to distribute impulses generated in the receptors among the cells of the ganglion layer and to feed back these impulses to other receptor cells as well. The cells of the ganglion layer are the site of origin of the impulses which emerge from the retina in the optic nerve, but the pattern of these impulses is not determined simply by events in single receptor cells connected with the corresponding ganglion cells. Rather the cells of the inner nuclear layer are in a position to modify or integrate the effects of receptor cell stimulation very considerably. The electroretinogram must represent some summation of all this activity and it is surprising that, with such complexity behind it, any analysis of the ERG has been possible at all.

The most intelligible analysis remains that of the impulses emerging from the retina in the axons of the optic nerve. By analogy with other receptors, these impulses presumably originate in the axon where it emerges from the ganglion cell and are aroused by a generator potential in that cell. Generator potentials have not been certainly identified in the eye as yet. When very small points of light are used to explore the surface of the eye for sensitivity it is found that any single optic nerve axon responds to

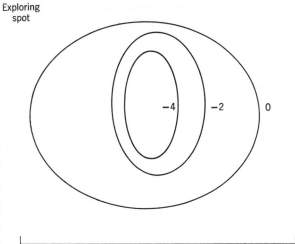

Fig. 7.12 The receptive field of a single optic nerve fiber in the eye of a frog. The numbers indicate the logarithms of the relative threshold intensity for a light spot of the size shown at the upper left, at a distance from the center of the field indicated by the numbered curves. (From H. K. Hartline, 1940, *J. Opt. Soc. Am.* **30** 239.)

light striking the retina over a rather large area. Thus in many vertebrates the receptive field at the surface of the retina for a single optic nerve axon has a diameter of the order of 1 mm (Figure 7.12). This is of course very much greater than the diameter of a single ganglion cell or of a single receptor. The large diameter can only mean that any one ganglion cell receives influences from receptors in a roughly circular area about 1 mm in diameter surrounding the ganglion cell. The sensitivity as measured by threshold values is maximal in the center of the receptive field and falls off logarithmically toward the edges. Likewise the frequency of the response to a given intensity is maximal in the center of the field and decreases toward the edges. This suggests that nervous impulses having their origin in receptor cells are transmitted by the cells of the inner nuclear layer to ganglion cells distributed over an area about 1 mm in diameter. Any one ganglion cell receives the largest number of connections from the receptors in its im-

mediate vicinity and progressively smaller numbers from more peripheral receptors. The degree of depolarization of any ganglion cell, and hence the frequency of discharge in its axon, would then be determined by the number of impulses reaching the ganglion cell in a given period of time, and this would depend on the number of receptors stimulated and on the intensity of the stimulus.

Taken by itself this arrangement would appear to sacrifice acuity to sensitivity, since the acuity depends on the number of discrete receptive fields. The interactions between adjacent fields, however, restore the balance. Thus any one receptive field has in its central portion either an *on*-response or an *off*-response. That is, in recording from a single fiber one will see an increased frequency of discharge when the center of the field is illuminated (type 1) or an inhibition of discharge during illumination followed by increased frequency at the end of illumination (type 2). As one moves the exploring light spot toward the periphery of the field, however, the response (still measured in the same axon) changes to the *on-off* type (type 3). Finally, at the periphery the response is opposite to that at the center—*on* at the periphery, if the center has an *off*-response and *off* at the periphery if the center has an *on*-response. The full explanation of this behavior will require more experimental study. It seems likely, however, that the inner nuclear layer and its synaptic connections are the major sites of action. If we assume that the receptors respond only to illumination and have no *off*-response we may then suppose that the nature of the synaptic connections lying between the receptor and the ganglion cell will determine whether the latter responds to illumination or to the cessation of illumination, and that these connections will be different according to whether the receptors are close to the ganglion cell or lie peripherally to it.

The effect of these interactions at the ganglion level is to sharpen the acuity of the eye without losing its sensitivity. Most normal visual stimuli are patterns in which the intensity varies considerably from region to region, and the pattern of impulses discharged in the optic axons may correspond rather closely to the pattern of intensity in the stimulus. Moreover the eye is probably never still but makes microscopic scanning movements, so that a regular alternation of *on-off* responses at the margins of regions of contrasting intensity may be produced.

Color Sensitivity

The responses of the receptors and their integration in the nervous connections in the eye will provide, when fully understood, a basis for the discrimination of the patterns of intensity in bright or dim light. The problem of discrimination of wavelength remains to be considered. There are two sorts of evidence indicating that certain eyes can discriminate color. The first is behavioral; many animals can be trained to respond differently to light of different wavelengths or can be shown to do so naturally. The second is subjective and rests on our own experience of color as an aspect of the visible world. One may suppose that our subjective experience and the behavioral responses of other animals have some common basis in the eye. It is this common basis in which we are interested. Strictly speaking the term "color vision" should be restricted to human subjective experience, but color sensitivity as shown by behavior is widespread, especially in diurnal animals.

The leading theory concerning color sensitivity is the "duplicity theory." This theory postulates two sets of receptors: one, generally identified with the rods, is sensitive to dim light but with no color discrimination, and the other, identified with the cones, is sensitive to bright light and able to discriminate wavelengths. Although the strict generality of this theory has been questioned, it remains the most satisfactory concept we have, if we do not attempt to apply strict anatomical criteria for rods and cones. Color discrimination is generally associated only with sensitivity to bright light.

Studies of the effects of light of varying wavelengths on the electroretinogram have been, as might be expected, difficult to interpret. However, the only interpretations which have been possible in the light-adapted eye require the assumption that there are

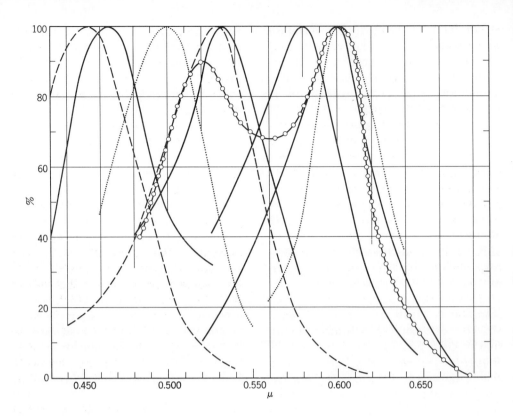

Fig. 7.13 Single-fiber responses in vertebrate eyes. Each curve gives the relative sensitivity (%), as measured in a single optic nerve fiber, to various wavelengths of monochromatic light of equal quantum intensity. Solid line, frog; open circles, snake; solid circles, rat; broken line, guinea pig. (From R. Granit, 1943, *Nature* **151** 11.)

three distinct substances in the receptors involved, each substance absorbing in a different wave-length region. The only cone substances isolated chemically are iodopsin and cyanopsin, and these are not normally found together in the same eye. However, as we pointed out earlier, the spectral sensitivity curve of the eye in bright light does not coincide with the absorption curve of iodopsin; hence we may expect that some other light-absorbing substance is functioning. Recent studies of the human eye by a reflection technique have provided evidence that the eye does have three pigments and

that absence of any one is associated with a specific type of color blindness.

When we study the effects of light at varying wavelengths on the discharge of nervous impulses in individual fibers of the optic nerve the results are much simpler. When the sensitivity of a single fiber is studied as a function of the wavelength, with careful control of intensity so that equal stimulating energies are used, two types of results are obtained. In some cases the curve relating wavelength to sensitivity is a broad bell-shaped one (Figure 7.13). In the dark-adapted eye the curve has a maximum near 500 mμ, and its shape is similar to the absorption curve for rhodopsin. The same nerve fiber in the light-adapted eye will give a broad sensitivity-wavelength curve with a maximum near 650 mμ, corresponding to the sensitivity curve for the whole eye in bright light but not corresponding exactly with the iodopsin absorption curve. In other experiments much narrower curves are found with maxima in different regions. Thus, the eye of the rat, which contains mostly rods, shows a broad band curve with maximum at 500 mμ in the dark-adapted eye, while the light-adapted eye has a very narrow band of sensitivity with the same maximum and a second narrow band with a maximum at 600 mμ. The snake, *Tropidonotus natrix,* has a cone eye with a broad curve maximum about 560 mμ but also two other maxima at 520 and 600 mμ. The frog, with broad curves at 500 and 560 mμ, also has narrower curves with peaks at 465, 530, 580, and 600 mμ. At present the most reasonable interpretation is that each of these curves represents a single photosensitive pigment. At present all of the purified pigments have broad absorption spectrum curves, and no eye has been shown to contain more than two pigments. On the other hand it has not proved possible to show, even theoretically, how the narrow sensitivity curves could be derived from the absorption curves of the known pigments, and there is a growing body of evidence for the existence of pigments which have not been purified.

In any case it is clear that the variations of wavelength sensitivity which exist are sufficient to provide the central nervous system with information which can be used to discriminate wavelength. Whether the central nervous system uses the information is another question. There is evidence, for example, that the eye of the cat responds differentially to spectral stimulation and that this difference reaches the brain. The cat, however, cannot learn to distinguish between red, blue, and green light, though it readily learns to distinguish between different intensities of these colors.

Summary

In this chapter we have, in the interest of brevity, concentrated on two types of sensory systems—mechanoreceptors and photoreceptors. The mechanoreceptors were shown to be able to convert various mechanical changes, such as changes in pressure or tension, into a pattern of nervous discharge in axons leading from the receptor to the central nervous system. The termini of these axons constitute the essential feature of the receptor. The cell membrane of this terminal region is polarized, and the degree of polarization can be altered by mechanical changes. The membrane is not, however, electrically excitable and cannot produce an action potential spike. The depolarized region serves as a sink for current flowing from the adjacent excitable region of the axon, and the spike or more often a series of spikes is generated here. The frequency here is a function of the amount of depolarization in the terminal and hence of the intensity of the mechanical stimulus.

In photoreceptors the basic event is the photochemical breakdown of a pigment-protein complex in the receptor cell. We do not know whether this produces an electrical change, but ultimately action potentials are aroused in an axon leading from the receptor organ. Such organs often have accessory structures of two types—structures such as lenses, iris diaphragms, and pigmented layers, which influence the source and amount of light impinging upon the receptor cells, and nerve plexuses, which integrate the responses from receptor cells into the final pattern of nerve impulses that emerges from the receptor organ. By mechanisms which are understood in some aspects but not in others, the most complex photoreceptors (eyes) are able to provide information as to intensity, wavelengths, pattern or images, and changes in pattern and images, distances and direction of the stimulating light sources. All of this information is transmitted as a complex code of nervous impulses to the central nervous system.

References

Sensory Mechanisms, General

Adrian, E. D. 1959. Sensory mechanisms. *Hdbk. Physiol. I: Neurophysiol.* 1 365–367.
Davis, H. 1961. Some principles of sensory receptor action. *Physiol. Rev.* 41 391–416.
Granit, R. 1955. *Receptors and Sensory Perception.* Yale Univ. Press, New Haven, Conn.
Gray, J. A. B. 1959. Initiation of impulses at receptors. *Hdbk. Physiol. I : Neurophysiol.* 1 123–145.
Rawdon-Smith, A. F. 1938. *Theories of Sensation.* Univ. Press; Cambridge, England.

Simple Mechanoreceptors

Cooper, S. 1960. Muscle spindles and other muscle receptors. *Structure and Function of Muscle* (G. H. Bourne ed.) 1 381–420.
Gray, J. A. B. 1959. Mechanical into electrical energy in certain mechanoreceptors. *Progr. Biophys.* 9 285–324.
Loewenstein, W. R. 1959. The generation of electrical activity in a nerve ending. *Annals N.Y. Acad. Sci.* 81 367–387.

Photoreceptors

Collins, F. D. 1954. The chemistry of vision. *Biol. Rev.* 29 453–477.

Crescitelli, F. 1958. The natural history of visual pigments. *Annals N.Y. Acad. Sci.* 74 230–255.
Dartnall, H. J. A. 1957. *The Visual Pigments.* Wiley, New York.
Davson, H. 1949. *The Physiology of the Eye.* Churchill, London.
Detwiler, S. R. 1956. The eye and its structural adaptations. *Am. Scientist* 44 45–72.
DeVries, H., and Kuiper, J. W. 1958. Optics of the insect eye. *Annals N.Y. Acad. Sci.* 74 196–203.
Fry, G. A. 1959. The image-forming mechanism of the eye. *Hdbk. Physiol. I: Neurophysiol.* 1 647–670.
Granit, R. 1959. Neural activity in the retina. *Hdbk. Physiol. I: Neurophysiol.* 1 693–712.
Hartline, H. K. 1959. Vision. *Hdbk. Physiol. I: Neurophysiol.* 1 615–619.
Hartridge, H. 1950. *Recent Advances in the Physiology of Vision.* Churchill, London.
Hecht, S. 1937. Rods, cones, and the chemical basis of vision. *Physiol. Rev.* 17 239–290.
Hubbard, R., and Kropf, A. 1959. Molecular aspects of visual excitation. *Annals N.Y. Acad. Sci.* 81 388–398.
Kennedy, D. 1958. Electrical activity of a "primitive" photoreceptor. *Annals N.Y. Acad. Sci.* 74 329–336.
Kropf, A. and Hubbard, R. 1958. The mechanism of bleaching rhodopsin. *Annals N.Y. Acad. Sci.* 74 266–280.
LeGrand, Y. 1957. *Light, Colour and Vision.* (tr. R. W. G. Hunt, J. W. T. Walsh and F. R. W. Hunt) Chapman, Hall, London.
Linksz, A. 1950–52. *Physiology of the Eye* (2 vols.) Grune and Stratton, New York.
Miller, W. H. 1960. Visual photoreceptor structures. *The Cell* 4 325–364.
Milne, L. J. and Milne, M. 1959. Photosensitivity in invertebrates. *Hdbk. Physiol. I: Neurophysiol.* 1 621–645.
Müller-Limroth, H. W. 1956. Die Theoren des Farbensehens. *Naturwiss.* 43 337–346, 364–370.
Pirenne, M. H. 1956. Physiological mechanisms of vision and the quantum nature of light. *Biol. Rev.* 31 194–241.
Pirenne, M. H. 1961. Light quanta and vision. *Endeavour* 20 192–209.
Ratliff, F., Miller, W. H., and Hartline, H. K. 1958. Neural interaction in the eye and the integration of receptor activity. *Annals N.Y. Acad. Sci.* 74 210–222.

Ronchi, V. 1957. *Optics, the Science of Vision.* (tr. E. Rosen) New York Univ. Press, New York.

Rushton, W. A. H. 1959. Visual pigments in man and animals and their relation to seeing. *Progr. Biophys.* **9** 239–283.

Tschermak-Seysenegg, A. von 1952. *Introduction to Physiological Optics* (tr. P. Boeder) Thomas, Springfield, Ill.

Wald, G. 1954. The molecular basis of visual excitation. *Am. Scientist* **42** 73–95.

Wald, G. 1959. The photoreceptor process in vision. *Hdbk. Physiol. I: Neurophysiol.* **1** 671–692.

Wald, G. 1960. The visual functions of the vitamins A. *Vitamins and Hormones* **18** 417–430.

Wolken, J. J. 1960. Photoreceptors, comparative studies. *Comparative Biochemistry of Photoreactive Systems.* (M. B. Allen ed.) 145–166. Academic Press, New York.

Wulff, V. J. 1956. Physiology of the compound eye. *Physiol. Rev.* **36** 145–163.

Other Receptors

Galambos, R. 1954. Neural mechanisms of audition. *Physiol. Rev.* **34** 497–528.

Hodgson, E. S. 1955. Problems in invertebrate chemoreception. *Quart. Rev. Biol.* **30** 331–347.

Maxwell, S. S. 1923. *Labyrinth and Equilibrium.* Lippincott, Philadelphia.

Moncrieff, R. W. 1946. *The Chemical Senses.* (out of print) Wiley, New York.

Wever, E. G. and Lawrence, M. 1954. *Physiological Acoustics.* Princeton Univ. Press, Princeton, N.J.

Zotterman, Y. 1959. The nervous mechanism of taste. *Annals N.Y. Acad. Sci.* **81** 358–366.

8 Transmission of excitation from cell to cell

In the preceding chapters we have considered the events of excitation as they are seen naturally in receptors and experimentally in isolated nerve axons, and we have examined the mechanism by which the state of excitation is conducted along the axon. Relatively early in the development of our knowledge about the physiology of excitation it became apparent to physiologists that the passage of a state of excitation from one cell to another may be qualitatively different from the passage of that state along a nerve fiber, which is simply an extension of a single cell. The first evidence was obtained in a classical experiment performed by the French physiologist Claude Bernard and reported in 1849. This experiment was not planned with the view of establishing any new physiological principle but merely as an exploration of a physiological and pharmacological curiosity.

As every reader of tales of exploration or detective novels knows, certain South American natives use, on the tips of their arrows, a poison which is unusually effective in very small quantities, producing paralysis and death. The poison is known as curare, and Bernard's experiment was an attempt to determine something of its mode of action. The drug was injected into a frog, which became paralyzed. When the sciatic nerve was stimulated electrically no response was observed in the leg muscles. On the other hand, when the leg muscles were stimulated by direct application of an electric shock to the muscle they proved capable of contraction. The experiment was then repeated in a somewhat different form. Before the drug was injected a tight ligature was tied around one leg, cutting off the circulation. When curare was injected into the frog stimulation of the nerve in the ligated leg produced contraction, but in the opposite leg, with normal circulation, stimulation of the nerve was ineffective. Moreover if the skin of the back of the curarized frog was pinched, the flexor muscles of the ligated leg contracted in typical fashion, but there was no response in a leg with normal circulation. This experiment proved that curare does not interfere with muscle function, since the muscles still contract upon direct stimulation, and that curare does not interfere with sensory reception or nervous conduction, since the leg which had no circulation and hence received no curare responded normally to sensory stimulation. By elimination the only possible sight of action of the drug is at the junction between nerve and muscle. The fact that the drug acts so specifically on this site suggests that the site has properties not found elsewhere.

The Synapse

Nerve and muscle are clearly, on both structural and functional grounds, different tissues. The question of whether transmission from one nerve cell to another is in any way different from conduction along the axon of a single nerve cell was not even formulated until the end of the nineteenth century when histologists, especially the Spanish neurohistologist Ramon y Cajal, developed the concept of the neuron as a distinct cellular unit; hence a basis was laid for the question whether any special properties are to be observed at the junction between one unit and the next. Physiological

evidence that there are such special properties was provided by many, but especially by the English neurophysiologist Sherrington. Sherrington introduced the concept of the synapse as a region of contact between anatomically distinct cells across which a state of excitation is transmitted in one direction only. The cell by which the excitation enters the synapse is called the presynaptic unit, and the cell by which the excitation leaves the synapse is called the postsynaptic unit.

Properties of Synapses

Of the classical properties which suggest that the process of synaptic transmission is in some way distinct from that of axonal conduction, we need only list polarity, delay, facilitation, and inhibition. Polarity means that, with exceptions confined to highly specialized situations in certain invertebrates, transmission between one nerve cell and another is normally unidirectional. The excitation moves only from presynaptic unit to postsynaptic unit, and these units never exchange roles. Delay means that the time required for the state of excitation to pass from a point before the presynaptic unit to a similar point beyond the postsynaptic unit is substantially greater than is the time required for conduction along a comparable length of axon.

Facilitation may be of two sorts: if several impulses enter a synapse through a single presynaptic unit in rapid succession the effect, in the form of impulses leaving through the postsynaptic unit, depends on the number and frequency of entering impulses. In general the number and frequency of impulses leaving the synapse will be greater as the number and frequency entering is greater, but the impulses leaving will not show a one-to-one correspondence with those entering. With low entering frequency there may be no postsynaptic impulses; as the entering frequency increases, or the duration is prolonged, postsynaptic impulses may appear, or their frequency may increase. These phenomena together constitute the property known as temporal facilitation. Many synapses are made up of several presynaptic units in contact with a single postsynaptic unit. In this sort of synapse stimulation of a single presynaptic unit may not result in excitation of the postsynaptic unit. Impulses may only be aroused in the postsynaptic unit when two or more presynaptic elements are stimulated. This phenomenon is known as spatial facilitation.

The effect of stimulation of certain presynaptic units is transmission of excitation to the postsynaptic unit, as we have seen. Stimulation of other units, however, may result either in the cessation of activity previously in progress or in prevention of the transmission of excitation from another presynaptic unit. Either of these phenomena is known as inhibition. The basic problem to which we will give our attention in this chapter is that of the nature of the events involved in transmission of a state of excitation across synapses and the relation of these events to the properties just described.

The Autonomic Nervous System

For most of the period following the realization that transmission has properties distinct from those of conduction, physiologists assumed that the differences could be explained in terms of the anatomical arrangement of the synapse, and that the essential process in transmission is the same as that in conduction, namely, propagation of an electrical change. The first suggestion that the transmission might, in some cases, involve chemical events as essential features was apparently made by Elliott in 1904, with respect to the mammalian autonomic nervous system. Students will recall that there is, in all the vertebrates, a set of ganglia located outside the central nervous system, though connected with it. These ganglia send axons to most organs and tissues of the body and are concerned in the control, usually involuntary, of a great many important actions. The relative independence of these ganglia and their nerves, functionally and structurally, from the rest of the nervous system makes the name autonomic an apt one. The system is further subdivided into two divisions, the thoracolumbar or sympathetic division and the craniosacral or parasympathetic division. Elliott's suggestion was that the sympathetic nerves transmit their effects by liberation at their peripheral endings of a chemical product, which then acts to excite or inhibit activity in the organ or tissue innervated. This suggestion has been brilliantly and thoroughly confirmed by many investigations and notably those of W. B. Cannon. For the moment, however, we shall confine our attention to the parasympathetic division.

Chemical Transmission in Parasympathetic Synapses

A major pair of nerves in the parasympathetic system are the vagi or tenth cranial nerves. The vagi innervate, among other viscera, the heart; and stimulation of a vagus nerve is followed by slowing or cessation of the beat of the heart. In 1914 the British pharmacologist Dale showed that the substance acetylcholine has in general the same actions on the heart as does the stimulation of the vagus and suggested again that the vagus might bring about its characteristic inhibitory action by liberating acetylcholine or some similar substance. This suggestion was temporarily neglected during the war, but in 1921 Otto Loewi published his classical experiment demonstrating the existence of a *Vagusstoff*. The experiment, once again, was very simple, though in this case it was specifically designed to test Dale's hypothesis (Figure 8.1). Two frog hearts were arranged so that saline solution could be passed through one heart and then subsequently through the second. The vagus nerve was left attached to the first heart. When the nerve was stimulated the first heart stopped beating, but saline solution was kept flowing. Shortly afterward the second heart also stopped, though the only connection between the two was the saline solution. This was a clear proof that the vagus, when stimulated, liberates something which is capable of causing in another heart the same response produced by excitation of the vagus. Subsequent studies showed that the active agent is, in all properties tested so far, the same as acetylcholine, and we now generally accept the view that acetylcholine is the *Vagusstoff* and that the vagus produces its effect on the heart by liberating acetylcholine from its peripheral endings.

Neuromuscular Junctions

Dale now turned his attention to the neuromuscular junction, where spinal nerve fibers terminate in the skeletal muscle of vertebrates in the characteristic motor endplate. Though this system has nothing to do with the parasympathetic system, some of the properties are similar. In 1936 Dale published results showing that when the motor nerves are stimulated a substance is released which has the pharmacological properties of acetylcholine. He and others were eventually able to gather evidence sufficient to establish acetylcholine as the transmitter substance at the motor endplate. Briefly this evidence includes the following points:

(1) Acetylcholine or a substance identical in behavior chemically, pharmacologically, and physiologically is liberated when the motor nerve to a muscle is stimulated. The amounts liberated are directly related to the amount of stimulation.

(2) Acetylcholine applied to the muscle causes a contraction which is essentially similar to normal contraction. It is effective only when applied to the endplate region and at concentrations of the same order of magnitude as those observed following nervous stimulation.

(3) The effects of nervous stimulation and of acetylcholine are blocked by curare.

(4) The effects of nervous stimulation and of acetylcholine are increased by the drug physostigmine (eserine).

(5) There is in the endplate region an enzyme, acetylcholinesterase, which hydrolyzes acetylcholine specifically. Its action is prevented by physostigmine.

Transmitter Agents

This evidence was conclusive in establishing acetylcholine as the transmitter substance at the neuromuscular junction. Similar evidence was obtained for a variety of parasympathetic pe-

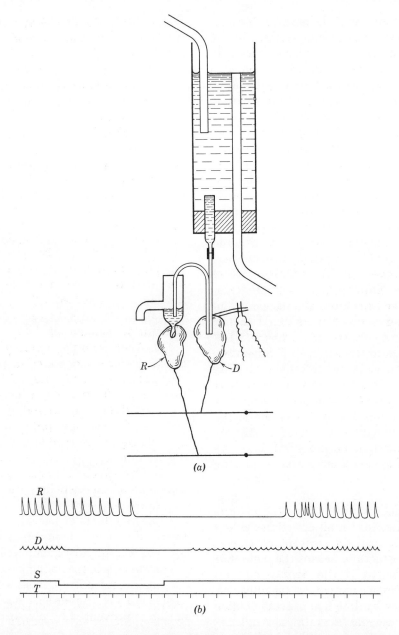

Fig. 8.1 Demonstration of humoral transmission during stimulation of the vagus. (*a*) One heart (*D*) is perfused with Ringer's solution from the reservoir, and electrical stimulation is applied to the vagus nerve connected to this heart. A second heart (*R*) receives perfusion fluid from the first, but is not connected with the first in any other way. (*b*) The contractions of the donor heart *D* stop soon after the stimulus *S* is applied; the time marker *T* is marked in 5 sec intervals. Some time after *D* has stopped completely, *R* also stops, showing that some inhibitory substance has been carried in the perfusion fluid from *D* to *R*. When the electrical stimulation is stopped, *D* resumes its beat after a time; some little time later, *R* also resumes beating. (From Bain, 1933, *Quart. J. Exp. Physiol.* **22** 269.)

ripheral endings. Likewise it became clear that the peripheral endings of the sympathetic nerves liberate specific substances which Cannon called sympathins. It has since been established that most, perhaps all, sympathetic endings liberate norepinephrine, that this substance duplicates closely the actions of sympathetic stimulation, and that both these effects are blocked or enhanced similarly by suitable drugs. There is, however, no known mechanism for the rapid destruction of norepinephrine at its site of action.

The foregoing might lead to the conclusion that, in general, transmission from nerve cell to muscle or other effector cell involves a chemical transmitter, but that this is no evidence for the occurrence of chemical transmission between one nerve cell and another. However, in the ganglia of the sympathetic nervous system, where presynaptic fibers from the central nervous system transmit excitation to the postsynaptic motor fibers, we have abundant evidence, similar to that for the neuromuscular junction, that acetylcholine is the transmitter.

Electrical Events in Transmission

In the central nervous system it becomes very difficult to obtain evidence establishing any specific substance as the transmitter, since there are enormous numbers of synapses, and one can stimulate only a small proportion at any one time. In consequence, the argument over electrical versus chemical transmission centered upon neuro-neural phenomena during the last decade. The decision in favor of chemical transmission for most, perhaps all, synapses as defined originally by Sherrington rested primarily upon electrical rather than chemical evidence and specifically on evidence obtained with microelectrodes, which can be inserted directly into nerve cells and can thus record events very close to the site of transmission.

When a microelectrode is inserted into or placed very close to the cell body of a postsynaptic unit, whether it be a nerve cell, a muscle cell, or a gland cell, the transmission of excitation is invariably accompanied by an electrical change known as the postsynaptic potential (Figure 8.2). This potential may be hyperpolarizing, increasing the potential difference across the cell membrane, or depolarizing, decreasing the membrane potential. Any particular postsynaptic unit may characteristically exhibit one of these two, or if it has connections with several presynaptic units it may exhibit either at different times. The postsynaptic potential is a local potential, comparable with the generator potential of a receptor, or the local potential observed on subthreshold stimulation of an axon. Like other local potentials it is not propagated but spreads with decreasing magnitude by electrical conduction (electrotonic), and it varies in magnitude and duration depending on the presynaptic stimulus.

The Nature of Transmitter Action

On the basis of those synapses studied thus far—and this includes many types—we may conclude that in general the postsynaptic unit cannot be excited electrically, but rather that the postsynaptic potential must always normally result from the action of a chemical transmitter released by the presynaptic unit. There are few known exceptions to this rule, and they occur in highly specialized situations. One can never of course be

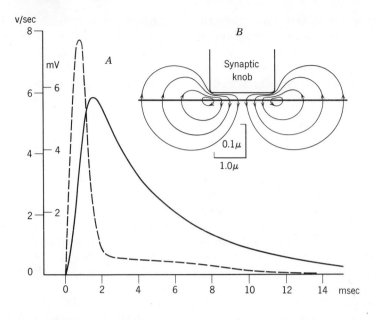

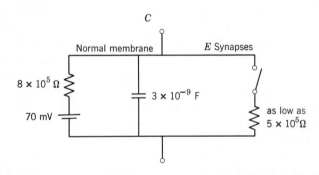

Fig. 8.2 Postsynaptic potentials. (*A*) The time course of an excitatory postsynaptic potential (EPSP) in millivolts is shown as a solid line, while the current flow required to generate this potential is represented as a broken line. (*B*) Idealized pattern of current flow in the synaptic region during the EPSP; note that the diagram is drawn with a horizontal scale different by tenfold from the vertical scale. (*C*) The equivalent electrical circuit for the postsynaptic membrane; closing of the "synaptic circuit" on the right would produce a potential change comparable to the EPSP. (From J. C. Eccles, 1960, *Handbook of Physiology: Neurophysiology* **1** 66, ed. J. Field, American Physiol. Soc., Washington.)

certain of this sort of generalization, since one good exception may overthrow it, but it fits the presently available data. The evidence on which the generalization is based may be summarized quite simply. First, postsynaptic potentials cannot be produced by any electrical stimulation applied to the region of the synapse unless the presynaptic unit is excited. Second, even when the postsynaptic unit can be excited by electrical stimuli applied to the synapse region this excitation occurs without any development of postsynaptic potentials, and it clearly results from depolarization of a portion of the postsynaptic unit (e.g., the axon of the neuron) remote from the synapse. Third, the postsynaptic potential has no refractory period and is not influenced by the simultaneous occurrence, in parts of the postsynaptic unit not involved in the synapse, of spike potentials.

These facts give us a picture of synaptic transmission similar in some respects to that which we developed for excitation of receptors. The impulse which enters along the presynaptic neuron causes, at the presynaptic terminal, liberation of a chemical transmitter. This transmitter then acts upon the adjacent postsynaptic unit to elicit a postsynaptic potential which is comparable to the generator potential of a receptor. If the postsynaptic potential is a depolarizing potential adjacent regions of the postsynaptic unit will be depolarized and may thus be excited in the usual way. If the postsynaptic potential is a hyperpolarizing potential the effect may be inhibitory. Delay at the synapse may be accounted for by the time required for liberation of the transmitter, its diffusion across the space (perhaps 100 Å wide) between units, and the processes involved in developing the postsynaptic potential. Facilitation can be accounted for by the accumulation of transmitter or its effects from successive impulses arriving along the same presynaptic unit (temporal facilitation) or simultaneous impulses arriving along several presynaptic units (spatial facilitation). Attempts to account for all of these phenomena by purely electrical mechanisms are much less satisfactory.

We are then faced with three problems: The nature of the transmitter, the mechanism of its release, and the mechanism of production of the postsynaptic potential. The first problem we have discussed already. Acetylcholine and norepinephrine are the only proven transmitters. The proof is adequate for acetylcholine at parasympathetic endings, at the neuromuscular junction, in sympathetic ganglia in the vertebrates, and in several invertebrate synapses and for norepinephrine at sympathetic endings in the vertebrates. A number of other substances have been suggested as possible transmitters, both for vertebrates and for invertebrates, but conclusive proof is lacking.

Mechanism of Transmitter Release

The problem of the release mechanism has been approached from both the physiological and the morphological viewpoints. Morphologically, small granules are characteristically seen in the cytoplasm adjacent to the presynaptic membrane. These granules show changes in structure following intensive presynaptic excitation, suggesting that they may contain, and on stimulation release, the transmitter. Physiologically, the principal evidence has arisen in connection with the studies of electrogenesis at the neuromuscular junction and should be discussed with that phenomenon.

Origin of the Postsynaptic Potential

Katz, with his collaborators Fatt and Del Castillo in London, has applied the microelectrode technique to the vertebrate motor endplate with great success. Others more recently have studied neuromuscular junctions in crustaceans. When a microelectrode is inserted into a muscle fiber in close proximity to the motor endplate a typical postsynaptic potential is observed on arrival of an impulse along the motor axon. If now the composition of the medium bathing the muscle is varied it is found that the magnitude of the postsynaptic potential depends on the ionic composition of the medium, in a manner which is not at all specific. In contrast to the axon spike, which is sensitive only to changes in sodium ion concentration, the endplate potential of the vertebrates depends on the total concentration of ions in the medium, rather than on the concentration of any one specific ion. This is interpreted to mean that the endplate potential is the result of a general increase in the ion permeability of the membrane, rather than an increase in the permeability to any particular ion.

In the course of these observations, measurements at very high amplification showed the existence in the resting vertebrate endplate of miniature endplate potentials. These small changes in potential, amounting to one millivolt or less, occur in a random fashion. Similar potentials occur in crustaceans. The distribution in time suggests that the miniature potentials may be the result of a spontaneous release of small amounts of transmitter at specific sites over the endplate surface. The relation between the calculated number of sites and the relative magnitudes of the miniature and normal endplate potentials suggest, moreover, that the normal endplate potential results from simultaneous discharge of all the sites. Taken with the morphological evidence, one might suppose that the presynaptic granules normally liberate in random fashion small amounts of transmitters spontaneously. The arrival of an impulse at the presynaptic ending in some way causes a simultaneous release of transmitter from all

the granules, and this results in a normal endplate potential.

The studies of Eccles and his collaborators in Australia have established a similar mechanism of electrogenesis in the spinal motor nerve cell bodies of mammals. They have used double-barreled micropipettes inserted into the cell body. One barrel is connected to an electrode and used to measure membrane potential. The other is used as a pipette for microinjection of solutions into the cell. The normal postsynaptic potential in this cell, when an excitatory afferent is stimulated, is depolarizing. As in the motor endplate, this depolarization is decreased by any change in ion concentration in a quite unspecific manner. When an inhibitory afferent is stimulated, however, the postsynaptic potential is hyperpolarizing. This postsynaptic potential is influenced by changes only in the potassium or chloride ion concentrations inside the cell. Changes in other ion concentrations were ineffective.

General Summary

In concluding this section, we might review and summarize briefly the major electrical phenomena in excitation, conduction, and transmission. All of these arise out of the resting membrane potential of the cell. This in turn is caused by the active transport of sodium ion and the resulting differences in ion concentration across the cell membrane, particularly sodium and potassium. The changes in potential which accompany nervous activity involve in general a change in the properties of the cell membrane which, in all cases studied so far, seems to be an increase in the passive permeability of the membrane to ions. In the axon the increase is highly specific and limited to sodium ion. Because of the nonequilibrium distribution of sodium ion produced by the sodium pump, sodium ion flows into the cell, and this further adds to the depolarization caused by the initial stimulus, resulting in an explosive reversal of polarization which is then readily propagated. None of the other potential changes, in receptors or at synapses, have this explosive character. They result from changes in permeability to sodium ion and to other ions, whose distribution is normally near equilibrium, as well. The result is a small change in potential which may be depolarizing or hyperpolarizing, depending on the ions involved, and which may require facilitation before it acquires sufficient magnitude to arouse excitation in the postsynaptic unit.

References

Bishop, G. H. 1956. Natural history of the nerve impulse. *Physiol. Rev.* **36** 326–399.

Brown, G. L. 1937. Transmission at nerve endings by acetylcholine. *Physiol. Rev.* **17** 485–514.

Brown, L. 1957. Chemical transmission at nerve endings. *Adv. Sci.* **14** 103–107.

Bullock, T. H. 1947. Problems in invertebrate neurophysiology. *Physiol. Rev.* **27** 643–664.

Cannon, W. B., and Rosenblueth, A. 1937. *Autonomic Neuroeffector Systems.* Macmillan, New York.

Dale, H. 1953. A chemical phase in the transmission of nervous effects. *Endeavour* **12** 117–123.

Del Castillo, J., and Katz, B. 1956. Biophysical aspects of neuromuscular transmission. *Progr. Biophys.* **6** 121–170.

Denny-Brown, D. 1960. Motor mechanisms. *Hdbk. Physiol. I: Neurophysiol.* **2** 781–796.

Eccles, J. C. 1959. Excitatory and inhibitory synaptic action. *Annals N.Y. Acad. Sci.* **81** 247–264.

Fatt, P. 1954. Biophysics of junctional transmission. *Physiol. Rev.* **34** 674–710.

Fatt, P. 1959. Skeletal neuromuscular transmission. *Hdbk. Physiol. I: Neurophysiol.* **1** 199–213.

Furshpan, E. J. 1959. Neuromuscular transmission in invertebrates. *Hdbk. Physiol. I: Neurophysiol.* **1** 239–254.

Grundfest, H. 1959. Synaptic and ephaptic transmission. *Hdbk. Physiol. I: Neurophysiol.* **1** 147–197.

Grundfest, H. 1961. General physiology and pharmacology of junctional transmission. *Biophysics of Physiological and Pharmacological Actions.* (A. M. Shanes, ed.) Am. Assn. Adv. Sci., Washington, D.C.

Hebb, C. O. 1959. Chemical agents of the nervous system. *Int. Rev. Neurobiol.* **1** 165–193.

Hoyle, G. 1957. *Comparative Physiology of the Nervous Control of Muscular Contraction.* Univ. Press, Cambridge, England.

Katz, B. 1949. Neuro-muscular transmission in invertebrates. *Biol. Rev.* **24** 1–20.

Kuffler, S. W. 1952. Transmission processes at nerve-muscle junctions. *Mod. Trends Physiol. Biochem.* 277–290.

Riker, W. F. Jr., Werner, L., Roberts, J., and Kuperman, A. 1959. The presynaptic element in neuromuscular transmission. *Annals N.Y. Acad. Sci.* **81** 328–344.

Rosenblueth, A. 1950. *The Transmission of Nerve Impulses at Neuro-effector Junctions and Peripheral Synapses.* (out of print) Wiley, New York.

Tasaki, I. 1953. *Nervous Transmission.* Thomas, Springfield, Ill.

Tiegs, O. W. 1953. Innervation of voluntary muscle. *Physiol. Rev.* **33** 90–144.

Welsh, J. H. 1957. Neurohormones or transmitter agents. *Rec. Adv. Invert. Physiol.* 161–170.

Wiersma, C. A. G. 1953. Neural transmission in invertebrates. *Physiol. Rev.* **33** 326–355.

Wilson, I. B. 1959. Molecular complementarity in antidotes for nerve gases. *Annals N.Y. Acad. Sci.* **81** 307–316.

part III
The vegetative activities of animals

In the first two sections of this book we have been concerned with phenomena that are common to many animals and that can be observed with very little change in any suitable species. In the discussion of this material we have followed the "general" approach, emphasizing the similarities and treating any particular kind of cell or tissue as typical of all similar cells or tissues. In the remaining sections we shall be concerned with phenomena that exhibit certain common features but also vary greatly in different animal species. In this section we shall examine the vegetative functions, those functions necessary for the normal maintenance of the living animal. This maintenance rests on provision of an adequate supply of energy to the cells in the form of foodstuffs and oxygen, on the removal of the end products of cellular activity, and on the transfer of intermediates from cell to cell. The variations we observe are in part systematic; in the course of evolution the various groups of animals have developed a variety of different mechanisms for the performance of similar functions. The variations are also in part adaptive, in that the requirements of life in different environmental situations will differ, and so individual species will utilize the basic organ systems of the class or phylum in individual adaptive patterns. To study such variations we use the "comparative" approach, in which the observed variations are analyzed in terms of variations in structure, presumed evolutionary relationships, and adaptations to special ecological situations.

9 Nutrition

By nutrition we mean the processes in which an animal obtains from his environment those materials required for life and growth other than oxygen. It is a matter of common experience that all animal organisms must have food to survive or grow. The basis for this need as regards growth can be deduced from the necessity of providing materials out of which new tissue can be formed. The basis as regards survival began to emerge with the development of the concepts of respiration as a combustion and the consequent requirement of fuel as outlined in Chapter 1 of the first part. One of the great tasks of physiological chemistry in the nineteenth century and in the first half of the twentieth century was to establish the concept of proteins, carbohydrates, and lipids as the major constituents of cells, of foods, and of the fuel for cellular respiration, and to work out in detail the structures of these compounds and their metabolic fates.

Nutritive Requirements

Early in the present century when the broad outlines of these concepts had been established, attempts were made to formulate purified diets, composed only of the pure basic foodstuffs. Such diets in general failed to support growth or even life, and the question arose in some minds whether the basic foodstuffs are alone sufficient. The first clue to the existence of dietary essentials other than proteins, fats, carbohydrates, and minerals came from accidental observations of chickens fed on polished rice. These animals developed a neuritis which was soon recognized as being comparable to the polyneuritis (beri-beri) widely observed in men in tropical climates. The accidental observation was that the chickens could be cured by feeding them material which was removed from the rice in polishing. This fact suggested that the rice polishings contained some essential nutrient not included among the basic foodstuffs. During the same period similar observations were made, or recalled from long experience, in several other diseases. Xerophthalmia, or hardening of the mucous tissues around and in the eyes, could be cured with butter or cod liver oil. Rickets, involving softening of the bone, could be cured by cod liver oil but not by butter in general. Scurvy had long been cured by feeding fresh vegetables or fruits, especially citrus fruits and juices. Out of this medical work, then, emerged the concept that certain foods contain essential nutrients which are not included among the basic foodstuffs. Initially, the chemical nature of these nutrients was unknown, and they were called by initials: fat-soluble A for the anti-xerophthalmic factor, water-soluble B for the anti-neuritis factor, C for the anti-scurvy factor, D for the anti-rickets factor. Early attempts to establish the chemical nature of B suggested that it might be an amine; hence the name vitamine, for vital amine, was coined. It later became clear that these substances have no common structure, and the word has been altered to vitamin.

Nature of the Vitamins

As soon as the concept was accepted, intensive chemical studies were directed at isolating and identifying the active factors. These studies were carried out by means of biological assays based on the prevention or cure of the deficiency diseases or of some of their symptoms. From such studies it very soon appeared that the water-soluble B is not a single substance, but that there are several B vitamins, designated at first as B_1, B_2, etc. Within the course of two decades or so all of the original vitamins had been isolated and identified, and the identity proved by synthesis. With isolation, trivial chemical names were given to the water-soluble vitamins. The fat-soluble vitamins, on the other hand, proved complex in a different way. There are several different naturally occurring substances which have vitamin A action and several substances which have vitamin D action. Hence the alphabetical terminology is still in use for these substances (Table 9.1).

Parallel with the experiments in animal nutrition, microbiologists were engaged in studies of growth factors—substances which, when added in small amounts to cultures of yeast or bacteria, stimulate or are essential to reproduction. As purified vitamins became available they were tested as growth factors for microorganisms, and it soon became clear that the same substance could often act in both situations. As a result, microbiological assays were developed which greatly simplified the task of assaying some of the vitamins. Microorganisms can be grown rapidly in enormous numbers, and assays using microbes may take hours instead of days or weeks, as with animals. Moreover the amount of material and space needed is very much less. The general identity of growth factors and vitamins also suggested tests of well-known microbial growth factors, such as biotin, on animals with

TABLE 9.1
The Vitamins

Name	Letter Symbol	Formula	Functions
—	A		Part of visual pigment in some animals
Ascorbic acid	C	$O:C$ ... $CH \cdot CHOH \cdot CH_2OH$ $HO \cdot C = C \cdot OH$	Probably involved in tissue oxidations, especially tyrosine catabolism
Biotin	—	$NH \quad NH$ $CH——CH \cdot CH_2 \cdot CH_2 \cdot CH_2 \cdot CH_2 \cdot COOH$ $CH_2 \quad CH_2$ S	Coenzyme for carboxylation
Choline	—	$HO—CH_2—CH_2—N^+{<}^{CH_3}_{CH_3}$ (with CH_3)	Methyl donor
Cobalamin	B_{12}	Cobalt-Porphyrin	May be involved in C_1 cycle and in transmethylation
—	D		Activates alkaline phosphatases, especially involved in Ca metabolism
Tocopherol	E		Not conclusively established
Inositol	—	OH HO OH HO OH OH	Not conclusively established
—	K		Not established
Niacin	—	$COOH$ N	Component of NAD, NADP (respiratory coenzymes)

TABLE 9.1 (*Cont.*)
The Vitamins

Name	Letter Symbol	Formula	Functions
Pantothenic acid		$HO \cdot CH_2 \cdot \overset{\displaystyle CH_3}{\underset{\displaystyle CH_3}{C}} \cdot CHOH \cdot CO \cdot NH \cdot CH_2 \cdot CH_2 \cdot COOH$	Component of Coenzyme A (acetylation)
Pteroylglutamic acid		$-CH_2 \cdot NH$ — CO $COOH$ $NH \cdot CH \cdot CH_2 \cdot CH_2 \cdot COOH$	Component of C_1 cycle (Figures 12.6, 12.7)
Pyridoxine	B_6		Coenzyme for amino acid decarboxylases and transaminases
Riboflavin	B_2	$CH_2 \cdot CHOH \cdot CHOH \cdot CHOH \cdot CH_2OH$	Component of flavo-proteins (respiratory enzymes)
Thiamin	B_1		Cocarboxylase (as pyrophosphate)
Thioctic acid (Lipoic acid)		$\cdot CH_2 \cdot CH_2 \cdot CH_2 \cdot CH_2 \cdot COOH$	Coenzyme of oxidative carboxylation

the result that the discovery of new dietary essentials for animals was greatly accelerated.

Function of the Vitamins

From a physiological viewpoint, the major question arising from these studies was that of the function of vitamins. Studies of the pathology of the deficiency diseases gave no useful clues. The only valuable suggestion came from the fact that the amounts of the pure vitamins required to cure deficiency diseases are so very small. The vitamins are effective in doses of milligrams or even micrograms. Hence we can suggest that their function must be a catalytic one. The proof that this is the correct suggestion came first from studies of respiratory enzymes and the efforts of biochemists to isolate and identify these substances. When the yellow enzymes of Warburg (page 32) were finally purified, they were found to be proteins having flavin nucleotides as prosthetic groups with riboflavin as the essential unit. Riboflavin had already been isolated and identified as vitamin B_2. Soon afterwards thiamin, or vitamin B_1, was identified as an essential component of the coenzyme of carboxylase, and the catalytic function of the vitamins seemed to be established.

Again, as with the discovery of the identity of vitamins and microbial growth factors, establishment of a general principle led to new discoveries. The coenzymes of the dehydrogenases were isolated and shown to be pyridine nucleotides, containing as their essential component the amide of nicotinic acid. This was not at the time known to be a vitamin but was very soon tested in two deficiency diseases for which no cure was known—black tongue in dogs and pellagra in man. In both cases it proved very effective. Nicotinic acid (or its amide) was also soon established as a growth factor for microorganisms and is now generally known as niacin.

During the first fifty years of the present century, then, the series of interrelated studies by pathologists, nutritionists, microbiologists, chemists, and enzymologists have led to a general concept. Most organisms, and specifically microorganisms, insects, and mammals require, in addition to external sources of energy, small amounts of substances known as vitamins or growth factors. In many cases these substances function as parts of enzyme systems, either as prosthetic groups or coenzymes.

Vitamin Requirements of Animals

We should now look at this general concept from the comparative viewpoint. This is made difficult in the case of animals by the fact that nutritional experiments can be performed only with a few species which will feed readily on synthetic diets and which can be maintained on such diets in the laboratory. Thus far, nutritional experiments have been confined to protozoans, insects, and mammals almost entirely, with only a few experiments on other groups. On the other hand, the results of such experiments are in such general agreement, and the groups studied represent such great structural and evolutionary diversity, that there is no reason to anticipate important discoveries in principle from the study of other groups.

A general summary of vitamin requirements is presented in Table 9.2. It should be kept in mind in using this table that the number of species studied in any one major group is relatively small compared to the total number of species in that group, and moreover that the species studied may be selected and hence not typical of the whole group. Thus with more information one might have to change the entries in the table, especially those (N, R) which are rather sweeping. In fact the most striking thing in the table is the great variation in vitamin requirements, considered only qualitatively. One might account for such variation in either of two ways. The difference in vitamin requirements might be the result of differences in synthetic ability. Organisms like green plants which carry out photosynthesis might be able to synthesize their vitamins and hence not require them in the food. Animals, and especially higher animals like the insects and the vertebrates, might lack the ability to synthesize some or all of the vitamins. Alternatively, the differences in requirements might arise out of func-

TABLE 9.2
Vitamin Requirements of Major Groups of Organisms

Vitamin or Growth Factor	Higher Plants	Fungi	Yeasts	Bacteria	Algae	Green Flagellates	Other Protozoa	Insects	Vertebrates
A_1, A_2, A_3	N	N	N	N	N	N	?	N	R
Ascorbic acid (C)	N	N	N	N	?	N	r	N	r
Biotin	N	r	r	r	r	N	r	r	r
Choline	N	r	N	r	N	N	N	r	r
Cobalamin	N	N	N	r	r	r	r	r	r
D	N	N	N	N	N	N	N	N	R
Tocopherol	N	N	N	N	N	N	N	N	r
Inositol	N	r	r	?	N	N	N	r	r
K	N	N	N	r	N	N	N	r	r
Niacin	N	r	r	r	N	N	r	r	R
Pantothenic acid	N	r	r	r	r	N	r	r	R
Pteroylglutamic acid	N	N	N	r	N	N	r	r	R
Pyridoxin	N	r	r	r	N	N	r	r	R
Riboflavin	N	r	N	r	N	N	r	r	R
Thiamin	N	r	r	r	r	r	r	r	R
Carnitine	N	N	N	N	N	N	N	r	N
Asparagine	N	N	N	r	N	N	N	N	N
Glutamine	N	N	N	r	N	N	N	N	N
Glutathione	N	N	N	r	N	N	N	N	N
Hematin	N	r	N	r	N	N	r	r	N
Thioctic acid	N	N	N	r	N	N	r	N	N

N—not required by any species tested; r—required by some species or strains; R—required by all species tested.

tional differences. If a vitamin is needed for a function which is carried out by a higher animal but not by a unicellular form, then, we might expect the higher animal to require the vitamin though the unicellular form does not.

The Evolution of Vitamin Requirements

The demonstration that the first of these two explanations applies to at least some vitamins was initiated by Lwoff in his studies of protozoan nutrition, studies which have since been elaborated upon and confirmed by others. Table 9.3 summarizes the nutritive requirements of a number of related flagellate protozoans, some of which have chlorophyll and some of which do not. In general the vitamin requirements are simple. Several species require no vitamins at all. Two species require only thiazole, which is the sulfur-containing ring of the thiamin molecule. Two species require, in addition to thiazole, the pyrimidine ring of the thiamin molecule. One species requires only the pyrimidine ring and not the thiazole; this species also requires cobalamine (vitamin B_{12}). None of these species requires thiamin as such, but in every case thiamin will substitute for thiazole or pyrimidine or both. Finally, two species do require thiamin as such. Neither the pyrimidine nor thiazole nor a mixture of the two will substitute in these two species, which incidentally also require B_{12}. This pattern of vitamin requirements suggested the following hypotheses to Lwoff: All of the species use thiamin in their metabolic processes. Those which have no vitamin requirement are able to synthesize thiamin from simple substances such as CO_2, H_2O, NH_3,

and SO_4. The process of thiamin synthesis can be represented by the following pathway:

$$H_2O, NH_3, CO_2 \xrightarrow{a}$$
$$\text{precursor 1} \xrightarrow{b} \text{pyrimidine} \searrow$$
$$\qquad\qquad\qquad\qquad\qquad\qquad e \quad \text{thiamin}$$
$$H_2O, NH_3, CO_2, SO_4 \xrightarrow{c}$$
$$\text{precursor 2} \xrightarrow{d} \text{thiazole} \nearrow$$

The species which have no vitamin requirement can carry out the whole series of reactions *a–e*. Those which require pyrimidine have somehow lost the ability to carry out part of the series of reactions *a–b* and hence must be supplied with pyrimidine in the medium. Those which require thiazole have lost reactions *c–d,* and those which require both have lost *a–d.* Finally, those which require thiamin as such have lost reaction *e* and possibly earlier reactions as well.

The loss of these synthetic abilities appears moreover to be part of an evolutionary process. If we arrange the species in Table 9.3 in order of increasing complexity of vitamin requirements we find that they also fall into a more or less consistent pattern of utilization of sources of carbon and nitrogen. The seven species which require no vitamins can utilize as carbon sources only CO_2 and organic acids. Three of them can use only CO_2 and three others can use only a limited number of simple organic acids. Only one of the species which requires one or more vitamins (*Euglena klebsii*) has such a limited pattern of carbon source utilization. Likewise, three of the seven species which do not require vitamins can use only NO_3^- and NH_3 as nitrogen sources, and two more can use only these two and a single amino acid. Many of the species which require vitamins are able to use a variety of amino acids, and only one of them

TABLE 9.3

Nutritional Requirements of Some Flagellate Protozoans

Species	Occurrence of Chlorophyll	Carbon Sources Used	Nitrogen Sources	Vitamins Required
Chlamydomonas agloeformis	+	CO_2, acetic, butyric	NO_3^-, NH_3, glycine	None
C. moewusii	+	CO_2	NO_3^-, NH_3	None
Chlorogonium elongatum	+	CO_2, acetic, butyric	NO_3^-, NH_3	None
C. euchlorum	+	CO_2, acetic, succinic	NO_3^-, NH_3	None
Polytoma caudatum	–	CO_2, pyruvic, butyric	NH_3	Thiazole
P. ocellatum	–	CO_2, acetic to decylic, lactic, pyruvic, ethanol, butanol, propanol, hexanol	NO_3^-, NH_3, alanine	Thiazole
P. obtusum	–	CO_2, acetic, butyric	NH_3, glycine	None
P. uvella	–	CO_2, acetic to valeric	NH_3, glycine	None
Polytomella caeca	–	CO_2, acetic to decylic, ethanol to hexanol	NH_3	Pyrimidine thiazole
Euglena anabaena	+	CO_2	NO_3^-, NH_3, ala, leu, phe, pro, val	None
E. stellata	+	CO_2	NO_3^-, NH_3, ala, arg, glu, gly, hist, leu, lys, phe, pro, ser, val	None
E. klebsii	+	CO_2	NO_3^-, NH_3, ala, arg, glu, gly, hist, leu, lys, pro, ser, val	Pyrimidine Thiazole
E. gracilis typica	+	CO_2, acetic to decylic, ethanol, to hexanol, lactic, malic, pyruvic, succinic	NH_3, ala, glu, gly, hist, leu, phe, pro, ser, val	Pyrimidine B_{12}
E. gracilis bacillaris	+	CO_2, acetic, butyric, malic, succinic, fumaric, phosphoglyceric, glucose	ala, gly	Thiamin B_{12}
E. gracilis urophora	+	CO_2, acetic to octylic, ethanol to hexanol, lactic, pyruvic, malic fumaric	NH_3, glu	Thiamin B_{12}

Amino acids indicated by initial 3 letters.

(*Polytoma ocellatum*) can use nitrate.

The pattern of carbon and nitrogen utilization we see in the species which do not require vitamins is characteristic of green plants: use of CO_2 as a carbon source and NO_3^- or NH_3 as a nitrogen source. The pattern we see in the species which do require vitamins approaches that of animals: use of organic sources for both carbon and nitrogen and ability to use a wide range of such sources. The flagellates contain many forms, including the species listed here, which can be classified either as animals or plants, and many biologists have considered that higher animals and higher plants may have developed from flagellate ancestors. If so, we can see evidence of such an evolutionary pattern in these nutritional requirements.

Genetic Control of Nutritive Requirements

The idea of loss of synthetic ability as an evolutionary process, suggested by Lwoff, gained support from the development of the gene-enzyme hypothesis. As we noted earlier, Beadle and Ephrussi first showed that the genes which control eye pigmentation in the fly *Drosophila melanogaster* act by controlling specific steps in the synthesis of the eye pigments. Beadle and Tatum then were able, in their work with the mold *Neurospora sitophila,* to obtain mutant strains with a series of vitamin requirements comparable to those which Lwoff had demonstrated in naturally occurring species and varieties of protozoans. *Neurospora* normally does not require thiamin or its precursors, but after irradiation mutant strains can be isolated which require pyrimidine, thiazole, a mixture of the two, or thiamin itself.

Again thiamin will substitute for any of these requirements. Genetic analysis shows that each major step in the synthesis *a, b, c, d, e,* is controlled by one or more specific genes. Mutation of any one of these genes then results in loss of the corresponding synthetic ability and hence in the appearance of a vitamin requirement.

Taken alone this loss of synthetic mechanisms appears to be a negative factor in evolution. A gene mutation which results in the development of a need for a vitamin would, by itself, be lethal unless the organism had already developed some compensating ability. Thus, suppose a variant of some plant-like photosynthetic flagellate develops in the course of evolution a habit of living in an environment rich in dissolved food material. With this habit the strain must also develop the necessary biochemical machinery to permit use of the food material. If now, a mutation occurs leading to development of a requirement for a vitamin, this mutation will not be lethal as long as the vitamin is present in the food material, and the mutation will be passed on to the progeny. This progeny will, however, be differentiated from its fellows by the inability to live without the vitamin. This, along with other accumulated differences, may separate the mutants from their more conservative fellows who retain their synthetic abilities and hence eventually lead to the formation of a separate species. The success of this species will depend not on its synthetic abilities but on its ability to obtain food which will compensate for any deficiency in synthetic ability. On this view, the development of vitamin requirements is one factor at the very basis of the evolution of animals as distinct from plants, and much of animal evolution may be seen as the consequence of the need to develop food-getting abilities to compensate for the synthetic abilities which plants have and which animals have lost.

A similar line of reasoning may be pursued for the amino acids (Table 9.4). Green plants, other than flagellates, do not require amino acids for growth but can synthesize their own. A few green flagellates, however, will grow only if one or more specific amino acids are supplied. The same is true of many species or strains of fungi, bacteria, and protozoa. Genetic analyses in fungi (*Neurospora*) have shown that specific amino acid requirements arise when a gene mutation occurs which interferes with a specific step in the synthesis of one amino acid. In the higher animals (insects, vertebrates) many amino acids are required, and one may see this as the gradual accumulation of gene mutations which have involved progressive losses of synthetic ability over the long course of evolution.

We can see some evidences of this evolutionary pattern in higher animals. Thus among the mammals only man, the anthropoid apes, and the cavy (guinea pig) are known to require ascorbic acid as a vitamin. None of the other mammals tested require this substance in the diet but all have it in their cells and tissues. It appears therefore that in the anthropoid group and in the cavy, separately of course, a mutation has occurred leading to loss of ability to synthesize vitamin C or ascorbic acid. On the other hand, it is difficult to account for the vitamin A requirements in this way. Vitamin A as such is relatively rare in the living world outside the vertebrate group. It occurs in the eyes of certain crustaceans and other invertebrates where it

is, as in the vertebrates, a component of the visual pigment. Otherwise the only compounds related to vitamin A are the carotenoid pigments. Some of these serve in the vertebrates as precursors of vitamin A, but they are not converted into vitamin A by any plant or by most animals. The function of vitamin A remains unknown save for its role in vision. But since the vitamin is essential for mammalian life, we must assume it has a more vital function; one may suppose that this function is either lacking in other organisms or performed by some other substance such as the carotenoids. There is no evidence, however, that the carotenoids are ever dietary essentials as such. Similar arguments apply to the other fat-soluble vitamins D and E (tocopherol). Insects require cholesterol in the diet, which is hence a vitamin for them, whereas this substance is synthesized by vertebrates.

Symbiotic Vitamin Synthesis

A rather remarkable form of evolutionary compensation for loss of synthetic abilities is seen in many insects and some vertebrates and possibly could be found very widely among animals generally. We can see from Table 9.2 that no one of the vitamins is required by all insects, suggesting that some insects can synthesize many of their own vitamins. Specifically, the beetle *Lasioderma serricorne* does not require thiamin, riboflavin, pyridoxin, or niacin. Most other insects require these vitamins, and all of them are essential to basic cellular functions. Similarly, the adult cow does not require any of these four vitamins, although most other vertebrates do. However, in a number of cases, animals have been raised in germ-free condi-

TABLE 9.4
Amino Acid Requirements and Utilization by Major Groups of Organisms

Amino Acid	Higher Plants	Fungi	Yeasts	Bacteria	Algae	Green Flagellates	Other Protozoa	Insects	Vertebrates
Leucine	N u	r u	r u	r u	N	N u	r u	R*	R
Lysine	N u	r u	u	r u	N	N u	r u	R	R
Methionine	N u	r u	r u	r u	N	r	r u	R	R
Phenylalanine	N u	r u	r u	r u	N	N u	r u	R*	R
Threonine	N u	r u	u	r u	N	–	r u	R*	R
Histidine	N u	r u	r u	r u	N u	r u	r u	R	R
Isoleucine	N u	r u	r u	r u	N u	–	r u	R	R
Tryptophan	N u	r u	r u	r u	N u	N	r u	R*	R
Valine	N u	r u	u	r u	N u	N u	r u	R*	R
Arginine	N u	r u	r u	r u	N u	N u	r u	R	r
Cystine-cysteine	N u	r u	u	r u	N u	–	u	R*	N
Glutamic	N u	r u	u	r u	N u	N u	u	r	r
Glycine	N u	r u	u	r u	N u	N u	r u	r	r
Proline	N u	r u	u	r u	N	N u	r u	r	r
Serine	N u	r u	u	r u	N	N u	r u	r	r
Alanine	N u	u	u	r u	N	N u	r u	r	N
Aspartic	N u	u	u	r u	N u	N u	u	r*	N
Tyrosine	N u	r u	u	r u	–	N	r u	N	N

N—not required by any; u—used by some; r—required by some; R—required by all tested.
* Some substitutions are possible. Thus phe will substitute for thre, try for val, val for leu, tyr for phe, met for cys, asp or glu for ala, glu for asp, in some species.

tion, and it is found that they then have extensive vitamin requirements. When the eggs of *L. serricorne* are sterilized and the animals are raised aseptically, the requirement for the B vitamins is the same as in other insects. Likewise, the young calf, before its rumen or paunch has developed and while it is still feeding on milk, requires these vitamins. When the rumen develops and the animal begins to eat grass, there develops, in the rumen, a vigorous population of bacteria and protozoa. In the insects, likewise, there are often symbiotic microorganisms in the intestines or in other tissues, and sometimes elaborate mechanisms insuring infection of the young with these microbes have been described. The evidence therefore clearly suggests that the microbes synthesize vitamins which are then used by the host animal.

Summary

To summarize current views on nutrition we may say that animals in general require in their food the following:

(1) The elementary components of cells and tissues. These include the major constituents C, H, N, O, P, and S and the mineral constituents Cu, Fe, Mg, Ca, Mn, Na, and K, which serve as components of enzymes or enzyme systems or as activators. In general, animals must have the C and N supplied in the form of specific organic compounds such as carbohydrates, organic acids, alcohols, or amino acids. This is in part because of a need for energy (2 below) and in part because of the inability of the animal organism to synthesize certain important molecules from simpler substances (3 and 4 below).

(2) A sufficient amount of organic compounds which can be oxidized in the cells to supply energy. The green flagellates, which were presumably the ancestors of the animal kingdom, were able to utilize solar light energy through the chlorophyll mechanism. A very early step in animal evolution must have involved loss of this mechanism. Many colorless flagellates, and some higher organisms, can obtain their energy from compounds as simple as acetic acid or ethanol, but most animals obtain their energy from carbohydrates, fatty acids, and amino acids, and their metabolic processes would probably be unable to utilize simpler compounds as exclusive sources of energy.

(3) An adequate supply of major organic tissue constituents which the organism is unable to synthesize from other dietary constituents. This category includes a number of amino acids (10 in most vertebrates, probably about the same number in other animals) and in some species smaller amounts of lipids, such as linoleic acid or cholesterol, and nitrogenous compounds, such as purines, pyrimidines, and choline.

(4) An adequate supply of a number of compounds known as vitamins. The absolute amounts of these substances required are small, ranging from a few micrograms to a few milligrams per day for most animals, but they cannot be synthesized by the organism and are absolutely essential, in those cases where the function is known, as components of enzyme systems.

Feeding, Digestion, and Absorption

With the exception of the elementary requirements (1), all of these needs have arisen out of a loss of synthetic abilities which in turn has resulted from accumulated gene mutations and consequent loss of specific synthetic enzyme systems. Along with these losses have necessarily gone adaptations, permitting the animal to utilize preformed organic matter derived from the synthetic activities of plants or of other animals. These adaptations involve four major types of processes: (1) feeding, in which the organic matter is concentrated and separated from the surroundings; (2) digestion, in which the organic matter is broken down mechanically and chemically to its component parts; (3) absorption, in which the organic matter is taken into the body of the organism across bounding membranes; and (4) assimilation, in which the organic matter becomes an integral part of the animal's body or is oxidized as an energy source. The order given here is not invariable; the second and third processes may occur in reverse order. Moreover, the details of the four processes show considerable variation, some of which has not been brought into any systematic pattern.

The feeding mechanisms of animals generally exhibit some relation to the type of food, as one would reasonably expect. It is probable, on the basis of the view of animal evolution which we have presented, that the most primitive animal organisms utilized organic matter in solution as their source of food. Many protozoans, many parasites, and a few other animals do this today, but there has been very little study of the mechanisms by which the dissolved food enters the cell. Mechanisms for absorption of dissolved organic matter have, however, been studied in bacteria and the cells of higher animals, with specific reference to monosaccharides and amino acids. In general it appears that these sub-stances are taken into the cell by a number of active sites, which are able to combine specifically with the compound absorbed and in some way pass it to the interior of the cell. There are distinct active sites for different monosaccharides, for example; each site is able to combine with sugars of a specific molecular structure. Whether similar situations prevail in protozoans is not known. An alternative and presumably nonspecific method for the absorption of materials from the medium would be the process of pinocytosis, in which minute droplets of medium are surrounded and engulfed by projections of the cell membrane. The occurrence of pinocytosis in a great variety of cells is well established, but we do not know what part, if any, the process plays in absorption.

Protozoans

At a relatively early stage in protozoan evolution, species probably arose which had the ability to ingest other organisms or parts of organisms smaller than themselves. A variety of mechanisms capable of doing this is found today among the protozoans (Figure 9.1). In the simplest case, the cytoplasm flows around the particle and engulfs it. This may possibly be an extension of pinocytosis which, in animals such as the amoeba, may engulf particles almost as large as the amoeba itself. Among the ciliate protozoans a variety of accessory devices involving production of water currents by cilia insure that the particles reach the mouth or portion of the animal where ingestion can occur. In other protozoans, notably the sessile Sarcodina, extensive nets or traps of sticky pseudopodia are extended, in which unwary

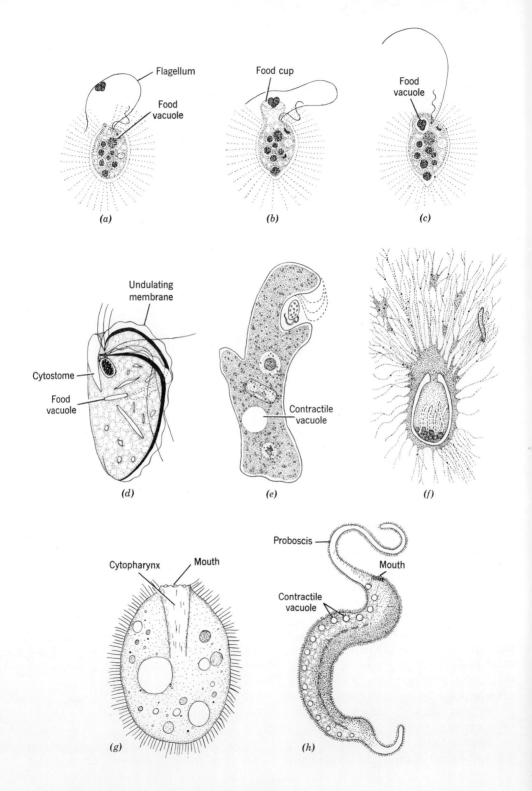

(a)

(b)

(c)

(d)

(e)

(f)

(g)

(h)

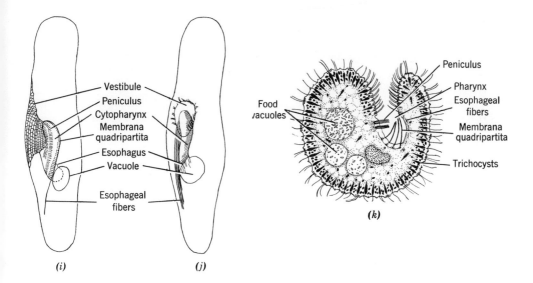

(i)   (j)

Fig. 9.1 Feeding mechanisms in protozoans. (*a*)(*b*)(*c*) Ingestion by food-cup formation in a flagellate, *Monas vestita.* (After Reynolds, 1934, *Arch. Protistenk.* **81** 399.) (*d*) The polymastigote flagellate, *Trichomonas termitides,* showing the cytostome or mouth and the undulating membrane and flagella used in bringing food into the cytostome; food vacuoles are formed at the inner end of the cytostome. (After Kofoid and Swezy, 1919, Univ. Calif. Publ. Zool. **20** 21.) (*e*) Ameboid ingestion in an amoeba (After Kepner and Taliaferro, 1913, *Biol. Bull.* **24** 411.) (*f*) Capture by pseudopodia in a rhizopod (Calkins, 1901, *The Protozoa,* Macmillan, New York.) (*g*) A ciliate (*Prorodon*) with permanent mouth but no oral groove (After Conn, 1905, State Geol. Nat. Hist. Survey Connecticut, Bulletin no. 2). (*h*) Another ciliate utilizing a proboscis in feeding (*Dileptus gigas*). (*i*) (*j*) (*k*) The ciliary feeding apparatus of the ciliate *Paramecium* (After Gelei, 1934, *Arch. Protistenk.* **82** 331.) (*i*) and (*j*) seen from right and left sides, respectively, (*k*) in cross-section.

moving organisms may become entangled and ultimately engulfed.

All of these protozoan mechanisms for engulfing particulate material raise problems of digestion and absorption. When material in solution is absorbed it presumably enters directly into the cytoplasm and is there attacked by cytoplasmic enzymes, but a large and perhaps active particle of food poses a somewhat different problem. In general, this problem has been solved among protozoans by the mechanism of the food vacuole. The ingested particle is retained within a spherical vacuole filled with fluid and surrounded by a membrane. Exactly what happens inside this vacuole is still not clear, in spite of the many observations which have been made. All we know is that the food particle slowly breaks down and disappears, and that there is a corresponding appearance of organic matter in the cytoplasm of the animal. We must therefore infer that enzymes somehow enter the vacuole and break down the food into constituents which can then pass into the cytoplasm and be assimilated.

Porifera

The method of feeding by currents, followed by engulfment in intracellular digestion, persists in highly specialized form in the sponges (Figure 9.2). Here the current is produced by the flagella of the collar cells which line certain interior cavities of the sponge. The current which these cells produce is relatively weak, but it carries into the sponge microscopic particles in suspension. In the internal cavities the total cross-sectional area is considerably greater than in the incurrent pores. Consequently the velocity of flow is reduced, and particles tend to settle out, to be engulfed by the collar cells. It may well be that the flagella of these cells exert some active efforts to bring the particles into the collar region as well. Digestion occurs in vacuoles, much as in protozoa, but the sponges with their multicellular organization require a distributing system. Apparently this function is performed by amoebocytes which transfer materials from the collar cells to other cells of the sponge body. The evidence for this view is limited to histological observation, however, and we know nothing of how the movements of the amoebocytes are controlled.

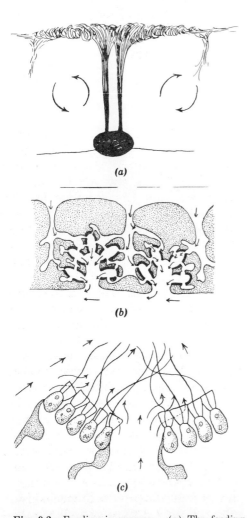

(a)

(b)

(c)

Fig. 9.2 Feeding in sponges. (*a*) The feeding currents around a sponge in quiet water. (*b*) The course of currents through the wall of a leuconoid sponge; the flagellated lining of the chambers is shown in heavy black. (*c*) A portion of the flagellated lining of one chamber, showing the currents utilized in feeding. (After Bidder, 1923, *Quart. J. Micr. Sci.* **67** 293.)

Coelenterata

Many coelenterates, like the sponges, are sessile animals, remaining in one location more or less permanently attached to the substratum. Even the medusae, which are free living, have little or no ability to direct their movements. Most coelenterates, however, use a trapping method rather than a current method of obtaining food. The food may range from microscopic particles to whole animals almost as large as the coelenterates, but it must in general consist of motile particles or less often of particles carried by an external current. The essential feature of the trapping mechanism is the cnidoblast (nematocyst), a complex structure consisting of a fine thread coiled inside a box-like chamber, the distal surface of which can open, on appropriate stimulation, like a trap door. Beside the trap door is a small hair, the cnidocil, which is evidently suitably located to serve as a receptor of contact stimuli. In fact, when a small animal bumps or brushes against the cnidocil, the trap door flies open, the thread shoots out, and the small animal is impaled upon or entangled in the thread (Figure 9.3).

Professor and Mrs. Pantin of Cambridge University have provided experimental evidence concerning the effective stimulus. In spite of the fact that the normal stimulus appears to be contact with the cnidocil, various investigators had shown that mechanical stimuli, with clean sand grains or glass rods for example, were ineffective even when the force involved was much greater than that normally involved in contact of the cnidocil with a moving animal. The Pantins showed that mechanical stimulation with the glass rod is effective if the rod is contaminated with a small amount of organic matter. On the other hand, organic matter alone—even extracts of normal food animals—will not by itself provoke discharge of nematocysts. If now the animal is first exposed to a tissue extract and then stimulated mechanically, the nematocysts will discharge. Clearly the nematocysts are only sensitive to mechanical stimuli when these are preceded or accompanied by a suitable chemical stimulus. Neither type of stimulation alone is adequate. The adaptive significance in preventing a response to stimuli which are not associated with edible particles is obvious.

When the food particle is impaled upon or entangled by the thread of the nematocyst, it is carried to the mouth of the animal by one or more of the tentacles which surround the mouth in one or more rings. The tentacles are long, muscular, and flexible and on appropriate stimulus bend toward the

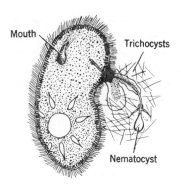

Fig. 9.3 A discharged nematocyst or cnidoblast, showing the effect on *Paramecium*. (After Zick *Zool. Anz.* **83** 295.)

mouth. Again, the effective stimulus is a combination of chemical and mechanical stimulation, though now the responding unit is not a single cell, but an organ; and the stimulus is not received directly by the responding cell but by a part of the nervous system which may be more or less removed from the responding muscle cells. The magnitude and extent of the response depend upon the intensity of the stimulus. A weak stimulus may cause a response only in the stimulated tentacles, while stronger stimuli cause adjacent tentacles to respond as well and may result in movement of the mouth towards the stimulated tentacles. Again, the adaptive significance in bringing a large and struggling prey into the mouth is obvious. We shall discuss the nervous mechanisms later.

The digestive mechanisms of some of the larger coelenterates differ significantly from the protozoan mechanism we discussed briefly above. When the prey, taken through the mouth into the coelenteron or gastrovascular cavity in the center of the body of the coelenterate, is very small by comparison with the endodermal cells lining the cavity, the prey may be engulfed and digested in a food vacuole as in the protozoans. On the other hand, many coelenterates take quite large organisms or particles as food, and these are digested in the cavity itself. No large quantity of enzymes ever appears in the coelenteron. Rather, the endodermal cells, including in some forms the cells of partitions or tentacles within the coelenteron, are applied closely to the surface of the food particle and secrete digestive enzymes directly onto the surface. These same cells then absorb the products of digestion as rapidly as they are formed, and hence there is no accumulation of these products in the coelenteron. This method of digestion is called "contact digestion." It probably arose by some modification of the function of the food vacuole. Vacuole formation is a characteristic feature of secretion in many animal cells, and one can imagine that the vacuole which is formed primitively around an engulfed food particle came to be formed even in the absence of the food particle. Digestive enzymes then might be secreted into the vacuole just as they apparently are when the food particles are present. Then the enzyme-filled vacuole moves to the surface of the cell and discharges its enzymes directly onto the external food particle. This picture is of course speculative and like many such speculations cannot be verified in detail, though such evidence as we have supports it.

Mollusca

Among the higher animals the variety of mechanisms utilized in feeding and digestion is so great that we must restrict ourselves to a few examples. Indeed, it is questionable whether a systematic survey would yield any general picture clear enough to justify the effort required in making it. Rather, we may leave these details to the specialists in the biology of particular groups who will find a comparative study very useful for their purposes, though it may involve too much detail for ours. Perhaps the clearest pattern of relationships among feeding and digestive mechanisms is that seen in the mollusks. We owe much of our general understanding of this pattern to C. M. Yonge, now at the University of Glasgow. He worked out the essentials of the feeding and digestive mechanisms in pelecypods and showed how these mechanisms are related to the pattern in other classes of the phylum.

Filter Feeding

We may begin with the pelecypod pattern as seen in oysters, clams, and mussels because Yonge has suggested, on what seem very reasonable grounds, that this pattern is a primitive one. These animals are sessile or have very limited powers of movement. They feed essentially by a filtering mechanism in which water is drawn in through an opening or tube (incurrent siphon), passed through a fine-meshed filter which strains out particulate matter, and ejected through another opening or tube (excurrent siphon). If we open the bivalve shell of a pelecypod, one of the most conspicuous features we see are the ctenidia or gills. These are thin membranous structures lying between the mantle tissue that lines the inner surface of the shell and the visceral mass or the main body of the animal. In cross section the ctenidia are seen as thin sheets pierced with many openings. If the animal is living and we examine the surface of the ctenidia with a binocular dissecting microscope, we see that this structure is made up of two sets of long bars, one running from top (dorsal) to bottom (ventral), the other, at right angles, from anterior to posterior. Moreover, we see that small particles of sand or debris are moving rather rapidly in the dorsoventral direction. Closer examination with high power and suitable illumination will show that the dorsoventral bars are heavily ciliated and that the movement of particles appears to be caused by the beating of cilia on the surface of the dorsoventral bars (Figure 9.4).

Yonge worked out in detail the arrangement on these bars of cilia, which occur in three well-defined groups: (1) The frontal cilia, on the exposed or frontal surfaces of the bars, beat in a direction parallel to the long axis of the bars, creating a current from the dorsal toward the ventral edge of the ctenidium. (2) The laterofrontal cilia, along the outer edges of the frontal surfaces of the bars, beat toward the frontal surface and are relatively long, strong, and few in number. (3) The lateral cilia, on the lateral surfaces between adjacent bars, are small and numerous and beat away from the frontal surface, creating a current which flows through the ctenidium between the bars. The horizontal bars,

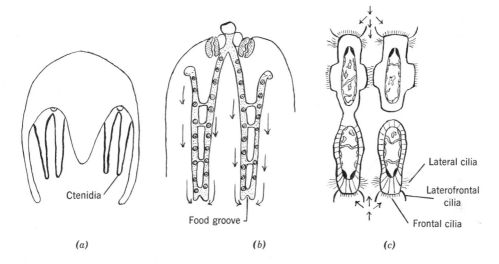

(a) (b) (c)

Fig. 9.4   The feeding mechanism of a pelecypod mollusk. (a) Cross section through a clam or mussel to show the position of the ctenidia in the mantle cavity with relation to the body mass and mantle shown in outline. (b) Enlarged diagram of one pair of ctenidia seen from the same aspect as in (a); the arrows indicate the direction of movement of food particles entrapped in mucus. (c) Section through the bars of a ctenidium, cut at right angles to the section of (b) to show the cilia. The frontal cilia beat in a ventral direction, moving the food particles and mucus downward toward the food groove. The laterofrontal cilia beat away from the surface of the ctenidium, holding the mucous sheet out of contact with the surface. The lateral cilia beat toward the inside of the ctenidium and set up the water current, which flows into the mantle cavity through the incurrent siphon, penetrates the mucous sheet covering the outer surfaces of the ctenidia, and leaves the mantle cavity through the excurrent siphon. Food and other particles are strained from this current as it passes through the mucous sheet. (After Borradaile and Potts, *The Invertebrata*, 1st edn., Macmillan, New York.)

running anteroposteriorly, are not ciliated and appear to be merely structural elements holding the vertical bars in their normal arrangement.

From this arrangement of cilia and the direction of beat, Yonge deduced the following functions: The lateral cilia produce the current of water which flows in through the incurrent siphon to the mantle cavity, through the spaces between the bars of the ctenidia, and out through the excurrent siphon. The water, in its passage through the sieve-like ctenidial structure, will be filtered; suspended particles will be caught by the laterofrontal cilia and thrown up onto the surface of the dorsoventral bars. Here they will be swept by the beat of the frontal cilia to the lower or ventral edge of the ctenidium where we shall examine their fate in a moment.

There was, however, one flaw in Yonge's argument which was brought out first by the study of the nutrition of mussels carried out by D. L. Fox. Fox, by ingenious use of the total matter and energy balance of the mussel, showed that the particulate matter (diatoms, dinoflagellates, bacteria, and other unicellular forms) available to this animal was not sufficient to pro-vide the matter and energy for the observed growth rates, even if all such cellular material ingested was digested and utilized (Table 9.5). In fact, much of the cellular material ingested passes through the digestive tract unchanged and even emerges alive in the feces. On the other hand, if we take into account the microscopic and colloidal organic detritus in the water, there is more than enough to provide for growth of the muscle. Consequently, the feeding mechanism must be able to remove such detritus, as well as cellular material, from the water. Meanwhile, G. E. MacGinitie was studying the feeding mechanisms of worms. The annelid worm *Chaetopterus,* for example, lives in a U-shaped burrow in tidal estuaries and feeds by passing a current of water through its burrow by means of movements of specialized parapodia (Figure 9.5). The worm spins a conical tube of mucus from special glands located on parapodia just behind the mouth. The rim of the open base of the cone is attached to these modified parapodia and the apex is held in a special ventral protuberance. When the animal pumps water through the burrow with the feeding cone in position, the water

TABLE 9.5
The Metabolic Balance Sheet of a Mussel

Metabolism		Food Intake	
Somatic tissue formed	1.6 gm	Diatoms	0.7 gm
Gametes formed	2.7 gm	Dinoflagellates	4.2 gm
Used in metabolism	38.0 gm	Bacteria	0.05 gm
Lost in feces	26.0 gm	Other organic matter	110.0 gm
Total used	68.3 gm		114.95 gm

Values are calculated for the second year in the life of the sea mussel *Mytilus californianus,* on a dry ash-free weight basis, and for a filtration rate of 2–3 liters of sea water per day. From D. L. Fox and W. R. Coe, *J. Exp. Zool.* **93** 205.

must pass through the mucous walls of the cone, and particles will then be strained out. The cone is secreted continuously and the small apical end is passed into a ciliated groove and passed, with its contained particles, to the mouth. MacGinitie showed by experiments with various materials that particles as small as large protein molecules are filtered out of the water by this mechanism, and he was consequently led to suggest that mucous filters might provide a means by which aquatic animals could utilize the abundant colloidal organic matter suspended in most waters.

This suggestion was then applied to pelecypods. The frontal surface of the ctenidium is normally covered by a thin sheet of mucus secreted by mucous glands on the surface. This sheet is held away from the surface by the beat of the latero-frontal cilia and moved continuously downward toward the ventral edge of the ctenidium. The water, which passes through the spaces between the bars of the ctenidium, is first filtered through the sheet of mucus which effectively removes particulate matter as small as 1 to 3 microns in diameter, depending on species. The lower or ventral edge of the ctenidium is folded into a groove, the food groove, which is lined with cilia. The marginal cilia along the edge of the groove beat toward the groove and thus pass the sheet of mucus into the groove. The cilia lining the groove itself beat in a spiral in such a pattern that the sheet of mucus is rolled into a thread, and the thread is passed forward toward the mouth. The whole apparatus thus constitutes a kind of conveyor belt combined with a sieve which filters the water and passes the collected material embedded in mucus in a steady stream toward the mouth.

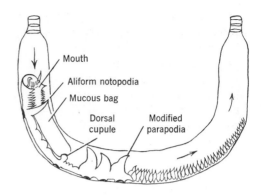

Fig. 9.5 The feeding mechanism of an annelid worm, *Chaetopterus variopedatus,* utilizing a mucous bag. (After G. E. MacGinitie, 1939, *Biol. Bull.* **77** 115.)

Digestion in Pelecypods

At the mouth the thread is received by a set of palps, also covered with cilia, which probably serve to pass the thread into the mouth, whence it passes along the short esophagus to the stomach. This structure is not analogous to the vertebrate stomach, since its primary function is that of sorting the food particles, and relatively little digestion occurs here. The pH of the stomach contents is generally more acid than sea water, and as a result the mucus brought in with the food tends to dissolve, freeing the entangled particles. The sorting mechanism involves a system of ciliated grooves and ridges. The cilia along the tops of the ridges beat in the direction from the esophagus toward the opening of the intestine. The cilia in the grooves beat in the direction toward the openings into the large digestive gland. Particles too large to enter the grooves are thus carried directly to the intestine, while smaller particles which can enter the grooves are diverted into the digestive gland. The latter structure consists of highly branched ciliated tubules. The smaller tubules are lined with cells that ingest the particles which reach them and digest these within food vacuoles. Yonge considers this pattern of intracellular digestion a primitive characteristic associated with the utilization of microscopic and submicroscopic particles as food.

The stomach of the pelecypods contains a curious structure, the crystalline style, which is a small clear cylinder of proteinaceous material projecting into the stomach from the style sac, a blind tube running parallel to the intestine (Figure 9.6). The free end of the style bears against the gastric shield, a thickened region of the stomach wall opposite the mouth of the style sac, and cilia which line the style sac cause the style to be forced against the shield and rotated slowly. As a result, the style slowly dissolves in the stomach contents, being replaced continuously at the other end by a secretion process in the style sac. The function of the style was long in dispute, but Yonge showed that it contained substantial amounts of amylase and suggested that this amylase is liberated as the style dissolves and hence may serve to initiate digestion of starch in the stomach. One wonders whether the amylase might serve to help dissolve the mucus brought in with the food since mucus is a polysaccharide-protein complex, but this has not been tested.

The Odontophore

In nearly all other mollusks, including the amphineurans of relatively primitive organization, the feeding process is entirely different and utilizes a structure peculiar to this phylum, the odontophore (Figure 9.7). The odontophore is a relatively complicated apparatus including an elongated piece of cartilage, occupying a position in the buccal cavity roughly comparable to that occupied by the tongue in many vertebrates, for example. The distal surface of the cartilage is covered by a ribbon-like structure, the radula, which bears on its exposed surface a complex set of low teeth, varying greatly in structure in different mollusks. This apparatus, consisting of cartilage and radula, is operated by two sets of muscles. One set can protrude the cartilage, rotate it in a ventrodorsal plane, and retract it. The other set can slide the radula back and forth around the distal end of the cartilage. In use as a feeding mechanism, these two sets of muscles act in a coordinated fashion along with the lip muscles. At rest, the whole structure is in the retracted position inside the buccal cavity, and the radula is pulled back so that most of its length is on the ventral side of the cartilage. The cartilage is then protruded until it touches the surface of the object to which the lips are applied. The radula is then rotated around the

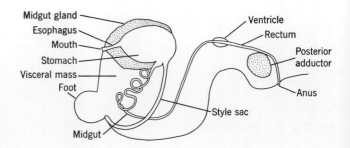

Fig. 9.6 The digestive tract of the clam, *Mya*. (After C. M. Yonge, 1923, *J. Exp. Biol.* **1** 15.)

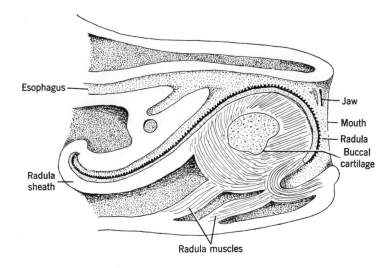

Fig. 9.7 The odontophore of a gastropod mollusk. (After Lang, *Lehrb. vergl. Anat. wirbellosen Thiere.*)

end of the cartilage so that the teeth scrape over the surface in a rasping motion. At the same time the cartilage moves over the surface and upward so that, as the radula completes its movement, the odontophore is retracted into the mouth, carrying with it any particles scraped off the surface. The whole movement resembles a licking motion, with the added touch of a sliding toothed ribbon to add to the rasping effectiveness.

This apparatus is most often used either to scrape attached unicellular algae and other materials off rocky surfaces or to rasp away plant tissues from the body of a larger multicellular plant. The material thus scraped off may be passed directly to the stomach to be sorted and passed into the digestive gland, much as in pelecypods, or it may first enter a crop and gizzard arrangement as in the pond snail, *Limnaea stagnalis*. The crop is merely an enlargement of the esophagus in which the food material is retained until it can pass through and into the stomach. The gizzard is a sac with muscular walls, which is kept filled with sand grains ingested by the snail. Contraction of the muscles of the gizzard causes a grinding action of the sand on food particles, reducing them to smaller size. The smallest particles are then passed by the ciliary sorting mechanism of the stomach into the digestive gland to be digested intracellularly, while the larger particles are either passed into the intestine or returned to the gizzard for further grinding.

Extracellular Digestion

In many gastropods, intracellular digestion has been partly or wholly supplanted by extracellular digestion. In such animals, digestive enzymes are secreted by the cells lining the tubules of the digestive gland. These enzymes enter the stomach and there hydrolyze the food particles. The products of digestion then enter the digestive tubules where they are absorbed by the cells lining the walls of the tubules. In general, the same cells appear to perform absorptive and secretory functions in different stages of their life cycle. In some animals the cell dies after liberating digestive enzymes and is replaced by new cells formed by mitosis. In other cases, the secretory cells may go through regular secretory cycles and secrete enzymes many times over during their lifetime. In animals which feed periodically the liberation of secretion is coordinated, probably through nervous mechanisms, with the entrance of food into the stomach.

Cephalopoda

In neither gastropods nor pelecypods is there evidence that the intestine has important digestive or absorptive functions. It serves, as far as we know, largely to form the material rejected by the stomach into feces and pass these to the anus. In cephalopods both the feeding and digestive processes are greatly elaborated by comparison with the other groups of mollusks. Cephalopods (octopus, squid) are all predators feeding on relatively large and active animals. The octopus, for example, feeds on crabs and other small animals which it captures by pouncing from a hiding place under rocks and seizing the prey with the long muscular arms lined with rows of suckers. There is a rather complex behavior involved in this feeding process which has served as a basis for a detailed analysis of brain function in these animals.

In squid, and probably in the octopus as well, prey is rapidly brought to the mouth, which is armed with a horny beak very similar to that of a bird, as well as with a radula. The prey is killed by poison glands, and the tissues are quickly and neatly removed from the shell or other coating and passed into the stomach with the aid of the radula and a lubricating saliva from the buccal glands. The stomach communicates with a blind sac or caecum which receives the secretion of two large digestive glands, the pancreas and the liver. The pancreatic secretion passes from the caecum into the stomach and digestion begins there. The caecum is separated from the stomach by a special spiral valve which permits the partly fluid material from the stomach to enter the caecum slowly. Here it meets the secretion of the liver which is kept separate from the pancreatic juice by the spiral valve. The digested material is absorbed from the caecum and also from the intestine. Undigested material is passed into the intestine from the stomach, bypassing the caecum. The food remains in the stomach for about 2 hours and in the caecum for about 4 hours. We do not have much information about the enzymatic composition of the pancreatic or hepatic secretions of cephalopods, but we would suspect that, as is the case in vertebrates, these secretions differ in enzymatic composition.

We have discussed the mollusks at some length because this phylum is the only one in which we have a complete sequence from the primitive condition of intracellular digestion to the relatively complex and advanced situation in the cephalopods, where digestion is entirely extracellular and the digestive glands have no absorptive but only secretory functions. In virtually all of the higher animals digestion is extracellular, though the feeding mechanisms vary greatly. The zoologist will find much of interest in comparing the uses to which the basic morphological equipment of each phylum is put in utilizing various types of food materials, but a detailed discussion of this topic here would not be justified in terms of the physiological principles which might emerge.

Vertebrata

Rather, we shall confine ourselves to a discussion of the vertebrate digestive system, which is very well known and which offers interesting contrast with the mollusks and other groups. The basic feeding mechanism of the vertebrates is a pair of apposed movable jaws. These are used in a variety of ways to capture and hold food material and to reduce the size of the food particles. In many cases a muscular tongue aids in the latter process and in moving the food from the buccal cavity into the esophagus. The latter is simply a conduction pathway in most vertebrates but contains a storage diverticulum or crop in the birds. This modification of the esophagus is encountered in many other groups of animals. We noted it in some gastropod mollusks; it is well known to most students of zoology in the earthworm and appears in some insects, to mention a few instances only.

The Stomach

The esophagus leads to the stomach which is exclusively a vertebrate feature in spite of the existence, in most of the invertebrates, of structures called stomachs. The unique features of the vertebrate stomach are in its digestive secretions rather than in its shape or position. Gland cells in the wall of the stomach secrete hydrochloric acid at a relatively high concentration, approaching $0.1M$ in some cases, and in addition secrete a unique enzyme, pepsin. Pepsin is a peptidase or pro-

teolytic enzyme with the unusual property of pH optimum near pH 1. This is in contrast with most other peptidases and indeed most other enzymes, which have their maximum activity within the pH range of 5 to 9.

Over the past half century a very large number of studies of the pH-activity relationship have been made for a great many digestive enzymes for a large number of animals, but the significant results obtained have been meager. From the point of view of the enzymologist many of the observations are relatively meaningless because the enzyme preparations used were nearly always mixtures of enzymes in very low concentrations and in very impure state. From the point of view of the physiologist, the only striking facts are that the vertebrate pattern—a highly acidic gastric secretion containing an enzyme with an acidic pH optimum, followed by a mildly alkaline set of intestinal secretions containing enzymes with pH optima near neutrality—is unique, and that the minor variations in pH of other digestive secretions and of pH optima of other digestive enzymes are of no obvious physiological significance.

The significance of the stomach seems to be first that it serves as a storage site from which partly digested food can be released into the intestines slowly. In this function, the hydrochloric acid serves to preserve the food during storage, to aid in its liquefaction by physical and chemical action, and possibly, in those animals which ingest living prey, to help kill the prey. The second role of the stomach is mechanical. The walls are provided with a typical musculature, a layer of circular and a layer of longitudinal muscles, but these are especially well developed in the stomach, and vigorous contractions following feeding, combined with the effects of HCl and of pepsin, are important in reducing the food, often taken in as large particles, to a semifluid suspension. The third gastric function is digestive. Pepsin, in acid solution, hydrolyzes specific peptide linkages and hence breaks the protein molecules of the food into smaller fragments. Specifically, pepsin acts to hydrolyze the peptide bond between an aromatic amino acid, such as tyrosine or phenylalanine, and a dicarboxylic amino acid, such as glutamic or aspartic acid, provided the second carboxyl group of the dicarboxylic acid is free and there is no free amino group near the aromatic amino acid. There are other proteolytic enzymes of this same specificity, but none of them has the distinctive pH optimum. The low pH optimum means, in effect, that pepsin will act only when it is positively charged and when the substrate is also positively charged. It should be clear that the product formed by pepsin action will depend on the location in the protein molecule of the specific peptide bonds on which pepsin can act; hence the common statement that pepsin action forms "proteoses and peptones" is meaningless.

The regulation of gastric secretion has been extensively studied in mammals. The primary normal regulation is nervous. Stimuli ranging from the sight and smell of food to apparently irrelevant stimuli which have come to be associated with food through the process of conditioning will initiate secretion of gastric juice. The effects of these stimuli are augmented by the action of food in the stomach, through mechanical and chemical effects, in further stimulating secretion. There is considerable evidence for the view that these direct effects, and possibly the nervous effects as well, are mediated by one or more hormones formed in the stomach wall, which in turn stimulate the gland cells to secrete. There may be two such hormones acting respectively on the secretion of HCl and of pepsin.

Two modifications of the stomach are well known and of some interest here. In the birds the proximal half of the stomach is modified to form a gizzard with heavy muscular walls and a tough inner lining. This structure is filled with stones ingested by the bird and serves to grind the food into small particles before it is passed into the pyloric portion of the stomach for digestion. The other modification is seen in the ruminant animals where the large stomach is divided into four portions. The food is received into the large paunch or rumen which supports a vigorous population of microorganisms. These help to digest cellulose and other components of the food. At intervals the solid portions are returned to the mouth for chewing (the cud), after the more fluid portion has been pressed out in the reticulum and passed on to the omasum. In the omasum the water is partly absorbed and the remaining material enters the abomasum, where the usual digestion is carried out. The cud is returned to the rumen for further bacterial action. Roughly 10 to 15% of the cellulose and protein in the food is digested by the microorganisms which, as we noted earlier, also contribute vitamins to the nutrition of their hosts. They contribute amino acids and fatty acids as well, synthesizing the amino acids from precursors such as NH_3 so that ruminants can, with the aid of their symbionts, use nonprotein nitrogen as a nitrogen source.

Intestinal Digestion

During gastric digestion, the food and gastric juice are held in the stomach by the pyloric sphincter or valve, a ring of circular muscle marking the boundary between stomach and intestine. When the stomach contents reach a semi-fluid state this valve begins to open as each peristaltic wave reaches it, and the stomach contents are thus periodically ejected into the intestine. Here they meet first the secretions of pancreas and liver, entering through the common bile duct in most vertebrates. The liver is another vertebrate feature; it does not secrete digestive enzymes but only a concentrated solution called bile whose function we will note later. The pancreas, on the other hand, secretes a complete set of digestive enzymes in a solution rendered mildly alkaline by $NaHCO_3$. The pancreatic enzymes include two peptidases, trypsin and chymotrypsin, as well as amylase and lipase. The peptidases are secreted in inactive form as trypsinogen and chymotrypsinogen and are activated by an intestinal enzyme, enterokinase, or by active trypsin once this has been formed. In the active state trypsin acts on peptide bonds in which dibasic amino acids, such as arginine or lysine, contribute the CO group, while chymotrypsin acts on peptide bonds in which aromatic amino acids, such as tyrosine and phenylalanine, contribute the CO group. Both enzymes operate in mildly alkaline solutions (pH 7–9), and the result of their action is similar to that of pepsin. They split protein molecules into fragments by hydrolyzing specific peptide bonds. Each of the three endopeptidases acts on a different kind of peptide bond; hence the effects of their actions are the reduction of the protein molecule to successively smaller units (Figure 9.8).

The limited specificity of the endopeptidases means that there will be relatively large units of the protein molecule which will not be attacked by any of these three enzymes. These remnants are acted upon by the exopeptidases, which are of two types. One type, known as carboxypeptidase, acts upon the terminal peptide bond in which the terminal amino acid has a free carboxyl group. The other type, known as an aminopeptidase, acts on the terminal peptide bond when the terminal amino acid has a free amino group. These two types of peptidases will then attack any polypeptide chain at opposite ends and hydrolyze the peptide bonds in succession to yield individual amino acids. In addition there are dipeptidases, which act on dipeptides to yield individual amino acids. The exopeptidases and dipeptidases, with enterokinase, amylase, disaccharases, and lipase, are found in the intestinal secretion which is formed in the cells lining the simple tubular glands in the walls of the upper portion of the small intestine.

Control of the pancreatic secretion is entirely humoral and involves the hormone secretin, the first hormone to be demonstrated experimentally. In 1902 Bayliss and Starling showed that the pancreas of the dog deprived of its nerves would still secrete when gastric juice or acid was introduced into the duodenum and that an acid extract of the duodenum injected into the blood stream would cause pancreatic secretion when there was no connection between the pancreas and intestine, other than the blood stream. They called the effective agent in their ex-

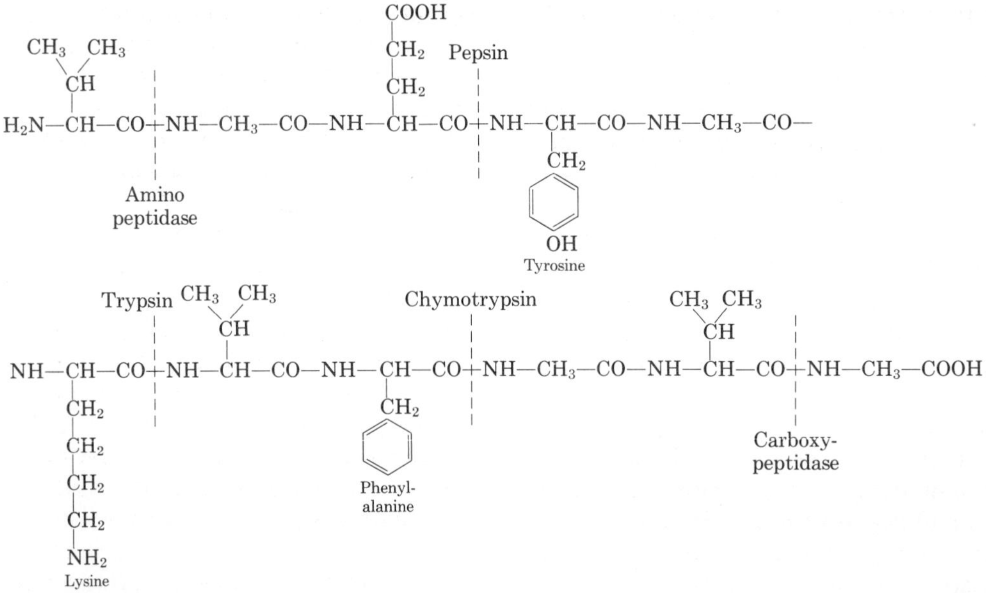

$$CH_3 \quad CH_3 \qquad\qquad\qquad\qquad COOH$$

Pepsin

$$CH \qquad\qquad\qquad\qquad\qquad CH_2$$

$$CH_2$$

$$H_2N-CH-CO \!+\! NH-CH_3-CO-NH-CH-CO \!+\! NH-CH-CO-NH-CH_3-CO-$$

$$CH_2$$

Amino peptidase

OH

Tyrosine

Trypsin $\quad CH_3 \quad CH_3$ $\qquad$ Chymotrypsin $\qquad\qquad CH_3 \quad CH_3$

$$CH \qquad\qquad\qquad\qquad\qquad\qquad\qquad CH$$

$$NH-CH-CO \!+\! NH-CH-CO-NH-CH-CO \!+\! NH-CH_3-CO-NH-CH-CO \!+\! NH-CH_3-COOH$$

$$CH_2 \qquad\qquad\qquad\qquad\qquad CH_2$$

$$CH_2 \qquad\qquad\qquad\qquad\qquad\qquad\qquad\qquad\qquad\qquad Carboxy\text{-}peptidase$$

$$CH_2$$

$$CH_2$$

Phenyl-alanine

$$NH_2$$

Lysine

Fig. 9.8 Points of action of peptidases on a hypothetical polypeptide. The names of the amino acid residues essential to the specificity of the enzyme are indicated (phenylalanine and tyrosine are interchangeable, as are arginine and lysine).

tracts secretin. It has since been established that at least three hormones are formed in the intestinal wall when the acidic gastric juice or chyme (mixture of partly digested food and digestive secretion) enters the intestine. Secretin itself elicits secretion by the pancreatic cells of a watery fluid containing $NaHCO_3$; pancreozymin elicits secretion of enzymes by the pancreatic cells, and cholecystokinin causes the gall bladder to contract, liberating bile into the intestine.

The role of bile in digestion is primarily a physical one. The bile acids (cholic acid for example) are products of metabolism of cholesterol and other steroids. They have the property of stabilizing emulsions of oils or fats in water. When they are thoroughly mixed with the chyme they help to form emulsions in which the fat droplets are reduced to colloidal dimensions.

In this condition the fat is more readily accessible to the water-soluble lipases and is also more readily absorbed without prior digestion.

Absorption

Absorption takes place by active processes in the distal portion of the small intestine. The process is facilitated by various devices which increase the absorptive surface, usually in the form of folds or villous protuberances in the intestinal wall. The mechanism of absorption is not fully understood, but it seems to be basically similar to the process by which all cells absorb organic materials selectively and actively. For sugars and amino acids this appears to involve a combination of the material to be absorbed with specific carriers in the cell membrane. For glucose phosphorylation of the sugar itself is not involved. The absorption of fats, in mammals at least, occurs in part without previous hydrolysis. The emulsified fat droplets are taken in directly, perhaps by pinocytosis, and passed into the tissue spaces whence they travel by the lymphatic system and ultimately enter the blood. The monosaccharides and amino acids, and probably those fats which are absorbed as fatty acid and glycerol after hydrolysis, enter the intestinal blood capillaries. The large intestine in most vertebrates is primarily a region of feces formation. In the mammals it has acquired the function of reabsorbing water, a part of the regulatory mechanisms to be discussed later.

Concluding Remarks

In a discussion of the comparative significance of the vertebrate digestive system, Professor Vonk has suggested that the general trend of evolution as regards digestive mechanism is away from the pool of enzymes, in which all the digestive enzymes work together in a single cavity, and toward a chain of enzymes, in which the successive stages of digestion are separated in space and time. The evidence for or against such a concept remains tenuous. In the mollusks the highest forms, the cephalopods, exhibit a two-stage digestive process, in the stomach first and later in the caecum, with a separate digestive fluid for each process. Until we know something about the enzymes in these two secretions we cannot say whether this arrangement constitutes a chain of enzymes. In a few vertebrates, including man, the two-stage digestive process, in stomach and intestine, has an earlier stage initiated by an amylase, secreted in the saliva, which continues to act in the stomach until its action is terminated by HCl. This is relatively rare and does not contribute greatly to the effectiveness of digestion. Likewise, in the vertebrates, pancreatic enzymes in part are responsible for stages in digestion distinct from and preliminary to those carried out by the enzymes of the intestine proper. There is then, in some degree, a chain of enzymes here. The most efficient digestive systems, in terms of rate of digestion in relation to mass of tissue involved, are probably those of certain insects, where digestion occurs in a short and simple midgut into which is poured a mixture of enzymes with no separation of processes in space or time. One therefore wonders whether the chain mechanism, even where it exists, is necessarily better than the pool arrangement.

For the future of the comparative physiology of nutrition and digestion, we would like to know much more than we now know about the adaptive and evolutionary aspects of digestion in relation to the mode of life of the animals. The whole complex of the feeding and digestive mechanisms is bound up with the type of food available and utilized by the animal, on the one hand, and with its metabolic needs on the other. We need to know much more about the quantitative capabilities of digestive tracts and feeding mechanisms as a basis for understanding the ecological roles of animals as consumers of plant and animal material on one hand, and producers of animal material on the other. In this regard, quantitative measures of the efficiency of digestion and of the efficiency of food utilization as developed especially by agricultural scientists would be of special interest. Quantities commonly used are:

$$\text{Digestive efficiency} = \frac{\text{Total organic intake—organic loss in feces}}{\text{Total intake}}$$

$$\text{Growth efficiency} = \frac{\text{Total organic matter assimilated}}{\text{Total intake}}$$

$$\text{Net growth efficiency} = \frac{\text{Total organic matter assimilated}}{\text{Total intake—maintenance energy}}$$

If these quantities can be measured in relation to specific ecological situations, they will offer a fruitful field for collaboration of physiologists and ecologists. The comparative physiologist will, moreover, find many fascinating problems in analyzing the physiological basis of such differences as may be found.

References

Nutritive requirements

Elvehjem, C. A. 1946. Biological significance of vitamins. *Curr. Biochem. Res.* 79–88.

Green, J., Diplock, A. T., Bunyan, J., Edwin, E. E., and McHale, D. 1961. Ubiquinone (coenzyme Q) and the function of vitamin E. *Nature* **190** 318–325.

Harris, L. J. 1953. The history of vitamins. *Biochem. Physiol. Nutr.* **1** 17–38.

Johnson, A. W. and A. Todd. 1956. Vitamin B$_{12}$. *Endeavour* **15** 29–33.

Kidder, G. W. 1953. The nutrition of invertebrate animals. *Biochem. Physiol. Nutr.* **2** 162–196.

Lardy, H. A., and Peanasky, R. 1953. Metabolic functions of biotin. *Physiol. Rev.* **33** 560–565.

Lusk, G. 1928. *The Elements of the Science of Nutrition.* 4th edn. Saunders, Philadelphia.

Morton, R. A. 1960. Vitamin A and metabolism. *Vitamins and Hormones* **18** 543–569.

Novelli, G. D. 1953. Metabolic functions of pantothenic acid. *Physiol. Rev.* **33** 525–543.

Reed, L. J. 1953. Metabolic functions of thiamin and lipoic acid. *Physiol. Rev.* **33** 544–559.

Sebrell, W. H. Jr., and Harris, R. S. 1954. *The Vitamins* (3 vols.). Academic Press, New York.

Snell, E. E. 1953. Summary of known functions of nicotinic acid, riboflavin, and vitamin B$_6$. *Physiol. Rev.* **33** 509–524.

Terroine, T. 1960. Physiology and biochemistry of biotin. *Vitamins and Hormones* **18** 1–42.

Williams, R. J. P. 1953. Metal ions in biological systems. *Biol. Rev.* **28** 381–415.

Feeding and Digestion

Babkin, B. P. 1950. *Secretory Mechanism of the Digestive Glands* (2nd edn.) Hoeber, New York.

Barker-Jørgensen, C. 1955. Quantitative aspects of filter-feeding in invertebrates. *Biol. Rev.* **30** 391–454.

Cuthbertson, D. P. (ed.) 1950. Microbial digestion in the alimentary tract. *Adv. Science* **6** 345–350.

Frazer, A. C. 1951. Le systéme d'absorption des graisses. *Bull. Soc. Chim. Biol.* **33** 961–967.

Fruton, J. S. 1946. Enzymic hydrolysis and synthesis of peptide bonds. *Curr. Biochem. Res.* 123–135.

Grossman, M. I. 1958. The physiology of secretin. *Vitamins and Hormones* **16** 179–203.

Holter, H. 1959. Pinocytosis. *Int. Rev. Cytol.* **8** 481–504.

Lindley, H. 1954. The mechanism of action of hydrolytic enzymes. *Adv. Enzymol.* **15** 271–299.

Morton, J. E. 1960. The functions of the gut in ciliary feeders. *Biol. Rev.* **35** 92–140.

Neurath, H. 1952. Some considerations of the chemical structure and biological activity of chymotrypsin. *Mod. Trends Physiol. Biochem.* 453–470.

Smith, E. L. 1951. The specificity of certain peptidases. *Adv. Enzymol.* **12** 191–257.

Vonk, H. J. 1937. The specificity and collaboration of digestive enzymes in metazoa. *Biol. Rev.* **12** 245–284.

Yonge, C. M. 1928. Feeding mechanisms in the invertebrates. *Biol. Rev.* **3** 21–76.

Yonge, C. M. 1937. Evolution and adaptation in the digestive system of the metazoa. *Biol. Rev.* **12** 87–115.

10 Transport: body fluids and respiration

The problem of transport arises with differentiation. As the parts of an organism become specialized in function, they develop needs which must be supplied by materials originating elsewhere in the organism, and they form products which must be transported to other parts of the organism. In the simplest situations, diffusion will be an adequate transport mechanism. As a material is used by a specialized structure, its local concentration will decrease, and the rate of diffusion into the specialized region will increase accordingly. If protein synthesis, for example, is localized in special cell structures, there will rapidly develop a stationary state in which the rate of diffusion of any amino acid into the region of protein synthesis will be equal to the rate of incorporation of that amino acid into the protein. In any

population of organisms which feed by absorbing organic matter from solution, however, those which can absorb the most food in the shortest time will have an evolutionary advantage.

When diffusion is the only transport mechanism the major determinants of diffusion rate are, as we have seen, the area of the surface across which diffusion occurs, the diffusion gradient across that surface, and the specific property of the surface which we call the diffusion or permeability coefficient. In competition for food, then, that organism with the largest surface area and the largest permeability coefficient, in relation to its metabolic rate or need for food, will have the evolutionary advantage. The metabolic rate will be, other things being equal, a function of body weight or volume; the exact nature of the relation will be discussed later. Since the volume increases with the cube of a linear dimension, and the surface area increases with the square of a linear dimension, it is easily seen that, of two organisms with the same shape, the smaller will have the advantage. The same principles will apply if we consider need for oxygen or need for removing end products of metabolism, such as CO_2 and NH_3.

There may well be some competitive advantage to increased size as well, and the animal that can solve its transport problem will then avail itself of this advantage. Variations in shape or in permeability may offer some possibilities, but they are very limited by comparison with the development of an active process, in which some of the energy of metabolism is used to increase the transport rate manyfold by comparison with the diffusion rate. In nutrition the active processes include the development of specific mechanisms for absorption of food substances such as carbohydrate or amino acid from solution and the whole range of feeding mechanisms. Development of feeding mechanisms in turn raises the problem of transporting the greatly increased food supply from the region of absorption to the other cells or parts of the body which do not participate in the absorption process. Likewise the greatly increased metabolic rate made possible by an increased food supply sets new problems in transporting oxygen to and carbon dioxide and ammonia away from the cells which use the food for a variety of functions.

In this chapter we shall be concerned with the transport mechanisms as they are seen in the highly differentiated multicellular animals. These mechanisms generally involve (1) a respiratory system which in one way or another facilitates the exchange of O_2 and CO_2 across the body wall, and (2) a circulatory system which facilitates the transport of materials within the body. These two systems may be clearly separable in the higher vertebrates, but their activities are so closely interrelated and the mechanisms involved are so diverse in the various animal groups that we shall consider them here as a functional unit, the transport system.

In general the transport system of multicellular animals consists of (1) the fluid (air or water) in immediate contact with the body; (2) the contents of the digestive system; (3) the areas of contact and exchange between these and (4) a set of internal fluids which intervene between the exchange areas and the cells of the body; and (5) various devices which move the fluids in relation to the parts of the body and to each other. We have somewhat arbitrarily excluded the excretory fluid or urine and the exchange area between this and the internal fluids from this scheme because we wish to consider these later as a part of the regulatory systems.

Body Fluids

We may look first at the internal fluids (4 above). They comprise all the aqueous fluids which are external to the body cells, and inside the boundaries of the body. Operationally they represent that fluid volume in which moderately large molecules, such as the polysaccharide inulin or the disaccharide sucrose, are readily distributed. This volume is approximately the same as the volume in which ions such as SCN^-, Br^-, Cl^-, or SO_4^{2-} are distributed, although these ions may penetrate cells to some extent or be eliminated by the excretory system during the period of measurement. The ideal technique for measurement of extracellular fluid volume is to infuse a substance such as inulin or sucrose into the body at a rate such that its concentration remains constant for a period of time. The amount of substance in the body (amount administered minus amount excreted) divided by its concentration in a sample of body fluid will then give the volume of fluid in which the material has become distributed. This method has thus far been applied only to mammals. An alternative method is to give a single injection of the test substance and then determine its concentration at intervals. By extrapolation of the curve to zero time the maximum concentration value can be determined and the volume calculated as before.

The results of such measurements give values of 10 to 40% of body volume for the extracellular fluid volume for those higher animals (mammals, birds, fishes, insects) studied; some mollusks fall outside this range with volumes as high as 80% in large marine slugs. In man the value is exceptionally high in the late fetal stage (60%), falling to about 35% at birth and still further to about 15% in young adults, with some increase toward old age. Values for other mammals and for the chicken are similar to those for man, while fishes have lower values in the range of 10 to 15%. In insects extracellular volumes are 15 to 40% in the few species studied, and in mollusks the range is from 10 to 80%. For mammals and fishes these values are to be compared with a total body-water content of 60 to 80%; the low values may be eliminated if the fat-free weight is used, when the range becomes 70 to 80% of the fat-free body weight.

Fluid Compartments

The extracellular fluid can be divided into several compartments in most species. Classically, this division has been anatomical, based on the structures in which the fluid is found and on the types of cells found in the fluid. Thus in man we distinguish blood, which contains erythrocytes and is found in the vessels of the circulatory system; lymph, which has no erythrocytes and is found in special lymphatic vessels; and a number of special fluids in the cavities of the central nervous system (cerebrospinal fluid), the eye (aqueous humor) and the joints (synovial fluid), for example. To some extent these anatomical distinctions correspond with operational physiological distinctions. Thus it is possible to measure a "blood volume" which corresponds to the anatomical definition of blood by injecting into the blood stream erythrocytes labeled with an appropriate radioisotope or proteins labeled with a dye (T-1824) or an isotope such as I^{131}, and then determining the volume of distribution of these materials. The plasma volume (fluid volume not including erythrocyte volume) determined in this way ranges from 3 to 6% of body weight for a considerable number of species of mammals and birds and falls most often between 4 and 5%, which is the range in man. Values for elasmobranchs are similar, but in the painted turtle (*Pseudemys*) and the frog (*Rana catesbeiana, Rana pipiens*) the values are higher (7 to 8%), while in the few fishes for which a value is available it is low (2 to 3%).

In the vertebrates the anatomical lymph cannot be distinguished by physiological methods from the rest of the extracellular fluid, outside the blood system. In many invertebrates, no distinction can be made between the blood and the extracellular fluid. These are the animals with an open circulatory system in which, as we shall see, the blood or hemolymph bathes the tissue cells directly or communicates with them across a permeable membrane. Other invertebrates, such as the annelid worms, have a distinct blood system, but the volume has not been measured accurately. For convenience, we shall use the word "blood" in a broad sense to include all fluid which moves for a part of its course through a definite system of vessels, and we shall use the term "tissue fluid" to describe all other types of fluids which come into direct contact with the general tissue cells of the body. We thus avoid the term hemolymph and recognize that in some species blood and tissue fluid are synonymous while in others they constitute separate fluid compartments. We shall not discuss here the special fluid compartments of the vertebrate central nervous system or eye, since these are small in volume and highly specialized in function.

Functions

The body fluids serve four major functions. The first of these is the subject of this section, namely, transport. The second, which we shall discuss in more detail later, is a part of the regulatory mechanisms of the body; the body fluids serve as a medium of more or less uniform composition in which cells can carry out their activities. This aspect of body fluid function was first noted by Claude Bernard, who spoke of the body fluids as a *milieu intérieur* or internal environment. The third function, often little

noticed, is a skeletal one of helping to give form to the body structure and providing an incompressible mass on which muscles can act. This function is especially evident in certain aquatic invertebrates and will be discussed briefly later. The fourth function is a part of the mechanisms for protection of the body against microbial infections. It is most evident in the higher vertebrates and will not be discussed here.

Gas Exchange

As a starting place for the examination of the transport function we may first examine the mechanisms for transport of the respiratory gases, O_2 and CO_2, and begin with the exchange areas between the body and the external medium. Primitively, the whole body surface served for this exchange, and the exchange involved only diffusion between the cytoplasm of the body cells and the external aqueous medium. The major changes which have occurred in evolution are (1) development of devices for moving the external medium with respect to the body, thus providing an increased diffusion gradient at the surface; (2) development of an internal fluid medium which comes into close contact with the external medium across a thin cellular membrane; (3) specialization of localized areas of the body surface with restriction of gas exchange to these areas; (4) ventilation of these areas as in (1) above; (5) development of modified exchange areas of various sorts suited to gas exchange in air.

To some extent, the first adaptation is seen in the habit of locomotion in protozoans and other microorganisms. If diffusion alone is involved in gas exchange in a stationary organism, the diffusion gradient will extend beyond the cell membrane or other body limit and may become rather small, if metabolic activity is high. Constant movement of the organism or movement of a current of fluid past the organism will insure constant renewal of the fluid at the body surface and hence a maximum concentration gradient across that surface. This is the basic principle of respiratory ventilation. Locomotion in microorganisms has adaptive significance in food transport and in gas transport on the basis of this principle.

In many larger organisms—the earthworm is a familiar example—the body surface as a whole may still serve for gas exchange, but internal diffusion rates may be inadequate for transport. The presence of an internal fluid aids in transport, but it may also be of considerable importance in the exchange process by providing internal ventilation of the exchange surface. In the earthworm, for example, there is a continuous flow of blood through the capillaries underlying the epidermis, and the region of diffusion is thus confined to the thickness of tissue between the external medium, which may be air or water in this case, and the blood.

Aquatic Respiration: Gills

The use of the entire body surface for respiratory exchange has numerous disadvantages in the large organism. Ideally, from the standpoint of exchange efficiency, the surface membrane across which diffusion occurs should be as thin as possible and readily permeable to O_2 and CO_2. A thin membrane is, however, very easily damaged, and a membrane permeable to O_2 and CO_2 will also in general be permeable to H_2O. The latter property is not always a disadvantage, but the former is. In consequence, we find in most higher animals that specialized portions of the body surface (gills or lungs) have retained the thin delicate exchange membrane and the vigorous internal circulation, while the remainder of the body surface has become hardened or covered with some sort of protective armor which is impervious to H_2O, O_2, and CO_2 alike. The shells of mollusks and the exoskeletons of arthropods are important and familiar examples, as are the tough skins bearing scales, hair, or feathers in various vertebrates. A specialized exchange area usually has, in aquatic animals especially, a very large surface as a result of a branched, folded, or lamellar structure. Thus, in fishes the gill surface area ranges from 200 to 2000 mm^2/gm of body weight, depending upon the activity of the fish; the higher figure may exceed the external body surface area.

The localization of respiratory exchange to limited portions of the body surface makes ventilation of the exchange area imperative, especially when the gill is enclosed in some sort of protective chamber, as is usually the case. The ventilating devices vary considerably; among mollusks ciliary action is the typical and primitive pattern, and in the pelecypods this ventilation mechanism has been utilized in the feeding process as well. In the cephalopod mollusks, which are both larger and more active than are most members of the phylum, a muscular mechanism utilizing the mantle replaces the ciliary action. These animals, or at least the living forms, have no external shell, and the mantle has acquired a set of muscles which can by their contractions enlarge or contract the mantle cavity. When the cavity is enlarged water flows in around the lower margins of the mantle. These margins are provided with valves, so that outflow by the same route is prevented. When the mantle cavity is constricted the water must then flow out through a small aperture, a siphon. This arrangement insures, first, that the water flows through the mantle cavity in a definite path, rather than in an ebb-and-flow pattern. Second, the discharged water leaves the cavity with some force and hence does not mix with the water which will enter in the next inspiration. Finally, the flow of water from the siphon can be used in locomotion by a jet propulsion technique, as in the rapid swimming of the squid or for such purposes as excavation of a hole under a rock by blowing away the sand, as the octopus often does.

In the higher crustaceans, the gills are either branches of the thoracic appendages or in some cases extend from the body wall near the base of a leg. They are generally enclosed in a chamber formed by part of the carapace, and this chamber is ventilated by a current set up by the small appendage, the epipodite of the maxillule in the ostracods or the scaphognathite of the second maxilla in decapods. Typically in the latter group the water enters along the posterior and ventral regions of the gill chamber and leaves anteriorly after flowing over the gill filaments.

In fishes the gills are associated with a series of openings (gill slits) in the wall of the pharynx, and the ventilation current is produced by the combined action of the mouth, which takes water in and forces it into the gill chamber in a swallowing motion, and of the operculum or gill cover, which

on opening aspirates water through the gills. The result is a continuous flow of water over the gills.

The measurement of the effectiveness of these exchange mechanisms involves two observations: the ventilation rate, or volume of water passed over the gills per unit of time, and the exchange efficiency or per cent of oxygen removed from the water. The exchange efficiency has been measured for many species and generally falls in the range of 30 to 80%. Ventilation rates have been measured only in a few forms. The ventilation rate is the major variable in the control of respiratory exchange, and it is regrettable that so few physiological studies of this quantity are available. The ventilation rate may easily show variations of tenfold to a hundredfold in one individual.

Aerial Respiration

The physiological problem of gaseous exchange in air is quite distinct from that in water. The principal dissimilarities arise from the difference in density of the two media and from the differences in the O_2 concentrations and diffusion coefficients. The specific gravity of dry air at 20°C and 1 atm pressure is 0.0012; that of water is, of course, 1.00 and of sea water about 1.03. At the same temperature, a liter of air contains about 250 mg of oxygen, but a liter of fresh water saturated with air contains only 9.4 mg of oxygen and the liter of sea water only 7.6 mg. Moreover, natural waters are often less than fully saturated with air. Obviously then, air is a better medium of respiratory exchange of oxygen than water. Concentration figures are in some ways deceptive. The effective diffusion force for a gas is not its concentration, as the word is used above, but its partial pressure, and the partial pressure of oxygen in water which is in equilibrium with air is the same as the partial pressure in the air. Thus the diffusion gradient between air and tissue will be the same as that between water saturated with air and tissue. However, the absolute amount of oxygen in a liter of water is less than that in the same quantity of air, and the diffusion coefficient in air is much higher than that in water. Consequently, the water at the exchange surface will more rapidly be exhausted of O_2, and the replacement by diffusion will be slow. Air, with its lower density, will tend to have more convection currents, and if ventilation occurs this will require less expenditure of energy with air than with water.

The primary difficulty in aerial respiration comes from the fact that air is often not saturated with water vapor. Since respiratory exchange surfaces are in general permeable to water there may then be a serious loss of water in aerial respiration. The transition from aqueous to aerial respiration has evidently occurred many times in the course of evolution, and the physiological adaptations involved have been of many kinds. These include the loss of gills (with utilization of the general body surface as in the earthworm), the modification of gills to permit aerial respiration, and the development of new structures specifically adapted to aerial respiration. In general, the first two expedients have not always been successful in that the animals showing this type of adaptation are confined to habitats in which the humidity is always high, can spend only limited periods of time respiring in air, or must confine their activity to times of the day or year when the humidity is high.

We shall not examine these animals here but turn instead to the two major groups in which a successful adaptation to air breathing has appeared, namely, the insects and the vertebrates.

Insects: Tracheal Respiration

In the insects, we see only the end results of the evolutionary process; the intervening stages, whatever they may have been, are lost. The respiratory system, as it appears in present-day insects in its simplest form, consists of a system of branching tubes, the tracheae. The unit of the system begins at an opening on the cuticle of the body surface known as a spiracle. The spiracle is provided with a valve which can be opened or closed by the action of small muscle fibers. Typically there is a pair of spiracles in each body section, one on each side. From the spiracle a cylindrical tube or trachea extends into the body of the insect. The tube is lined internally with a chitinous cuticle continuous with the outer covering of the body of the insect. The trachea branches repeatedly, ending finally in tiny tracheoles which penetrate directly into the body tissues, coming in close contact with the nerve, muscle, and other tissue cells. The terminal portion of the tracheole has no cuticular lining but is walled only by a thin membrane. The tracheole ends blindly, and its terminal region may be filled with liquid; the greater part of the system, however, is gas-filled.

In the smaller insects, this system operates entirely by diffusion. There is a gradient of O_2 and CO_2 between tissues and spiracle which is sufficient to cause a diffusion exchange, even when the spiracles are open only a part of the time. In the larger insects this system no longer suffices for diffusion exchange, and a part of the system is ventilated. Typically, the tracheae are connected by a longitudinal system of tracheal trunks running from one segment to the next. These trunks may also have diverticula or air sacs. Ventilation is accomplished by a coordinated cycle of spiracular opening and closing and muscular body movements. Thus, at the beginning of the cycle, the thoracic tracheae are closed, and the abdominal tracheae are opened. The abdomen is then dilated, drawing air in through the abdominal spiracles. The latter are closed, and the abdomen is constricted, increasing the pressure in the system. Then the thoracic spiracles open, and the air is forced out. Thus the gas in the main trunks is renewed, and some gas is forced into the branching segmental tracheae in each cycle. In a few insects with aquatic larvae the tracheal system has been readapted to respiration in water by the remarkable tracheal gill, in which exchange of gas occurs across a membrane from the water into the air chambers of the tracheal system. The tracheal system is remarkable also in that the ultimate exchange of gases is directly from trachea through tissue fluid to cells, and in that the circulation of the fluid plays little or no part in the gas transport.

Vertebrates: Evolution of
Air Breathing

For the evolution of the vertebrate lung we have a little more evidence. A great many living fishes are capable of aerial respiration, in a few cases for quite extended periods. This adaptation occurs under three kinds of circumstances. In tropical fresh waters, especially in shaded jungle habitats,

the vigorous bacterial action combined with low rates of photosynthesis results in deoxygenation of the water, and the fish come to the surface to gulp air. In many regions of the world, especially in parts of Africa, there are long dry seasons in which bodies of fresh water dry up. The fishes in these regions undergo a period of estivation, living in cavities in the dried mud or in cocoon-like structures and breathing air. Finally, some fishes leave the water for land or even to climb trees in search of food or in migrating from one body of water to another.

The adaptations to these situations are varied. In many cases, the pharynx, or branchial chamber, develops a specialized epithelial lining or special diverticula which function in gas exchange between air and blood. In a few fishes the skin serves for gas exchange; even the stomach or intestine may be used. The most interesting adaptation from the point of view of evolution is the use of the swim bladder in the lung fishes. This structure, which typically serves to regulate specific gravity and hence buoyancy in fishes, has become modified by the development of a very thin epithelial lining, and an increased surface circulation, into a lung. Air is moved into and out of the structure, essentially a blind sac, through a duct which opens into the pharynx, by muscular movements. The mode of gas exchange through this structure has not been determined, but the lung has been shown to be essential for life out of water or in oxygen-free water. These fish, of course, also have gills, and the conditions under which they use aquatic or aerial respiration have been studied for one species, *Erythrinus unitaeniatus*. This fish dwells in South American swamps and its respiratory behavior depends upon both O_2 and CO_2 content of the water. When the O_2 is high (greater than 1.5 cc per liter) and the CO_2 moderate (10–25 cc per liter) the gills are used. A decrease in O_2 or a change in CO_2, above or below the limits stated, leads to mixed respiration or if carried farther to an entirely aerial respiration (Figure 10.1). The factors controlling this behavior have not been analyzed experimentally. The significance of the modern lung fish seems to be that at some stages of vertebrate evolution the ancestors of the amphibians and higher vertebrates made a similar adaptation.

Lungs

In most modern amphibians the gills are present only in larval forms and are lost in the adult. The urodeles and many anurans (e.g., the frog) can live for extended periods under water, but they use the skin with its vigorous blood supply for respiratory exchange

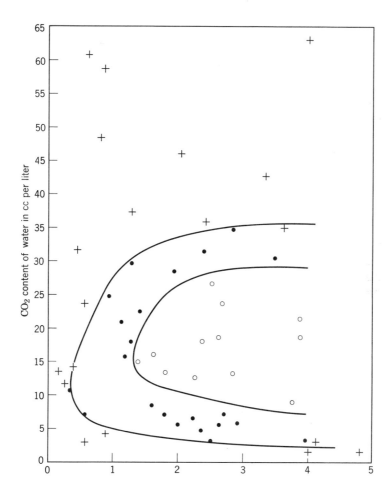

Fig. 10.1 Environmental determinants of respiratory patterns in a tropical fish; ordinate CO_2 content, abscissa O_2 content of the water in cc/l. ○ Aquatic respiration; ● Intermediate respiration; + Aerial respiration. (From E. N. Willmer, 1933, *J. Exp. Biol.* **11** 292.)

in water. In addition, nearly all the amphibians are able to live for extended periods out of the water, and a few have become entirely independent of water. In aerial respiration most of the gas exchange occurs through the lungs, which are considerably more highly developed than those in the lung fishes. The lungs are paired blind sacs, divided up into many simple pouch-like alveoli and lined with a very thin epithelium across which the gas in the alveolus comes into close contact with the vigorous flow of blood through the lung capillaries. This same pattern is characteristic of all of the higher vertebrates—reptiles, birds, and mammals—as regards the lung, but the respiratory function of the skin is entirely lost. The means of ventilating the lungs varies. Two main patterns are seen: a primitive one in which the lungs are filled by a swallowing action in the buccal cavity, and a more advanced one in which the filling action is the result of aspiration from an increase in the volume of the thoracic cavity by movements of ribs, and in mammals of a muscular diaphragm.

The ventilation of the lungs in all the vertebrates is relatively inefficient; that is, only a part of the gas in the lungs is exchanged with each respiration. The classical figure for men is, for a total lung capacity of 6 liters at maximum inspiration, a tidal air (amount exchanged in a normal inspiration-expiration cycle) of 0.5 liter. The maximum exchange is 4.5 liters— a ninefold range—which leaves a residual volume not expelled even after a maximum inspiration followed by a maximum expiration of 1.5 liters. The result of this partial exchange is that the air in the lung always has somewhat less O_2 and considerably more CO_2 than does the outside air. Thus

in men the alveolar air at rest contains CO_2 at a partial pressure of 40 mm Hg and O_2 at 100 mm compared with values of 0.3 and 158 for the inspired air. In the swim bladder of the lung fish, *Lepidosteus,* the gas composition is 3.8% O_2 and 2.4% CO_2 between inspirations and 7.2% O_2 and 1.6% CO_2 immediately after an inspiration. The alveolar air will be closer to the first values.

Birds exhibit an adaptation which probably improves the efficiency of respiratory ventilation. They have, connected with the lungs, relatively large air sacs; the sacs surround the lung and communicate with the trachea by relatively large channels, the bronchi (Figure 10.2). The bronchi are in turn perforated by small openings leading into "air capillaries" which replace the alveoli and where the gas exchange takes place. Krogh originally suggested that there is an oscillatory movement of air through the bronchi, but recent evidence suggests a circulatory movement into the air sacs and thence through the air capillaries back to the bronchi, thus permitting a more or less complete flushing of the air capillaries. The respiratory movements of birds involve primarily the thoracic muscles, which are also used in flying. The latter activity therefore causes a great increase in respiratory ventilation at a time when metabolic activity is also greatly increased.

Gas Transport

In many higher animals, the process of diffusion is limited to the thin membrane, normally two cells thick, separating the water which moves over the gills in the ventilation stream or the air in the alveoli of the lung from the blood, which moves rapidly through the capillaries. We shall consider now the transport of gases in the blood before turning to the problem of the movement of the blood itself.

Transport of Carbon Dioxide

The transport of CO_2 is greatly aided by its solubility in water. This in turn is the result of the hydration reaction in which carbonic acid is formed:

$$H_2O + CO_2 \rightleftharpoons H_2CO_3$$

The hydration reaction is catalyzed by an enzyme, carbonic anhydrase, which is present in gill and lung tissue especially. Carbonic acid in turn dissociates as a weak acid:

$$H_2CO_3 \rightleftharpoons H^+ + HCO_3^-$$

The second dissociation, of bicarbonate to form carbonate, is of little or no importance under physiological conditions. We may write a mass action equation for the equilibrium constant K_1 of the dissociation:

$$K_1 = \frac{[HCO_3^-][H^+]}{[H_2CO_3]}$$

There is no reliable method of estimating the H_2CO_3 or HCO_3^- content of the blood independently of the H^+ concentration, hence we must rely on measurements of total CO_2 content, the pressure of CO_2 in equilibrium with the blood, and the hydrogen ion concentration to evaluate the equilibrium constant. Mass action theory gives us for carbonic acid

$$K_0 = \frac{[H_2CO_3]}{[CO_2]}$$

where $[CO_2]$ is the concentration of free CO_2 in the solution. The free CO_2 is in turn related to the partial pressure of CO_2 by

$$[CO_2] = kP_{CO_2}$$

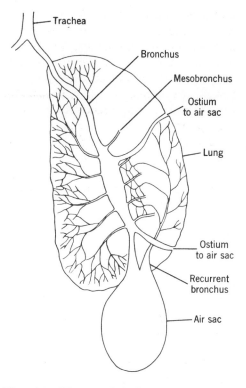

Fig. 10.2 Diagram of the lung and air sacs of a bird. The air capillaries are shown connecting the mesobronchi and leading to the recurrent bronchus. (After Krogh, 1941, *Comparative Physiology of Respiratory Mechanisms,* Univ. Pennsylvania Press, Philadelphia.)

so that we may write that

$$[H_2CO_3] = K_0kP_{CO_2}$$

and

$$K_1 = \frac{[HCO_3^-][H^+]}{K_0kP_{CO_2}}$$

If we call the CO_2 concentration, in all forms $[\Sigma CO_2]$, and if we define an apparent dissociation constant K_1' by

$$K_1' = K_1K_0$$

then

$$[HCO_3^-] = [\Sigma CO_2] - [H_2CO_3] - [CO_3^{2-}]$$

and, if we neglect the $[CO_3^{2-}]$,

$$K_1' = \frac{([\Sigma CO_2] - kP_{CO_2})[H^+]}{kP_{CO_2}}$$

This is the Henderson-Hasselbalch equation, which is more easily used in its logarithmic form because we usually measure hydrogen ion on the pH scale, where

$$pH = -\log_{10}[H^+]$$

so we have

$$pK_1' = pH - \log_{10}\frac{[\Sigma CO_2] - kP_{CO_2}}{kP_{CO_2}}$$

The pH of human blood is normally very close to 7.40. The value of k is 0.0314 mM per liter per mm CO_2 pressure, and the value of pK_1' is 6.10. The student should be able to demonstrate the conditions under which we are justified in neglecting the CO_3^{2-} concentration and to calculate total CO_2 for the pH value given and for pH values higher or lower. It is clear that the CO_2 carrying capacity depends closely upon the pH of the blood, and

we shall later discuss some of the factors maintaining the pH constant. Table 10.1 gives some typical values and ranges for blood pH and CO_2 for various vertebrates. The pK_1' changes in the amount of 0.005 unit per degree C and the k changes 0.0007 mM/liter/mm CO_2/degree C. The student should verify the Henderson-Hasselbalch equation for several cases in Table 10.1. The pH values for the blood of insects are generally lower than those for vertebrate blood, usually falling between 6 and 7; this difference may be connected with the fact that insect blood is not greatly involved in gas transport. Crustacean blood, by contrast, has pH values between 7.4 and 8.4.

As evidence of transport, in contrast to mere presence, the arteriovenous differences in CO_2 content are quite useful, since all the arterial blood has passed through the lungs or gills in a vertebrate. The few available values are tabulated in Table 10.2. It is clear that only a fraction of the CO_2 in the blood is normally exchanged.

TABLE 10.1
Acid-Base Values in Vertebrate Blood

Animal	Temperature, °C	pH	CO_2 mM/l	P_{CO_2} mm Hg	Na$^+$ mM/l	Cl$^-$ mM/l
Man, arterial	37	7.38	27.0	43.1	138	102
venous		7.68	29.5	51.0		
Cat, mixed	38.6	7.35	20.4	36	153	120
Rat, arterial	38.2	7.35	24.0	42	144	104
Chicken, venous	41.7	7.54	23.0	26	154	117
Alligator, mixed	5	7.74	36.1	15		
	26	7,30	23.5	38	154	107
	34	7.43	19.8	29		
Iguana, mixed	26	7.48	24.4	27	157	118
Carp, venous	20	7.39	17.7	22	130	107
Skate, arterial	10.4	7.82	3.5	1.3	254	255

From *Blood and Body Fluids,* Federation of American Societies for Experimental Biology, ed. P. L. Altman & D. S. Pittner, Washington.

TABLE 10.2
Arteriovenous Differences in CO_2 and O_2 Content of Blood

Species	CO_2 Content of Blood (vol. %)		O_2 Content of Blood (vol. %)		O_2 Capacity (vol. %)
	Arterial	Venous	Arterial	Venous	
Man, at rest	48.2	54.8	19.6	12.9	20
Frog (*Rana catesbeiana*)	58.2	70.1	—	—	—
Skate (*Raja ocellata*)	7.7	10.8	93*	32*	5.7
Squid (*Loligo pealii*)	3.82	8.27	4.27	0.37	—
Lobster (*Homarus americanus*)	5.2	6.0	0.44	0.18	3.0†
Rock Lobster (*Panulirus interruptus*)	10.1	10.6	0.82	0.35	1.8‡
King Crab (*Loxorhynchus grandis*)	18.6	18.8	0.41	0.71	—
Spider Crab (*Maja squinado*)	4.9	9.7	—	—	1.75
Sea Water	—	—	—	—	0.5

* Per cent saturation of hemoglobin.
† *H. vulgaris.*
‡ *Palinurus vulgaris.*

Transport of Oxygen: Respiratory Proteins

Oxygen, by contrast with CO_2, is not readily soluble in water and does not enter into a reaction with water. The oxygen capacity of blood (i.e., the amount of O_2 which dissolves in unit volume of blood saturated with air) is considerably greater than that of water in many species, as seen from Table 10.2. The difference results from the presence in the blood of a protein which combines reversibly with oxygen. Such a protein is called a respiratory protein because of its potential role in transporting respiratory oxygen. The respiratory proteins are usually colored and hence are often called respiratory pigments. The most widely distributed of these pigments is called hemoglobin. It is a protein of the class known as globins, with a porphyrin prosthetic group called heme (Chapter 1). The porphyrins and the cytochromes, which also have porphyrin prosthetic groups, are of almost universal occurrence. Hemoglobin is found in many kinds of animals in a distribution which suggests independent evolution in several instances. These facts led Redfield to suggest that hemoglobins evolved from cytochromes by changes in protein structure and mode of linkage of heme to protein. The details of the structure of one of the mammalian hemoglobins have been worked out, and a representation of the general form of the molecule, deduced from X-ray evidence, is given in Figure 1.5.

A somewhat less widespread respiratory protein is known as hemocyanin. This word is derived differently from hemoglobin—which means "blood globin." Hemocyanin means "blood blue," a reference to the fact that, when combined with oxygen, the protein acquires a deep blue color. It is colorless in the deoxygenated state, while hemoglobin is always colored, changing from a purplish to a scarlet hue on oxygenation. Hemocyanin is a copper-containing protein, and the exact structural relation of the copper to the rest of the molecule is still not known. Heme can be separated readily from hemoglobin, but the copper is not readily detached from hemocyanin. When copper is removed from hemocyanin, one SH group is exposed for every four atoms of copper, suggesting that the copper forms a coordination complex with cysteine residues in the protein. When the pigment combines with oxygen half of the copper molecules are oxidized.

Hemocyanins are found in many crustaceans and mollusks but not in any other animal group. The most likely evolutionary precursors of the hemocyanins are the phenol-oxidases. These enzymes contain copper and play a part in oxidative reactions of crustaceans, mollusks, and other animals as well. Whatever the origin, it seems likely that crustacean and molluscan hemocyanins represent separate evolutions, since the protein components are very different in the two cases. The hemocyanins of mollusks have molecular weights ranging from 3×10^6 to 7×10^6 and hence are among the largest of protein molecules. Crustacean hemocyanins have molecular weights in the range of 4×10^5 to 8×10^5. The copper content of hemocyanin from crustaceans is 0.15 to 0.19%. The comparable figure for mollusks is 0.24 to 0.26%. The hemocyanin of the horseshoe crab *Limulus,* generally regarded as a primitive form of arthropod belonging to a rather isolated group, has a weight of 1.3×10^6 and a copper content of 0.17%.

The annelids, which are biochemically a rather remarkable group, exhibit a considerable variety of iron-containing respiratory pigments. If it were not for this group and its near relatives we could confine our discussion to hemoglobin and hemocyanin, but some species of annelids have in their blood a red iron-containing protein called hemerythrin, and others have a green iron-containing protein called chlorocruorin. Hemocyanin has not been observed in the annelids, but hemoglobin occurs in some species.

Chlorocruorin is a heme-containing protein similar to hemoglobin but with a different heme and a different protein. The heme has one of the two vinyl groups on the 4-pyrrol ring oxidized to formol, and the amino acid composition of the protein differs from that of the hemoglobins. Chlorocruorin occurs only in the annelid families Sabellidae and Serpulidae, and in some species of these families it is accompanied by or replaced by hemoglobin. The heme of the tissues of these animals is that of hemoglobin, but the porphyrin of chlorocruorin is found in the tissues of some starfish, which have no respiratory protein.

Hemerythrin contains iron and is red, but the iron is not bound in a porphyrin. The iron content is 0.81% as compared with 0.3 to 0.4% for hemoglobins and 1.3% for chlorocru-orin. The iron is bound in part through SH groups. In this respiratory protein oxygenation involves a change in the valence state of the iron from Fe^{2+} to Fe^{3+}. Oxygenation of hemocyanin also involves a valence change. In the hemoglobins and chlorocruorin the oxygen is loosely bound through coordination bonds which do not involve a valence change in the metal. For this reason we speak of oxygenation of hemoglobin rather than oxidation. It will be recalled that the functioning of the cytochromes involves oxidation.

The nature of the respiratory proteins has been discussed in some detail because these substances illustrate an important principle of comparative physiology: the use of varied means for the same function. In addition to the variation of chemical composition in the respiratory proteins, we find differences in location. The proteins are found in solution, in the blood cells, or in tissue cells. In all cases the function, where one is established, is in the transport or occasionally the storage of oxygen. Moreover, we will find the same properties relative to these functions occurring in each of the major groups of compounds. The distribution of the compounds is summarized in Table 10.3 along with some characteristic properties. It appears from the table that the molecular size of the protein depends upon its location. In general, those proteins which occur in cells have molecular weights below 10^6, while those which occur in blood plasma may have molecular weights which are above this level.

Oxygen-dissociation Curves

If these proteins are to function effectively in the transport of oxygen they must not only combine with this gas but must also liberate it in the tissues. Table 10.2 gives arteriovenous differences in O_2 content of the blood of various species. These data show that a substantial part, but by no means all, of the O_2 which is taken up in the gills or lungs, and hence appears in the arterial blood, is removed from the tissues, leaving a lower O_2 content in the venous blood. Careful comparative studies of these quantities are still rare, and most of our ideas about respiratory gas transport are inferences from studies of the properties of the blood *in vitro* or of purified respiratory pigments. Some of these inferences may in consequence be quite unreliable if we are interested in the physiology of the intact animal.

The classical approach to the study of the properties of the respiratory proteins is the measurement of the oxygen dissociation curve. This measurement takes advantage of the fact that the respiratory proteins in general change color on oxygenation. Thus hemoglobin has its maximum absorption near 560 mμ in the deoxygenated state but at 540 and 560 mμ in the oxygenated state. Values for chlorocruorin are about 600 and 560 mμ respectively. Hemocyanin is colorless in the absence of oxygen and has a diffuse band at 570 mμ when oxygenated. Thus by measuring the absorption of light at a wavelength characteristic of the deoxygenated pigment and the absorption at another wavelength characteristic of the oxygenated pigment, it is possible to calculate the per cent of the total pigment which is in the oxygenated form. This per cent is known as the per cent saturation of the protein with oxygen. The dissociation curve is a representation of the general equilibrium for hemoglobin (Hb), for example,

TABLE 10.3
Chemical Properties and Distribution of Respiratory Proteins

Respiratory Protein	Prosthetic Group	Ratio Metal Atoms per O_2 Molecule	Molecular Weight	Occurrence
Hemoglobin	Protoheme (iron porphyrin)	1:1	7×10^4	Red blood corpuscles of nearly all fishes, all amphibians, reptiles, birds, and mammals
			2×10^4	Red blood corpuscles of cyclostomes
			3×10^4	Blood cells of some holothurians and some polychaetes, tracheal cells of some insects
			3×10^4	Blood cells of echiuroid and phoronid worms, some pelecypods
			4×10^5	Blood plasma of some crustaceans; tissue cells of various mollusks, parasitic roundworms, annelids
Myoglobin	Protoheme (iron porphyrin)	1:1	2×10^4	Muscles of vertebrates and some invertebrates
			3×10^6	Blood plasma of various annelids
			1.5×10^6	Blood plasma of planorbid snails
Chlorocruorin	Chlorocruoheme (iron porphyrin)	1:1	3×10^6	Blood plasma of serpulid and sabellid worms
Hemerythrin	Iron	3:1	7×10^4 1×10^5	Blood corpuscles of sipunculids, a few annelids, and brachiopods
Hemocyanin	Copper	2:1	4×10^5 3×10^5	Blood plasma of crustaceans
			1×10^6	Blood plasma of xiphosuran
			3×10^6 7×10^6	Blood plasma of mollusks

$$O_2 + Hb \rightleftharpoons HbO_2$$

and is constructed by plotting the ratio of HbO_2 to $Hb + HbO_2$ against the partial pressure of oxygen in equilibrium with the blood or the hemoglobin solution.

We may examine first the curve for adult men taken on whole blood at a temperature of 38°C (normal body temperature) and a pH of 7.4 (Figure 10.3). The curve is seen to be sigmoid in shape; one would predict a rectangular hyperbola from strict mass-law relations. The S-shape probably arises largely from lack of homogeneity in the hemoglobin molecules, so that one observes a statistical distribution of oxygen-combining properties. In addition the salts and other proteins of the blood have some action, and the curve for purified hemoglobin is much closer to a rectangular hyperbola. In nearly all cases the curves for whole blood are sigmoid.

To relate this curve to actual conditions during gas transport we shall need to examine the points corresponding to conditions in the alveoli of the lungs and in the tissues. The O_2 pressure in arterial blood is 93 mm Hg, and at this point the hemoglobin is 98% saturated. The O_2 pressure in mixed venous blood, which we may take as comparable to the condition in the tissues at rest, is 39.4 mm Hg, and at this point the hemoglobin is 74% saturated. The hemoglobin content of blood in an adult man is about 160 gm per liter; the iron content of hemoglobin is 0.339%. If one O_2 combines with each iron atom we can calculate the O_2 capacity for saturation of hemoglobin at 21.3 vol. %, close to the observed value.

The student should verify this calculation and also calculate the amount of O_2 transported from lungs to tissues by each liter of blood. The normal output of blood from the heart is 6

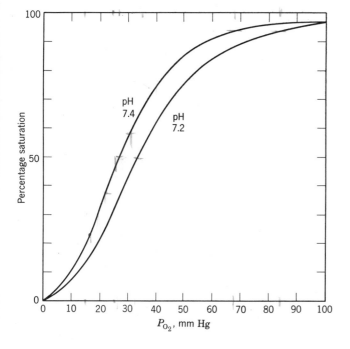

Fig. 10.3 The oxygen-dissociation curve of human blood, and the effect of a decrease in pH from the normal value of 7.4. (From *Blood and Body Fluids,* ed. P. Altman and D. S. Pittner, Fed. Am. Soc. Exp. Biol., Washington.)

liters per minute; the student should calculate the resting O_2 consumption and compare the value with that obtained experimentally, 230 cc O_2 per min. Note that, in the resting condition, the hemoglobin is still 74% saturated. There is, in other words, a considerable reserve of oxygen present even in the venous blood.

Suppose now that as a result of exercise the oxygen pressure in the tissues decreases slightly to about 25 mm Hg. Now the per cent saturation will be only 50%, and now 38% of the oxygen held by hemoglobin will be liberated at each circulation. A further fall in tissue O_2 to 15 mm will bring saturation down to 30% and liberate 78% of the O_2 held at each circulation. The S-shaped curve is now seen to have special significance. Even a small decrease in P_{O_2} will cause a very large increase in amount of O_2 liberated in the tissues in that part of the curve lying below the resting value of the P_{O_2}. In other words, the shape and position of the curve are such that in the resting condition only a small proportion of the combined O_2 is liberated, but a small increase in activity will then produce a relatively large increase in the amount of O_2 liberated from the hemoglobin in the tissues.

It is then of special interest to compare dissociation for various species to learn whether these properties of the curves show the same adaptive relations. To avoid the necessity of drawing curves for each species it has become customary to consider two points as characterizing the curve. The shape of the curves is in general so similar that this will serve for approximate comparisons, though the whole curve is required for accurate study. The points chosen are the P_L or P_{95}, the oxygen pressure (sometimes called tension) at which the blood pigment is

95% saturated, and the P_U or P_{50}, the pressure for 50% saturation. The first is called the pressure of loading (P_L) because it is assumed that this pressure may correspond to that in the lungs or the gills where loading of the pigment occurs. The second is called the pressure of unloading (P_U) for similar reasons. The abbreviations P_{95} and P_{50} are preferred here because we do not wish to beg the question of adaptive significance. One may, as a further simplification and approximation, use only the P_{50} value. The remainder of the curve can then be calculated by using a factor, since the ratio of the per cent saturation at any P_{O_2} for one pigment to the per cent saturation at the same P_{O_2} for another will be approximately constant over the whole curve, if the shapes are the same. Table 10.4 gives P_{50} values for a number of cases which we wish to analyze in more detail. Full curves will also be presented for some of these.

Effect of Carbon Dioxide and Temperature

One factor which must be kept in mind is that the O_2-dissociation curve is influenced by pH—or by P_{CO_2}, which as we have seen is closely related to pH. Thus, in human blood a decrease in pH increases the value of P_{50}, and an increase in pH decreases P_{50} as seen in the figure. This phenomenon is known as the Bohr effect, after its discoverer. The physiological significance at rest is probably small, but in activity it may come to be considerable. Normally, the arteriovenous pH difference at rest in adults is no more than 0.05 pH units ($A = 7.42$, $V = 7.37$). In vigorous muscular activity, however, CO_2 and lactic and pyruvic acids are produced by the muscles and liberated into the blood with the probable re-

TABLE 10.4

P_{50} Values for Respiratory Proteins

Animal	Temperature, °C	pH	P_{CO_2} mm Hg	P_{50} mm Hg
Vertebrates				
Mammals				
Man	37	7.40	44	26.3
Cat	37	7.40		38.0
Dog	37.5	7.40	58	28.0
Horse	37.5	7.40	50	27.0
Mouse	38	—	40	72.0
Porpoise	38	—	46	30.0
Rat (white)	37	—	40	56.0
Birds				
Chicken	40	7.14	37	51.0
Duck	37.5	7.10	—	45.0
Pigeon	37.5	7.10	—	40.0
Reptiles				
Alligator	29.0	7.60	42.0	28.0
Gila monster	20.0	7.40	36.0	32.0
(*Heloderma suspectus*)	20.0	7.32	37.0	31.0
	37.0	7.40	32.0	59.0
Turtle (*Pseudemys elegans*)	25.0	—	27.0	28.0
Amphibians				
Frog (*Rana*	20.0	6.28	—	3.6
catesbeiana)	20.0	7.32	—	4.6
larva	25.4	6.80	—	5.0
	25.4	7.38	—	6.0
adult	20.0	7.40	—	13.5
	25.4	7.38	—	26.0
Newt (*Triturus* sp.)	25.4	7.38	—	7.5
Toad (*Bufo* sp.)	25.4	7.38	—	30.0
Fishes				
Carp (*Cyprinus carpio*)	15.0	—	1–2	5.0
	18.0	—	30.0	13.0
Catfish (*Ictalurus* sp.)	15.0	—	0–1	1.4
Cod (*Gadus* sp.)	14.0	—	0	15.0
Mackerel (*Scomber scombrus*)	20.0	8.0	1.0	17.0
Salmon (*Salmo salar*)	15.0	—	1–2	21.0
(in fresh water)			10.0	35.0
Toadfish (*Opsanus tau*)	20.0	—	1–2	14.0
			10.0	33.0
Brook trout (*Salvelinus*	15.0	—	1–2	17.0
fontinalis)			10.0	42.0
Elasmobranchs				
Dogfish (*Squalus suckleyi*)				
Embryo	25.0	7.53	—	12.7
Adult	25.0	7.53	—	16.8
Ray (*Raja oscillata*)	10.4	7.80	1.0	20.0
	25.0		1.0	45.0
	37.0		1.0	98.0

TABLE 10.4 (*Cont.*)
P_{50} Values for Respiratory Proteins

Animal	Temperature, °C	pH	P_{CO_2} mm Hg	P_{50} mm Hg
Cyclostomes				
Hagfish (*Polistotrema stouti*)	18.0	6.7–9.0	—	3–4
Crustaceans				
Crab (*Cancer* sp.)(HCy)	23.0	—	0	12.0
Ceriodaphnia	17.0	—	0	0.8
Daphnia	17.0	—	0	3.1
Mollusks				
Busycon (HCy)	23.0	—	13.5	6.0
Helix (HCy)	20.0	8.20	—	11.0
Loligo (HCy)	23.0	—	0	36.0
Octopus (HCy)	25.0	—	0.6	3.0
Planorbis	17.0	—	0	1.9
	20.0	—	0	7.0
Annelids and other worms				
Arenicola	17.0	—	0	1.8
Phascolosoma (He)	19.0	—	—	8.0
Sipunculus (He)	19.0	—	0–80	8.0
Spirographis (Cc)	20.0	7.70	—	27.0
Tubifex	17.0	—	0	0.6
Urechis	19.0	—	8.6	12.3

From *Blood and Other Body Fluids,* Fed. Am. Soc. Exp. Biol., Washington. Cc = chlorocruorin, He = Hemerythrin, Hcy = Hemocyanin; blood pigment is hemoglobin unless otherwise noted.

sult that the pH in the muscle capillaries will fall appreciably. To see the effect of this, assume that the P_{O_2} in the muscles is 25 mm Hg, and read from the curve the per cent dissociation at the normal pH of 7.4 and at a pH of 7.2. From the data given earlier, the student can calculate the amount of additional O_2 which would then be transported to the muscles as a result of the Bohr effect.

The Bohr effect is of rather general occurrence but varies quantitatively from one species to another. Among fishes, for example, those with very small Bohr effects (*Ameiurus* the catfish, *Cyprinus* the carp) also have low P_{50} values. Those with large Bohr effects (*Prionotus,* the sea robin, *Scom-*

ber, the mackerel, and the salmonids) also have high P_{50} values. The salmonids and mackerel are active dwellers in well-aerated waters, while the catfish and carp are sluggish dwellers in poorly aerated waters, where the CO_2 content of the water may well be as high as that of the blood. An extreme case is that of the large gastropod mollusk, *Busycon canaliculatum* (the whelk), which has a negative Bohr effect and a very low P_{50} in the presence of CO_2 (Figure 10.4). This animal has hemocyanin as its respiratory protein, and it may be compared for example with the squid, *Loligo,* which has a relatively high P_{50}, greatly increased by CO_2. The curve of the active pelagic squid resembles that of an active fish

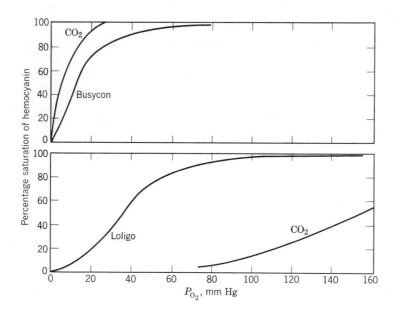

Fig. 10.4 The oxygen-dissociation curves of the bloods of two mollusks, and the effects of CO_2. The curves marked CO_2 were determined in the presence of P_{CO_2} of about 13 mm Hg. (From Redfield et al., 1926, *J. Biol. Chem.* **69** 475.)

such as the trout, in spite of the difference in the respiratory protein. The whelk, by contrast, is a sluggish animal which lives in mud on the sea bottom where P_{O_2} will often be low and P_{CO_2} relatively high. One may suppose that in general the absence of a Bohr effect— or the rare negative Bohr effect—serves to prevent the inactivation of the transport system which would occur at high P_{CO_2} values in blood with a large Bohr effect. In an active fish or a squid high P_{CO_2} would lower the P_{95} so that the blood could take on relatively little O_2 in the gills. Air-breathing animals in general have a large positive Bohr effect. They do not encounter high P_{CO_2} values although there is always some CO_2 in the lungs.

Temperature also has a marked effect on the O_2-dissociation curve. In mammals and birds, with constant body temperature, this is not important

physiologically. However, in the heterothermic animals whose body temperature varies with that of the environment a marked change in temperature may seriously impair the function of the respiratory protein, since the O_2 affinity is decreased by an increase in temperature, while the metabolic rate and hence the need for oxygen is increased by increase in temperature. Since the increases in P_{50} and P_{95} are roughly proportional, and P_{50} is less than P_{95} the effect of increasing temperature in absolute terms of the amount of O_2 transported is quite considerable. In a few fishes living in polar waters, where the temperature is always near $0°C$, the blood contains no hemoglobin at all. The solubility of O_2 in blood at these low temperatures is sufficient to permit adequate O_2 transport to support metabolism— which is at about the same levels as seen in other fish in warmer waters.

The comparison which we noted earlier between the squid and the trout suggests that the O_2-dissociation curves may not be related specifically either to the nature of the pigment or to its occurrence in or outside of cells, and this is entirely true. We can find examples for each of the major pigment types of high, medium, and low O_2 affinities and of large and small Bohr effects. Similar variations can be found for hemoglobin in cells and hemoglobin free in solution in the plasma. In fact, experimentally, it may in some cases make little difference in the O_2-dissociation curve of vertebrate blood if the blood is hemolyzed so that the hemoglobin escapes from the erythrocytes. In other cases, the properties of blood are altered by hemolysis.

Embryonic Respiratory Pigments

The most obvious factors correlated with the properties of the respiratory protein are the environment and the activity of the animal. This in turn means that the respiratory proteins must have undergone, in each species, an evolutionary adaptation to the habits and habitat of the species. This adaptation is seen, perhaps in its most striking form, in embryonic development. The hemoglobin of the embryo of the spiny dogfish, *Squalus suckleyi,* has a P_{50} of 12.7 mm Hg, while the adult value is 16.8. These elasmobranchs are viviparous, hence the higher O_2 affinity of the embryonic hemoglobin is probably of adaptive significance in O_2 transfer from mother to embryo. The P_{50} of the hemoglobin of the bullfrog tadpole is 6.0 compared with the value of 26.0 for the adult at the same temperature and P_{CO_2}. The

tadpole lives an aquatic life of low activity, often in relatively poorly aerated waters. The adult spends part of its time on land, breathing with the aid of lungs. The hemoglobin of the chick embryo, soon after the blood first appears, has a P_{50} of 11 in solution. By the time of hatching the value has risen to 17, and the rise continues to reach adult values of about 50 as the size and activity of the bird increases.

In mammals, where the embryo depends upon the maternal blood for its O_2 supply, there must be a special relation between the O_2-combining properties of the fetal and maternal blood. In the goat the fetal blood has a P_{50} of about 18 mm Hg at 60 to 120 days as compared with 30 for the adult. At a P_{O_2} of 30, where the maternal blood is 50% saturated, the fetal blood is 82% saturated so that a substantial transfer of O_2 can occur from the maternal to the fetal blood, even if the former is not fully saturated. At birth, the P_{50} of goat blood has risen only slightly, but it changes rapidly after birth, reaching adult levels in about two weeks. This change involves a complete replacement of a fetal type hemoglobin by the adult type; the two are distinctly different proteins.

The adaptations of the properties of the respiratory proteins which have been discovered this far are entirely of an evolutionary type. There is no known instance where exposure to altered conditions produces any change in the properties of the respiratory proteins during the lifetime of the organism. The change from fetal to adult hemoglobins is undoubtedly genetically rather than environmentally determined, though it is possible that hormonal factors initiate the change. There are, however, quantitative changes in hemoglobin content in response to environmental influences. Several aquatic arthropods which have hemoglobin in the blood show a marked increase in the amount after a period of exposure to water lacking O_2. Men who move from low to high altitudes develop an increased hemoglobin content in the blood after a period of exposure to the lower oxygen pressure at altitude. The factors which control these responses are not fully known.

Transport of Oxygen: Direct Measurements

In the foregoing paragraphs we have been drawing inferences from the properties of proteins, studied outside the body, about the physiological processes occurring inside the body. To what extent are these inferences justified? For hemoglobin we have a simple means of testing the inferences. Hemoglobin and other iron-containing proteins combine with carbon monoxide in the same way as they do with oxygen, but the affinity for CO is much greater than for O_2. The result is that in the presence of relatively low CO concentrations this gas entirely replaces O_2 in the blood protein and hence blocks O_2 transport by these proteins completely. When the higher vertebrates are exposed to CO the effect is almost immediate death. Clearly, mammals and birds cannot survive without the O_2 carried by hemoglobin. By contrast, the goldfish is reported to survive at all normally tolerated temperatures and with normal activity in the presence of CO sufficient to block O_2 transport. This observation requires further verification.

Among the invertebrates, the CO technique has been applied only to a few annelid worms and aquatic insect larva. Carbon monoxide has no effect on the oxygen consumption of the earthworm *Lumbricus* below a P_{O_2} of about 10 mm Hg. At a P_{O_2} of 35 mm as much as 40% of the oxygen consumption depends on the hemoglobin. The proportion declines again to 20% at 150 mm. The P_{50} for *Lumbricus* blood at 20°C is 8 mm Hg. Hemoglobin is more important in the free-living polychaet *Nereis diversicolor;* CO blocks 50% of O_2 consumption at about 20 mm Hg and all O_2 consumption below 10 mm Hg. *Nereis* consumes oxygen about ten times as rapidly as does *Lumbricus,* but we have no information about O_2 dissociation curves for *Nereis.* The tube-dwelling worm, *Sabella pavonina,* has chlorocruorin as a respiratory pigment; roughly 30% of the oxygen consumption is eliminated by CO in water saturated with air, and the proportion remains the same at the lowest P_{O_2} levels measured, about 30 mm Hg, which is the P_{50} level for the pigment.

In many annelids and arthropods, especially those living in conditions where the O_2 supply may at times fall to quite low levels, the P_{50} is exceedingly low, at about 0.6 mm Hg. It has been questioned whether a protein with such properties can function in oxygen transport, and these properties suggest that the protein may serve only in emergencies, when tissue P_{O_2} may fall essentially to zero. Studies with CO show that at P_{O_2} values above 25 mm, hemoglobins of the worm *Tubifex* and the insect larva *Chironomus plumosus* account for a constant amount (not proportion) of the oxygen consumed. At lower P_{O_2} values, CO inhibits a progressively smaller proportion of the oxygen consumption. Study of the absorption spectrum of the blood in the animal shows that the P_{50} is probably nearer 10 mm than 1 mm Hg. The reason for this disparity in values is not clear, but a CO_2 effect might be involved. Another suggested function for respiratory proteins with low P_{50} values is that they serve as an oxygen store. Calculations for various species show that the O_2 combined with the protein will last the animal 3 to 60 minutes. In some cases, this might aid in survival as when a burrow is temporarily blocked or exposed at low tide.

When it is not possible—as with hemocyanin—to use CO as an inhibitor it is necessary to use physiological criteria of the effectiveness of the protein in respiratory transport. We carried out a computation of this sort for man at the beginning of this section, but this has been done for very few other animals. In the squid, *Loligo,* about 90% of the O_2 of the blood is removed by the tissues (Table 10.2), and the blood can be seen to change from colorless to blue as it passes through the gills. The P_{95} and P_{50} values (Figure 10.4) are at a level consistent with functional activity of the hemocyanin, and there is a marked Bohr effect which would reinforce that activity.

In crustaceans, there has been uncertainty as to the role of hemocyanin, since the blood taken from the pericardium, and corresponding to arterial blood, is usually colorless, suggesting that the hemocyanin is not oxygenated. Redmond has studied the problem in three large crustaceans; the lobster, *Homarus americanus,* the rock lobster, *Panulirus interruptus,* and the king crab, *Loxorhynchus grandis. P_{50}* values for lobster and king crab are 27 mm, and for rock lobster, 14 mm, at 25°. The oxygen capacities are low, amounting to 1 to 2 vol. % and the blood taken from the pericardium contains less than half of its maximum O_2 capacity and only

about the same amount of O_2 as the surrounding sea water. The hemocyanin of arterial blood is only 50 to 70% saturated with O_2, hence the pale color. However, the venous blood is 30% saturated, and computations based on these values show that 90 to 97% of the O_2 in the blood is in fact combined with hemocyanin. The P_{O_2} of arterial blood is only 7 mm when that of the surrounding sea water is 100 mm. This means, then, that these crustaceans operate on the lower half of the O_2-dissociation curve rather than the upper half as with most animals. The tissues can apparently operate at very low P_{O_2} values, a fact which permits the development of a very high diffusion gradient for oxygen across the gills. The system will operate quite well under normal conditions but might be expected to break down during vigorous activity and increased O_2 demand. The results of this study point up the caution that we gave at the beginning: the pressure of loading for a large decapod crustacean is not P_{95} but P_{50}, and the pressure of unloading is about P_{20}.

There is a minor but important relation between the transport of O_2 and that of CO_2 in mammals, and probably in other forms as well. Hemoglobin, like all proteins, combines with hydrogen ions as a weak acid.

$$HHb \rightleftharpoons Hb + H^+$$

Oxyhemoglobin is a somewhat stronger acid than deoxygenated hemoglobin. Hence, when hemoglobin is oxygenated in the lungs, some H^+ is given off, with the result that HCO_3^- is converted to CO_2. In the tissues the reverse change occurs. The result is that the blood can carry somewhat more CO_2 as a result of this change in acid dissociation. The same phenomenon occurs in crustaceans and mollusks, with hemocyanin as the respiratory protein. In addition, some CO_2 may combine directly with hemoglobin or hemocyanin to form a carbamino compound. The importance of the latter in transport is questionable.

Gas Transport: Summary

We have given considerable attention to the problem of gas transport because the subject permits some interesting comparative generalizations. In conclusion, these will be summarized briefly. The respiratory proteins vary considerably in chemical nature and especially in the nature of the prosthetic group. Outside the annelids there are two major types, known as hemoglobin and hemocyanin. The hemoglobins differ considerably in the protein portion but have the same protoheme prosthetic group. The hemocyanins likewise differ in protein but have in common copper as an essential part of the O_2-transporting mechanism. Evidence from distribution of the substances suggests that each has evolved independently in several different groups of animals. This view is consistent with the occurrence among annelids of two other proteins, chlorocruorin and hemerythrin, which appear to have arisen independently in this phylum alone. Proteins may occur in solution in the plasma or in blood cells or in other tissues. In some animals there may be two kinds of protein in different locations. Myoglobin, a variant of the hemoglobin type, may occur in the muscles or nervous system of animals having hemocyanin in the blood plasma, but hemocyanin is found only in the blood plasma and never in cells or tissues.

In spite of the diversity in chemical structure the properties of the proteins in combining with oxygen are related to the habitat and habits of the animal, rather than to the type of protein. Hemocyanins and hemoglobins alike exhibit a wide range of oxygen affinities, and these are generally correlated with the activity of the animal and the levels of oxygen content encountered in the environment. Sluggish animals and those living in environments in which low O_2 levels occur generally have respiratory proteins of high O_2 affinity. Active animals and those living in surroundings of high O_2 content have respiratory proteins with low O_2 affinity and a marked effect of CO_2 on the O_2 affinity. These properties must, of course, ultimately be related to differences in protein structure. The conclusions, as to function, which are drawn from the properties of the proteins studied *in vitro* are not reliable unless verified by careful physiological study *in vivo*. This has been done only in a few cases.

References

Barcroft, J. 1928. *The Respiratory Function of the Blood.* Univ. Press, Cambridge, England.

Florkin, M. 1948. La biologie des hématino-proteids oxygènables. *Experientia* 4 176–191.

Fox, H. M. 1949. Blood pigments. *Endeavour* 8 43–47.

Gilding, H. P. 1951. The physiology of the capillaries. *Adv. Sci.* 81 194–203.

Goor, H. van. 1949. Carbonic anhydrase, its properties, distribution, and significance for carbon dioxide transport. *Enzymologia* 13 73–164.

Haldane, J. S. 1922. *Respiration.* Yale Univ. Press, New Haven, Conn.

Jones, F. R. H., and Marshall, N. B. 1953. The structure and function of the teleostean swim bladder. *Biol. Rev.* 28 16–83.

Krogh, A. 1916. *Respiratory Exchange of Animals and Man.* Longmans, Green, London.

Krogh, A. 1941. *Comparative Physiology of Respiratory Mechanisms.* Univ. Pennsylvania Press, Philadelphia.

Pappenheimer, J. R. 1953. Passage of molecules through capillary walls. *Physiol. Rev.* **33** 387–423.

Redfield, A. C. 1934. The hemocyanins. *Biol. Rev.* **9** 175–212.

Rossier, P. H., Buhlmann, A. A., and Weisinger, K. 1960. *Respiration.* (P. C. Luchsinger and K. M. Moser, ed. & transl.) Mosby, St. Louis, Mo.

Roughton, F. J. W. 1935. Recent work on carbon dioxide transport by the blood. *Physiol. Rev.* **15** 241–296.

11 Transport: circulation of body fluids

We now turn to the mechanisms by which the body fluids are moved from one part of the body to another in the transport of gases and other substances. The study of this aspect of transport mechanisms is one of the oldest branches of physiology, going back to the demonstration by William Harvey that the blood of the vertebrates moves in a path which, ideally, may be regarded as circular. Harvey made very effective use of the comparative method in his studies, examining the hearts of heterothermic animals, where the rate of beating is relatively slow, to verify some of his concepts.

More recent comparative studies have shown that there are two basic patterns of circulation. In the familiar vertebrate pattern a specialized fluid, the blood, circulates through a system of vessels which is closed, in the sense that the blood flows at all times in a system of tubes of relatively small diameter. In many invertebrates, on the other hand, blood flows through a system of vessels in no more than a part of its circular path; in a part of the path the blood flows out into extensive tissue spaces. Such a system is called an open system. There may be two types of open systems. In one the tissue spaces, called sinuses, are lined by a cellular membrane which keeps the blood separated from the tissue cells. In the other type the blood spaces, called lacunae, are not lined by a cellular membrane, and the blood bathes the tissues directly. Both sinuses and lacunae may exist in the same system. In either closed or open systems the blood must be moved through the body, where it will encounter frictional resistance. The continuous movement will then require the exertion of a force. This force, in all circulatory systems with the exception of those of certain echinoderms, is provided by muscular contraction. In the simplest and probably the most primitive case, as seen in some annelid forms, the muscular force is exerted by a peristaltic wave. This basic pattern persists to some degree in the most highly specialized hearts in the sense that the "beat" of the heart is a propagated wave of muscular contraction. Insect hearts, particularly in larval forms, exhibit this peristaltic character quite clearly.

The peristaltic wave will give direction to flow by its direction of propagation, but there will generally be some back flow. In most circulatory systems the back flow is prevented by the appearance, at one or more points in the system, of competent valves. There are, however, notably in the ascidians, circulatory systems in which reversal of the direction of the flow is a regular feature. The heart, as we see it in higher forms, may be regarded as a concentration of muscle tissue in one limited portion of the circulatory system. This tissue by its contraction provides the motive force and is associated with valves restricting the flow to one direction only. In the following pages we shall describe structure and function in several types of circulatory systems as representative of the major groups of animals. These will to some extent be generalizations.

Annelids

The annelid type of system consists of several longitudinal vessels, with lateral connectives. Typically there is a large dorsal vessel, a subintestinal vessel, and a neural vessel. Each of these has lateral branches in each segment running to the skin or parapodia or both, and there is a pair of direct connectives between one of the ventral vessels and the dorsal vessel in each segment. The general pattern of flow is anterior in the dorsal, and posterior in the ventral vessels. Most of the vessels are contractile, and peristalsis is the motive force. The lateral segmental vessels lead to a network of anastomosing small vessels, and the dorsal vessel terminates anteriorly in a plexus of small vessels in the brain. There are also networks of vessels in the intestinal wall and the ventral ganglia of the nervous system. The arrangement in oligochaetes such as the familiar earthworm, where several of the anterior segmental connectives have developed into hearts with valves, is exceptional. The annelid system is generally closed and exists in parallel with a large coelom filled with tissue fluid. The small vessels of the circulatory system are functionally capillaries, but structurally they differ from vertebrate capillaries in having a more complex wall. From morphology one would deduce that the coelomic fluid, which is confined segmentally by the septa between segments, would have some part in exchanges between blood and tissues, but physiological evidence for such a role is lacking. Moreover, we have no information on the dynamics of blood flow in the annelid system.

The extreme form of the open circulatory system is seen in worms such as the sipunculids and echiuroids, which are clearly related to annelids but have lost the intersegmental septa and the vessels of the circulatory system. Here, blood and tissue fluid are indistinguishable, and there is no regular flow of either. Instead, the body fluid is continually mixed by the movements of the body wall in burrowing or pumping water through the burrow. The large volume of body fluid free in the body cavity serves an important function as the "hydrostatic skeleton." Localized muscular contractions act against the incompressible fluid to cause changes in body shape, which are very effective in burrowing. The same function is performed, perhaps less effectively, by the coelomic fluid in annelids. The origin of open circulatory systems, inherently less efficient in transport than closed systems, may well result in some cases from the need in certain situations for a hydrostatic skeleton.

Mollusks

The molluscan type of circulatory system is quite different from that of the annelids in two respects; it is more or less open, and there is a single distinct systemic heart (Figure 11.1). The coelom has become reduced to a small pericardial space surrounding the heart. The heart consists of a muscular ventricle with one or more afferent vessels, the number being related to the number of gills. These afferent vessels are often called atria, but their contractile function is not certainly established. The blood enters the heart through vessels leading from the gill to the atria. Each atrium is separated from the ventricle by a valve. If there are two atria they open typically into a single ventricle. The ventricle is, in turn, a muscular chamber connected with an aorta which generally extends toward the cerebral ganglia. The beat of the heart produces a unidirectional flow of blood from gill vessels to aorta. The aorta branches in patterns which vary in the different groups, but in the amphineurans and gastropods these branches ultimately end by opening into the sinuses or tissue spaces. In pelecypods these sinuses are confined to the foot and in cephalopods to a small region around the intestine, and most of the course of the blood flow is vascular. In the cephalopods the blood is separate from the extracellular fluid, the respective volumes being about 6 and 28% of the body weight. In the amphineurans and the gastropods the large foot operates with the aid of the hydrostatic

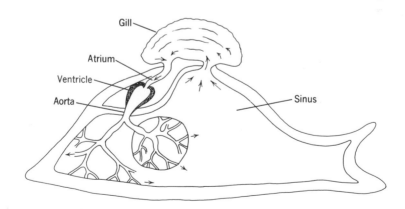

Fig. 11.1 Molluscan circulatory system. Simple type with single systemic heart and extensive sinuses, as in the slug, *Aplysia*. (From Winterstein, *Handbuch vergl. Physiol.*)

skeleton provided by the blood in the pedal sinuses. The blood is collected from the sinuses by vessels leading to the gills, is diffused there through a plexus of small vessels, and collected again in the vessels leading to the atria. In pelecypods and cephalopods the flow of the gills may be aided by small accessory gill hearts.

Dynamics

In the dynamics of blood flow, the basic principle is expressed in Poiseuille's law for streamlined flow:

$$V = \left(\frac{\pi r^4}{8L\eta}\right)P$$

V is the velocity of flow (ml per sec) of a fluid of viscosity η through a cylindrical vessel of radius r and length L when impelled by a pressure difference P. The quantity in parentheses can be called the resistance to flow.

In mollusks we have little information about circulatory dynamics, but blood pressures have been measured in a few cases. The values are, with the exception of cephalopods, quite low, of the order 1 to 10 mm Hg. More important, in the very few cases where pressures have been measured in the heart and in other parts of the system (sinuses) in the same animal, the differences are quite small and quite variable. In particular, body movements can readily produce a tenfold increase in pressure in the sinuses, putting this well above the pressure in the heart. These studies have been made only for the large marine slug *Aplysia* and for the freshwater mussel *Anodonta*, and further study is needed. One gets the impression that the circulation in some resting mollusks is quite sluggish, while body activity might result in vigorous surges of blood through the system. The role of the heart would then be limited, in the less active animals, to (a) providing a sluggish flow at rest and (b) serving as a valve to prevent back flow during activity, when the real motive power would come from the body muscles. This impression is, however, based on too limited evidence to be reliable.

In the cephalopod mollusks, by contrast, we have evidence of a more vigorous role for the heart. The course of the circulation in these remarkable animals is shown in the diagram (Figure 11.2) along with blood pressures as measured in resting unanesthetized animals. The systemic heart consists of a single muscular ventricle, which, by its contraction, forces blood into the thick-walled aorta. There are two sets of valves in the ventricle. One is a pair that prevents back flow of blood from ventricle to efferent branchial vessels, and there is a single valve that prevents back flow from aorta to ventricle. As in all circulatory systems, the pressure in the aorta undergoes a regular rhythmic oscillation as the heart alternately contracts and ejects blood into the vessel, and relaxes. The minimum point in this oscillation is called the systolic pressure, and in the resting octopus this amounts to 30 to 50 mm Hg. The minimum point is known as the diastolic pressure. The difference between the two is the pulse pressure. The pulse pressure in the octopus is 15 mm Hg.

From the aorta, branching arteries lead to capillary beds and sinuses in various parts of the body. The blood is collected in veins from these regions and returned to the cephalic or anterior vena cava. This vessel branches into lateral venae cavae which pass through the kidneys to a pair of branchial hearts, each again consisting of a single

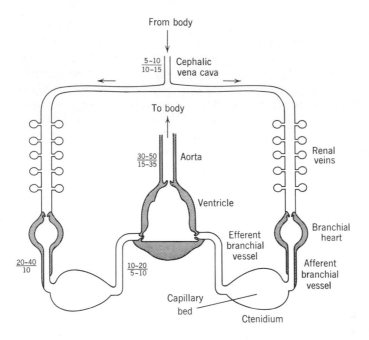

From body

$\frac{5-10}{10-15}$ Cephalic vena cava

To body

$\frac{30-50}{15-35}$ Aorta

Renal veins

Ventricle

Efferent branchial vessel

Branchial heart

$\frac{20-40}{10}$

$\frac{10-20}{5-10}$

Afferent branchial vessel

Capillary bed

Ctenidium

Fig. 11.2 A diagram of the central portion of the circulatory system of *Octopus*. The numbers are the approximate ranges of the systolic/diastolic pressures in mm Hg. (After Johansen and Martin, 1962, *Comp. Biochem. Physiol.* **5** 161.)

muscular ventricle. The systolic pressure in the cephalic vena cava is 5 to 10 mm Hg. The loss in pressure is doubtless the result of frictional resistance in the small vessels of the systemic circulation. The actual loss is probably greater than the pressure figures show, however, since the contractions of the mantle musculature in respiration cause rhythmic increases in pressure in all the vessels and since part of this appears in the venous pressure. There is a pulse pressure of 3 to 5 mm Hg in the vena cava.

The contraction of the branchial hearts, which have a single valve each between the vena cava and the ventricle, forces blood into the ctenidia or gills with a pressure nearly equal to that produced by the systemic heart (20 to 40 mm Hg). Roughly half of this pressure is lost in overcoming the resistance of the gill capillaries, so that the blood in the efferent branchial vessels leading to the systemic heart flows under a reasonable pressure head. The portions of the efferent branchial vessels near the heart have been regarded as atria, but these structures appear to exert no contractile force and hence should probably be regarded merely as large blood vessels. This observation raises questions about the functional significance of the atria in other mollusks.

When the octopus becomes active in walking or swimming there is an immediate marked increase in the arterial pressure, amounting in moderate exercise to 50%. The pulse pressure also increases somewhat, as does the heart rate. The increase in pressure might be attributed to constriction of peripheral blood vessels. Examination of

Poiseuille's equation will show that decreased diameter without change in rate of flow will result in increased resistance to flow and hence increased pressure. Alternatively the increased pressure could result from an increased blood flow. If the body movements force blood from veins and sinuses into the vena cava and thence to the hearts there will be an increased output from the hearts. This relation has been demonstrated experimentally in the hearts of mammals, but not in the octopus. Increased flow of blood stretches the heart muscle. Stretched muscles contract more vigorously than unstretched, and as a result the extra blood that flows in at each diastole is ejected in each systole. The fact that in the octopus the pressure change appears immediately on the beginning of exercise suggests vasoconstriction as the initial cause. There is a later further increase in pressure which may be due to increased cardiac output. Measurements of the latter quantity have not been made.

Arthropods

The arthropods have an open circulatory system which differs in a number of respects from that of mollusks (Figure 11.3). One can imagine the arthropod heart to be derived from the contractile dorsal vessel of annelids—though there is no proof that it is in fact so derived—by concentration of the contractile portion of the dorsal vessel into a small proportion of the whole length, and elimination of much of the rest of the annelid vascular system. The blood flowing anteriorly from the dorsal heart in the arthropods flows out of the arteries into sinuses or lacunae, the large annelid coelom and its fluid having disappeared. The blood re-

turns to the heart through a pericardial space and enters the heart through parallel openings or ostia, which might represent the openings into the dorsal vessel of the annelid lateral connectives.

Structure

Whatever the merits of this hypothetical evolutionary relation, the facts are these. The arthropod heart is dorsal, typically tubular in form with paired lateral openings through which blood flows from the pericardial space into the cavity of the heart itself. Blood is forced from the heart into arteries which in turn drain into lacunae or sinuses. From the sinuses the blood is returned through vessels to the pericardial space; in crustaceans, it passes through the gills *en route*. The ostia are provided with valves, and there is typically a valve between the heart and the aorta or other arteries. Valves may also occur in the venous portion of the system between sinuses and pericardial space. The heart is unique in being suspended in the pericardial space by ligaments and in some cases by muscles (alary muscles) as well. The contraction of the heart forces blood into the arteries and stretches the suspensory ligaments. When the heart muscle relaxes the elastic rebound of the ligaments, and in some cases contraction of the alary muscles as well, restores the heart to its original volume. The result is an active aspiration of blood from the pericardial cavity into the heart; in all other animals, flow of blood into the heart depends entirely on the venous pressure, which must therefore be higher than the pressure in the relaxed heart. In arthropods the pressure in the pericardial space may be the lowest in the system.

Dynamics

For a consideration of the dynamics of arthropod circulation we may use the lobster *Homarus americanus,* which has been studied in some detail. The general pattern of the circulatory system is shown in the diagram (Figure 11.3) with values of the blood pressure indicated. The principal motive force in this system, judging from pressure relationships, is the contraction of the heart. The pulse pressure in the heart itself is considerably greater than that in the large arteries leaving the heart, since the diastolic pressure does not fall as low in these vessels. Flow from ventral sinus to pericardial space through the gills is brought about by a pressure difference resulting in part from the aspirating effect of the heart contraction. The arterial system in the decapods is extensive and supplies arterial blood to all the major regions of the body. The ends of the arteries open into sinuses which ultimately lead to the large ventral sinus in the thorax

and thence through vessels to the gills. There is an accessory heart, the cor frontale, which consists of an enlargement of the anterior aorta in the region near the stomach. Small specialized skeletal muscles insert on the walls of the artery and presumably exert some pumping action by rhythmic movements. The significance of the organ has not been studied experimentally, but it is presumably connected with the blood supply to the cephalic ganglia.

The cardiac output of several crustaceans including the lobster has been estimated at roughly 5 to 8% of the body weight per minute. This figure is comparable to values for vertebrates, but the blood volume of the crustaceans is about 20% of the body weight, while that of the vertebrates ranges from 2 to 8%. On the other hand the total extracellular fluid volume in the vertebrate is not greatly different from that of the lobster. The two systems thus differ quantitatively. In the vertebrate a portion of the extracellular fluid is

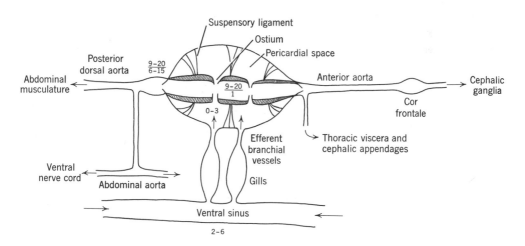

Fig. 11.3 A diagram of the central portion of the circulatory system of a lobster or crayfish, with approximate values of ranges of systolic/diastolic pressures for *Homarus americanus* in mm Hg.

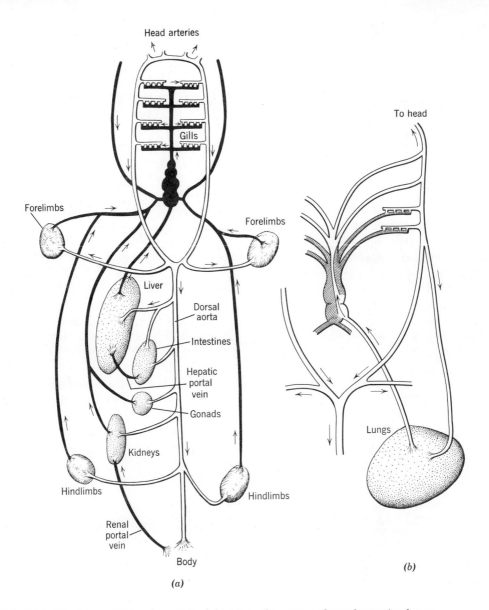

Fig. 11.4 Diagrams of the course of blood flow in various types of vertebrate circulatory systems. (*a*) Fish, (*b*) Modifications of flow in a lungfish, (*c*) Amphibian, (*d*) Mammal. (From Scheer, 1948, *Comparative Physiology,* Wiley, New York.)

circulated rapidly in vessels, while the remainder moves much more slowly in tissues and exchanges with the circulating portion by diffusion. In the crustaceans the whole of the extracellular fluid is circulated, with exchange by mixing in large sinuses.

The circulatory system of insects is in principle similar to that of crustaceans, but with one important physiological distinction. In insects there are no gills, hence no gill circulation, and the blood has little or no respiratory function. The blood returns from

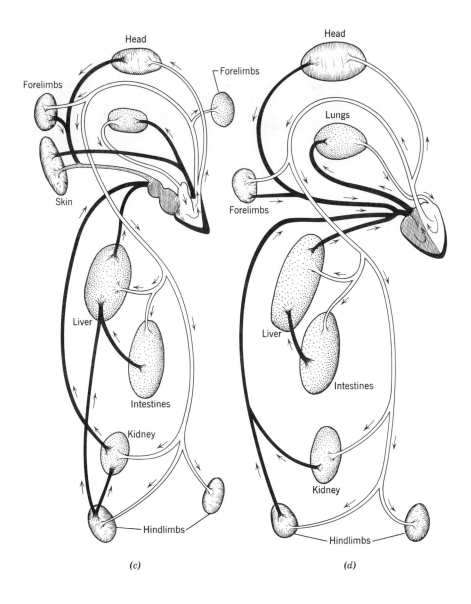

Head
Forelimbs
Forelimbs
Skin
Liver
Intestines
Kidney
Hindlimbs

Head
Lungs
Forelimbs
Liver
Intestines
Kidney
Hindlimbs

(c)

(d)

the sinuses directly to the pericardial chamber. The detailed morphology of the circulatory system varies considerably in different groups of insects and in the various stages of the life history. In particular, there may be accessory hearts pumping blood into the limbs of the larger adult insects, and the systemic heart varies in length and number of ostia. The dynamics of circulation have been little investigated in the insects, partly because of the technical problems associated with the small size of these animals.

Vertebrates

The circulatory system of the vertebrates (Figure 11.4) stands in sharp contrast to that of the arthropods in several respects, most of which are related to the fact that the vertebrate system is closed, with the entire course of the blood flow confined to vessels of relatively small diameter. Circulatory dynamics of the mammals are very well known after more than three centuries of scientific study. We know less about the lower vertebrates. The vertebrate circulatory system is of great interest from a comparative viewpoint in that we can trace, in the existing major classes, the probable stages of evolutionary development within the phylum. This has been done in great detail with respect to morphology, and we shall assume familiarity with the comparative anatomy of the circulatory system. We do not have as much information on physiology, but we can trace some developments.

Structure

The typical circulatory pattern of the primitive vertebrate as seen in modern cyclostomes, elasmobranchs, and fishes is distinctly different from that of mollusks and arthropods in that the output of the heart passes through the gills before, not after, it has passed through the tissues. Several important consequences follow. First, the heart itself contains deoxygenated blood and hence requires an external blood supply. Coronary arteries which meet this need are present in most vertebrates. Second, the blood flow through the gills is considerably more vigorous than it is in mollusks or arthropods with the possible exception of those species having accessory gill hearts. Third, a considerable proportion of the work of the heart is expended in forcing the blood through the gills, leaving a smaller proportion of total force for propulsion through the tissues than is the case in the invertebrates. The overall course of the flow is diagrammed

in Figure 11.4. A further significant aspect of the pattern is the existence of portal systems in both liver and kidney; thus blood from the intestines and the trunk muscles passes wholly or in part through one or the other of these regulatory organs before returning to the general circulation. The physiological significance of the renal portal system is not clear, but the importance of the hepatic portal system is considerable and will be discussed in connection with metabolism.

The heart of the fish shows, more clearly than that of the higher vertebrates, its presumed relation to a tube. Typically the heart consists of four chambers arranged in series and somewhat twisted on themselves. Blood from the tissues enters a sinus venosus. It passes through a sinu-atrial valve to the atrium, a relatively thin-walled but large chamber. Thence, it is propelled through atrioventricular valves to the ventricle, with heavier walls and a smaller lumen. Vigorous ventricular contraction forces the blood into the bulbus (or conus) arteriosus through a third set of valves. In elasmobranchs and Dipnoi there are several sets of valves in the conus. Available evidence, though limited, suggests that the valves are competent to prevent back flow of blood. The heart receives an external blood supply to the myocardium (muscle tissue) through coronary arteries, arising from the arteries and the dorsal aorta in most cases.

Cardiac Function

The chambers normally contract in the same sequence noted above for blood flow. The beat begins in the sinus venosus and progresses in turn through atrium, ventricle, and bulbus arteriosus. The peripheral vessels are apparently not contractile, except that in the cyclostomes the gill vessels contract and there are accessory hearts in the portal, cardinal, and caudal portions of the venous system. The initiation and coordination of the heart beat was a subject of controversy for many years and led to extensive comparative investigations. In many and probably all vertebrates we are now convinced that the beat arises in the muscle tissue or myocardium, itself, and is in no way dependent on nervous tissue. The most convincing evidence for this view originally was that the embryonic heart begins to pulsate long before any nervous tissue invades the heart. The search for evidence concerning the origin of heart beats led A. J. Carlson to make his classic observations on the heart of the xiphosuran arthropod, *Limulus polyphemus* (horseshoe crab). The heart of this animal, like most arthropod hearts, has on its dorsal surface a ganglionic mass of nerve cells. Carlson was able to remove this ganglion and show that while the denervated heart muscle retains its excitability the spontaneous rhythmic contractions cease. The heart beat in this animal is therefore termed neurogenic, since it originates in the nervous tissue. Curiously enough, the heart of the *Limulus* embryo begins to beat before it is innervated. The vertebrate heart beat and the embryonic *Limulus* heart beat are termed myogenic, since they originate in the muscle tissue. The vertebrate heart has no ganglionic tissue, only postganglionic fibers. Comparisons of the responses of hearts to drugs show that the beat of the vertebrate heart is slowed by acetylcholine, while those arthropod hearts which are clearly neurogenic are accelerated by this drug. Acetylcholine is consequently used as a standard test for myogenic and neurogenic beats. Table 11.1 shows the results for several kinds of animals, correlated with the presence of nervous tissue.

In the course of the studies of the origin of the heart beat the concept of the pacemaker was introduced. If a vertebrate heart is removed from the body and placed in a physiological saline solution it will continue to beat for some time. Moreover, the excised heart can be cut into portions, each of which may beat spontaneously or resume a beat following an initial stimulus. These parts, however, beat at different rates, and the rate is normally highest in the part that normally beats first. Moreover, the rate of beating of the whole heart can be changed, either when it is in place in the animal or after removal from the animal, by local changes in temperature. Thus when a warm glass rod is applied locally to the sinus venosus of the heart of an elasmobranch or an eel the rate of beating of the whole heart increases. A cold glass rod causes a decreased rate. Applications to the atrium or ventricle do not have this effect if there is no spread of the heating or cooling to the sinus. In most fishes, heating and cooling of the sinus in general are ineffective, and only a small area of specialized tissues (the sinu-atrial or s-a node) at the junction of sinus and atrium respond. There is, in both elasmobranchs and fishes, a second bundle of tissue—the atrioventricular or a-v node at the atrioventricular junction. Warming this region causes a shift in the normal pattern of beat, which now begins at the a-v node and increases toward the atrium and sinus and through the ventricle to the bulbus. Finally, the elasmobranch heart has a third center

TABLE 11.1
Evidence of Cholinergic Innervation of Hearts

Group	Effect of Acetylcholine (+ = acceleration, - = inhibition)	Ganglionic Pacemaker (+ = present, - = absent)	Acetyl Choline (+ = present, - = absent, f = formed on stim.)	Choline Esterase (+ = present, - = absent)	Eserine Action (+ = increases effects of nerve stim., - = decreases)	Atropine Action (+ = increases Ach effect, - = decreases)
Annelida	+(2)	+(2)	-	-	-	-(1)
Crustacea						
Decapoda	+(8)	+(8)	+(4)	-	variable	-(4)
Amphipoda	+(2)	-	-	-	-	-
Branchiopoda	-(1) 0(2)	-(1)	-	-	-	-
Xiphosura						
embryo	0(1)	-(1)	-		-	
adult	+(1)	+(1)	-	+	-	
Insecta	+(4)	+(4)	-	-	-	-(1)
Gastropoda	-(5)	-(2)	+(3)	+(2)	-	0(3)
Pelecypoda	-(4)	-(1)	+(2)f(1)	+(2)	+(1)	0(1)
Cephalopoda	-(3)	-(1)	-(1)	-	0(1)	0(1)
Chordata						
Urochorda	+(1) 0(1)	+(1) -(3)	-	-	-	-
Vertebrata						
embryo	0(2)	-(2)		-	-	-
adult	-	-	f(1)	-	+	-

The numbers in parenthesis indicate the number of species for which results are recorded. (After C. L. Prosser et al., 1950, *Comparative Animal Physiology*, Saunders, Philadelphia.)

in the conus arteriosus, warming of which induces a reversal in the normal direction of propagation of the beat. These regions have been called pacemakers, since they can determine the rate and point of origin of the heart beat (Figure 11.5).

Electrical evidence supplements the direct observation of heart contraction in developing the pacemaker concept. In those vertebrate hearts which have been studied the earliest detectable electrical change appears in the s-a node (or sinus venosus in the eel) and then spreads in succession through the atrium, the ventricle, and the bulbus. This evidence coincides with the older classical evidence from ligatures. If a tight ligature is passed around (or a clamp applied to) the s-a junction the contraction of the sinus continues, while the remainder of the heart either stops beating or beats at a slower rate. Similarly, ligature at the a-v junction stops the beat in the ventricle. If the ventricle is stimulated it may resume beating, but at a slower rate than is seen in the sinus and atrium.

In general then, the vertebrate heart contains centers which are capable of originating, from internal processes, a state of excitation in a rhythmic pattern. The centers are most often located at the s-a and a-v junctions, but in elasmobranchs the whole sinus is such a center and there is no s-a node. In the eel the sinus is a center, and there is also an s-a node. From the center the state of excitation spreads through the myocardium and is followed by contraction. The electrical evidence shows the state of excitation to be comparable to that of other muscle tissue and represented by a typical action potential. The rhythmicity is likewise comparable to what we see in sense organs or in nerve axons

under certain conditions in which repolarization is followed in an oscillatory pattern by depolarization. That region which has the highest inherent rhythmicity will be the pacemaker, and the basic underlying determinant of rhythmicity is probably metabolic rate.

The basic dynamic principle of heart action was worked out by Starling in the dog and expressed as Starling's law of the heart, namely

$$\text{output} = \text{input}$$

This seems obvious, since the heart cannot expel more blood than it receives and would soon encounter diffi-

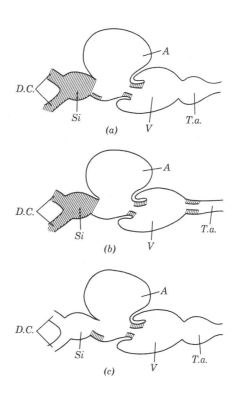

Fig. 11.5 Location of pacemakers in fish hearts. (a) Eel, (b) Elasmobranch, (c) Teleost. Si = sinus venosus; A = atrium; V = ventricle; $T.a.$ = truncus arteriosus. (After Skramlik, from Mott, 1957 in *Physiology of Fishes* 1 88; ed. M. E. Braun, Academic Press, New York.)

culty if it were to expel less than it receives. In fact, in individual beats and for very short periods the heart may not always expel at each beat all of the blood which enters, but over any period of significant length it must do so. This fact has the obvious consequence that a change in the heart rate will in itself have no effect on the amount of blood flowing out of the heart in unit time (cardiac output or minute volume). The general relation is

input = output =
$$\text{stroke volume} \times \text{rate}$$

The stroke volume is normally expressed as milliliters of blood expelled per beat, the rate as beats per minute and the output as milliliters per minute. The physiological basis for Starling's law lies in the general property of striated muscle tissue, in which the force of contraction is directly related to the length of the muscle at the beginning of the contraction. Thus if there is an increase in input the heart muscle will be stretched, and the succeeding contraction will be greater; hence the force and the stroke volume will be greater.

Dynamics: Lower Vertebrates

We may now return specifically to the lower vertebrates and examine what is known as the dynamics of the circulation. The cardiac output has been estimated by indirect methods at 10 to 15 ml per kg body weight per min for one elasmobranch (*Squalus acanthias*) and three fishes. These values are regarded as minimum values. They are only 15% of comparable figures for a lobster, for example, although the lobster has a much larger heart. On the other hand the fish has a blood volume of 20 to 30 ml/kg, while the lobster's blood volume is 200 ml/kg. The result is that the fish circulates about the same proportion of his total blood per minute as does the lobster.

The principal difference between the fish and the lobster is seen in the pressure against which the fish heart must work. The pressure in the ventral aorta between the heart and gills is 3 to 8 mm Hg in the hagfish (Cyclostomata), between 15 and 30 mm in elasmobranchs, about 40 mm in an eel, and 75 mm in a salmon. A good part of the force of the heart beat is dissipated in the gills. The pressure in the dorsal aorta leaving the gills is about 4 mm or less in the hagfish and 6 to 20 mm in the elasmobranchs, amounting to a drop in pressure of 30 to 70% in various species under various conditions. Comparable values for the eel are 20 mm (50%) and for the salmon 50 mm (30%). Pulse pressures range from 5 to 15 mm in the bulbus and ventral aorta and appear from the limited data to be larger when the systolic pressure is small. In general the pressure figures in fishes are quite comparable to those in the octopus, but are substantially greater than those in the lobster. Nearly all of the pressure remaining in the dorsal aorta and head arteries is lost in the tissues, so that the pressure in the sinus venosus is quite low. The venous return to the heart must depend largely on this residual pressure, possibly supplemented considerably by compression of the veins in the bodily movements of swimming. The role of the latter has not been determined.

Adaptive Variations

In those fishes with accessory respiratory organs, and especially those in which the swim bladder has become modified to a functional lung, there are associated modifications in the circulatory system. In several cases the efferent artery of the sixth aortic arch supplies the lung. Alternatively, the lung is supplied by the coeliac artery. The return to the venous end of the heart varies and may be through the hepatic vein, the posterior cardinal vein, or a special vein direct to the atrium. Whatever the arrangement, the lung circulation is essentially parallel to the gill circulation, which on anatomical grounds appears to remain functional, though ineffective in gas transport. The result is that the oxygenated blood from the lung is mixed in the venous system with the deoxygenated blood from the tissues, and the level of oxygenation in the blood will never approach saturation. It has been suggested on anatomical grounds that in the dipnoans, with a direct return of blood from lung to atrium, there may be some separation, in the atrium, of oxygenated from deoxygenated blood, so that the deoxygenated blood flows to the tissues; however, this has not been demonstrated physiologically.

A partial solution to the problem is seen in the amphibians where the atrium is divided by a septum into two chambers, one of which receives the venous return from the lungs and the other, the return from the tissues (Figure 11.4). The gill arches are reduced, and the arterial supply to lungs and skin through the pulmocutaneous arches is probably a larger fraction of the total cardiac output than in the lung fishes. The ventricle remains as a single chamber, but studies of the toad, *Xenopus laevis,* suggest that, in this animal, there is considerable separation of the oxygenated from the

deoxygenated blood. The right atrium receives the deoxygenated blood from the tissues; contraction of the right atrium which slightly precedes that of the left atrium forces blood into the ventricle. The left atrium receives the oxygenated blood from the lungs and skin and forces this blood into the ventricle as well. The evidence suggests that there is relatively little mixing, and nearly all of the output of the right atrium goes to the pulmocutaneous arches, along with a part of the output of the left atrium. The pressure in the two portions of the arterial system—pulmocutaneous and systemic—is about the same, amounting in the frog, *Rana temporaria,* to $15/8$ mm and in the toad, *Bufo bufo,* to $26/19$ mm, but the resistance of the pulmocutaneous system is less, and hence the blood flow through this part of the system is greater.

The hearts of reptiles show a variety of ventricular structures. In all of the living reptiles which have been studied there is some division of the ventricle, but only in the Crocodilia is this complete, with the ventricle divided into two chambers connected respectively with right and left atria. In the turtle, with only a partial septum, separation of blood is also only partial. Ten per cent or less of the blood from the right atrium gets into the aorta, but considerably more than 10% of the blood of the left atrium gets into the pulmonary artery. In lizards and snakes, though the septum is also incomplete, the separation of blood from right and left atria is much more complete.

The birds and mammals have complete ventricular septa, resulting in a complete double circulation, pulmonary and systemic. The double heart nevertheless beats as a unit, and the output of the two sides must be the same. Foxon has concluded on morphological grounds that the avian ventricular septum is not homologous with that of mammals, but is with that of reptiles, and that the first tetrapods probably had a ventricular septum. This has been lost in modern amphibians and partly lost in many reptiles, according to his view. From a physiological viewpoint it is hard to envision a situation in which loss of ventricular septum would confer, or be associated with another characteristic which would confer, an evolutionary advantage.

The hearts of birds and mammals have specialized conducting systems which are not found in the lower vertebrates, although some elements appear in reptiles. In turtles there are special fibers, resembling smooth muscle but embedded in collagenous tissue, which extend from the sinus venosus through the myocardium of the atria, become concentrated in the region of the a-v junction, and extend thence through the ventricular myocardium. Their function has not been studied experimentally. In mammals, the nineteenth century morphologists Purkinje and His described a system consisting of the bundle of His, a strand of specialized tissue running down the interventricular septum and ramifying in branches from the apex over the walls of the ventricles. The fibers in this system are called Purkinje fibers, and they are recognized today as conducting tissue derived from muscle fibers that have lost their contractile function. Similar tissue is found in the sinus node and the a-v node. The sinus venosus has disappeared in mammals; the s-a node of the lower vertebrates is found in the tissue of the right atrium near the entrance of the vena cava, and referred to as the sinus node. Birds have a similar system which Davies and Francis consider to have evolved independently of the mammalian system.

The conducting function of the system in mammals is very well established. From studies of pathology and physiology we know that the excitation originates in the sinus node and spreads through the myocardium of the atria. It is delayed at the a-v node, where the conducting fibers are arranged normal to the direction of conduction from atria to ventricles, thus forcing the state of excitation to cross several intercellular junctions. This arrangement permits atrial contraction to be initiated before the excitation passes into the ventricle. In the ventricle, the excitation moves rapidly down the bundle of His to the apex and then spreads back from the apex towards the a-v junction. This insures that the ventricular contraction begins at the apex and spreads upward, a matter of importance since the aorta and pulmonary artery have their openings at the base of the ventricle, that is, at the a-v junction.

Dynamics: Higher Vertebrates

The circulatory system of mammals and birds is also distinguished from that of the lower vertebrates by a much higher blood pressure—systolic pressures from 90 mm to almost 200 mm Hg—and in mammals, at least, by a higher cardiac output, as much as 100 ml/kg/min. The double circulation, of course, gives a large advantage in permitting the whole force of the left ventricular contraction to be used to propel blood through the tissues, while the force of the right ventricle overcomes the resistance of the lung vessels. The heart of mammals is much larger than that of fishes, probably in direct relation to the larger output in the double function. The blood is circulated much more rapidly, the whole volume being circulated roughly 3 to 4 times per minute through either half of the double system. The result is an extremely effective transport system.

In the mammal we know a great deal about the peripheral portion of the circulatory system as well. The vessels which constitute this system vary in structure in the different parts of the system. The major arteries have heavy walls, with relatively large amounts of elastic tissue (Figure 11.6). The inner lining is a smooth, thin, cellular endothelium which is continuous throughout the system. In the smaller branches (the arterioles) muscular tissue predominates over elastic. These vessels are contractile and constitute the major variable factor in the control of blood pressure and blood flow. In the capillaries the muscular coat disappears and the vessels become mere tubes of endothelium. At intervals the Rouget cells extend their long projections around the vessels. The capillaries are complex in their branching and anastomosis, forming a network. The endothelial wall is quite permeable to all the plasma constituents, save the larger protein molecules and cells. The leucocytes, however, are able to push through the spaces between the endothelial cells, wandering freely between blood and tissue fluid. The flow through the capillaries can be shut off, probably by contractions of arteriolar muscle near the point where the arteriole merges with the capillary. The venules and veins regain their outer coatings, including muscle layers in some regions, but their role in the circulation is mostly passive. The

larger veins in many mammals have at intervals internal valves which serve to prevent flow away from the heart. The discovery of these valves by Fabricius was one of the basic observations which ultimately led Harvey to the concept of circulation.

The principal source of the blood pressure in mammals is the resistance offered by the arterioles to the flow of blood under the force of the contraction of the heart. Roughly 80% of the pressure drop between the arterial and venous side of the heart occurs in these vessels. If we recall Poiseuille's law (page 228) we see that the resistance is a sensitive function of the radius, and the high resistance of the arterioles is directly attributable to the small radius. We also noted earlier that this radius can vary, and the variation constitutes the major basis for control of blood pressure and blood flow.

As we shall see later, there are important reflex mechanisms controlling the heart rate and the blood pressure in all of the vertebrates. We can therefore assume that under normal conditions the pressure is constant, and the blood flow through the whole system or any part of it is a function simply of the resistance, which in turn is a function of the radii of the arterioles. Thus if the radii of the arterioles in a part of a system increase there will be an increase in blood flow through that part of the system.

The radius of the arterioles is under a dual control, nervous and chemical. The nervous control is a part of the system for maintenance of constant blood pressure and hence can be regarded as a constant influence for the present. The chemical control is in part exerted by metabolites, products of tissue activity such as CO_2 and other substances not conclusively identified.

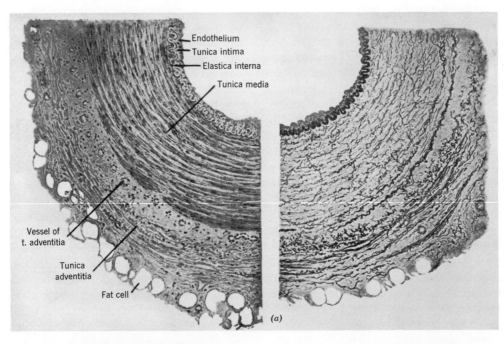

- Endothelium
- Tunica intima
- Elastica interna
- Tunica media
- Vessel of t. adventitia
- Tunica adventitia
- Fat cell

(a)

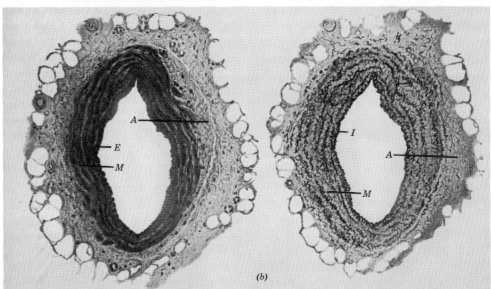

(b)

Fig. 11.6 Cross sections of an artery (*a*) and of a vein (*b*). Differences in appearance in the sections are due to staining technique. (From Maximow and Bloom, *Textbook of Histology,* 5th edn., Saunders, Philadelphia.)

Thus an increase in tissue activity generally results in dilation of the arterioles in the tissue, and hence an increased blood flow through the tissue. The adaptive significance is obvious. These aspects of the regulatory mechanisms will be discussed later.

In a normal man the cardiac output is 6 to 7 liters per minute. All of this of course goes through the pulmonary circulation. The capacity of the lung vessels can vary, thus varying the amount of blood in the lungs at any time and affording a "blood storage," though a very mobile one. In the systemic circulation, the flow divides in the major arterial branches. The brain, liver, and kidney get a large share of this flow. The flow to the brain is under close nervous regulation and changes very little. It amounts to 0.75 liter per minute in man. The liver gets about one fourth of the total flow, and the kidney slightly less; the rest is divided among muscles and skin. The liver flow depends largely on the flow through the intestines, and this in turn normally depends on digestive activity and is highly variable. The kidney flow is under nervous and hormonal regulation in man; the flow to the muscles depends on their activity and is highly variable. The flow to the skin also is highly variable. As we shall see, the skin is an important part of the temperature control mechanism, and the blood flow is closely related to this function, under nervous control. The interplay among digestive tract, muscles, and skin provides the major variation in blood flow, with the lungs serving as a variable reservoir to balance the first three.

The flow through the capillaries is also controlled, probably by the local mechanisms operative on the arterioles. The capillaries are the major site of exchange between blood and tissue fluid or lymph. There is free diffusion of most blood components across the capillary membrane, and the large total diameter of the capillary network ensures a slow blood flow, giving time for the exchange. There is a small net total flow of fluid across the walls of the capillaries into the tissue spaces, regulated by the difference between the hydrostatic pressure in the capillary and the colloid osmotic pressure of the blood. The fact that the blood proteins cannot diffuse across capillary walls gives them an osmotic effect, small because of the large molecular weight but still appreciable. The result is a tendency for water to diffuse from lymph to blood. This is opposed by the hydrostatic pressure in the capillary tending to force fluid out. The result in normal conditions is that at the arteriole end of the capillary there is a net outflux of fluid and at the venous end, a net influx, since the pressure decreases along the length of the capillary and the protein concentration, as a consequence of fluid loss, increases.

The overall effect is a small net loss to the tissues. The fluid thus exuded becomes the lymph. It enters by diffusion into small blind-ended capillaries (lymphatic capillaries) and is moved from these into larger lymphatic vessels by muscular contractions in the tissues surrounding the lymphatics. The larger lymphatics have valves like those in the veins, and there is consequently a general flow toward the major lymph trunks, which drain into the venous system near the heart.

This general pattern of blood flow and its control is probably characteristic of all of the vertebrates though it has not been studied in detail in most. Variable features include the valves in the veins (lacking in fish and probably many others), the role of the skin (which functions in temperature regulation only in birds and mammals, and in respiration only in amphibians and a few fishes), and the lymph circulation (involving lymph hearts in frogs, for example). The details of circulatory regulation will be discussed in Part IV.

References

Chapman, G. 1958. The hydrostatic skeleton in the invertebrates. *Biol. Rev.* **33** 338–371.

Danielli, J. F., and Stock, A. 1944. The structure and permeability of blood capillaries. *Biol. Rev.* **19** 81–94.

Davies, F., and Francis, E. T. B. 1946. The conducting system of the vertebrate heart. *Biol. Rev.* **21** 173–188.

Foxon, G. E. H. 1955. Problems of the double circulation in vertebrates. *Biol. Rev.* **30** 196–228.

Krijgsman, B. J. 1952. Contractile and pacemaker mechanisms of the heart of arthropods. *Biol. Rev.* **27** 320–346.

Krijgsman, B. J. 1956. Contractile and pacemaker mechanisms of the heart of tunicates. *Biol. Rev.* **31** 288–312.

Krijgsman, B. J., and Divaris, G. A. 1955. Contractile and pacemaker mechanisms of the heart of molluscs. *Biol. Rev.* **30** 1–39.

MacFarlane, R. G. 1956. Blood coagulation, with particular reference to the early stages. *Physiol. Rev.* **36** 479–502.

McDowall, R. J. S. 1935. The nervous control of the blood vessels. *Physiol. Rev.* **15** 98–174.

McMichael, J. (ed.) 1958. *Circulation.* Blackwell, Oxford, England.

Pappenheimer, J. R. 1953. Passage of molecules through capillary walls. *Physiol. Rev.* **33** 387–423.

Sjöstrand, T. 1953. Volume and distribution of blood and their significance in regulating circulation. *Physiol. Rev.* **33** 202–228.

Skramlik, E. von. 1954. Die Regelung der Strömungsrichtung des Blutes. *Experientia* **11** 441–454.

12 Intermediary metabolism

In earlier chapters we discussed the exchanges of matter and energy at the cellular level and the details of the chemical processes involved. In one sense, the metabolism of the whole multicellular organism is merely the sum of the cellular processes in all the body cells, but in another sense the metabolism of the whole organism has properties we cannot interpret as an algebraic sum, or even an integral, of the properties of individual cells. The first such group of properties we shall consider here is a consequence of cellular differentiation and the adaptation of the organism to specific environmental conditions. The second such group of properties, to be considered in the next section of the book, results from the fact that the metabolism and activities of individual cells are subordinated, by means of regulatory mechanisms, to the requirements and activities of the organism as a whole.

Total Metabolism

The word metabolism refers to the total exchanges of matter and energy in the organism. Since, from the first law of thermodynamics, the energy taken up by the organism must equal that given off, plus the amount retained by the organism, a measurement of either side of the equation would give us a quantitative estimate of metabolism. In an animal, energy is normally taken up only in the form of chemical potential energy (food) and heat, and is given off only in the form of heat, mechanical work, and chemical-potential energy (excretory and reproductive products and secretions). Energy is retained primarily in connection with growth and storage processes and the synthesis of organic matter in such processes. The simplest accurate method of measuring metabolism is the exact measurement of the energy equivalent of food consumed, under conditions in which no heat is absorbed by the organism, and no growth or storage processes occur. This method is, rather surprisingly, very rarely used. An alternative is the measurement of energy output. This is most accurately accomplished by calorimetry, in which the heat production of the organism is measured and corrections are applied for the energy loss in the excreta, etc. Direct calorimetry has been carried out for man and several common domestic animals but has rarely been applied to other species. The apparatus required for accurate work by this method is rather complex, and the technical problems are considerable.

Oxygen Consumption

The simplest and most widely used method of measuring metabolism is based on the assumption, valid for most animals under most normal conditions, that all of the processes yielding energy involve oxidation by molecular oxygen and production of CO_2, and a further assumption, much less reliable, that there is a dependable ratio between the amount of oxygen consumed or CO_2 produced and the amount of energy yielded. In its most elaborate form this method is known as indirect calorimetry. A full protocol of an experiment on a cow is given in Table 12.1. More frequently only oxygen consumption is measured, and an energy equivalent for oxygen consumption is used to compute the energy balance. Usually the equivalent is 4.8 kcal per liter of O_2, but this value obviously depends on the nature of the foodstuffs being metabolized during the test and probably also varies somewhat with species. Thus, as we shall see later, the formation of urea or uric acid instead of NH_3 as an end product of nitrogen metabolism will influence the energy yield of protein metabolism. Also, we cannot assume that the oxygen consumption measured during a brief experimental period is a reliable measure of the oxygen consumption for extended periods under natural conditions. Most of these sources of error are eliminated by measuring the long-term food-energy consumption, when this is possible, and this method is recommended as a check on O_2 consumption measurements.

The ease of the latter measurements has given us a vast literature on oxygen consumption in a wide variety of organisms under a wide range of conditions, and we shall summarize here the main factors which seem to influence the oxygen consumption. The factor which we must consider first, since it affects all the others, is that of body size. The importance of this factor was first noted by Rubner in some of the first modern quantitative studies of heat production, using dogs. He found that, in dogs of varying size, the heat production per unit of body weight is greater in small dogs than in large dogs. On the other hand, when he computed the rate of heat production per unit of body surface area, he found no difference between small and large dogs. This observation led to the surface law, which states that the rate of metabolism, however measured, is proportional to body surface area, not to body weight. Rigorous testing of this law is made difficult by the fact that, in general, measurements of body surface area are difficult. Measurements of body weight, on the other hand, are quite simple. As a result, a variety of empirical relations between surface area and other more readily measurable quantities is normally used in computing metabolic rates. Thus, the metabolic rate in man is normally expressed in kilogram calories per square meter per hour (kcal/m²/hr), but a formula such as that of DuBois and DuBois,

$$A = 0.007184 \ (W)^{0.425} \ (S)^{0.725} \quad (1)$$

where A is the surface area in square meters, W the weight in kilograms, and S the height in centimeters, is used for the calculation. Similar equations are available for other mammals.

Rubner considered that the surface law was somehow related to heat loss from the body surface, an important factor in body temperature regulation in mammals. Studies of heterothermic animals, which do not regulate body temperature, have shown that a similar relationship prevails in general for all animals; the metabolic rate (or more

TABLE 12.1
Indirect Determination of Mass Balance and Heat Production by a Fasting Cow

Item	Basis of Calculation	
Mass Balance		Weight, gm
N loss in urine	Measured, as urea	53
Protein catabolized	53 × 5.88 (1 gm N = 5.88 gm protein)	311
C in protein catabolized	311 × 0.52 (1 gm protein contains 0.52 gm C)	162
C from protein in urea excreted	53 × 0.43 (1 gm urea N = 0.43 gm urea C)	23
C from protein in respiratory CO_2	162 − 23	139
C lost in respiratory CO_2	Measured, 1275 liters STP (1 liter = 1/22.4 mole = 12/22.4 or 0.532 gm C)	697
C from fat catabolized	697 − 139	558
Fat catabolized	558/0.765 (1 gm fat contains 0.765 gm C)	729
O_2 consumed	Measured, 1730 liters STP	2420
Heat Production		Heat, kcal
Heat produced, protein	311 × 4.8 (1 gm protein yields 4.8 kcal)	1490
Heat produced, fat	729 × 9.5 (1 gm fat yields 9.5 kcal)	6890
Total heat from N and C balances		8380
Heat produced, O_2 consumption	1730 × 4.7 (1 liter O_2 yields 4.2 kcal)	8132

From M. Kleiber, 1961, *The Fire of Life,* Wiley, New York.

specifically the rate of oxygen consumption) can be expressed by the empirical equation

$$M = aW^b \qquad (2)$$

In general, b is less than 1, and the mean value is close to 0.73 for a very wide range of organisms. The ideal value for a spherical organism, assuming that metabolic rate is in fact proportional to surface area, would be of course 2/3 or 0.667. Values for individual species range from 0.5 to 1.0. Many attempts to explain this relationship have been made. Kleiber has recently reviewed the problem and concludes that of six hypotheses proposed, only two are basically sound: (1) the relation of metabolic rate to rate of heat transfer—hence to body surface—and (2) the relation to cardiac output. He suggests the following statement as being justified by the present state of our knowledge: In natural selection those animals proved to be better fit whose rate of oxygen consumption is regulated so as to permit the more efficient temperature regulation as well as the more efficient transport of oxygen and nutrients. His considerations concern mammals only, and it would be interesting to know whether the relation to circulation can be generalized.

The metabolic rates of individual tissues from large and small animals of the same species have in some cases shown the same relation to body size as prevails in the whole animal, but this is not always the case. The discrepancies may arise from the conditions under which tissue or cell metabolism is measured; these are different from those prevailing in the intact organism. The constant a in the metabolism equation will of course depend on the units used for M and W, but in addition it is characteristic of individual species and varies widely in relation to many factors, some of which we shall consider below. It has been suggested that the oxygen consumption of isolated tissues measured experimentally $(Q_{O_2}t)$ may bear a simple general relationship to the oxygen consumption of the whole animal (Q_{O_2}) of the form

$$\frac{Q_{O_2}t}{Q_{O_2}} = rW^b \qquad (3)$$

where r varies from one tissue to another. In view of the generality of the relation between body size and metabolic rate and the likelihood that surface area is only one factor and perhaps the least general factor in this relation, it seems quite reasonable to hope that all measurements of metabolic rates, and of other quantities reasonably relatable to metabolic rates, will be reported in terms of the constants a and b of equation (2) and not merely in terms of body weight and surface area.

Variations in Metabolic Rate

However it is reported, the metabolic rate or the rate of oxygen consumption of an organism will depend on many factors external to the organism itself, among which we may note oxygen pressure, CO_2 pressure, temperature, and in aquatic forms the salt concentration of the medium. In addition, many intrinsic factors other than body size influence the metabolic rate. Among the most obvious are activity, state of nutrition, sex, time of day, season of the year, and age or stage of development. Physiologists, in attempting to study metabolic rates on a comparative basis, have tried to minimize these sources of variation in some systematic way.

In man it is customary to measure a "basal metabolic rate" defined as the rate of energy exchange in kilogram calories per square meter per hour when the subject is at rest in temperature equilibrium (no net heat gain or loss) and in a postabsorptive state (i.e., after digestion and absorption have been completed). ˙ For animals, other than man, these conditions are difficult to attain, and measurements of "standard" or resting metabolism are made in conditions of minimal motor activity and temperature equilibrium, as far as possible. The postabsorptive condition and that of absolute rest are not generally met. Measurements of this sort are useful as a basis of interspecific comparisons, but they often have little relevance to the problems of the ecologist, who is interested in the total energy requirements of the organism. They are also useful to the physiologist in the study of the effects of some specific factor such as temperature, oxygen pressure, or sex on metabolic rates; however, even in such a study there is a great deal to be said for examining the metabolism in an active as well as a resting condition, since the effect to be studied might well be different in the two states.

The relation of motor activity to metabolic rate is obvious. The more active an animal is, the more energy must be expended to maintain the activity. The specific energy cost of various activities has been measured for man, for some of the common domestic animals, and for fishes and insects. This sort of measurement might provide quite valuable information to the ecologist and zoologist, since the energy cost of certain activities might easily become the limiting factor in survival or distribution. The effect of activity on metabolism, and the relation to basal rates, can be seen in man in the following example. The mean basal metabolic rate for men 25

years old is 38 kcal/m²/hr. If a man weighs 65 kg and is 70 cm tall, his basal rate is equivalent to 1670 kcal in 24 hr. A man of this age and weight, leading a sedentary existence and eating a normal diet, would actually use about 2500 kcal per day. Vigorous normal activity raises the figure to 3200, and the heaviest work to 4800 kcal.

The problem of relating basal metabolic rate to the metabolism of the fed animal has been a source of much confusion. Rubner first measured heat production in fasting animals, and then repeated the measurement after feeding. The rate of heat production of the fed animals was greater, especially if they had been fed protein. Rubner described this phenomenon by the phrase "specific dynamic effect" of food; Kleiber, in reviewing the subject recently, prefers the descriptive term "calorigenic effect." Most of the theoretical attempts to "explain" the phenomenon actually confused the issue by bringing in, explicitly or implicitly, fallacious assumptions about the nature of metabolism. The true explanation lies, in part, in cellular regulatory processes that are still poorly understood. Part of the calorigenic effect arises from the chemical work required to convert ammonia, derived from deamination of amino acids, into urea or other excretory product (Page 264). The rest of the effect is probably the result of a change in the stationary state of cellular processes from the fasting to the fed condition.

The basal metabolic rate appears in general to decrease with age, though this has been explored in detail in only a few species. Sexual differences are marked in some species, less evident in others. There are many intrinsic factors related to regulatory mechanisms that influence metabolic rate and will be discussed later.

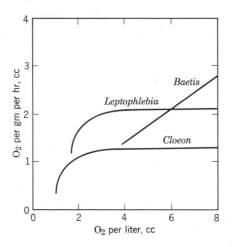

Fig. 12.1 The relation of oxygen consumption (ordinate) to oxygen concentration (abscissa) in three genera of aquatic insect larvae. *Cloeon* inhabits ponds, *Leptophlebia* inhabits lakes, and *Baetis* lives in swift streams. (Data from H. M. Fox et al., 1937, *J. Exp. Biol.* **14** 210.)

Of the extrinsic factors, the most obvious is temperature. All chemical processes are influenced by temperature; metabolism, complex though it is, is no exception. Among the heterothermic animals the metabolic rate and all correlated phenomena increase with temperature, from the lowest level tolerated to a level near the upper lethal limit. The increase is usually exponential, so that a 10°C rise in temperature approximately doubles the metabolic rate. In the homeothermic animals the existence of internal mechanisms for regulation of body temperature destroys this relationship, and the metabolic rate is usually constant over a fairly wide range of temperature, increasing at the lower and the upper ends of the range.

The relation of oxygen consumption and metabolic rate to the environmental oxygen pressure varies between two patterns (Figure 12.1). The first pattern (called conformity by Prosser) is that of a direct linear relation of Q_{O_2} (the amount of O_2 consumed per unit of weight per unit time) and P_{O_2}. This is seen in a variety of aquatic animals, belonging to most of the major groups, with the whole range of naturally occurring levels of P_{O_2} and in nearly all aquatic animals at very low P_{O_2} values. The second pattern (called regulation by Prosser) is one of complete independence between Q_{O_2} and P_{O_2} above a critical level of P_{O_2}. This pattern is characteristic of terrestrial animals and of the more highly organized aquatic animals, but also of most protozoans. The present author prefers the word independence to regulation for this second type of relation, since it is not established that the pattern is invariably the result of regulatory processes. Thus in protozoans it is likely that the metabolic rate is limited at low external P_{O_2} values by the rate of diffusion, but at high P_{O_2} values the rate limiting factor is the diffusion of something other than O_2. This is hardly regulation. On the other hand, in higher animals as we shall see later there is clear evidence for a regulatory process controlling the ventilation rate of the respiratory organs, and this in turn may assure independence of oxygen consumption from oxygen pressure. The critical level of P_{O_2}, which is not always sharp, is simply that level at which the P_{O_2} is no longer a limiting factor for oxygen consumption. The limiting factor at higher P_{O_2} levels in O_2-independent forms may be a regulatory process, or it may be something over which the animal has no control, such as diffusion of substrates. An effect of external P_{CO_2} on Q_{O_2} has been noted only in a few cases. Clearly, this could be a consequence of the Bohr effect on respiratory proteins in some cases.

Intermediary Metabolism

Thus far we have been discussing total metabolism. We may also dissect this total process into its component parts in either of two ways: by analyzing the fate of individual foodstuffs (intermediary metabolism) or by analyzing the metabolism of the component body parts (tissue metabolism, cellular metabolism). The two approaches are in fact inseparable in the higher animals, and the connecting link lies in the differentiation of tissues and organs in these animals. Although the basic events of cellular metabolism as discussed earlier are apparently the same in all cells, the steps of preparation of substrates for cellular metabolism (transport from one part of the body to another) and disposal of the end products of cellular metabolism differ considerably in different kinds of animals, and the various steps in these processes are carried out in specialized organs. The best known situation is that in the mammals, and we shall begin with this group. What we say here of mammals should not be assumed for animals generally; we shall try to point out known differences as we go, and more differences may be expected as study of other animals continues.

Metabolism of Carbohydrate

We begin with carbohydrate. The end products of digestion—monosaccharides: glucose, galactose, fructose primarily—enter the capillaries of the hepatic portal system and are carried to the liver. Here they are largely removed from the blood, to be converted into glucose or fructose phosphates. Liver contains the enzyme system for conversion of galactose phosphate to glucose phosphate. The hexose phosphate may then enter into (1) glycolysis, (2) oxidation through the pentose shunt, or (3) glycogenesis or conversion to glycogen. The relative proportions in these three pathways depend on cellular regulatory mechanisms, which in turn are under hormonal control, but basically the level of supply of glucose, ATP, NADP, and O_2 will determine the pathways.

Transport and Storage in Mammals

The blood leaving the liver typically contains glucose at a level of about 90 mg per 100 ml of whole blood or plasma in man, 40 to 100 mg for other vertebrates. There is virtually no other monosaccharide in the blood. Free fructose levels are about 7 mg per 100 ml. There are carbohydrates bound to protein in the blood, but these are not in general available to the cells for direct metabolic use. We must therefore conclude that glucose is the main transport form of carbohydrate in mammals and probably in all the vertebrates, though this statement is based more on the absence of contrary information than on positive evidence.

The origin of blood glucose, aside from that which may escape the liver during absorption from the intestine, is the liver glycogen store. This fact was recognized first by Claude Bernard and has been confirmed abundantly since. The glycogen is broken down (glycogenolysis) by the enzyme phosphorylase to yield glucose-1-phosphate, which in turn is hydrolyzed by phosphatase to yield glucose. Glycogen is replenished from carbohydrate absorbed following digestion, from pyruvic and lactic acid absorbed from the blood or formed in liver metabolism, from glycerol absorbed from the intestine or formed from hydrolysis of fats, and from the keto acids formed by deamination of amino acids. The synthesis of glycogen from noncarbohydrate precursors is known as gluconeogenesis. From a chemical viewpoint, acetic acid residues from fatty acid oxidation can also enter into glycogen synthesis, but the energy requirement for such a synthesis is considerable, and it is unlikely that fatty acids form an important source of glycogen normally. The balance of glycogen synthesis and break-down is determined by the internal cellular regulatory mechanisms of the liver which in turn reflect the state of energy balance in the liver cells. The cellular regulatory mechanisms in turn are under control of external regulatory mechanisms of a hormonal nature from the pancreatic islets, the anterior pituitary, and the adrenal cortex, as will be discussed later.

The blood glucose, which is held at a remarkably constant level by the regulatory mechanisms, is absorbed by the various tissue cells, where again it may be converted to glycogen or utilized in cellular metabolism. The tissues which make major use of glucose in the mammals are the muscles and the brain. Quantitatively the muscles are the heaviest users. The process of absorption and glycogen synthesis appears to be the same in muscle as in liver, but muscle is unable to return glucose to the blood. This inability results from the effective absence of phosphatase. That glucose which is not incorporated into glycogen, or which subsequently is converted from glycogen to glucose-1-phosphate, must be broken down to pyruvate or lactate before it can re-enter the blood stream. Most muscles can carry on vigorous activity for considerable periods on energy derived from anaerobic glycolysis, with formation of lactic acid from glycogen. As we have seen, the discovery of anaerobic glycolysis in muscle was one of the major factors in the development of our understanding of the chemistry of cellular metabolism. Physiologically, anaerobic glycolysis constitutes the most important anaerobic energy source in animals.

Muscles have very limited capacity for gluconeogenesis. The frog muscles studied by Meyerhof could convert some lactic acid to glycogen at the expense of energy derived from oxidation of more lactic acid, but this situation appears to be rare, and in most mammals any lactic acid which is not oxidized in the muscle enters the blood and returns to the liver, there to be converted to glycogen. Glycogen synthesis from amino acids does not occur in muscle in general. The brain of mammals is very sensitive to alterations in blood sugar levels. Glucose is used as an important substrate for aerobic and anaerobic metabolism alike, in both cases through the glycolytic pathway. The glycogen store of nervous tissue is quite small as compared, for example, with muscle. The generality of this picture of carbohydrate metabolism (Figure 12.2) remains to be established.

Invertebrates

Glycogen is by far the most generally encountered storage form for carbohydrate. Certain gastropod mollusks also accumulate galactogen, a comparable polysaccharide derived from galactose, but its role is primarily that of an energy store in the ova, and glycogen is the normal adult energy store. Protozoans appear to have a variety of storage carbohydrates, few of which have been characterized chemically.

Glycogen has been demonstrated

histochemically or chemically or both in a great variety of tissues throughout the animal kingdom. Some of these demonstrations may be unreliable, since the methods used are not entirely specific. Thus, the carbohydrate precipitated by alcohol from acid extracts of crustacean epidermis was found on careful examination to be a mucopolysaccharide; this tissue contains no true glycogen. Physiological studies of variations of glycogen content are relatively few, but there is enough evidence to justify a cautious statement that tissues such as the mid-gut gland or hepatopancreas of mollusks and crustaceans, the fat body of insects, and the chloragogue tissue of annelids do store glycogen derived from dietary carbohydrate or other foodstuffs, and that this glycogen is later transported to other tissues and utilized there. In some crustaceans the tissue glycogen stores appear to be utilized primarily in chitin synthesis and muscular activity.

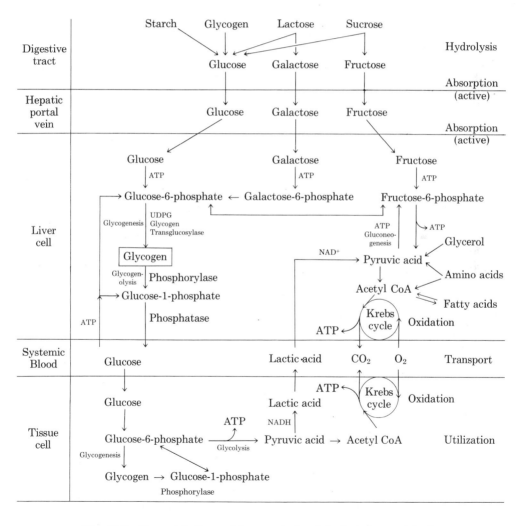

Fig. 12.2 The metabolism and transport of carbohydrate in a vertebrate.

The transport of carbohydrate in the blood of invertebrates has only been studied in arthropods. In nearly all invertebrates the blood sugar, as determined by classical reducing methods, is quite low. Injection of glucose into mollusks or echinoderms results in a brief increase in blood levels, followed by rapid return to the normal very low values. Experiments of this sort have been very few in number, but they suggest that there is rapid tissue utilization of glucose and no regulatory mechanism. In insects the blood sugar values vary greatly with species and in a few cases, notably the honey bee, attain quite high values, as much as 2%. Detailed analysis has shown that the sugar may be largely glucose in some species, but may also include other sugars as well. Fructose often occurs in relatively high concentrations, as does the disaccharide trehalose.

Trehalose is of particular interest. Its significance was first made clear in a study by Treherne at Cambridge on the intestinal absorption of sugar by the locust. He found that glucose was absorbed from the intestine in a pattern which suggested active transport but that the glucose did not appear entirely as such in the blood; rather, when the glucose concentration in the intestine was low, nearly all of the glucose appeared as trehalose. He considered trehalose formation to be a part of the absorption mechanism, permitting transfer of glucose from the intestine to the blood. It has since been shown that trehalose synthesis and break down can also occur in the fat body and that trehalose can be converted to glycogen. This latter process, of course, involves preliminary break down of trehalose to glucose-6-phosphate. The general relations in carbohydrate transport in the locust are shown in Figure 12.3. Trehalose occurs rather widely in the insects as in many other invertebrates, but its

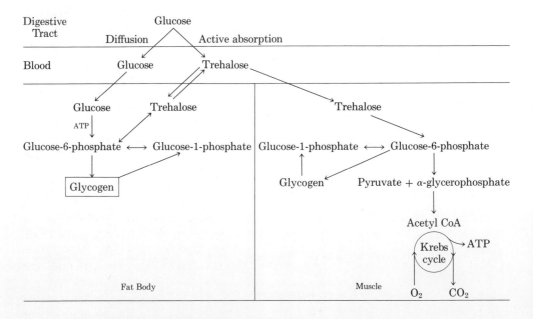

Fig. 12.3 The metabolism and transport of glucose in an insect.

physiological role in these other forms has not been established.

In certain crabs and crayfish, the transport mechanism appears to be different. There is no trehalose in the blood which instead contains, in addition to small amounts of glucose, glucose-6-phosphate, the disaccharide maltose, and related polymers of glucose containing 3 and 4 glucose molecules. When crabs are given glucose by mouth the sugar appears first in maltose. When the sugar is injected glucose-6-phosphate is the first detectable product. These observations suggest that maltose is the normal transport form for glucose in these animals. Maltose can in principle be converted directly to glycogen without previous hydrolysis. It seems likely that further study may reveal a variety of mechanisms of carbohydrate transport in the animal kingdom.

Metabolism of Amino Acids

The amino acids absorbed from the digestive tract of a vertebrate, like the carbohydrates, enter the hepatic portal system and are largely removed from the blood by the liver. In nearly every case the first step in the metabolism of the amino acids in the liver is removal of the amino group to form a keto acid. The reaction may involve a transfer of the amino group to another amino acid (transamination) or it may involve oxidative or hydrolytic removal of the amino group (deamination).

Deamination and Transamination

The central agent in transamination is α-ketoglutarate and its amino homologue, glutamate. These two interact with amino acids such as aspartate, alanine, leucine, isoleucine, valine, or tyrosine thus:

$$
\begin{array}{ccc}
\begin{array}{l} COO^- \\ | \\ CH_2 \\ | \\ CH_2 \\ | \\ C{=}O \\ | \\ COO^- \end{array}
&
+ \begin{array}{l} R \\ | \\ C{-}NH_3^+ \\ | \\ COO^- \end{array}
& \rightleftharpoons
\end{array}
\begin{array}{ccc}
\begin{array}{l} COO^- \\ | \\ CH_2 \\ | \\ CH_2 \\ | \\ HCNH_3^+ \\ | \\ COO^- \end{array}
&
+ \begin{array}{l} R \\ | \\ C{=}O \\ | \\ COO^- \end{array}
\end{array}
$$

The products of the reaction with aspartate and alanine are respectively oxaloacetate and pyruvate. These three amino-keto acid pairs then can all interact readily; the keto acid members are all directly involved in the tricarboxylic acid cycle and can thus be formed readily from either carbohydrate or fat or can readily be converted back to these substances or can be oxidized to CO_2 and H_2O. The three reaction pairs constitute a system which can readily absorb $-NH_2$ groups in large numbers and transfer these reversibly to other keto acids, forming new amino acids (Figure 12.4). In consequence, these three reaction pairs constitute the central feature of a nitrogen pool which can readily absorb or supply NH_2 groups.

The nitrogen pool is not an inert store of nitrogen but merely a pool in a stream which flows from food to tissues during digestion and absorption, and is slowly depleted in fasting. Its existence was first clearly demonstrated with the aid of isotopes in a classical experiment performed by Schoenheimer and Rittenberg at Columbia University. They administered glycine labeled with the heavy isotope of nitrogen, N^{15}, to rats and found that, within a relatively short period, the fraction of the isotope which had not been excreted was distributed through virtually all of the amino acids of the body, including many found in proteins.

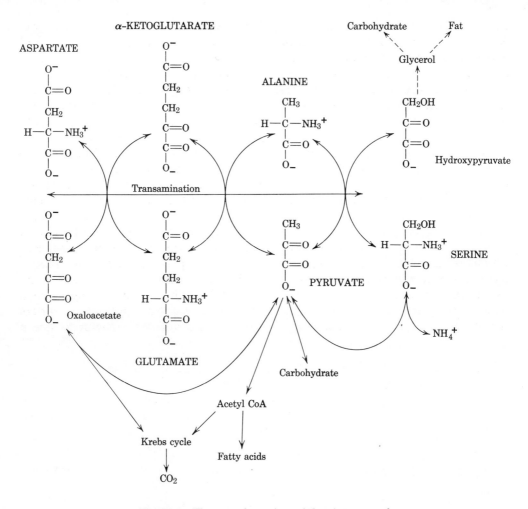

Fig. 12.4 The central reactions of the nitrogen pool.

Deamination rather than transamination appears to be the normal method for removal of —NH$_2$ from amino acids such as lysine, threonine, and cysteine (Figure 12.5). This process, which forms NH$_4^+$ at physiological pH, is less readily reversible than transamination, but free NH$_4^+$ can enter the nitrogen pool, as Schoenheimer and Rittenberg demonstrated, by administering labeled NH$_4^+$ salts to rats and finding the isotope in NH$_2$ groups of many amino acids. Deamination of

glutamate also forms NH$_4^+$, which can be incorporated into, and readily liberated from, the amide group of glutamine. We shall discuss the conversion of NH$_4^+$ into special excretory products such as urea and uric acid later.

Metabolism of Keto Acids

The fates of the keto acids formed by deamination or transamination vary. Many are, of course, reaminated and utilized for protein synthesis in the liver or passed into the blood stream. Those keto acids which are not reconverted to the parent amino acids are degraded through one or more of three pathways: to pyruvate, to other tricarboxylic acid cycle intermediates, or to acetyl coenzyme A. We noted this fact earlier in pointing out that the final pathway of catabolism is the same for all the major foodstuffs. It is worth some time here to explore some of the pathways of amino acid catabolism to show how these processes are interwoven.

We look first at those amino acids which are converted to pyruvate. Since pyruvate stands at the crossroads between oxidation and synthesis of carbohydrate, these amino acids can readily be converted to carbohydrate.

Likewise, pyruvate is the normal precursor of acetyl coenzyme A, and hence these amino acids readily serve as material for fatty acid synthesis. Alanine is converted directly to pyruvate by transamination. Cysteine can be deaminated and desulfurated, again forming pyruvate directly.

The relation of glycine and serine to pyruvate and other substances is complex, and these two amino acids are involved in two cyclic reaction systems (Figures 12.6, 12.7). One of these systems is involved in the formation and break down of ethanolamine and choline, important constituents of phosphatides. The other system is involved in the transfer of one-carbon units, as between glycine and serine, and is an important factor in break

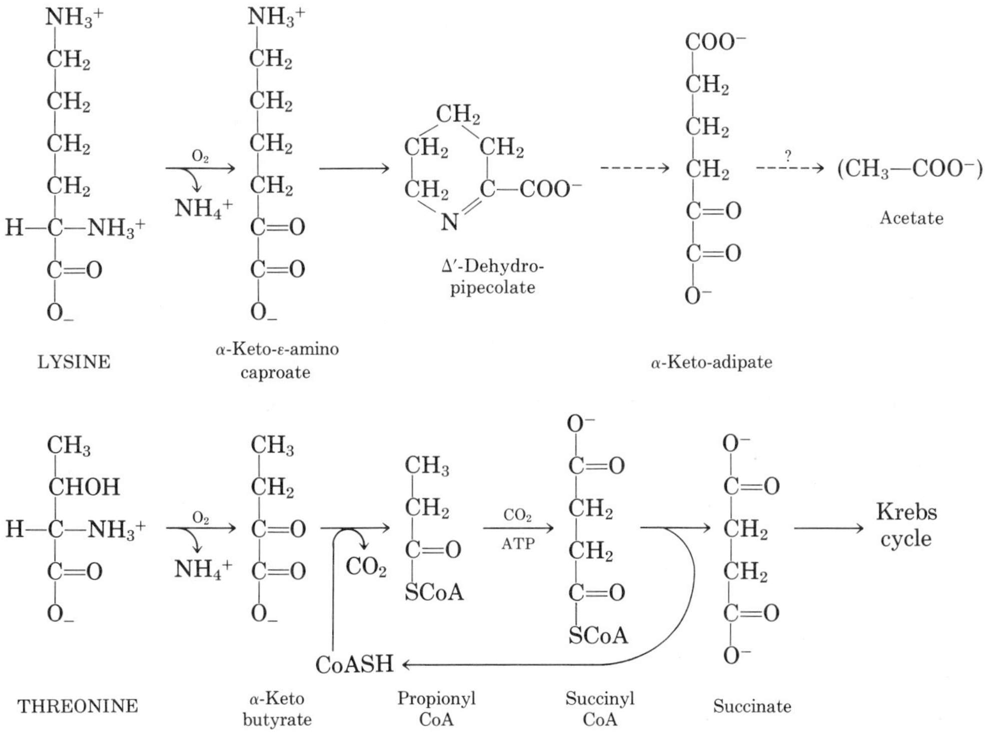

Fig. 12.5 The catabolism of lysine and threonine.

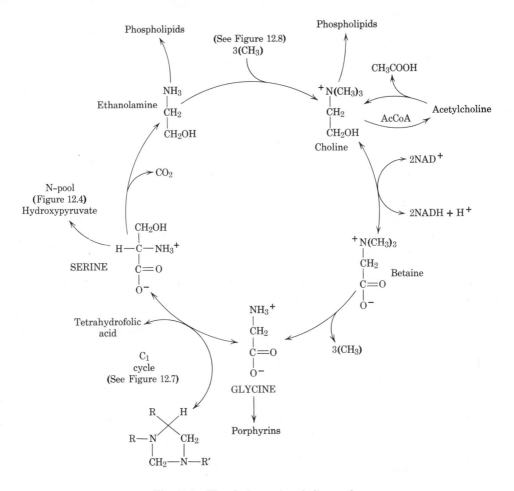

Fig. 12.6 The glycine-serine-choline cycle.

down of certain amino acids and in synthesis of purines as we shall see later. Glycine serves also as a building block for the very important porphyrins of hemoglobin and the cytochromes. It is catabolized only after conversion to serine; serine may be transaminated to hydroxypyruvate, which can then be converted to glycerol.

Serine is also involved in the metabolism of methionine (Figure 12.8). The methyl group of the latter amino acid can be transferred, with the aid of ATP energy, to form methylated compounds such as choline or creatine, with conversion of the methionine to homocysteine. This in turn combines with serine to form a complex which breaks up to cysteine and homoserine. The cysteine derived from serine goes to pyruvate; homoserine is metabolized like threonine, which will be discussed later.

Tryptophan is unique among the amino acids in its degradation pathway (Figure 12.9). The first step is not removal of the —NH2 group but an irreversible oxidation to break the pyr-

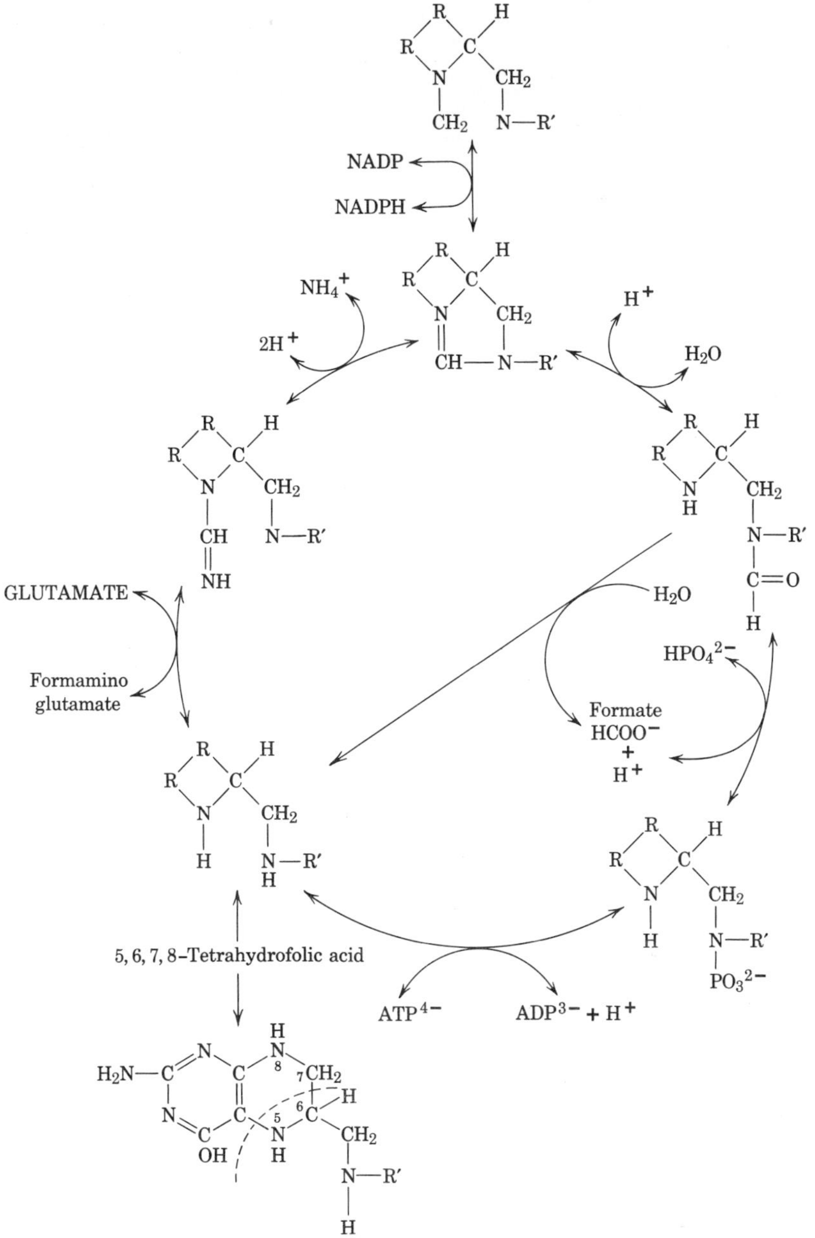

Fig. 12.7 The C_1 or tetrahydrofolic acid (THFA) cycle (See Figure 12.6 for relation to serine and glycine).

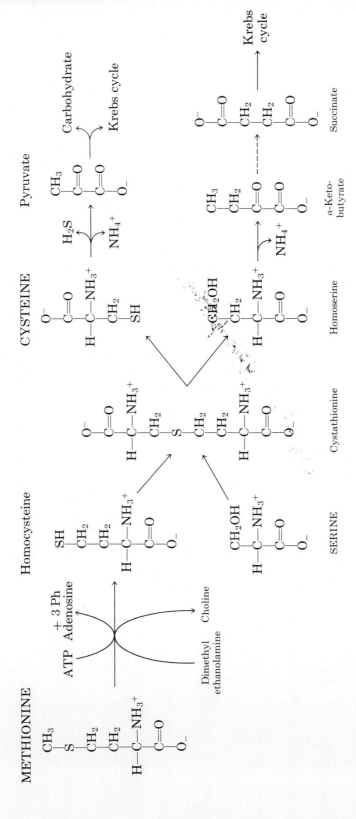

Fig. 12.8 Catabolic interrelations of methionine, serine, and cysteine.

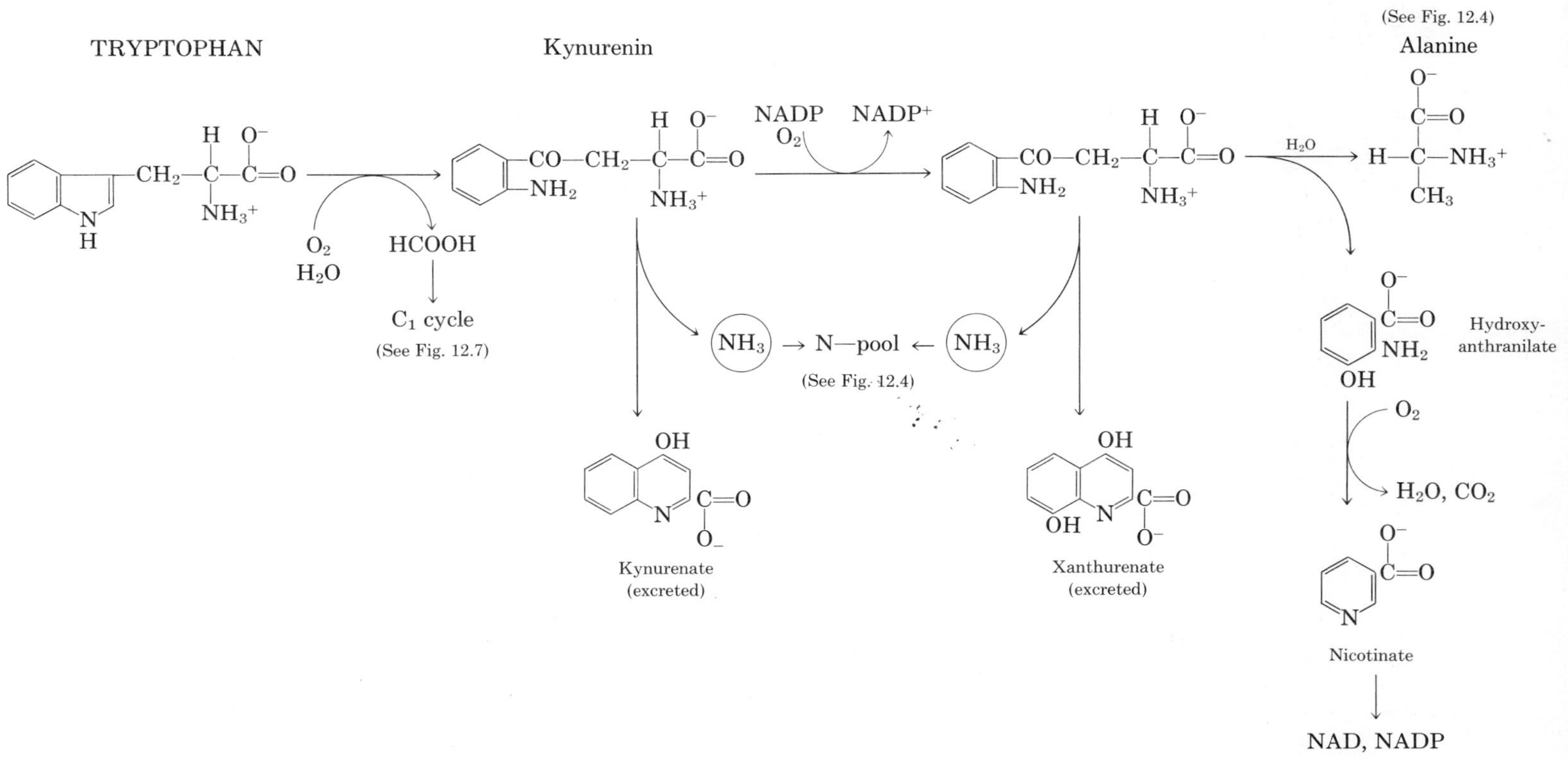

Fig. 12.9 The catabolism of tryptophan.

rol ring, with formation of formic acid, which enters the THFA C_1 cycle (Figure 12.7). The product of this oxidation is the amino acid kynurenin, which may undergo transamination to kynurenate and be excreted in this form; further oxidation of kynurenin produces hydroxykynurenin, which in turn is readily transaminated to xanthurenate, another excretory product. Hydrolysis of hydroxykynurenin forms alanine and hydroxyanthranilate; the latter can be oxidized to nicotinic acid, an essential component of the pyridine nucleotides. Animals with limited capacity to carry out these reaction sequences require nicotinate as a vitamin. Kynurenin also has had an important role in genetics, as one of the precursors of the eye pigments of *Drosophila melanogaster.*

Aspartic and glutamic acids form tricarboxylic acid intermediates directly by transamination. A number of amino acids are converted to glutamate in the course of catabolism. Proline and hydroxyproline are oxidized as the first step in catabolism with splitting of the ring to form glutamic semi-aldehyde, which may be oxidized to glutamate or undergo transamination to form ornithine, the fate of which we consider later. Histidine is deaminated to form urocanic acid and this is hydrated to formamino glutamic acid. Transfer of the formamino (—CH=NH) group to the C_1 THFA cycle then yields glutamate. Arginine may be hydrolyzed by arginase to form urea and ornithine. The latter amino acid is converted by transamination to glutamate.

Transamination of valine yields α-keto *iso*valerate, which is metabolized in the fatty acid pattern; that is, it is oxidized, carboxylated, and conjugated with coenzyme A (Figure 12.10). The

resulting *iso*butyryl coenzyme A is further oxidized and hydrated to yield β-hydroxy *iso*butyrate, which ultimately forms succinate. Threonine and homoserine follow a similar path. The deamination involved yields a keto acid which is decarboxylated and combined with coenzyme A to form propionyl coenzyme A. Carboxylation then yields succinyl coenzyme A, which enters directly into the tricarboxylic acid cycle. *Iso*leucine similarly first undergoes transamination and then acylation with coenzyme A. It is ultimately oxidized to α-methyl acetoacetyl coenzyme A, which then is acylated and split to acetyl coenzyme A and propionyl coenzyme A. The latter is carboxylated to succinyl coenzyme A and thus enters the tricarboxylic acid cycle. Leucine follows a similar course to a different end (Figure 12.10). Transamination of this amino acid forms α-keto *iso*caproate, which is decarboxylated and conjugated with coenzyme A. Oxidation and carboxylation yields β-hydroxy β-methyl glutaryl coenzyme A which then splits to acetoacetate and acetyl coenzyme A. Acetyl coenzyme A, of course, enters directly into the Krebs cycle or may be converted to fatty acid, but acetoacetate is not as readily metabolized. In the presence of sufficient supplies of ATP it can be converted to two molecules of acetyl coenzyme A, with transfer of coenzyme A from succinyl coenzyme A or a similar compound, but in diabetes or fasting this reaction does not progress and acetoacetate may be reduced to β-hydroxy butyrate or acetone. These three compounds together are the acetone bodies characteristic of diabetes.

The pathway for lysine is still not fully worked out (Figure 12.5). The α—NH_2 group is removed by deami-

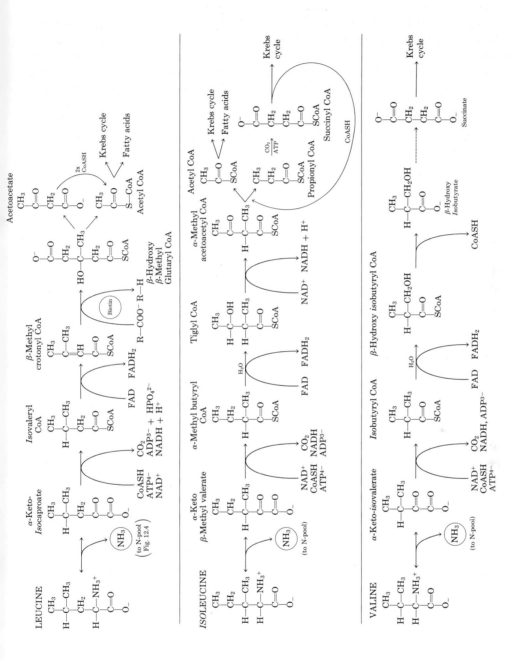

Fig. 12.10 The catabolism of leucine, *isoleucine*, and valine.

263

nation and the α-keto ε-amino caproate is converted by decarboxylation and oxidation to α-amino adipate which can then undergo reversible transamination to α-keto adipate. Catabolism of the latter involves acetate or acetyl coenzyme A as an intermediate. Phenylalanine (Figure 12.11) is first oxidized to tyrosine. The first step in tyrosine metabolism is transamination through phenylpyruvic acid, which in turn is oxidized to homogentisic acid. Excretion of these phenols in man is evidence of gene deficiencies connected respectively with oxidation of phenylpyruvate and of homogentisate. The inability to oxidize phenylpyruvate is associated with mental deficiency. Oxidation of homogentisate involves splitting of the benzene nucleus; the resulting eight-carbon acid is hydrolyzed to acetoacetate and fumarate. Thus the carbon skeletons of the amino acids are almost entirely oxidized through the Krebs cycle, with consequent liberation of energy. They may, alternatively, be utilized as a basis for formation of fatty acids when the end product is acetyl coenzyme A or for formation of carbohydrate when the end product is pyruvate, oxaloacetate, or a precursor of oxaloacetate. The interrelations are shown in Figure 12.12.

Free Amino Acids

The free amino acids in the blood of various animal species differ quantitatively in a complex fashion which has only been partly explored. Further exploration is likely to be informative only if directed by some general concept. We would like to know for instance to what extent concentrations of individual amino acids are regulated and by what mechanism. In man, the most abundant amino compound in the blood is glutamine (8 mg/100 ml), followed by alanine, lysine, proline, and valine at about one third this level. The pattern differs both quantitatively and qualitatively in other mammals. The general levels of amino acid concentration in the blood of invertebrates are of the same order of magnitude as in the vertebrates, with a single exception, the insects. Where the blood of man contains 4 mg of amino-acid nitrogen per 100 ml, and most other animals have no more than three times this amount, the amino-acid nitrogen of insect blood falls in the range of 50 to 300 mg per 100 ml. The distribution of this nitrogen among the various amino acids varies with species and also in the stages of the life history. The physiological significance of the high level is not known, but the level of amino acids in insect tissues is also high. Curiously enough, the tissue amino acid level is also high in crustaceans, though the blood levels in these animals are not exceptional. This means that crustaceans, unlike either mammals or insects, have a considerable concentration gradient of amino acid between tissue and blood. Moreover, the qualitative composition of the tissue amino acids is different from that in the blood.

Tissue utilization of amino acids has not been studied in great detail. Glutamine and glutamic acid have a special role in the mammalian brain, where glutamic acid is an important energy source. Otherwise the amino acids probably serve primarily for protein synthesis outside the liver. In the liver they are important precursors both of carbohydrate and of lipid.

Elimination of Ammonia

Deamination of the amino acids, followed by use of the keto acids as energy sources, leaves a residue of

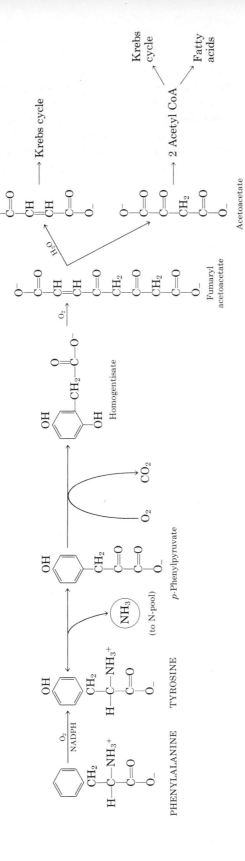

Fig. 12.11 The catabolism of phenylalanine and tyrosine.

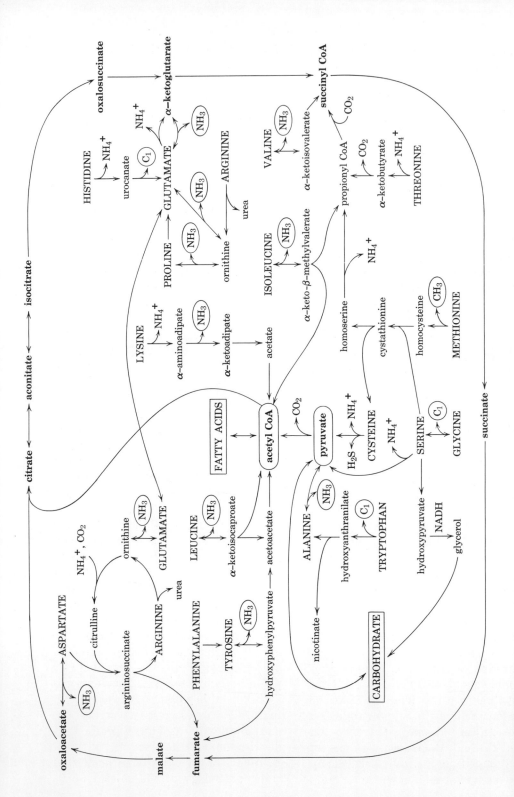

Fig. 12.12 The relations of amino acid catabolism to the Krebs tricarboxylic acid cycle. Amino acids which are normal constituents of proteins are shown in CAPITALS, other foodstuffs are shown in CAPITALS enclosed in boxes, and intermediates common to catabolism of protein, lipid, and carbohydrate are in **bold face** type. NH_3 represents ammonia entering the nitrogen pool (Figure 12.4). CH_3 represents methyl groups entering the choline cycle (Figure 12.6). C_1 represents formic acid entering the C_1 cycle (Figure 12.7).

ammonia which must be eliminated. Three major compounds of nitrogen are found in the excreta of animals: ammonia, urea, and uric acid; guanine occurs in a few forms. The major relations among these compounds are shown in Figure 12.13. The basic synthetic mechanism for urea is a part of the reaction systems of amino acid metabolism (Figure 12.14), while the synthetic mechanism for uric acid is a modification of the normal mechanism for purine synthesis (Figure 12.15). The chemical form in which the ammonia is eliminated shows some very interesting systematic variations which were first brought to general attention by Joseph Needham and Ernest Baldwin of Cambridge University. Table 12.2 summarizes, in general terms, the kinds of nitrogenous compounds eliminated by members of the major animal groups. The data from which this table has been compiled are not all equally reliable. In some groups a large number of species has been studied, and in others only a small number. The figures for amphibians and protozoans are derived from two or three species of a single genus; those for fishes, selachians, birds, echinoderms, annelids, and cephalopod mollusks, from a few genera only; the others represent enough different species to give one some confidence in their representative character.

The problem of collecting all of the excreted nitrogen is sometimes a serious one. In mammals most of the nitrogen is excreted in the urine, but in other animals this is rarely the case. Thus the values for the frog may not be representative of the total nitrogenous excretion, since some nitrogen is excreted through the cloaca. Values for the composition of urine in fishes and mollusks have been shown to be quite unrepresentative of the total nitrogen excretion.

In spite of these difficulties, we can see certain trends in the data recorded in the table. Ammonia is the primary end product in representatives of most of the invertebrate groups, with the notable exception of the insects. In many invertebrates, unidentified nitrogenous compounds make up a substantial portion of the excreted nitrogen. In a few gastropods and annelids urea is an important constituent. Among the vertebrates, ammonia is a major end product only in the fishes and the alligator. Urea is the major nitrogenous constituent in the selachians, some turtles, the frog, and in mammals. Uric acid, which accounts for only a very small proportion of the excreted nitrogen in most invertebrates, becomes very important in insects, the squamate reptiles (lizards and snakes), some turtles, and the birds.

In the attempt to interpret this distribution we may first look at systematic relations. Among the vertebrates, if for a moment we neglect the selachians and assume that the frog is representative of the amphibian class, we can see progression in the accepted phylogenetic sequence of fishes to amphibians to reptiles from ammonia to urea to uric acid. The general view that mammals and birds evolved from separate reptilian stock is consistent with the universal excretion of urea by mammals and the excretion of uric acid by birds; the excretion of ammonia by alligators may be regarded as a primitive characteristic. Needham was struck by this pattern and was accordingly led to investigate the nitrogenous end products formed during embryonic development of the chick. It is a commonplace of zoological knowledge that the morphology of the chick embryo

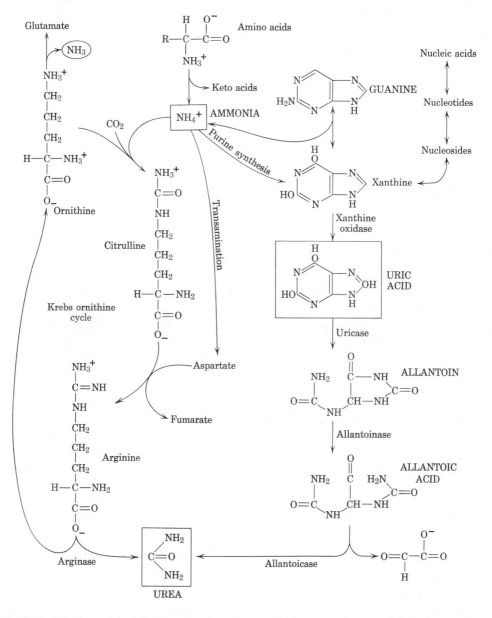

Fig. 12.13 The formation of nitrogenous end products; major known products are indicated by CAPITALS. The succeeding Figures 12.14 and 12.15 give details of the reactions summarized here.

has, at various stages in development, characteristics similar to those in its presumed phylogenetic ancestry. Needham found evidence suggesting a biochemical recapitulation as well. His measurements appeared to show that

the early embryo forms ammonia; the later embryo forms first urea, and then in turn uric acid. Subsequent studies with more modern techniques have thrown this sequence into doubt and suggest, rather, that both ammonia

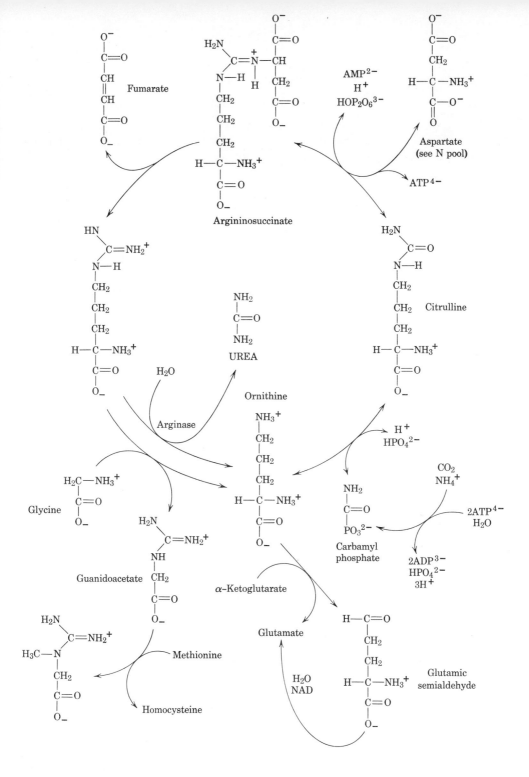

Fig. 12.14 The Krebs ornithine cycle in relation to urea formation. This system of reactions is a normal part of amino acid catabolism and anabolism in all animals, but in those which form urea as a nitrogenous end product, the system has become especially active.

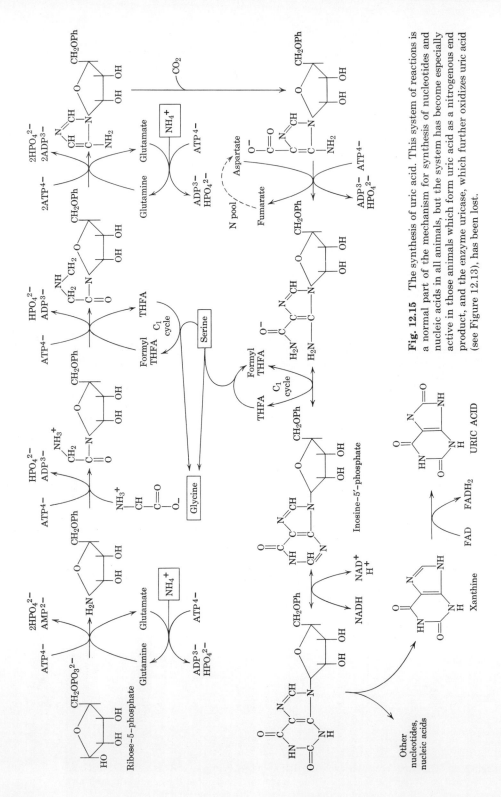

Fig. 12.15 The synthesis of uric acid. This system of reactions is a normal part of the mechanism for synthesis of nucleotides and nucleic acids in all animals, but the system has become especially active in those animals which form uric acid as a nitrogenous end product, and the enzyme uricase, which further oxidizes uric acid (see Figure 12.13), has been lost.

TABLE 12.2

Partition of Excreted Nitrogen among Various End Products

Group	Ammonia	Urea	Uric Acid	Allantoin	Amino Acids	Purine	Unident.
				Approximate per cent of total nitrogen excreted as			
Vertebrata							
Mammalia*	2–20	**30–90**	0–4	0–20	1–2	0.2–0.6	3–20
Aves	2–20	1–10	**60–90**	—	5	8	0–30
Reptilia							
Alligator	**40–80**	1–20	10–40	—	—	—	0–20
Turtles	4–20	**10–90**	**1–60**	0–1	5–20	—	0–40
Squamata	4–10	0–2	**60–95**	0–2	1–5	0.3–2	0–40
Amphibia (*Rana*)*	2–40	**60–90**	0–0.4	—	—	—	1–10
Pisces	**50–70**	10–20	—	—	3–15	—	1–10
Selachia	2–10	**80–90**	—	—	1–20	—	4–10
Arthropoda							
Insecta	2–20	0–10	**50–90**	—	0–10	—	5–40
Crustacea	**30–99**	0–10	0–10	—	0–30	0–40	**2–70**
Mollusca							
Cephalopoda	**30–70**	1–15	1–2	—	10–20	5–20	10–20
Gastropoda	10–40	**2–60**	1–10	—	1–30	5–30	**3–80**
Pelecypoda	5–60	3–5	0–2	—	10–40	5–20	**5–80**
Annelida	20–90	**4–90**	0–1	—	1–20	3–20	10–30
Echinodermata	20–40	5–20	0–1	—	20–30	5–10	20–30
Protozoa (*Paramecium*)	**60–90**	0	0	—	—	—	—

* Urine only.

271

and urea are formed in the early stages, while uric acid appears later.

We must conclude that the concept of a phylogenetic sequence in a nitrogenous excretion is attractive, but by no means established as a fact. In any case we wonder what possible adaptive significance these patterns of nitrogenous excretion might have to ensure their selection in the course of evolution. This question of course occurred to Needham and Baldwin, and they developed some ingenious answers. If we look first at those forms which excrete uric acid as the major nitrogenous end product, we must consider what birds, squamate reptiles, and insects have in common. Two things are obvious: a terrestrial existence and the habit of laying yolky eggs enclosed in an egg shell or other covering relatively impervious to water. The embryo which develops for a considerable period in a closed or cleidoic egg will, in the course of development, oxidize amino acids as energy sources. The ammonia liberated by this process would, in the enclosed space of the egg, be quite toxic. Uric acid, on the other hand, is quite insoluble in water. It can then be retained in the egg until development is completed, without harming the embryo, as a solid nontoxic material. The adaptive significance is obvious.

This adaptive significance must be balanced against the cost of synthesizing uric acid. This amounts to about 2.5 ATP molecules per nitrogen atom from the energy standpoint. It also involves the elimination of 5 carbon atoms for every 4 nitrogen atoms eliminated. One may then ask what advantage there is to the adult in retaining this expensive method of elimination. The adult could conceivably eliminate nitrogen by some other and less expensive mechanism. The answer to this question appears to be that uric acid permits the elimination of nitrogen with a minimum of water loss. The urine of all the uric acid excretors is eliminated through a cloaca or through the intestine in the form of a thick paste or even of dry pellets. No energy is required to separate the insoluble uric acid from water. Considerable energy would be required to separate urea, and those animals which utilize urea or NH_3 as end products normally either live in water or eliminate a fluid urine with consequent loss of water. An interesting variant of this pattern is seen in the spiders, which apparently eliminate the purine guanine instead of uric acid. Guanine is also relatively insoluble in water and contains equal numbers of carbon and nitrogen atoms.

Urea, like uric acid, is not toxic; it is however quite soluble in water. Its accumulation in a cleidoic egg would have serious osmotic consequences, since it does not readily penetrate cell membranes. The energy cost of urea synthesis is essentially the same as that for the synthesis of uric acid (2 molecules of ATP per atom of nitrogen); the carbon/nitrogen ratio is 1/2. In the embryonic development of a mammal, urea formed by embryonic metabolism is readily eliminated in the maternal circulation. In the adult the absence of toxicity, in a terrestrial form where the urine is normally concentrated as a part of the water conservation mechanism, is advantageous. Uric acid might offer some advantages in the adult, but the mammalian excretory system can handle only limited amounts of uric acid. On the other hand, the ability of the mammalian kidney to remove water from the urine as it is formed is considerable, and desert mammals can concentrate urea to a surprising extent; no other vertebrates can do this. In semi-aquatic forms such as many turtles and frogs, the ability to form urea offers distinct advantages over NH_3 when an animal is not in the water. Baldwin and his collaborators have recently shown that in amphibians the pattern of nitrogen elimination changes with environmental factors in the same animal. Frogs living in water eliminate more ammonia and less urea than frogs living in air, and progressive dehydration increases the proportion of urea.

If our reasoning so far is congruent with fact, we should find a good correlation between the patterns of excretion and habitat in related animals of the same group. The turtles, which have been studied in considerable detail, offer a test. Approximate values of urinary nitrogen partition are presented in Table 12.3, and we can see that the aquatic and semi-aquatic forms generally eliminate ammonia or urea and the terrestrial forms, urea or uric acid. The pattern is not, however,

entirely clear-cut; some of the lack of definition may be due to physiological variations which are not controlled in the studies. Some of it is simply biological variability, and the generalization that NH_3 is the characteristic end product in aquatic forms, urea the characteristic in semi-terrestrial forms, and uric acid the end product in terrestrial animals is clearly no more than a rough guide.

We must, however, still account for the selachians—marine animals which excrete urea. Marine vertebrates in general have a salt concentration in the blood which is substantially lower than the salt concentration of the sea. Bony fishes living in the sea have, as we shall see, a regulation problem as a result, but the osmotic concentration of elasmobranch blood is always slightly greater than that of sea water. The osmotic deficit of salts is made up by urea, which is present in elasmobranch blood at concentrations of 2 to $2\frac{1}{2}$%. The excretion of urea is no doubt a consequence of a physiological overproduction of this substance as an

TABLE 12.3
Urinary N Partition of Turtles

Species	Habitat	Percent of Urinary N as		
		Ammonia	Urea	Uric Acid
Chelone mydas	Aquatic	40	6	4
Pelusios derbianus	Aquatic	19	24	5
Kinixys youngii	Aquatic	6	44	6
Chrysemys pinta	Aquatic	11	24	14
Kinosternon subrubrum	Semi-aquatic	24	23	0.7
Emys orbicularis	Semi-aquatic	14	47	3
Testudo denticulata	Terrestrial	6	29	7
Kinixys erosa	Terrestrial	6	61	4
Testudo graeca	Terrestrial	4	22	52
Testudo elegans	Dry terrestrial	6	9	56

osmotic adaptation. Recently, a species of frog, which frequently enters sea water in quest of food and can live for considerable periods in sea water, has been studied. When this frog is placed in sea water, the urea concentration of the blood increases sharply, again as an osmotic adaptation. The same adaptive response has been found in other anuran amphibians.

The elimination of urea by certain gastropod mollusks is less clearly associated with environment. The sea slug *Aplysia* excretes relatively small amounts of urea while the terrestrial slug *Limax,* the snail *Helix,* and the semi-terrestrial periwinkle *Littorina* eliminate much more. The pond snail *Lymnaea* is, however, also reported to excrete urea in quantity. Among the annelids, urea is excreted in relatively high proportion by earthworms but not by marine annelids or leeches. Among crustaceans, on the other hand, there is little relation between urea excretion and habitat. The true land crabs have not been studied in this respect and might prove interesting. Both crustaceans and mollusks eliminate considerable amounts of nitrogen in forms not yet identified, and a study of these substances in relation to habitat might also prove interesting.

In conclusion, comparative studies have shown general relations between the pattern of nitrogen elimination, the habitat of the animal in the adult state, and the conditions of development of the embryo. In general, these relations are more closely correlated with habitat and developmental conditions than with systematic or phylogenetic considerations. Terrestrial animals generally form urea or uric acid as the major nitrogenous end product. Those forms in which development occurs in a cleidoic egg utilize uric acid, but the mammals, viviparous and

with a kidney capable of producing a highly concentrated urine, utilize urea. Aquatic animals eliminate nitrogen mostly as ammonia or urea. Urea may have an osmotic function in some forms and in general is utilized in preference to ammonia by semi-terrestrial animals. In a general way these relations can be rationalized on the basis of chemical properties of the substances. It is likely that more detailed study of special groups of animals will yield further information of interest in broadening or modifying these conclusions.

Metabolism of Lipids

The study of the metabolism of lipids has lagged behind that of the other foodstuffs, in part because the chemistry of lipids and the techniques for the study of their metabolism have lagged. Consequently the following account will describe the situation in mammals, where it is best known, with only minor notes on other forms (Figure 12.16). During the absorption of fats from the intestine, the triglycerides of the food are to a very large extent reconstituted, either by hydrolysis in the intestine followed by resynthesis in the mucosa or by exchanges of fatty acids in the mucosa among triglyceride molecules absorbed without previous hydrolysis. The bulk of the fat of the food appears in the lymphatic vessels of the intestine (the lacteals) in the form of colloidal particles with variable diameter, known as chylomicrons. A small portion of the fat consisting mostly of the short-chain fatty acids enters the portal blood. The chylomicrons move with the lymph into the blood through the thoracic lymph duct, and hence initially bypass the liver; they are the only major foodstuffs to do so.

The blood in certain conditions contains a lipase which can break up the chylomicrons. The quantitative importance of this "clearing" factor is not established. In any case the liver rapidly removes the chylomicrons from the blood, and the fatty acids enter into the general fatty acid pool of the liver. The liver is the only tissue known to be able to remove chylomicrons. Consequently, from a functional viewpoint, the liver has the same role with respect to fat that it has respecting the other foodstuffs. All the foodstuffs are absorbed by the liver after digestion and before transport to other tissues.

In the liver the fatty acids may be converted to liver triglycerides or to liver phosphatides, or they may be oxidized to acetyl coenzyme A. The acetyl coenzyme A in turn may serve for synthesis of other fatty acids, cholesterol or other lipids, or be oxidized through the tricarboxylic acid cycle. The liver fatty acid pool may also be replenished by conversion of carbohydrates to acetyl coenzyme A and thence to fatty acids or by conversion of amino acid residues to fatty acids, again through acetyl coenzyme A. Finally, the liver may absorb free fatty acids from the blood; the source of these will

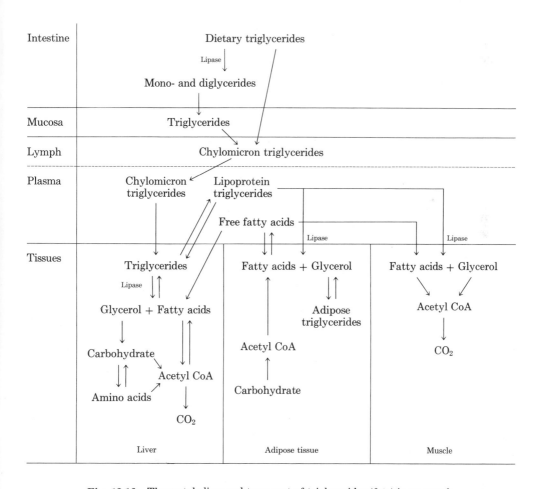

Fig. 12.16 The metabolism and transport of triglycerides (fats) in mammals.

be discussed below. From the pool of liver fatty acids, triglycerides are passed into the blood in the form of lipoprotein complexes. These are distinct from the chylomicron particles, having a higher protein content and much smaller particle size. They can be taken up by the various tissues, including adipose tissue; the half life of a lipoprotein glyceride in the blood of a mammal is only about 5 minutes.

Adipose tissue is a form of connective tissue heavily impregnated with lipid, mostly in the form of triglycerides. In mammals certain regions, known as fat depots, readily develop adipose tissue. The fat in the depots is derived in part from blood triglycerides and is in part synthesized in the tissue from carbohydrate or amino acid. The relative importance of liver and adipose tissue for *de novo* synthesis of fatty acids is not known. The depots liberate their stored material into the blood during fasting periods largely, perhaps entirely, in the form of free fatty acids. These free fatty acids are very readily absorbed and oxidized in the liver and other tissues, especially muscle. The half life of free fatty acids in mammalian blood is about 2 minutes, and these materials appear to be taken up by tissues and returned to the blood in several cycles before they are oxidized. The oxidation of free fatty acids can support the entire energy needs of the heart, and probably of other muscles, under fasting conditions.

We have said nothing here about the phosphatides. The known functions of these lipids are at cellular levels and little is known about their transport between tissues. The blood phosphatides are apparently not concerned in transport.

The foregoing account is a current interpretation of available evidence and requires verification in some points. It is clear, first, that the liver plays a central role in lipid metabolism. Second, there are at least three distinct transport forms for lipids: chylomicrons, between intestine and liver; lipoproteins, probably from liver to tissues, and free fatty acids from fat depots to liver and other tissues (Figure 12.16). The regulation of the various possible pathways of fatty acid metabolism is very poorly understood but is clearly linked closely with the metabolism of carbohydrates and amino acids. In particular, the balance between net synthesis and net break down of fats and between tissue utilization of fats or carbohydrates for energy depends closely on nutritional state and is probably also controlled by hormones.

We have no idea as to the generality in the animal kingdom of the picture just presented for mammals. Only vertebrates and insects store substantial amounts of triglycerides as energy stores; most invertebrates rely more on carbohydrates, or they store little reserve energy and utilize tissue proteins during a fast. Fat has the distinct advantage of providing a compact fuel, since the energy yielded by oxidation of a gram of fat is more than twice that from the same weight of carbohydrate. In addition, adipose tissue contains relatively little water, while tissues that store carbohydrate have 80% or more water. The weight factor is of undoubted importance in insects and in birds, where the relation of payload to fuel is as important as it is in mechanical aircraft. Recent evidence has shown clearly that migratory birds utilize fat as an energy source in preference to carbohydrate, during the nightly fast of sleep and during migration. A similar utilization of fat has been described in a migratory insect, the monarch butterfly. The transport mechanisms for lipids are entirely unknown outside the mammalian group.

References

Metabolism, General

Brand, T. von. 1946. *Anaerobiosis in invertebrates.* Biodynamica, Normandy, Mo.

Davies, M. 1961. On body size and tissue respiration. *J. Cell. Comp. Physiol.* **57** 135–147.

Holmes, E. 1937. *The Metabolism of Living Tissues.* Univ. Press, Cambridge, England.

Kayser, C. 1951. La loi des surfaces. *Rev. Scientifique* **89** 267–278.

Kleiber, M. 1947. Body size and metabolic rate. *Physiol. Rev.* **27** 511–541.

Kleiber, M. 1961. *The Fire of Life.* Wiley, New York.

Nicolaysen, R., Eeg-Larsen, N., and Malm, O. J. 1953. Physiology of calcium metabolism. *Physiol. Rev.* **33** 424–444.

Peters, J. P. 1951. The interrelationships of foodstuffs in metabolism. *Yale J. Biol. Med.* **24** 48–72.

Schoenheimer, R. 1942. *The Dynamic State of Body Constituents.* Harvard Univ. Press; Cambridge, Mass.

Schoenheimer, R., and Rittenberg, D. 1940. The study of intermediary metabolism of animals with the aid of isotopes. *Physiol. Rev.* **20** 218–248.

Zeuthen, E. 1953. Oxygen uptake as related to body size in organisms. *Quart. Rev. Biol.* **28** 1–12.

Metabolism of Foodstuffs: Carbohydrate, Protein, Lipid.

Bach, S. J. 1952. *The Metabolism of Protein Constituents in the Mammalian Body.* Clarendon Press, Oxford, England.

Buchanan, J. M., and Hartman, S. C. 1959. Enzymic reactions in the synthesis of purines. *Adv. Enzymol.* **21** 199–261.

Chaikoff, I. L., and Brown, G. W. 1954. Fat metabolism and acetoacetate formation. *Chem. Path. Metab.* **1** 277–348.

Cohen, P. P. 1954. Nitrogen metabolism of amino acids. *Chem. Path. Metab.* **2** 1–46.

Dawson, R. M. C. 1957. The animal phospholipids, their structure, metabolism, and biological significance. *Biol. Rev.* **32** 188–229.

Deuel, H. J., Jr. 1951–7. *The Lipids* (3 vols.) Interscience, New York.

Florkin, M. 1945. L'evolution du métabolisme des substances azotées chez les animaux. *Actual. Biochim.* **3** 5–66.

Greenberg, D. M. 1954. Carbon catabolism of amino acids. *Chem. Path. Metab.* **2** 47–111.

Greenberg, D. M. 1954. Synthetic processes involving amino acids. *Chem. Path. Metab.* **2** 113–147.

Huennekens, F. M., and Osborn, M. J. 1959. Folic acid coenzymes and one-carbon metabolism. *Adv. Enzymol.* **21** 369–446.

Keilin, J. 1959. The biological significance of uric acid and guanine excretion. *Biol. Rev.* **34** 265–296.

McElroy, W. D., and Glass, H. B. (eds.) 1955. *Amino Acid Metabolism.* Johns Hopkins Press, Baltimore, Md.

Meister, A. 1955. Transamination. *Adv. Enzymol.* **16** 185–246.

Meister, A. 1953. Amino acids. *Biochem. Physiol. Nutr.* **1** 102–187.

Munro, H. N. 1951. Carbohydrate and fat as factors in protein utilization and metabolism. *Physiol. Rev.* **31** 449–488.

Needham, J. 1930. The biochemical aspect of the recapitulation theory. *Biol. Rev.* **5** 142–158.

Needham, J. 1938. Contributions of chemical physiology to the problem of reversibility in evolution. *Biol. Rev.* **13** 225–251.

Ratner, S. 1954. Urea synthesis and metabolism of arginine and citrulline. *Adv. Enzymol.* **15** 319–387.

Sourkes, T. L. 1953. Carbohydrate metabolism. *Biochem. Physiol. Nutr.* **1** 57–101.

part IV
Integrative functions
in animals

13 Nature and mechanisms of integration

The Nature of Integration

The term integration, as we shall use it here, refers to the ordering of the manifold activities of the cells and tissues—the contraction of muscles, the secretion of gland cells, the metabolic activities of all the cells in the body—in such a way that they contribute to the activity of the organism as a whole. In a sense, the activity of the whole organism is the sum of the activities of the cells, but these cellular activities are not random; they are integrated.

Teleology and Adaptation

We are tempted to say that the activities are directed toward an aim or a goal—the aim of securing food, of reproducing, or merely of keeping alive, perhaps. In an Aristotelian sense, as an expression of a final cause, such a statement is true, but in science the teleological argument, the argument from final causes, is invalid. We are conscious within ourselves of aims and goals, and of directing our activities toward such aims and goals. It may be that many animals have the same consciousness, but it would be unwise to attempt to base scientific explanations on an analogy to our conscious experience. For one thing, the psychologists have made it clear that our conscious aims may be greatly influenced by factors of which we are unconscious and hence may be an unreliable basis for explaining our behavior. More important, centuries of experience have shown that the teleological argument is a facile one which can be used to explain the same body of phenomena in any of several ways, all equally valid in logic. By contrast, the practice of science, over the last four centuries, of restricting our considerations to efficient causes has yielded explanations on which general agreement is possible and from which fruitful consequences in theory and practice emerge.

The theory of evolution by natural selection has provided us with an alternative to teleology in the concept of adaptation. We may suppose that, in general, the activities of animals must contribute to survival and to the perpetuation of the species; otherwise the species would be eliminated by natural selection. Even here one must move with caution, for an activity which is adaptive in a situation familiar to the species in its normal habitat may become quite the opposite in an abnormal situation. An animal may tolerate a certain number of activities which have little or no adaptive value, if these activities are offset sufficiently by others with adaptive value. So in the sections to follow, as in the earlier sections of this book, we shall confine ourselves to the description of phenomena and to explanations of those phenomena in terms of efficient causes and not attempt to use arguments based on the presumed adaptive value of the phenomenon, or on its relation to the "aims" of the animal. This is not a denial that such aims exist but merely a statement that, in scientific analysis, their existence is irrelevant.

Types of Integration

In considering the phenomena of integration, we shall be concerned with two aspects: the integration of cellular activities to provide regulation of the internal conditions within the animal and the integration of these activities to provide for the manifold actions on

and reactions to the surroundings of the animal, which we know as behavior. The concept of regulation we owe primarily to Claude Bernard. He was one of the first to extend cell theory to physiology and to think of the activities of the organism as made up of cellular activities. He was also one of the first to realize that, in higher animals at least, there are numerous mechanisms concerned in providing a medium of constant chemical composition and physical properties in which the cellular activities take place. The concept of regulation which he introduced has formed a major basis of physiological thought ever since and has been given the convenient name *homeostasis* by W. B. Cannon. There are many physiological mechanisms concerned in keeping constant the properties of the blood and tissue fluids in which the cellular activities are carried on in higher animals. We shall discuss some of these in Chapter 14 under the heading of conservative regulation.

There are, however, a number of types of regulation which lead not to constancy but to regular ordered change. One such regulation is involved in growth and development. The ordered series of changes in form and size which occur between the zygote and the adult in the development of an animal are clearly regulated. We still know very little about the physiology of this regulation, especially in the embryonic stages, but in the later postembryonic stages we have considerable information for a few cases, and this will be discussed in Chapter 15.

When the animal reaches the adult condition, there may still be regular variations in activity of many sorts. Among the most familiar and the best understood are the cycles of molting and of reproduction. These two are regulated by mechanisms similar to those involved in control of growth and development. The difference is that, in growth and development, the organism is, at the end of the process, quite different in size and form from its condition at the beginning. In cyclical processes the organism passes through a sequence of changes to return essentially to its condition at the beginning of the sequence (Chapter 15).

In contrast to the relative uniformity and dependability of these regulatory processes stand the phenomena of behavior, which often seem capricious and unpredictable. We cannot here enter into this large field, but we can go a little way into the physiological mechanisms which underly behavior, and more specifically those aspects of behavior which clearly result from external stimuli. This aspect we have called reactive integration, the integration of reactions to stimuli originating in the environment (Chapter 16).

General Features of Integrative Mechanisms

In the present chapter we shall begin by proposing in very general terms a hypothetical description of the integrating mechanism. With this background we can, in the succeeding chapters, turn to the exploration of specific cases. In our hypothetical description we shall find it convenient to use the language (or jargon) of communication theory. The use of this language does not mean either that we improve our understanding of the processes described thereby or that we have explored or intend here to explore the phenomena of integration in terms of communication theory. The biological study of integration and the physical study of electrical and electronic systems for communication have much in common however, and have frequently found useful areas of common interest. In consequence, the language of communication theory is especially apt for the description of the processes of biological integration.

The systems we shall study are best considered by beginning with the input of information into the regulatory system. The information entering the system may come from outside the organism—from the environment—or from inside. If it arises inside the organism, it may come from the current activities of the organism or from a memory—a body of stored information which can be drawn upon under appropriate conditions. The information is always in the form of energy and may be of mechanical, chemical, thermal, or photic type. It becomes information instead of noise when it has some order and is not merely random. Much of the task of the integrative mechanism is that of separating the information from the noise.

To translate the above into some more familiar terms we might return to our discussion of receptors (Chapter 7). There we described mechanisms capable of responding to mechanical, photic, and other stimuli. Some of these receptors are located in the body surface, where they are exposed to stimuli from the exterior. Others are located in internal situations, where the only stimuli that normally reach them are those arising from muscular activity or other internal processes. We are all familiar from conscious experience with the nervous type of memory, which may act as a stimulus for action on our part. A very different sort of memory is that contained in the chromosomes, providing a set of instructions for the whole process of growth and development and in many cases for specific patterns of behavior as well and transmitted from generation to generation.

Coding

The information which enters at the input is either already in the form of a code—as in nervous memory or in the chromosomes—or it is encoded by the receptor. This is to say that the information, once it has entered the system, is not transmitted as such but is rather translated into a new form or code. This is analogous to the use of Morse code for a wireless message, in which a system of dots and dashes represent the letters of the alphabet in the original information, the letters in turn being part of the code by which we express facts, ideas, relations. The biological code may be nervous, as we saw earlier; information about the strength and duration of the stimulus acting on a receptor leaves the receptor as a pattern of action potentials in the axon. The organism also has chemical codes, in which information is contained in specific chemical substances. The most elaborate such code is that in the deoxyribonucleic acid of the chromosomes. Here, a great variety of hereditary information is contained in a code which must involve definite sequences of the four nitrogenous bases of the nucleic acid molecule.

Once encoded, the information is then transmitted from the input to a center. The transmission is nervous when the code is nervous, humoral when the code is chemical. Humoral transmission may be by diffusion, within cells and from cell to cell in the body fluids or more rapidly in the blood of the circulatory system. In the course of transmission, the nervous code may be translated into a chemical

code and this again back into a nervous code. We have discussed the details of such a translation mechanism in our consideration of synaptic transmission (Chapter 8).

The Center

The center is the most varied, often the most complex, and in consequence the most important part of the communication system. In the simplest case, the center is located in or identical with the effector, and its task is merely to formulate or to formulate and carry out a response appropriate to the information transmitted to it. Thus in a very simple case of an independent effector such as the cnidoblast or nematocyst of the coelenterate discussed in Chapter 9, the effector receives information in the form of mechanical and chemical stimuli. It will not respond to either alone but will respond to the two together if the chemical stimulus is an appropriate one. Here there is, as far as we know, no coding, and the transmission is confined to a single cell, but two sorts of information are integrated to elicit a response which has evident adaptive significance in food gathering and protection from predators.

A more complex situation in terms of mechanism is the knee-jerk reflex. A sharp blow on the stretched patellar tendon of a mammal is the information input. This information is encoded in the tendon stretch receptors in the form of a sharp burst of action potentials which first is conducted along the afferent axons to the center in the spinal cord. The center here is represented by synapses of the afferent axons from the stretch receptors of the patellar tendon on the large ventral horn cell bodies, connected through efferent neurons with the extensor muscles of the thigh. The nervous code of the input channels (afferent axons) is translated into a chemical code at the synapse. In the nervous code, intensity of stimulus is represented by frequency of action potentials. In the chemical code the intensity is represented by the amount of transmitter agent liberated. The chemical code is then translated back into a nervous code in the efferent axons (output channels of the center) to the neuro- muscular junction. Here the instructions to the muscle fibers are formulated, again in chemical terms, with contraction signaled by a threshold concentration of acetylcholine, the transmitter (Figure 13.1 and Table 13.1).

With these very simple cases in mind we can now formulate in outline form the general functions of the center. It receives information, usually in code form, along one or more input channels. If the information enters only

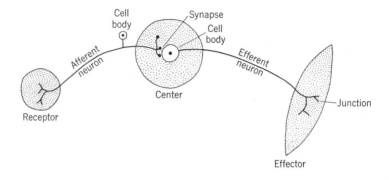

Fig. 13.1   Diagram of a simple reflex arc.

TABLE 13.1

The Mechanisms of Coding and Transmission in the Neuromuscular System

Unit	Information	Mode of Coding	Code
Receptor	Stimulus intensity	Generator potential	Depolarization
Afferent neuron	Generator potential	Spike (action potential)	Frequency
Synapse	Spike frequency	Transmitter	Concentration
Postsynaptic cell body	Transmitter concentration	Postsynaptic potential	Depolarization or hyperpolarization
Efferent neuron	Postsynaptic potential	Spike	Frequency
Neuroeffector junction	Spike frequency	Transmitter	Junctional potential

along a single channel it may be transmitted without change—that is, in the same code and in identical form. Alternatively it may be modified: transduced into another form, filtered to eliminate certain frequencies, or to reduce the frequencies, gated to eliminate the range of low or high frequencies, for example. If information enters along more than one input channel, the two or more bits of information are combined before transmission in any of a potentially infinite number of ways. The center itself may contain a memory, or the center may have some intrinsic pattern of activity, and either or both of these will influence the way in which the input is handled. Ultimately—and the time involved is normally not great—the center produces an output which is distributed along one or more channels. Typically these channels lead to effectors, and the output of the center consists of an organized pattern of instructions responsible for an integrated response of one or many effectors. In higher animals, at least, some central outputs go only to a memory, and in nearly all animals with central nervous systems the outputs of some centers go to other higher centers, to form part of the information used by these latter centers in formulating still more complex patterns of instructions for response. The output channels of the center may involve either nervous or chemical (hormonal, neurohumoral) codes.

Feedback

This, complex though it may sound, is not the end of the matter. The effectors responding to instructions from the center, in turn, can provide information concerning their response or the consequences thereof. If there are receptors to gather this information, it may in turn be transmitted to the center rapidly enough to permit the center to modify or correct the response while it is still in progress. This process, in which part of the output of the center is fed back into the center and there modifies the output, is known to communications theory as feedback. It may be positive, if the returning information increases the output of the center or negative, if the returning information decreases the output of the center. We will not give examples of these processes here, since the remainder of the book will be devoted primarily to such examples. Rather, we shall examine some of the properties of nervous centers on which their integrative activity depends and some of the chemical mechanisms involved in the humoral coordination.

Nervous Integrative Mechanisms

Morphologically, all the nervous centers we know are aggregations of nerve cell bodies with their synapses. The synapses are extremely diverse and varied in structure, so much so that they defy a systematic classification. Moreover, the experimental study of the events in synaptic transmission, which must be the crucial events in the integrative function of the center, have been carried out at the cellular level for only a few highly specialized synapses. Nevertheless, by combining what we know about these few synapses with the vastly greater body of information from experimental studies, in which the properties of the nervous input to a synapse or a collection of synapses have been compared with the properties of the nervous output from the same, we can develop at least a partial picture of the integrative process.

As we have seen earlier, the essential event in synaptic transmission seems to be the liberation from the presynaptic ending of a transmitter agent which in turn alters the properties of the adjacent portion of the membrane of the postsynaptic cell body or its dendrites. This alteration in turn causes a change in membrane potential of the cell body. In general, depolarization of the cell body, of sufficient magnitude, leads to excitation of adjacent portions of the efferent axon. We may now add to this picture of the transmission process—which seems to be quite general as far as studies have gone—the properties of synapses seen from outside. The most important, from a standpoint of integration, is the relation of input frequency to output frequency. A very few synapses show a 1:1 relation over the whole range of possible frequencies; that is, they have no integrative function. These few turn out to be the few in which transmission is electrical and which in consequence are not functional synapses at all. At the other extreme lie those synapses in which output frequency is completely independent of input frequency. The integrative function of such synapses must be confined to passing on the information that the input is "on" or "off" but nothing about the nature of the input information. Between these two extremes lie many synapses in which output frequency bears some relation to input frequency. The common pattern is a 1:1 relation up to a critical level, with less accurate following above that level.

Another pattern, also very common, is that of temporal facilitation. In this sort of synapse single input signals at low frequency are not transmitted. When the input frequency reaches a critical level, the second or third or tenth signal, and all succeeding signals at that frequency, are transmitted. Clearly, each signal produces a transitory change in the synapse, and when the signals come sufficiently close together their effects are cumulative and result in initiation of transmission as a consequence of accumulation of transmitter agent or of its effect. The related phenomenon of spatial facilitation, in which signals coming along separate input channels interact to produce output signals where signals coming in one channel alone would be ineffective, has a similar explanation. The integrative effects may be quite different in that the output of the center now depends upon two input channels, which may have different origins.

Another central interaction of great importance is that of inhibition. This phenomenon is seen when stimulation of one input channel prevents or stops transmission of information coming along another input channel. In the few cases studied at the cellular level, stimulation of the inhibitory afferent results in a hyperpolarization of the central cell body and hence a decrease in its excitability. There is also the possibility of more complex interactions of many sorts through the action of interneurons—neurons which run their whole course within the ganglion. These neurons may provide various sorts of feedback circuits within the center prolonging the effect of the input, amplifying or stimulating the input, or distributing it among many central neurons. Finally, there is the possibility that the neurons in a particular center are all in a controlled state of excitability, which varies from time to time, as a consequence of multiple effects from complex neuron chains. This type of mechanism becomes very difficult to analyze in detail. The ultimate in complex interaction is probably manifest experimentally in the spontaneous discharge patterns characteristic of all central nervous systems. If electrodes are applied to such systems one can record complex patterns of action potentials in the absence of any external stimulus. We shall return to this aspect of nervous systems briefly in Chapter 16.

Humoral Integrative Mechanisms

We have mentioned from time to time the possibility of chemical coding of information and have considered specifically the neuroneural and neuromuscular transmitters as examples of a chemical code. During the past few decades, the concept of neurohumors, developed especially by G. H. Parker, has gained increasing currency. Parker's concept was that many kinds of nerve cells produce their ultimate effects by forming and liberating a secretory product or neurohumor. This product may be liberated in very close proximity to the element on which it is to act, as in a synapse, or it may be liberated at a considerable distance from that element. Parker derived his concept of neurohumors to a large extent from his studies of color change in the vertebrates. The effectors in color change are the chromatophores, large cells with cytoplasmic extensions ramifying widely in the skin and elsewhere and containing pigment granules. Migration of the granules into the ramifying branches makes the pigment evident in the color of the skin. Concentration of the granules into a small area in the central portion of the cell minimizes the effect of the pigment on the color of the skin. In vertebrates, Parker discovered a whole range of

control mechanisms, from direct nervous action, produced by liberation of a transmitter such as acetylcholine or norepinephrin from a nerve ending closely applied to the chromatophore to effects transmitted through the blood stream by hormones liberated from the pars intermedia of the hypophysis and the medulla of the adrenal gland. The embryological and histological evidence showing that the adrenal medulla is in fact derived from sympathetic nervous tissue suggested to Parker that nerve cells in general might transmit their effect by liberating specific chemical agents, and that these might in some cases be liberated close to the target cell or organ and in other cases be liberated at some distance away, depending on the nature of the process to be controlled.

Neurosecretion and Endocrine Glands

The idea of neurohumors has gained strong support on one side from the evidence that virtually all neuroneural and neuromuscular transmission involves specific humoral substances as transmitters. It has gained another source of support from the histological demonstration by Ernst Scharrer, Bargmann, and many others that the central nervous system of animals having such systems contain cells which are, from their structure and connections, nerve cells but which contain distinctive secretory granules. Typically, these granules are formed in the cytoplasm of the cell body and move into the axon, to be carried to the axon terminus where the granule contents are liberated from the cell. Axonal transport has been demonstrated in fixed material in experimental studies, and observed in living material as well. In addition, some neurosecretory cells have been seen to liberate their products from the cell body directly. The product has been identified chemically in only a few cases. The neurosecretory cells of the vertebrate hypothalamus-posterior pituitary system contain and liberate the peptide hormones vasopressin, oxytocin, and vasotocin, for example. The biological effects of a variety of neurosecretory systems are known, and some will be discussed in the subsequent chapters.

The neurosecretory cells are doubtless activated through the nervous system, presumably by some sort of synaptic transmission. There are numerous instances demonstrating the activation or inhibition of neurosecretion by light, for example, through the medium of the eyes and optic nerves, and in a few rather crude experiments, vigorous electrical stimulation has been shown to have effects on neurosecretion. Action potentials have been demonstrated in neurosecretory cells, but the relation to the formation and transport of the secretory product is not clear. We still have much to learn about the cellular physiology of neurosecretion. In a general functional sense, however, we can regard the neurosecretory cells as output channels from the center specialized for chemical, not electrical, conduction as in the typical motor or efferent neuron. The neurosecretory material is typically liberated into the bloodstream rather than in immediate proximity to the target cells, but one could describe a range of situations between the intimate contact seen in a neuromuscular junction and the remote discharge from a neurosecretory axon terminus into the bloodstream.

From the neurosecretory cell, it is only a short step to the endocrine gland. Endocrine glands are structures which form hormones, and hormones we shall define here as specific chemical substances formed by definite cells or organs and transmitted in body fluids to other cells, tissues, or organs, where at low concentration they exert specific effects. This definition of hormones includes many neurohumors as special cases, and some of the recognized endocrine glands (the neurohypophysis and adrenal medulla of vertebrates, the sinus glands of crustaceans) are merely neurosecretory end organs made up of the termini of secretory axons; there are in addition a number of structures which are not derived from nervous tissue and which may even have no significant nervous connections, but are clearly endocrine glands. As a basis for subsequent discussion we shall describe in general terms the neuro-endocrine systems of the vertebrates and the arthropods, including as well an account of the known hormones and their mode of action (Table 13.2).

Neurosecretion in the Vertebrates

The two major neurosecretory connections with the non-nervous endocrine system of the vertebrates occur in the adrenal medulla and the neurohypophysis. The chromaffin cells, which in mammals and some other vertebrates are aggregated into a distinct structure in the central portion of a pair of adrenal glands located just cephalad of the kidneys, are in principle highly specialized nerve endings of the postganglionic sympathetic nervous system. They form and liberate epinephrin (adrenin, adrenalin) and norepinephrin (noradrenin, noradrenalin) into the blood stream. These agents have a great variety of actions, paralleling in part the more localized

TABLE 13.2
Hormones and Neurohumors

Name	Site of Formation	Chemical Nature	General Action or Function
Acetylcholine	Peripheral nerve endings of many animals	Ester	Transmitter
Adrenalin (see epinephrin)			
Adrenin (see epinephrin)			
Adrenocorticotrophic hormone (ACTH)	Anterior lobe of pituitary, vertebrates	Polypeptide (39 amino acid residues)	Initiates and maintains secretory function in adrenal cortex or interrenal bodies
Adrenoglomerulotrophin	Diencephalon, mammals	Carboline	Stimulates secretion of aldosterone by glomerulosa cells of adrenal cortex
Aldosterone	Glomerulosa cells of adrenal cortex, vertebrates	Steroid	Stimulates active transport of Na^+ across membranes
Cholecystokinin	Duodenal mucosa, mammals	Peptide?	Stimulates contraction of gall bladder
Cortisol	Adrenal cortex or interrenal bodies, vertebrates	Steroid	Stimulates gluconeogenesis, protein catabolism, and Na^+ transport
Corticosterone	Fasciculata cells of adrenal cortex, vertebrates	Steroid	Stimulates gluconeogenesis and protein catabolism, lymphocytosis; anti-inflammatory
Cortisone	Fasciculata cells of adrenal cortex, vertebrates	Steroid	As for corticosterone
Ecdyson	Thoracic gland, insects, Gabe's y-organ, crustaceans	Unsaturated ketone, $C_{18} H_{30} O_4$	Activates epidermis; promotes growth and cuticle secretion in this tissue and related processes in other tissues
Enterogastrone	Duodenum, mammals	Peptide?	Inhibits gastric secretion

TABLE 13.2 (*Cont.*)
Hormones and Neurohumors

Hormone	Source	Chemical nature	Action
Epinephrin	Chromaffin cells of adrenal, vertebrates	Methylaminodiphenol	Increases phosphorolysis of glycogen
Estradiol	Interstitial cells of ovary, vertebrates	Steroid	Stimulates development of female secondary sex characters and female sexual behavior
Follicle-stimulating hormone (FSH)	Anterior lobe of pituitary, vertebrates	Glycoprotein	Stimulates growth of ovarian follicle in female, spermatogenesis in male
Gastrin	Gastric mucosa, mammals	Peptide?	Stimulates gastric secretion
Glucagon	α-cells, islets of Langerhans, vertebrate pancreas	Peptide	Increases phosphorolysis of glycogen, liver
Hydrocortisone (see cortisol)			
Insulin	β-cells, islets of Langerhans, vertebrate pancreas	Protein	Increases uptake and oxidation of glucose by tissue cells
Interstitial cell-stimulating hormones (ICSH)	Anterior lobe of pituitary, vertebrates	Glycoproteins	Stimulate secretion of estrogen and progesterone by ovary, testosterone by testis
Juvenile hormone	Corpus allatum, insects	Hydrocarbon alcohol?	Restrains adult development in epidermis and other tissues
Luteinizing hormone (LH) (See Interstitial cell-stimulating hormone)			
Luteotrophic hormone (LTH)	Anterior lobe of pituitary, vertebrates	Protein	Varied actions related to reproduction
Melanocyte-stimulating hormones (MSH)	Intermediate lobe of pituitary, vertebrates	Polypeptides	Stimulate dispersion of pigment in melanophores
Noradrenalin (see norepinephrin)			
Norepinephrin	Peripheral endings of sympathetic neurons, vertebrates	Amino diphenol	Transmitter

TABLE 13.2 (*Cont.*)

Hormones and Neurohumors

Name	Site of Formation	Chemical Nature	General Action or Function
Oxytocin	Hypothalamic neurosecretory system, vertebrates	Cyclic peptide	Stimulates contraction of smooth muscle in uterus and mammary glands
Pancreozymin	Duodenum, mammals	Peptide?	Stimulates enzyme secretion, pancreas
Parathormone	Parathyroid gland, vertebrates	Peptide	Promotes Ca withdrawal from bones and P excretion by kidney.
Progesterone	Corpus luteum of ovary, mammals	Steroid	Variety of actions in reproductive cycle of female
Prolactin (see luteotrophic hormone)			
Secretin	Duodenum, vertebrates	Peptide	Stimulates alkaline fluid secretion by pancreas
Somatotrophic hormones (STH)	Anterior lobe of pituitary, vertebrates	Proteins	Stimulate protein synthesis and other growth processes; inhibit glucose uptake by tissues
Testosterone	Interstitial cells of vertebrate testes	Steroid	Stimulates development of male secondary sex characters and behavior
Thyrotrophic hormone (TSH)	Anterior lobe of pituitary, vertebrates	Glycoprotein	Stimulates growth and secretion of thyroid gland
Thyroxin	Thyroid gland, vertebrates	Iodinated amino acid	Stimulates tissue oxidation (mammals) and metamorphosis (amphibians)
Vasopressin	Hypothalamic neurosecretory system, mammals	Cyclic peptide	Increases permeability of membranes to water; stimulates Na$^+$ transport
Vasotocin	Hypothalamic neurosecretory system, lower vertebrates	Cyclic peptide	As for vasopressin

Only those are listed for which there is reasonable evidence of function, and which have been at least partly purified. The site of formation and action or function are the known ones; others are possible and in many cases probable.

actions of the postganglionic sympathetic fibers distributed throughout the rest of the body. The major physiological effects of secretory activity by the adrenal medulla are: (1) widespread vasoconstriction in the splanchnic area (the abdominal viscera) with resultant diversion of blood from that area into the peripheral circulation and (2) mobilization of glucose from the liver into the blood by a stimulation of glycogenolysis. The mechanism of the latter action has been explored in detail. It appears to rest on an increase in the activity of phosphorylase in the liver, with resultant increased rate of phosphorolysis of glycogen. The increase in phosphorylase activity depends on conversion of the inactive form of phosphorylase to the active form, and this is in turn brought about by an increase in the concentration of the nucleotide cyclic 3′,5′-adenosinemonophosphate (AMP). The details of the process by which formation of cyclic AMP is caused by epinephrin are not known.

The hypothalamic-neurohypophysial neurosecretory system is more complex in its actions than the adrenal medulla. The system consists of groups of cell bodies in the preoptic and paraventricular nuclei of the hypothalamus which send axons down the pituitary stalk, to end on the walls of the capillaries in the posterior or neural lobe of the pituitary (Figure 13.2). The neural derivation of this structure, as an out-

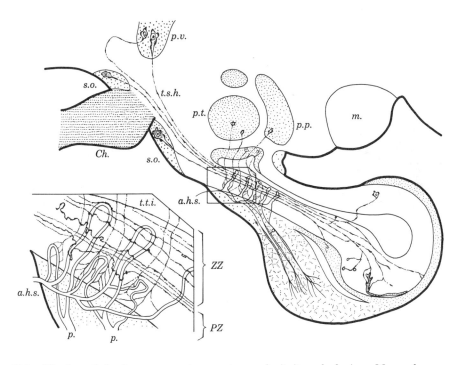

Fig. 13.2 The hypothalamic neurosecretory system and pituitary body in a Mammal. *p.v.* = paraventricular nucleus; *s.o.* = supraoptic nucleus; *a.h.s.* ≡ superior hypophyseal artery; *p.* = portal vessels. The inset shows the detailed arrangement of neurosecretory fibers with the capillaries of the portal vessels of the anterior lobe. (From Ortmann, 1961, *Handbook of Physiology: Neurophysiology* **2** 1041, ed. J. Field, Am. Physiol. Soc. Washington.)

growth of the embryonic brain, had long been known, but proof of its neurosecretory character began with Scharrer's observations in 1928.

The neurosecretory cells form, in various vertebrates, at least five polypeptide hormones—arginine vasopressin, lysine vasopressin, arginine vasotocin, oxytocin, and isotocin, recently isolated from a fish. Most vertebrates appear to have only two of these; in amphibians, reptiles, birds, and mammals oxytocin and vasotocin have been identified in posterior pituitary extracts, and in mammals one of the vasopressins replaces vasotocin. Most mammals have arginine vasopressin, but the pig and hippopotamus have lysine vasopressin. The primary function of vasopressin appears to be that of controlling the pore size of cellular membranes in situations such as the wall of the kidney tubule. The effect of treatment with vasopressin is to enlarge the apparent pore diameter, with a resultant increase in the passive diffusion of water and in the active transport rate of sodium ion. The suggestion has been made that the increased rate of sodium transport is simply a result of increased entry of sodium passively into the cells. Whether this general mechanism is proved to be correct or not, the action of vasopressin or vasotocin is to stimulate active sodium transport across membranes such as the wall of the kidney tubule or the skin or bladder of a frog or toad, and to increase the permeability of these membranes to water. In the course of its action, vasopressin is temporarily bound to the membrane on which it acts through the formation of disulfide bonds with substances, presumably proteins, in the membrane. Also, like epinephrin, it causes an increase in the cyclic AMP concentration of certain cells. The relation of these actions to the specific effect on salt and water transport remains to be worked out in detail.

The normal action of oxytocin is not fully understood as yet. It has effects on uterine contractions which may be important in parturition in mammals, and it acts as the milk letdown hormone in stimulating lactation, also in mammals. Probably there are more fundamental effects and mechanisms of action. There is physiological evidence that the neurohypophysis contains a corticotrophin-releasing factor, in addition to the peptides noted above. This substance has not yet been conclusively identified, and its function will be discussed later. In addition, there is evidence that the liberation of the gonadotrophic hormones from the anterior lobe and the melanocyte-stimulating hormones from the intermediate lobe may be under hypothalamic control.

The Adenohypophysis

The intermediate lobe and the anterior lobe of the pituitary are known together as the adenohypophysis. They are closely associated morphologically with the neurohypophysis, but have entirely different origins (Figure 13.2). The posterior lobe arises as an outgrowth of the embryonic brain, while the intermediate and the anterior lobes arise from a diverticulum of the roof of the embryonic buccal cavity known as Rathke's pouch. The anterior lobe forms at least six hormones, several of which act specifically on other endocrine glands. On the other hand, the adenohypophysis is to some degree influenced by the neurohypophysial hormones. It therefore occupies the position of a center in the vertebrate system of chemical integration, with chemical input from the neurohypophysis and chemical outputs to various endocrine glands in the body (Figure 13.3).

The products of the intermediate lobe are two melanocyte-stimulating hormones—peptides which, in those vertebrates provided with chromatophores, cause dispersion of the black melanin pigment in the melanophores or melanocytes. It is unlikely that this is the only function of the melanocyte-stimulating hormones.

The morphological aspects of the communication between neurohypophysis and adenohypophysis have attracted special attention in recent years. The axon termini of the hypothalamic neurosecretory cells are closely associated in the neurohypoph-

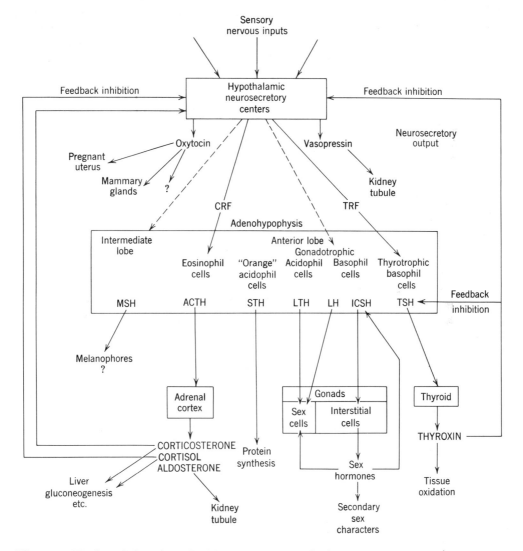

Fig. 13.3 The hypothalamo-hypophysial neurosecretory-endocrine system as a center in humoral integration in a vertebrate.

ysis with the walls of capillaries in the capillary network of that organ. In addition, in mammals, there are capillaries surrounding the neurosecretory axons in the median eminence of the diencephalon, where the axons often show an accumulation of neurosecretory material. The presumption is that the secretory products of the nerve cells are discharged from the axons and axon termini into the blood of these capillaries. In the lower vertebrates, some of the neurosecretory axons enter into the tissue of the adenohypophysis as well. The capillary network of the median eminence, and sometimes of the neurohypophysis, communicates directly with the capillary network of the adenohypophysis, usually through a system of portal vessels; that is, the capillaries unite into larger vessels which then again give rise to a capillary network in the adenohypophysis. Structurally, this provides an ideal situation for chemical transmission from the hypothalamic neurosecretory cells to the anterior lobe. As we shall see presently, there is experimental evidence indicating that neurohypophysial principles do act on the cells of the anterior lobe.

The six hormones of the anterior lobe are known respectively as the growth hormone or somatotrophic hormone (STH), the adrenocorticotrophic hormone (ACTH), the thyrotrophic or thyroid-stimulating hormone (TSH), the gonadotrophic or follicle-stimulating hormone (FSH), the luteinizing hormone or interstitial cell-stimulating hormone (LH or ICSH), and prolactin or the luteotrophic hormone (LTH). The termination -trophic means supporting or maintaining, while the alternative termination -tropic means attracted to or directed toward. The two are aften used interchangeably, but they have different meanings. The nomenclature of these hormones is related to the sequence of events in their discovery, and one should be careful to guard against the assumption that the name fully describes the function. Thus some hormones have two common names in consequence of the fact that two separate functions, such as stimulation of secretion by the corpus luteum on the one hand—hence luteotrophic hormone—and stimulation of growth and preparation for secretion in the mammary glands on the other—hence prolactin—are performed by the same hormone. As we shall see, these two functions do not by any means exhaust the range of activities of this hormone. All of the hormones of the anterior lobe are proteins, and the structures vary according to the function and often according to species as well. Thus the growth hormones of the various vertebrate species vary somewhat in structure. The growth hormones of various mammals, for example, act as antigens in man and hence cannot be used for treatment of growth defects arising from a natural deficiency of STH.

The growth hormones are formed in special cells in the anterior lobe, staining with the acid dye orange G in histological preparations. The hormones have two well-established modes of action. In the whole animal, and in tissue and cell preparations *in vitro,* they stimulate uptake of amino acids across the cell membrane and incorporation of amino acids into protein; it seems probable that this action will account for the growth-promoting effect, though there may be other related actions as well. In some mammals STH is also a diabetogenic factor, antagonizing the hormone insulin (see below and Chapter 14). The primary effect here seems to be exerted on the mechanism by which glucose penetrates cells. STH and insulin probably compete for some active site on the cell surface involved in glucose transport—STH interfering with the function of this site and insulin removing STH from the site. There are numerous other physiological effects of STH, but none of these is sufficiently well understood to be considered as directly involved in the normal mode of action. There is no adequate evidence concerning the normal control of STH secretion or the detailed relation of this secretion to normal patterns of growth.

The adrenocorticotrophic hormones (ACTH) differ less in their structure than do the growth hormones. The ACTH of beef contains 39 amino acids, and its structure has been fully worked out by C. H. Li and his collaborators at Berkeley, California. Human ACTH differs in having two additional amino acids (valine and tyrosine) near the amino end of the chain. The structure of ACTH is of interest in that it contains a sequence in common with the smaller molecules of the melanocyte-stimulating hormones, namely methionine, glutamine, histidine, phenylalanine, arginine, tryptophan, glycine. In consequence, ACTH has MSH activity as well, a fact which led to much confusion in the earlier stages of isolation of these hormones. The MSH hormones have, as is evident from Figure 13.4, much smaller molecules than ACTH. The MSH end of the ACTH molecule is apparently not its functional end as regards stimulation of the adrenal cortex. This stimulation is fully reproduced by a synthetic polypeptide comprising the last 23 amino acids of the ACTH chain. The evidence suggests that ACTH arises in those cells of the anterior lobe which take up eosin in histological preparations. The only known physiological action of ACTH is that implied in its name: it stimulates the cells of the adrenal cortex to form and liberate their steroid hormonal secretions. We shall discuss the details of this effect later. The mechanism of action is not certainly established, but recent evidence suggests that the primary effect may involve stimulation of formation of cyclic AMP. Note that a similar mechanism has been proposed for the actions of vasopressin and of epinephrin. Cyclic AMP in turn activates phosphorylase, which by increasing glycogen break down makes available increased supplies of reduced nicotinamide-adenine dinucleotide phosphate (NADPH), and NADPH in turn is the source of hydrogen for the synthesis of steroids. Whether this mechanism will prove to be the correct explanation of ACTH action can be learned only by further experimental study.

The control of ACTH secretion has also been a subject of much inquiry. A great variety of external stimuli, especially those of a potentially harmful nature, will elicit secretion of ACTH. The bulk of the evidence suggests that these stimuli ultimately act through the hypothalamic neurosecretory pathways. The effective agent has been called the corticotrophin releasing factor or CRF, and interest has centered recently around the relation of this factor to the known posterior pituitary hormones. One group of investigators consider that the functional CRF is related to, but not identical with, oxytocin.

The thyrotrophic hormone (TSH) is produced by basophilic cells in the anterior lobe. Its structure is not known in detail, but it is a glycoprotein of about 10,000 molecular weight. Its

ACTH, man

H Ser Tyr Ser Met Glu His Phe Arg Try Gly Lys Pro Val Gly Lys Lys Arg Arg Pro Val Lys Val Tyr Pro Asp Gly Glu Ala Glu Asp Ser Ala Glu Ala Phe Pro Leu Glu Phe NH$_2$

ACTH

H Ser Tyr Ser Met Glu His Phe Arg Try Gly Lys Pro Val NH$_2$ α-MSH (pig, horse, ox, monkey)

H Met Glu His Phe Arg Try Gly NH$_2$ Synthetic: MSH and CRF activity

H Asp Ser Gly Pro Tyr Lys Met Glu His Phe Arg Try Gly Ser Pro Pro Lys Arg NH$_2$ β-MSH (ox)

H His Phe Arg Try Gly NH$_2$ Synthetic: MSH activity

H Asp Glu Gly Pro Tyr Lys Met Glu His Phe Arg Try Gly Ser Pro Pro Lys Arg NH$_2$ β-MSH (pig)

H Asp Glu Gly Pro Tyr Arg Met Glu His Phe Arg Try Gly Ser Pro Pro Lys Arg NH$_2$ β-MSH (monkey)

H Ala Glu Lys Asp Glu Gly Pro Tyr Arg Met Glu His Phe Arg Try Gly Ser Pro Pro Lys Asp NH$_2$ β-MSH (man)

MSH

CRF

Fig. 13.4 The amino acid sequences of pituitary hormones. The names of the amino acids are indicated by their three initial letters. Groupings of amino acids common to several hormones and having melanophore-stimulating hormone activity (MSH) or corticotrophin-releasing factor (CRF) activity and the synthetic peptide having ACTH activity are enclosed in boxes.

primary action is in stimulating the synthesis and release of the hormone of the thyroid gland. A secondary and perhaps unrelated effect is that of causing uptake of water and fat, especially in the eyes of mammals and probably elsewhere. There is evidence suggesting hypothalamic regulation of TSH secretion, possibly as part of a feedback mechanism in which elevated levels of thyroid hormone in the blood act upon the hypothalamus to inhibit secretion of the factor which normally stimulates secretion of TSH. The identity of this hypothalamic factor is unknown.

The remaining hormones of the anterior lobe fall into the category of gonadotrophins. They stimulate various activities of the gonads. The follicle-stimulating hormone (FSH) stimulates growth of the ovarian follicles in the female and spermatogenesis in the male. It is a glycoprotein, produced by basophilic cells different from those which form TSH. The interstitial cell-stimulating hormones (ICSH), also known as the luteinizing hormones (LH), are also glycoproteins, produced apparently by the same basophilic cells which form FSH, but ICSH varies greatly in molecular weight and probably in structure from one species to another and may not even be homogeneous in a single species. The action by which this group of substances is identified is a stimulation of sex hormone secretion by the interstitial cells of the gonads. In females the hormones formed by the interstitial cells of the ovary are estrogen and progesterone. In males the hormone is testosterone. All of the sex hormones are steroids. The secretion of ICSH is under control by the hypothalamo-neurohypophysial system, and the stimuli which excite this system to action

vary greatly from species to species and from time to time in relation to the normal pattern of sexual activity in the species concerned.

Prolactin or the luteotrophic hormone (LTH) is a protein, molecular weight of about 25,000, produced by a special group of acidophil cells in the anterior lobe. Its original name (lactogenic hormone or prolactin) was given because of its role in milk production by the mammary glands. However, the hormone is formed by the adenohypophysis of all vertebrates studied and has known functions in many nonmammalian vertebrates. These functions are rather diverse but all have some connection with reproduction. In mammals the development of the mammary glands depends on stimulation by the female sex hormones estrogen and progesterone, and by prolactin. The secretion of milk depends on the thyroid hormone, the steroids of the adrenal cortex and prolactin, and the actual ejection of milk on oxytocin. Prolactin is clearly not alone in this complex process. The name luteotrophic hormone (LTH) which we shall use henceforth refers to the stimulation of secretion of progesterone by the corpus luteum of the mammalian ovary, formed after ovulation under the influence of the luteinizing hormone (LH or ICSH). LTH also has marked effects on behavior, stimulating the characteristic maternal behavior in vertebrates from mammals to fishes. It stimulates the crop gland of pigeons to form the milk on which the young are nourished for a time; it induces the newt *Triturus viridescens* to return to the water on approach of the breeding season, and it aids in the development of the sexual coloration pattern in certain fishes. There is as yet no known cellular basis for these varied actions, and one wonders if there can be a single common basis. From a biological point of view, LTH offers the first of several examples we shall see of the diversity of actions of a single hormone, in this case all directed toward the same biological end of reproduction.

Thyroid Gland

The thyroid gland is typically located on the ventral side of the pharynx, from which it arises as an evagination during embryonic development. There is also clear evidence that the thyroid has a homologue in the endostyle of the protochordates and the ammocoetes larva of the lamprey. This structure is a ciliated groove in the pharynx and constitutes part of the ciliary mucous feeding mechanism of those animals in which it occurs. Certain portions of the endostyle absorb iodide, incorporate it in a mucoprotein, and eliminate the protein with the normal secretion of the endostyle. There is no evidence that the product has any specific function in these animals. In structure, the thyroid gland of the vertebrates consists of numerous follicles, lined internally with a secretory epithelium. The cells of this epithelium actively absorb inorganic iodide from the blood and oxidize it to I_2; the I_2 in turn reacts with thyronine, an amino acid derived from tyrosine, to form a series of mono-, di-, tri-, and tetra-iodothyronines. The last of these, known as thyroxin, was the first hormone to be identified and have its structure proved by synthesis. Thyroxin, and smaller amounts of the other iodothyronines, are liberated from the follicles into the blood, where they combine with the plasma proteins in a loose union. The whole process of synthesis and release is stimulated by TSH from the pituitary. In the absence of this hormone, the thyroid ceases its secretory activity and undergoes atrophy.

The thyroid has two well-defined actions in the vertebrates, and there is no evidence that the two involve the same mechanism. The first action is a stimulation of oxygen consumption and heat production in mammals and birds. The mechanism of this action is not fully established, but there is an increasing body of evidence in favor of a mechanism by which thyroxin decreases the efficiency of oxidative phosphorylation. In this view the increased heat production results from a decreased P/O ratio in cellular oxidation, with the result that more of the energy produced by oxidation appears as heat and less as useful work (ATP). At first, this decrease in efficiency appeared as a consequence of a structural effect of thyroxin on the mitochondrion. More recent evidence favors the view that thyroxin acts by stimulating the enzyme which transfers hydrogen between nicotinamide-adenine dinucleotide and its phosphate.

$$NADH + NADP^+ \rightleftharpoons NAD^+ + NADPH$$

Increased thyroxin results in decreased concentration of NADPH, and this in turn diverts oxidative metabolism from the efficient Embden-Meyerhof glycolysis pathway to the inefficient pentose shunt pathway. Further study is required before this mechanism of action can be regarded as established.

The other effect of thyroid hormones which is very well-established is that of accelerating the metamorphosis of amphibians. This effect has been very thoroughly studied from many points of view. In spite of the wealth of information available, we cannot identify the exact point or points of action of the hormone. On the contrary, a great many related phenomena are probably influenced directly by the hormone, and among these are included neither the rate of oxygen consumption (or heat production) nor the efficiency of oxygen consumption of the whole animal. A possibility which has not been explored is that the thyroid hormones act by an effect in oxidative phosphorylation in certain critical tissues, with consequent developmental effects. On present evidence it seems probable that this possibility will not be established as fact, since there is considerable divergence in the actions of the many synthetic substances similar in structure to thyroxine which have been tested for effects both on metabolism and metamorphosis. Some of these substances are relatively more active on metamorphosis than on metabolism; others are more effective on metabolism than on metamorphosis; and some will influence one phenomenon only with no effect on the other.

Studies on other vertebrates suggest that neither the effect on metabolism seen in mammals nor the effect on metamorphosis seen in amphibians is universal. In general, the oxygen consumption of the poikilothermic vertebrates is not increased by thyroxin, though there are numerous reports of increases in individual species or special conditions, even in invertebrates and microorganisms. Extensive comparative studies on the effects of thyroxin on oxidative phosphorylation in the vertebrates are lacking and should be carried out, though for the reasons noted above the chances of arriving at a unified mechanism are small.

A third effect of thyroxin, thus far demonstrated only in mammals, is exerted on lipid metabolism. In thyroid deficiency the cholesterol content of mammalian blood increases, leading ultimately to deposition of cholesterol in the arterial walls in some cases. Thyroxin and a large number of related compounds will cause a decrease in levels of blood cholesterol. There is no consistent relation between this effect and the effect on total heat production, though a change in NADPH levels could conceivably account for both.

Parathyroid Glands

The parathyroid glands, like the thyroid, are formed from pharyngeal pouches in the embryo. They produce a protein hormone, parathormone, which has recently been partly purified and seems to be a relatively small molecule (mol wt about 7000). The mechanism of action is unknown, but the primary effects are on the metabolism of phosphate and calcium, with particular reference to blood levels and the formation of bone. In bone, where calcium and phosphate are mutually involved in the formation of bone substance, parathormone causes movement of calcium and phosphorus from bone to blood. In the kidneys it increases phosphate excretion. We do not know which of these two sites of action is the primary one; both may be involved. Whatever the mechanism, removal of the parathyroid causes a fall in blood calcium with consequent severe effects on excitability of nerve and muscle, as well as other effects on cell permeability and metabolism. The control of parathormone secretion appears to involve a direct feedback mechanism in which low levels of calcium in the blood stimulate secretion.

Endocrine Functions of the Pancreas

The islets of Langerhans, groups of endocrine cells embedded in and embryologically derived from the exocrine cells of the pancreas, secrete two hormones. The first of these, secreted by the beta cells, is the well-known insulin. This is the first protein hormone to be isolated and the first protein to have its structure fully worked out. Its role in the treatment of diabetes mellitus, a congenital disease resulting from deficient secretion by the beta cells, has been of great medical importance. The structure of insulin is now known in terms of amino acid sequence.

Insulin has two sites of action: at the cell surface in mammalian muscle and probably other cells as well, it facilitates the entrance of glucose across the cell membrane. As we noted earlier, this process appears to involve a relatively specific temporary combination of glucose with a constituent of the membrane. In this action, insulin is directly antagonized by the growth hormone (STH) of the anterior lobe of the pituitary. Within the cell, insulin accelerates the oxidation of glucose and synthesis of protein from amino acids. This last effect may be a consequence of increased energy availability from the increase in carbohydrate metabolism, or it may be independent. The mechanism of stimulation of glucose oxidation is not known. An earlier hypothesis, that insulin acts by stimulation of phosphorylation of glucose through the hexokinase system, has been abandoned because the experiments on which this hypothesis was based could not be repeated.

The other hormone of the islets is glucagon, a polypeptide of 29 amino acids, formed in the alpha cells. Glucagon was discovered first as a contaminant of commercial insulin preparations and named because of the effect which led to its discovery. The net effect of insulin administration is to decrease the concentration of glucose in the blood by increasing its utilization by tissues, especially muscle. The effect of glucagon administration is to increase the concentration of sugar in the blood by increasing the breakdown of glycogen to glucose in the liver. We can easily see how contamination of insulin with glucagon would raise serious medical problems in patients taking insulin to decrease blood sugar levels.

The secretion of both insulin and glucagon is regulated by a direct feedback mechanism in which increased levels of glucose in the blood stimulate insulin secretion, while decreased levels stimulate liberation of glucagon. The relative numbers of alpha and beta cells, and by implication the relative importance of insulin and glucagon secretion, vary in the different vertebrate groups. Herbivorous mammals and most reptiles and birds have largely alpha cells, while carnivorous mammals, rodents, and amphibians have mostly beta cells. The significance of these variations will be discussed in connection with the regulation of blood-sugar levels in the next chapter.

The Adrenal Cortex

The adrenal cortex, though closely associated structurally with the adrenal medulla in mammals, is functionally quite distinct. In the lower vertebrates the adrenal cortex has its homologue in the interrenal tissue located in more or less discrete clumps surrounding the renal arteries as they enter the kidneys. The interrenal tissue may be separated in part or wholly from the chromaffin tissue formed by the sympathetic nerve endings and homologous with the adrenal medulla in man. For the remainder of this discussion of adrenal function we shall be concerned only with the adrenal cortex and that part of the interrenal bodies which corresponds functionally with it. We shall refer to both of these as the adrenals. The adrenal cortex in mammals is more or less distinctly divided into an outer layer (the zona glomerulosa), a middle layer (the zona fasciculata), and an inner layer (the zona reticularis). No comparable differentiation has been described in the other vertebrates.

The hormones of the adrenals are steroids, and the number of these which can be extracted from the glands is considerable. Only four, however, are generally found either in the blood plasma or in the material liberated when the isolated adrenal tissue is stimulated to secrete *in vitro* by ACTH. These are cortisol or hydrocortisone, cortisone, corticosterone, and aldosterone. In man, the major normal products are cortisol and cortisone. The total amount of these two formed and liberated per day is about 20 mg. Roughly 0.1 of this amount of corticosterone is liberated, and less than that amount of aldosterone. There is not much quantitative evidence for other vertebrates, but qualitatively the same hormones seem to be formed in all the major classes. In mammals cortisol and cortisone are formed in the zona fasciculata, and aldosterone in the zona glomerulosa, while corticosterone is formed in both. The role of the zona reticularis is not established since in the experiments on which the above

statement is based the reticularis could not be separated from the fasciculata. The details of the synthetic processes are outlined in Figure 13.5. The source of all the normal adrenal hormones is progesterone, which is also a sex hormone formed by the gonads. This will be discussed later. The physiological importance of sex hormone liberation by the adrenals has not been established.

The actions of the adrenal steroids are generally grouped into two categories: actions on carbohydrate metabolism and actions on mineral or salt metabolism. Parallel to this, it is customary to classify the four common adrenal steroids as either glucosteroids or mineralosteroids, as their principal effect is on one or the other of these two aspects of metabolism. Such a classification is definitely an oversimplification and may obscure important physiological relations. Cortisone is perhaps the closest to a pure glucosteroid in that it has marked effects on carbohydrate metabolism and relatively little direct effect on mineral metabolism. On the other hand, the known effects of cortisone extend well beyond those on carbohydrate metabolism as such. The principal effects are increased synthesis of glycogen in the liver, mostly from protein (gluconeogenesis), increased protein breakdown, increased eosinophil leucocyte count in the blood, and decreased inflammatory reactions to tissue damage. The effect of increasing gluconeogenesis might result from the increased protein breakdown, but there is some evidence suggesting an independent effect on carbohydrate metabolism as such. The mechanisms of the metabolic and other effects are not known.

The other three steroids all have the same effects in various degrees. The

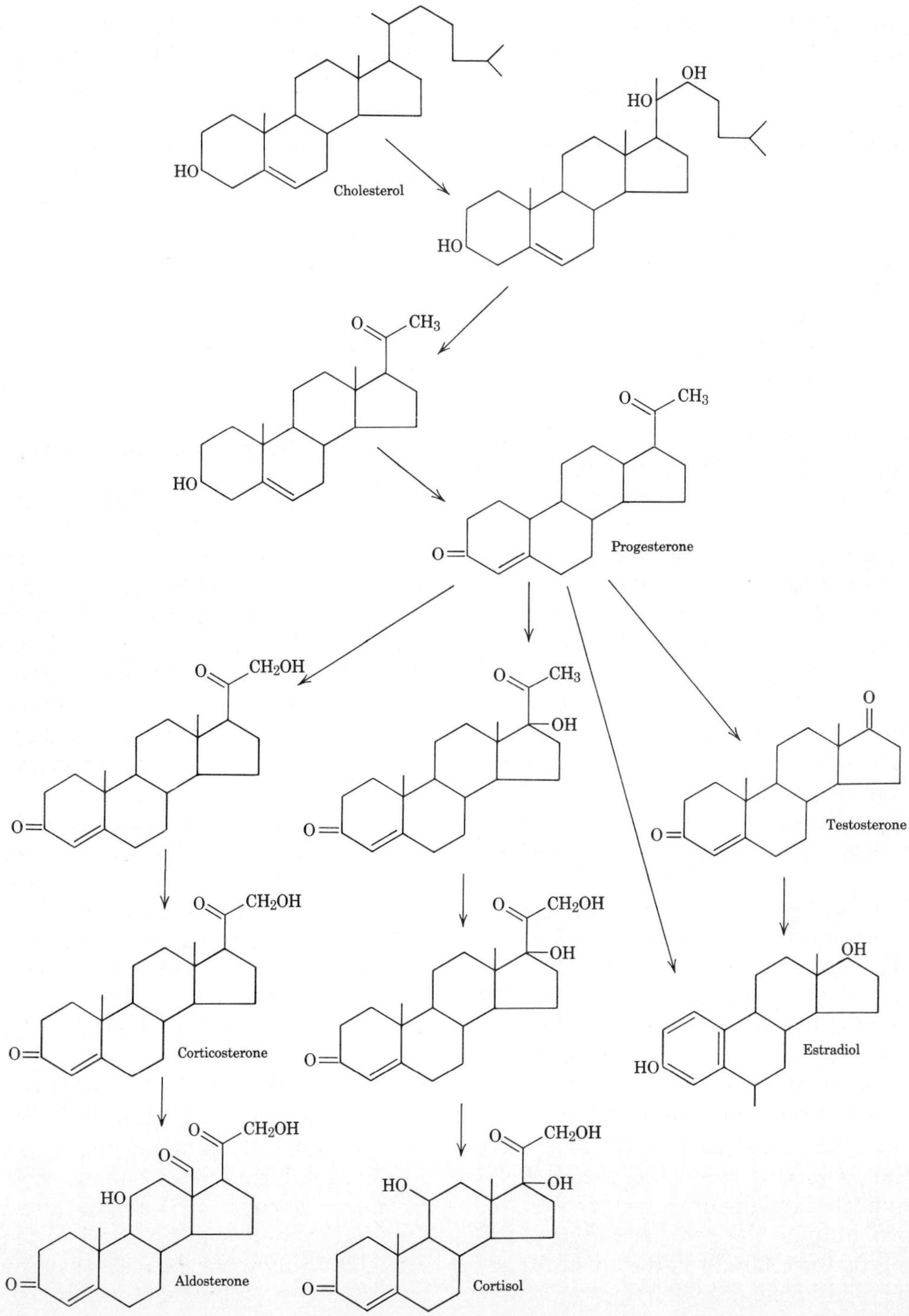

Fig. 13.5 Synthetic pathways for steroid hormones.

mineral effect of aldosterone, however, in mammals, at least, far exceeds the mineral effect of the other steroids. The prime action of aldosterone is in stimulating the active transport of sodium ion across the kidney tubule, and in amphibians across the skin of the frog or the bladder of the toad. The mechanism of this action is also unknown. Cortisol has the same effect as aldosterone on frog skin, but its action and that of corticosterone are not marked in the mammalian kidney.

The best known control over adrenal secretion is through ACTH, the adrenocorticotrophic hormone of the adenohypophysis. Removal of the anterior lobe of the hypophysis results in atrophy of the adrenal and especially of the zona fasciculata. Persistence of the glomerulosa cells has suggested to some that these cells are not under ACTH control, but ACTH will stimulate aldosterone secretion along with secretion of larger amounts of other steroids in isolated adrenals. Recent evidence points to the diencephalic region of the brain as a source of a second stimulating factor, which has been purified and synthesized and is called adrenoglomerulotrophin. It is a heterocyclic nitrogenous base of the carboline group. Its action is to stimulate aldosterone secretion, but its normal functional significance has not been established. Renin, an endocrine product of mammalian kidneys, also stimulates aldosterone secretion.

As we noted earlier, ACTH secretion is in turn regulated through the hypothalamic neurosecretory system, probably by the corticotrophin-releasing factor related to other neurohypophysial hormones. The normal stimulus to the hypothalamus is not known, but two experimental effects have been studied. In mammals, any severe stimulus such as tissue damage, extreme emotion, or cold will increase hypothalamic neurosecretory activity, ACTH secretion, and adrenal secretion. In frogs, the reverse sequence can be brought about by exposure to an isotonic salt solution, with the ultimate consequence that active sodium transport across the skin and kidney tubule is decreased. This sequence of responses appears to be adaptive; the "stress" reaction in mammals may also be.

Arthropod Neuro-endocrine System

The neuro-endocrine system of the arthropods shows several contrasts with that of the vertebrates, the principal one being the relative scarcity of true endocrine glands in the arthropods (Figure 13.6). Neurosecretory cells are widespread throughout the central nervous systems of all arthropods studied, and their peripheral endings are in many instances grouped in specialized end organs which were for a time considered to be endocrine glands. In crustaceans the best known of these end organs is the sinus gland, first clearly described by Hanström. This structure is made up of axon termini of neurosecretory cells with cell bodies in the brain or in the ganglia of the eyestalk. Experimental studies by B. Hanström in Sweden and by F. A. Brown and others in the United States showed that the sinus gland contains chromatophorotrophic hormones and a molt-inhibiting hormone as well. However, removal of the sinus gland does not prevent molting, and Passano was able to show conclusively that the molt-inhibiting hormone arises in neurosecretory cells in the eyestalk ganglia and is merely liberated from the sinus gland. In many crustaceans the eye-

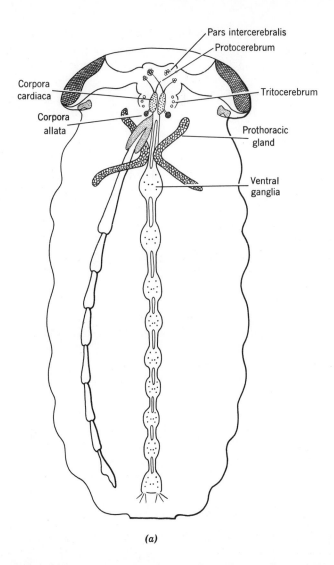

Corpora
cardiaca

Corpora
allata

Pars intercerebralis
Protocerebrum

Tritocerebrum

Prothoracic
gland

Ventral
ganglia

(a)

Fig. 13.6 The neuroendocrine systems of arthropods. (*a*) Insects (after Novak, 1959, *Insektenhormone*, Czech Acad. Sci., Prague). (*b*) Crustaceans (after Gorbman and Bern, 1962, *Textbook of Comparative Endocrinology*, Wiley, New York; and Carlisle and Knowles, 1959, *Endocrine Control in the Crustacea*, Cambridge Univ. Press, Cambridge).

stalk also contains another end organ, the X-organ or the organ of Bellonci, made up of axon termini from neurosecretory cells in the brain and optic ganglia.

In insects the neurosecretory cells of the brain send axons to two paired end organs located just posterior to the

brain, and known as the corpora allata and corpora cardiaca. Corpora allata appear to have intrinsic non-nervous secretory cells as well as axon termini and hence are true endocrine organs. The corpora allata form a fat-soluble juvenile hormone which has not been identified chemically, but which has

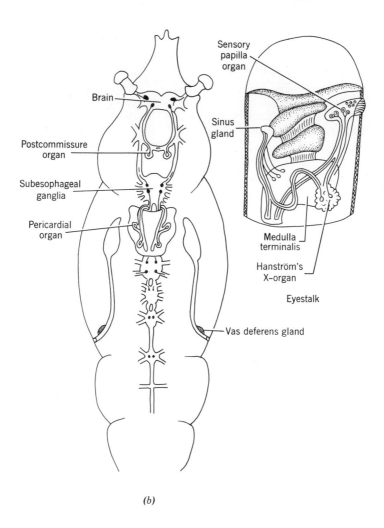

Brain

Sensory
papilla
organ

Postcommissure
organ

Sinus
gland

Subesophageal
ganglia

Pericardial
organ

Medulla
terminalis

Hanström's
X–organ

Eyestalk

Vas deferens gland

(b)

specific developmental actions in retarding the appearance of adult characteristics. Similar end organs occur in other arthropods, and in addition there are many neurosecretory cells whose axons do not form a specific end organ.

The principal endocrine organ of the arthropods, as distinct from neurosecretory structures, is the molt gland, variously known in insects as the prothoracic or thoracic gland and in crustaceans as the Y-organ or ventral gland. Removal of this structure prevents molting in many insects and in

those crustaceans tested, and its implantation restores the ability to molt. The development of the gland is closely correlated with the onset of processes leading to molt. A hormone known as ecdyson has been isolated from insects and crustaceans by Karlson and Butenandt in Germany. This hormone duplicates the actions of the molt gland, but its origin from that gland and its chemical structure have not been established conclusively. The development and activity of the molt gland are stimulated in insects by neurosecretory cells in the brain which probably liberate their product through the corpora cardiaca. The molt gland of crustaceans is inhibited by a factor from the eyestalks, in all probability the molt-inhibiting hormone.

Many crustaceans also have a distinct male sex gland, the secretion of which is responsible for development of male secondary sexual characteristics. This structure is typically located on the wall of the vas deferens and it is a non-nervous structure. In those crustaceans which lack a discrete male gland, the same function is performed by the interstitial cells of the testes, and the vas deferens gland may be made up of interstitial cells which have migrated out of the testes. Insects have no comparable structure as far as is known.

References

(Detailed references concerning certain topics considered in this chapter will also be found following chapters 14, 15, and 16.)

Endocrine mechanisms, general

Gorbman, A., and Bern, H. A. 1962. *A Textbook of Comparative Endocrinology.* Wiley, New York.

Haynes, R. C. Jr., Sutherland, E. W., and Rall, T. W. 1960. The role of cyclic adenylic acid in hormone action. *Rec. Adv. Horm. Res.* 16 121–133.

Jenkin, P. M. 1962. *Animal Hormones.* Pergamon, Oxford.

Levine, R. 1957. On the mechanisms of action of hormones on cells. *Survey of Biological Progress* (B. Glass ed.) 3 185–213.

Pincus, G. 1956. The hormones, their present significance, their future. *Curr. Biochem. Res.* 1956. 176–197.

Turner, C. D. 1955. *General Endocrinology.* (2nd ed.) Saunders, Philadelphia.

Neurohumors

DuVigneaud, V. 1960. Experiences in the polypeptide field, insulin to oxytocin. *Annals N.Y. Acad. Sci.* 88 537–548.

Fingerman, M. 1959. The physiology of chromatophores. *Int. Rev. Cytol.* 8 175–210.

Gabe, M. 1954. La neurosécrétion chez les invertébrés. *L'Année Biol.* Ser. 3 30 5–62.

Gaddum, J. H., and Holzbauer, M. 1957. Adrenaline and noradrenaline. *Vitamins and Hormones* 15 152–203.

Gellhorn, E. 1957. *Autonomic Imbalance and the Hypothalamus.* Univ. Minnesota Press, Minneapolis, Minn.

Gersch, M. 1957. Wesen und Wirkungsweise von Neurohormonen im Tierreich. *Naturwiss.* 44 525–532.

Fields, W. S., Guillemin, R., and Carton, C. A. (eds.) 1956. *Hypothalamic-Hypophysial Relationships.* Thomas, Springfield, Ill.

Hanström, B. 1953. Neurosecretory pathways in the head of crustaceans, insects and vertebrates. *Nature* 171 72–73.

Harris, G. W. 1960. Central control of pituitary secretion. *Hdbk. Physiol. I: Neurophysiol.* 3 1007–1038.

Landgrebe, F. W., Ketterer, B., and Waring, H. 1955. Hormones of the posterior pituitary. *The Hormones* 3 389–431.

Ortmann, R. 1960. Neurosecretion. *Hdbk. Physiol. I: Neurophysiol.* 3 1039–1065.

Parker, G. H. 1955. Background adaptations. *Quart. Rev. Biol.* 30 105–115.

Scharrer, E., and Scharrer, B. 1954. Hormones produced by neurosecretory cells. *Rec. Progr. Horm. Res.* 10 183–232.

Sloper, J. C. 1958. Hypothalamo-neurohypophysial neurosecretion. *Int. Rev. Cytol.* 7 337–389.

Welsh, J. H. 1955. Neurohormones. *The Hormones* 3 97–151.

Adenohypophysis

Astwood, E. B. 1955. Growth hormone and corticotropin. *The Hormones* 3 235–308.

Hays, E. E., and Steelman, S. L. 1955. Chemistry of the anterior pituitary hormones. *The Hormones* 3 201–234.

Jutisz, M., and de la Llosa, P. 1961. Relations entre la structure chimique et l'activité biologique des hormones hypophysaires. *L'Année Biol.* Ser. 3 34 81–105.

Rose, S., Nelson, J., and Bradley, T. R. 1960. Regulation of TSH release. *Annals N.Y. Acad. Sci.* 86 647–666.

Sonenberg, M. 1958. Chemistry and physiology of the thyroid-stimulating hormone. *Vitamins and Hormones* 16 205–261.

Waring H., and Ketterer, B. 1953. Relation of adrenocorticotrophin (ACTH) to the melanophore expanding (B) hormone of the pituitary. *Nature* 171 862–864.

Thyroid and Parathyroid

Firschein, H. E., Neuman, W. F., Martin, G. R., and Mulryan, B. J. 1959. Studies on the mechanism of action of the parathyroid hormone. *Rec. Progr. Horm. Res.* 15 427–448.

Gorbman, A. 1955. Some aspects of the comparative biochemistry of iodine utilization and the evolution of thyroid function. *Physiol. Rev.* **35** 336–346.

Greep, R. O., and Kenny, A. D. 1955. Physiology and chemistry of the parathyroids. *The Hormones* **3** 153–174.

Lardy, H. A., Lee, Y. P., and Takemori, A. 1960. Enzyme responses to thyroid hormones. *Annals N.Y. Acad. Sci.* **86** 506–511.

Leloup, J., and Fontaine, M. 1960. Iodine metabolism in lower vertebrates. *Annals N.Y. Acad. Sci.* **86** 316–353.

Munson, P. L. 1960. Recent advances in parathyroid hormone research. *Fed. Proc.* **19** 593–601.

Rawson, R. W., Rall, M. E., and Sonenberg, M. 1955. The chemistry and physiology of the thyroid. *The Hormones* **3** 433–519.

Pitt-Rivers, R. 1961. Iodine metabolism in the thyroid gland. *Cell. Mech. Hormone Prod. Act.* 71–78.

Roche, J., and Michel, R. 1955. Nature, biosynthesis, and metabolism of thyroid hormones. *Physiol. Rev.* **35** 583–610.

Roche, J., and Michel, R. 1956. Nature and metabolism of thyroid hormones. *Rec. Progr. Horm. Res.* **12** 1–22.

The Pancreatic Islets

Behrens, O. K., and Bromer, W. W. 1958. Glucagon. *Vitamins and Hormones* **16** 263–301.

Foa, P. P., Galansino, G., and Pozza, G. 1957. Glucagon, a second pancreatic hormone. *Rec. Progr. Horm. Res.* **13** 473–510.

Holt, C. von. 1955. Glukagon, das Hormon der A-Zellen der Langerhansschen Inseln. *Zeit. Vit. Horm. Fermentforsch.* **7** 138–152.

Sanger, F. 1956. The structure of insulin. *Curr. Biochem. Res. 1956.* 434–459.

Smith, G. H., Randle, P. J., and Battaglia, F. C. 1961. The mechanism of action of insulin in muscle. *Cell. Mech. Hormone Prod. Act.* 124–133.

Stadie, W. C. 1954. Current concepts of the action of insulin. *Physiol. Rev.* **34** 52–100.

Stetten, D. Jr., and Bloom, B. 1955. The hormones of the islets of Langerhans. *The Hormones* **3** 175–199.

Zimmerman, B. 1952. *Endocrine Functions of the Pancreas.* Thomas, Springfield, Ill.

The Adrenal Cortex

Farrell, G. 1958. Regulation of aldosterone secretion. *Physiol. Rev.* **38** 709–728.

Farrell, G. 1959. The physiological factors which influence the secretion of aldosterone. *Rec. Progr. Horm. Res.* **15** 275–310.

Farrell, G. 1960. Epiphysis cerebri in the control of steroid secretion. *Fed. Proc.* **19** 601–604.

Grant, J. K. 1961. The action of corticotrophin on the adrenal cortex in man. *Cell. Mech. Horm. Prod. Act.* 144–148.

Hechter, O., and Pincus, G. 1954. Genesis of the adrenocortical secretion. *Physiol. Rev.* **34** 459–496.

Ingle, D. 1959. Current status of adrenocortical research. *Am. Scientist* **47** 413–426.

Jones, I. C. 1957. *The Adrenal Cortex.* Univ. Press, Cambridge, England.

Muller, A. F., and O'Connor, C. M. (eds.) 1958. *Aldosterone.* Churchill, London.

Yoffey, J. M. (ed.) 1953. *The Suprarenal Cortex.* Butterworths; London.

Young, F. G. 1953. Adrenal steroids and ACTH. *Discovery* **14** 75–78.

Wettstein, A. 1954. Advances in the field of adrenal cortical hormones. *Experientia* **10** 397–416.

Arthropod Hormones

Carlisle, D. B., and Knowles, F. G. W. 1959. *Endocrine Control in Crustacea.* Univ. Press, Cambridge, England.

Knowles, F. G. W., and Carlisle, D. B. 1956. Endocrine control in the crustacea. *Biol. Rev.* **31** 396–473.

Scharrer, B. 1955. Hormones in invertebrates. *The Hormones* **3** 57–95.

Scheer, B. T. 1960. The neuroendocrine system of arthropods. *Vitamins and Hormones* **18** 141–204.

14 Conservative regulation

Organisms in general, and animals in particular, are characterized by their ability to maintain certain features of structure, chemical composition, and chemical processes constant, in spite of variations in the environment and in the flux of matter and energy between organism and environment. This characteristic was recognized long ago by the French physiologist Claude Bernard. In his book *Phénomènes de la vie* he developed in particular the view that the cells of a higher organism live in an "internal environment" which is different from the external environment surrounding the organism. In animals this internal environment is the body fluid, and in many animals the composition of the body fluid is not only different from that of the water or air surrounding the animal, but is held relatively constant when the composition of the external environment changes or when various substances are introduced into the body in the food or otherwise. Bernard expressed his basic concept in the aphorism: "The constancy of the internal environment is the condition of a free and independent life." By this he meant that the ability of an animal to move freely from one set of environmental conditions to another, and to continue normal activity when the environmental conditions change, depends on the ability to maintain the internal environment unchanged. The phenomenon of a constant internal environment we call *homeostasis;* the processes by which this constancy is maintained are those of conservative regulation.

Bernard's aphorism, quoted above, is only a part of his statement, which might be rephrased in the light of our current knowledge to read: The constancy of cellular activity is a condition of the free life; the constancy of the internal environment is one means of insuring the constancy of cellular activity. In fact, as we now know, many animals can survive rather extensive change in the environment, and even continue normal activity in spite of such changes, by a process which we shall call adjustment. In adjustment, the properties of the internal environment and of the cells themselves may change, but the internal cellular processes also change until the total activity reaches a new level of constancy, often not far different from that which prevailed in quite different conditions. The basic principle underlying such adjustment is known. Any complex set of processes involving a flow of energy tends toward a condition known as the stationary state, in which the composition of the system remains constant with time, and the rates of the component processes likewise remain constant. From a descriptive point of view, we can see how this comes about; in a process such as glycolysis, for example, the accumulation of any intermediate in excess will tend to increase the rate of the reaction by which that intermediate is removed. Likewise, if some intermediate is exhausted, the rate of reactions involving that intermediate will tend to decrease. Thus, ultimately, a concentration of intermediates will be reached in which all rates are constant.

In an unchanging environment, the cell and the organism must nevertheless maintain specific conditions essential to their respective existences. An organism, from a physicochemical point of view, is a highly improbable system, which is to say a highly unstable system. Such a system can be main-

tained in its unstable condition only by the continual expenditure of energy. The amount of energy which must be expended, and the way in which it must be expended, vary with the conditions in the environment, but there can be no interruption of the expenditure while life continues. The real subject of this chapter, then, is the regulation of the energy balance, considered in its broadest sense, in the organism, whether the organism is in a constant or changing environment.

Cellular Regulation

The first thing which must be regulated is the structure and composition of the cell itself. The cell is made up of proteins, carbohydrates, lipids, nucleic acids, and other compounds which must exist in the presence of enzymes capable of breaking them down. When a cell is injured or when its energy supply is cut off the cellular constituents sooner or later undergo a process of autolysis, in which the cellular enzymes act to break down the structure and composition of the cell. In the living cell, however, the constituents remain remarkably constant in their quantity and arrangement, so much so that a cytologist or histologist has no difficulty in recognizing particular kinds of cells or tissues on the basis of constant structural features.

Dynamic Steady States

The clue to this paradox came first from the classical studies of mammalian nitrogen metabolism carried out in the late 1930's by Schoenheimer and Rittenberg. These studies were among the first to use purified isotopes as "tracers". Rats were fed amino acids which had been synthesized using the heavy isotope of nitrogen, N^{15}, to label the amino groups. After a period of time varying from a few hours to a few days, the animals were killed, and the amino acids were separated from their tissues and analyzed, to determine the distribution of the N^{15}. It soon became apparent that nitrogen, introduced in the amino group of glycine, was found in the amino groups of nearly all the other amino acids, not only in the free amino acids but also in those which were combined in tissue proteins. The only possible conclusion was that the amino acids and proteins of tissues are continuously undergoing processes of breakdown and resynthesis, and that the constant structure which we observe is the consequence of a dynamic stationary state.

The nature of a dynamic stationary state can be simply illustrated by the device in which a lightweight ball is kept suspended by a jet of water or air. The ball can be kept motionless, or nearly so, as long as the jet flows constantly and smoothly. The position of the ball is not an equilibrium position, in the strict sense, since it can only be maintained by the constant expenditure of energy. The position is, however, determined by an equilibrium of forces; the upward force exerted by the jet is exactly equal to the downward force of gravity.

The situation in the cell, though more complex, is essentially similar. The cellular constituents would, if left alone, be broken down by the enzymes; this is the downward force tending toward disintegration of cellular structure. The upward force is the energy derived from the continuous oxidative metabolism of foodstuffs. The connection between the two lies in the energy-transfer agents such as ATP. The constant oxidative metabolism provides a constant level of ATP, which in turn maintains the synthetic processes at a steady level, exactly compensating or opposing the forces tending to the breakdown of cell constituents.

The problem of the dynamic stationary state of cell structure then is related to the question of the regulation of the oxidative metabolism of the cell. How is this maintained at a constant level when the supply of foodstuffs from outside is variable, and how is the energy available for maintenance of cell structure kept constant when the demands for energy for other cellular processes, such as contraction or secretion are intermittent and variable? The answer is not simple, and is not in any case fully known. We can state a physicochemical principle, that any complex system involving the degradation of energy tends toward a stationary state, which is then maintained while the energy supply lasts. In cells, this energy supply is provided by readily available stores of carbohydrate or lipid or both, and in the absence of these, by the breakdown of part of the cell structure. But this simple statement does not do justice to the elaborateness or to the delicacy of the balance which seems to prevail in the cell, and which we are just beginning to understand.

Catabolic Regulation

We have seen, in earlier sections, that both oxidative and synthetic processes proceed through a complex sequence of reactions, in which the energy is transferred from one chemical substance to another without conversion into another intermediate form of energy. The basic elements in this energy transfer process are the enzyme systems concerned in glycolysis and oxidative phosphorylation, and the nucleotides such as NAD and ATP. These latter two compounds serve as the principal reservoirs and exchangers of energy among the various cellular processes. The balance of oxidative and synthetic processes is probably held by the ATP level in the cell, since this compound and the related nucleotides such as UTP are the energy donors for all synthetic processes. There is evidence that the ATP level, and the ATP/inorganic phosphate ratio, are both held constant in many cells.

A well-known aspect of cellular regulatory mechanisms concerns the relation of oxidation to glycolysis. Pasteur first observed the effect which still bears his name; oxygen inhibits glycolysis. The phenomenon has been an almost continuous subject of investigation, but its mechanism is still not entirely clear. A crucial aspect of this and other regulatory mechanisms at the cellular level lies in the spatial separation of certain processes. Thus glycolysis and the synthesis of proteins and carbohydrates are confined largely to the cytoplasm outside the mitochondria, while oxidative phosphorylation and the synthesis of lipids occur primarily inside these structures. Many substances can move with relative freedom across the mitochondrial membrane, but two very important ones, namely NAD and ATP, apparently cannot. In anaerobic glycolysis, we would expect that the cytoplasmic supply of ATP would be built up at the expense of inorganic phosphate, which would consequently be less available for the mitochondria. The admission of oxygen to a glycolyzing cell would have two effects; by permitting the Krebs cycle to operate, it would further deplete the phosphate supply, and by drawing off pyruvate from the cyto-

plasm, it would cause accumulation of NADH in the cytoplasm. These changes, in turn, might be expected to slow the oxidative step between phosphoglyceraldehyde and phosphoglycerate in the glycolysis sequence. Whether this is the true explanation of the Pasteur effect can only be determined by further study.

It is of interest that many cells, especially those which depend largely on aerobic metabolism, have an active α-glycerophosphate dehydrogenase. This enzyme can act to utilize NADH from phosphoglyceraldehyde oxidation, forming α-glycerophosphate, which in turn can enter and be oxidized in the mitochondria, thus disposing at once of the problem of NADH accumulation and of phosphate deficiency. This system is especially characteristic, for example, of insect flight muscle, which must carry on a high level of oxidative activity in normal function.

Inhibition Induction and Repression

Another aspect of regulation at the cellular level is a more specific regulation of particular synthetic or catabolic processes. This sort of regulation has been studied especially in microorganisms, where it plays an important role in adaptation to altered environmental conditions. Three sorts of phenomena have been observed: In "feedback inhibition," the end product of a synthetic process inhibits specifically an early step in the same process. In enzyme induction, the presence of a substrate results in the synthesis of an enzyme involved in the metabolism of that or a related substrate. In enzyme repression, the presence of a substrate prevents the synthesis of an enzyme concerned in the metabolism of that or a related substrate. Feedback inhibition appears to be qualitatively different from the phenomena of induction and repression in that it involves an inhibitory effect on an enzyme already present, while induction and repression involve enzyme synthesis. Feedback inhibition can be illustrated by the case of aspartate transcarbamylase, which catalyzes the reaction

aspartate + carbamyl phosphate $\longrightarrow$
carbamyl aspartate + phosphate

This reaction is an early step in the synthesis of pyrimidines, and it is inhibited by pyrimidines, and more especially by cytidine triphosphate. This cannot be a simple mass-action phenomenon, since the amounts of inhibitor required are too small; the result of the phenomenon is to keep the level of products of the reaction sequence low and constant. This phenomenon has been demonstrated in higher vertebrates as well as in microorganisms.

Perhaps the best instance of enzyme repression in animals is the repression of hemoglobin synthesis in certain crustaceans by oxygen. When species of *Daphnia* are raised in well-aerated water, the blood contains little hemoglobin. Transfer to poorly aerated water results in a rapid synthesis of hemoglobin. In the vertebrates, creatine is synthesized by a series of reactions starting with glycine, which is converted to guanidoacetic acid by the enzyme glycine transamidinase; the guanidoacetic acid then forms creatine. If creatine is added to the diet of chicks raised on a creatine-free diet, the level of glycine transamidinase in the liver at once begins to decrease, though the other enzymes in the pathway, and unrelated enzymes, do not change in concentration. There is evidence, moreover, that the reappearance of the enzyme when the chicks are returned to a creatine-free diet involves synthesis of new enzyme, not merely activation of pre-existing enzyme.

There are a number of cases, in the vertebrates, in which addition to the diet of large amounts of a substance such as tryptophan or tyrosine, for example, is followed by an increase in the activity of enzymes involved in metabolism of these substances in the tissues. So far, however, in the cases of tryptophan pyrrolase and tyrosine-α-ketoglutarate transaminase, for example, the increase appears to be an activation of pre-existing enzyme, rather than a true induction resulting in synthesis of new enzyme. We shall mention later, and have mentioned in the preceding chapter, a number of instances in which hormones produce regulatory effects by altering enzyme activity; in most cases, these seem to be activating effects, rather than inductions.

The significance, in cellular regulation in higher animals, of enzyme repression and enzyme induction remains to be established. One factor which would tend to minimize the importance of these phenomena is the relatively stable character of the internal environment, which would normally prevent the occurrence of variations sufficient in magnitude to act as stimulus for repression and induction. On the other hand, it would be unwise to dismiss these phenomena as of no importance.

We should also note here that the phenomena of induction and repression are related to genetic factors (Chapter 3). Thus, the induction of an enzyme can occur only in an organism which has the requisite genes for production of the enzyme. Recent evidence, moreover, suggests that the phenomena of induction and repression themselves are under genetic control; there may be genes whose function is to control synthesis of a "repressor" substance, which in turn represses synthesis of an enzyme under control of another gene. The inducer then might act by removal of this repressor. If this rather complicated scheme is verified, it would provide an interesting point of attack for hormones which might, in higher animals, control specific enzyme synthesis by removing a repressor.

In all this, we have wandered somewhat from our point. There is clear evidence that cells have within themselves regulatory mechanisms of many sorts, but these mechanisms are only poorly understood at present. In most of what follows, we shall be concerned with levels of organization above the cellular level, but the student should keep in mind that the lower level is also important.

Regulation of Salts and Water

At the level of the differentiated multicellular organism, one of the most widely distributed forms of regulation is that concerned with salts and water. Organisms which live in the open sea generally do not experience any great changes in the concentration of salts or water in the medium; animals which live in the littoral zone may experience concentrations of the salts in the medium by evaporation of water from tide pools and other restricted bodies of water, or dilution of salts by influx of rain water. Estuarine animals are normally exposed to daily changes in the salt concentration of the medium as the tides ebb and flow, and in extreme cases, a given locality may be bathed in sea water at one time and fresh water at another time in the same day or tidal cycle. Alternately, any

place in the littoral zone, animals may be exposed to the air for a period of time, either daily or for brief periods during spring tides only, but with consequent water loss through evaporation in either case. Fresh-water animals maintain body fluids with salt concentrations well above the concentration in the external medium. Finally, terrestrial animals are exposed to constant danger of water loss by evaporation. All these factors present to organisms problems which must be met in various ways and at various levels, and in many cases the problem is met by regulation.

Ionic Regulation

One of the problems is that of the concentrations of individual ions. There is a very large body of experimental evidence concerning the effects of variation in concentration of one or another of the principal ions of the medium on the functional activity of various cells, and especially of contractile cells such as heart muscle. Much of this information has never been adequately summarized, and the theoretical interpretations which have been made are very limited indeed. The experiments themselves are quite easy to do, and this fact accounts for the abundance of experimental results, but for the interpretation of these results we need to know what changes in ionic composition occur within the cell when the external composition is changed, and what is the connection between the functional alteration in the cell and the concentration changes.

The major results thus far may be summarized thus: (1) Large changes in the concentration of any of the major cations (Na^+, K^+, Ca^{2+}, Mg^{2+}) in the medium of most cells will result in changes of function which, if not too long continued, are reversible. (2) Changes in the anion concentration are generally less effective, but replacement of Cl^- by other anions will alter the behavior of some tissues. (3) Anion effects, when they exist, are usually not specific, in that the effect of one anion is qualitatively similar to that of any other; anions can usually be arranged in some sort of series in terms of the relation between ion concentration and effectiveness, but the series for different effects are not necessarily the same. (4) Cation effects are usually rather specific and show the phenomenon of antagonism. Thus the effects of an increase in K^+ can be offset by increasing the Ca^{2+} concentration at the same time, and Mg^{2+} effects may be antagonized by decreasing K^+ or increasing Ca^{2+}.

In a few cases, especially in relation to cation effects on the excitability of nerve axons, we have some idea as to the mechanism. A decrease in Na^+ results in a decrease in excitability, and this can be explained by the essential rôle Na^+ plays in the generation of the action potential. Likewise, increasing K^+ leads to inexcitability because of the effect of such an increase in lowering the resting potential of the axon membrane. But the effects of Ca^{2+} and Mg^{2+} on the axon membrane, where decreasing Ca^{2+} leads to increased excitability while increasing Mg^{2+} may decrease excitability, remain to be explained. The other major ionic effects, in altering metabolism, on ciliary activity and on muscular contraction, for example, are very little understood. With a few exceptions, such as dietary deficiency of calcium in a terrestrial mammal or movement of a fresh-water animal from an environment with much calcium in solu-

tion to another with little, variations in the concentrations of individual ions in the medium sufficient to cause physiological disturbance are rare. The failure of internal regulatory mechanisms in higher organisms may, however, produce such variations in the blood or other body fluids.

Osmotic Regulation

A more common source of difficulty for organisms is the change in the osmotic concentration—that is, in the effective concentration of water—in the external environment. The membranes of most cells, and the respiratory surfaces of the bodies of most aquatic organisms, are much more readily permeable to water than to salts. Any change in the osmotic concentration of the medium surrounding the cell, or in contact with the respiratory surface of an animal, will then result in an osmotic flow of water across the membrane. This in turn, if long enough continued, may result in damage to the cell or organism, or at least in some modification of cellular activities. The same consequences will follow upon loss of water by evaporation.

The animal may meet this problem to some extent by a decrease in the water permeability of the body surfaces or by developing an increased tolerance, within a limited range, to the changes, without any sort of regulatory response. Such tolerance will in general involve some alterations in the activities of the animal as a direct consequence of the changed conditions. A third alternative is some adjustment in cellular or bodily processes such that normal activities can continue in the changed medium Finally, the animal may respond to the changes in a regulatory fashion, opposing the environmental change by some internal process which prevents, retards, or minimizes any change in the internal conditions.

Patterns of Osmotic and Ionic Regulation

With respect to salts and water, we can distinguish two sorts of regulatory processes. The first and simplest involves maintenance of a constant gradient of concentration between internal and external media, regardless of external conditions. The second involves maintenance of a constant level of concentration in some region such as the blood or body fluid, regardless of external conditions. The first sort of regulation is seen in certain fresh-water crayfish, for example, in which the level of osmotic concentration (or of NaCl concentration) in the blood is directly proportional to the external concentration, but is always higher than the external concentration. The second sort of regulation is seen in the prawn *Palaemonetes varians* or in the eel *Anguilla vulgaris,* both of which can maintain a nearly constant osmotic level in the blood when exposed to a wide range of variation in the external osmotic concentration.

The type of regulation which maintains a constant gradient in general involves some sort of "pump," which constantly pumps salts or possibly, in some cases, water against the gradient. The type of regulation which maintains a constant level of concentration requires, in addition to a pump, some means of sensing changes in concentration and some means of adjusting the rate and even the direction of pumping in such a way as to minimize or prevent changes in concentration. It

has been customary to speak of osmo-regulation or the regulation of water concentration, ionic regulation or the regulation of the concentration of individual ions, and volume regulation or the regulation of body volume as separate entities. The separation of any sort of regulation of salts and water into such categories must be in part arbitrary, since a change in water concentration must also usually involve a change in salt concentration, and often of the body volume as well. In the evidence thus far available, the examples cited in illustration of osmo-regulation generally involve the regulation of sodium chloride concentration rather than of water concentration, and the best known instances of true water regulation do not occur in aquatic animals. We shall therefore not use the customary categories, but discuss the problem of salt and water regulation as a single problem, which has been met in different ways by different organisms.

Protozoans

Marine and parasitic protozoans evidently have no means of regulating water content, with the exception of those marine protozoans which have contractile vacuoles. For the others, exposure to a diluted medium is followed by an increase in volume and presumably by dilution of the internal salt concentration consequent on an osmotic inflow of water. Similarly, in concentrated media, water is lost and the animal shrinks. The permeability to salts is evidently low, since there is little salt loss. Whether there is any active regulation of the internal concentration of individual ions is not known, but it seems likely that there may be such regulation.

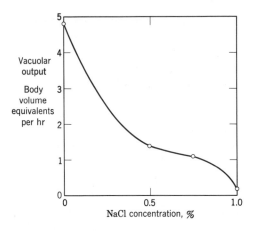

Fig. 14.1 The volume eliminated by the contractile vacuole of *Paramecium caudatum* as a function of NaCl concentration in the medium. (Data from A. Herfs, 1922, *Arch. Protistenkunde* **44** 277.)

Fresh-water protozoans normally occupy a medium in which the osmotic concentration is far below that within the cell. If, however, they are transferred to a more concentrated medium, the cell volume does not change. All fresh water protozoans, and some marine forms as well, have a structure called the contractile vacuole, from its rhythmic cycle of slow increase and rapid decrease in size. It is clear that this cycle results from a filling of the vacuole with fluid, followed by expulsion of this fluid to the exterior. The activity of the vacuole can be inhibited by treating the protozoan with a low concentration of cyanide or by removing the oxygen from the medium. When this is done, with the animal in fresh water, the body volume at once begins to increase; if oxygen is readmitted, or the cyanide is removed, the vacuolar activity resumes at an increased rate, and the body volume returns to normal. If the same experiment is carried out in a series of media of varying osmotic concentration, either

salt solutions or solutions of a nonelectrolyte such as sucrose, the vacuolar activity decreases as the concentration increases, until a solution is found in which there is no vacuolar activity (Figure 14.1). Those marine protozoans with contractile vacuoles have a very low rate of vacuolar activity while in sea water; if the sea water is diluted, however, vacuolar activity increases, and the body volume of the animals remains constant. It appears clear from these observations that the function of the vacuole is to remove water which has diffused into the body of the protozoan by osmosis and hence that the vacuole is a true osmoregulatory organ. The vacuole in marine protozoans serves to remove water taken in with the food. Contractile vacuoles occur occasionally in the cells of higher animals but are not generally present. The phenomenon of pinocytosis, which has recently been described in the cells of many higher animals and which involves the intake of fluid by formation of small vacuoles at the cell membrane, could conceivably serve for regulation of the water content of the cell, but evidence is lacking to determine this at present.

Marine Metazoans

In a great many marine animals, there is no evidence of osmotic regulation at all. If the animals are exposed to a series of dilutions of sea water and we follow the relation of the concentration of the internal medium to that of the external medium, as indicated for example by the depression of freezing point, we will find the two to be equal over the entire range (Figure 14.2). Within a certain part of this range the internal changes will not be lethal; outside that range of tolerance

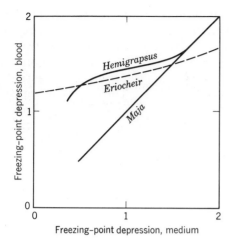

Fig. 14.2 Osmotic concentration of the blood of 3 crabs in relation to the concentration of the external medium. (Modified from Prosser and Brown, 1961, *Comparative Animal Physiology*, 2nd edn., Saunders, Philadelphia.)

the animal cannot survive. If we examine the body volume (or more easily, the body weight) as a function of time after exposure to a diluted medium, we will generally observe that the volume at first increases to a maximum, and then decreases, returning eventually in many cases to its original level. The increase is accompanied by an osmotic inflow of water and by loss of salts to the medium, with ultimate attainment of equilibrium when the internal osmotic concentration becomes identical with the external. Such a pattern is the consequence of purely passive phenomena and does not constitute regulation as we are using the term here. In some instances, the decrease in body volume appears to be accelerated by muscular contractions in the body walls, which force some water out; this may be regarded as a simple instance of a regulatory phenomenon and could most properly be called volume regulation, since the re-

sponse is probably a response to stretching of the body musculature.

If we now examine, instead of the osmotic concentration of the body fluid, the salt concentration (e.g., chloride concentration) of the entire animal following exposure to dilute or concentrated media, we will in many instances observe evidence of regulation at the cellular level. Within the range of salinities tolerated by the sea mussel *Mytilus californianus,* for example, the total chloride content of the animal, expressed in grams per cubic centimeter decreases more rapidly than the chloride concentration in the external medium as the medium is diluted (Figure 14.3). If we assume, however, that all of the body chloride is in the extracellular water of the body, we find the chloride concentration in the extracellular water to be the same as that in the external medium over the range studied. This means, in turn, either that the cells are impermeable to chlo-

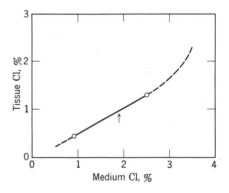

Fig. 14.3 Concentration of chloride in the tissues of the sea mussel, *Mytilus californianus*, in relation to the chloride concentration of the medium. The animals survive indefinitely in the concentrations of the solid part of the curve. The normal value for the concentration of the medium (sea water) is shown by the arrow. The broken line shows the concentration range tolerated only for brief periods. (After D. L. Fox, 1941, *Biol. Bull.* **80** 111.)

ride or that they are able to exclude chloride by some active means. When dilution or concentration of the medium is carried beyond the range which the animal will tolerate, the cells then take up chloride in the concentrated solutions, or lose small amounts in the dilute solutions. This means either that the regulatory mechanism breaks down or that the impermeability breaks down. From what we know of other cells, one may suggest that the chloride is kept out of the cells of the mussel by the electric potential gradient across the cell membrane (membrane potential), and that this gradient in turn is a consequence of the active extrusion from the cell of sodium ion. This, however, has not been established for the cells of mussels.

If, instead of the total osmotic concentration of the body fluid of marine animals, we examine the concentration of individual ions in the body fluid, we will find evidence of regulation of ionic concentration (Table 14.1). On the basis of the limited evidence available, it appears that the potassium ion concentration of the blood or body fluid is higher than that of the medium in many marine animals. There is a high internal concentration of calcium ion in mollusks and arthropods, perhaps associated with the calcareous exoskeletons of these forms. In addition, nearly all arthropods studied exhibit lower concentrations of magnesium and sulfate ions in the blood than are found in the surrounding sea water. It is very likely that these concentration differences are maintained by some regulatory process, and such evidence as we have suggests that the regulatory processes will be found in the gills, the absorptive membranes of the alimentary tract, and the nephridia. However, the study of ionic

regulation in marine animals has barely begun.

Estuarine Forms

If we examine the salt and water relations of estuarine animals and littoral forms which dwell in tide pools and other relatively exposed situations, we find a variety of patterns. Again, the simplest measurement we can make is to compare the freezing points of internal and external media when the osmotic concentration of the latter is varied. In general, these are not equal over the entire range in littoral or estuarine forms (Figure 14.2). We may compare, for example, two annelid worms, one of which burrows in the mud at or below the normal tide levels in regions where there is no fresh water inflow of consequence, while the other lives in estuaries where there is periodic dilution with fresh water. In the latter case, the body fluid is found to be always hypertonic to the medium when the medium is more dilute than normal sea water. This pattern of regulation in hypotonic solutions is also found in many estuarine and littoral crustaceans. The mechanism has been worked out in detail for only a few cases, but in these cases it appears to be primarily a mechanism for regulation of sodium ion concentration. The Chinese crab *Eriocheir sinensis* has been imported into Europe, where it lives in brackish water and may penetrate into completely fresh water for considerable periods. The principal regulatory mechanism in this crab appears to be active absorption of sodium ion across the gill membrane.

Fresh-water Animals

In fresh-water organisms, similar mechanisms seem to be involved.

TABLE 14.1

Ion Concentrations in the Body Fluids of Marine Invertebrates, mM/l and the Ratio of Concentration in Undialyzed Body Fluid to Concentration in Fluid Dialyzed against Sea Water

Group	Na	K	Ca	Mg	Cl	SO_4
Coelenterata	454 0.99	10.2 1.05	9.7 0.96	51 0.99	554 1.03	14.6 0.55
Echinodermata	444–489 1.0	9.6–10.8 1.12	9.9–11.0 1.0	50.2–58.5 0.98	522–573 1.0	26.5–39.0 1.0
Mollusca						
Pelecypoda	502–544 0.99:1.01	12.5–14.7 1.07:1.55	10.9–12.5 1.00:1.08	55.6 0.99:1.02	585 1.00	29.4 0.27:1.01
Gastropoda	492 0.97:1.00	9.7 1.17:1.97	13.3 1.03:1.32	49.0 0.97:1.07	543 1.00	28.2 0.90:1.02
Cephalopoda	460 0.92:0.97	23.7 1.52:2.05	10.8 0.91:1.07	56.9 0.98:1.03	589 1.02:1.05	4.7 0.77:0.22
Crustacea						
Decapoda	328–545 0.94:1.13	7.6–12.7 0.79:1.34	11.4–17.5 0.92:1.37	6.8–52.2 0.17:0.81	430–569 0.87:1.04	2.6–42 0.46:1.35

From J. D. Robertson, 1949, 1953 *J. Exp. Biol.* **20** 182; **30** 277.

Many species of crayfish appear to be able to absorb sodium ion actively across the gill membrane, and in addition have developed the ability to reabsorb sodium ion from the urine to a considerable extent. The antennary gland of the crayfish consists of a single complex nephridial unit made up of four distinct regions (Figure 14.4). At the proximal end is the coelomosac, the contents of which are identical in composition with the blood, except that the blood proteins have been filtered out. Following this is the labyrinth, a convoluted tubular region, in which the salt concentration at least remains unchanged, or even increases slightly. There follows a less convoluted region, the nephridial canal, in which there is a marked decrease in salt concentration, until the bladder is reached, when the salt level is only 5% of that in the blood. The nephridial canal is not found in marine crustaceans and is considered to be the site of active salt absorption. The result of its operation is that the urine finally released has a very low salt concentration. The urine is also relatively copious. The result of this combination of mechanisms for active salt absorption is an effective osmotic regulation. Water which diffuses into the animal across the gills is eliminated by the nephridia, with relatively small loss of salts. This salt loss can be made up by absorption of salts from the food, and across the gill membrane. It should be emphasized,

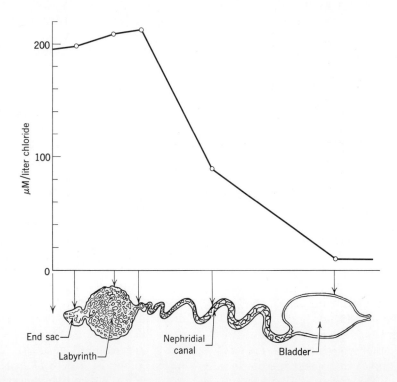

Fig. 14.4 Structure and function in the crayfish kidney. The graph shows the concentrations of chloride in the various regions of the crayfish nephridium, the structure of which is diagrammed below. (From Parry, 1960, *Physiology of Crustacea* 1 357, ed. T. H. Waterman, Academic Press, New York.)

however, that the "pumps" involved in this regulatory process are salt pumps, not water pumps. The regulatory mechanisms in the crayfish seem to be set at a constant rate of activity, since exposure of the crayfish to diluted sea water or other salt solutions results in an increase in the osmotic concentration of the blood.

The same general pattern of regulation operates in fresh-water teleost fishes and in amphibians such as the frog. In the fishes, the gills are the site of salt absorption, while in the frog, the skin performs this function. In addition, the frog has a sodium-absorbing mechanism in the large intestine, and certain frogs and toads have such a mechanism in the urinary bladder. The operation of the vertebrate kidney has been much studied. The kidney is made up of a large number of units, each of which is known as a nephron. The nephron is a long convoluted tubule, the proximal end of which is a thin-walled capsule (Bowman's capsule) which surrounds a knot of blood capillaries known as the glomerulus. The pressure of the blood in the capillaries causes filtration of blood through the walls of capillaries and capsule into the lumen of the capsule. It was shown by withdrawing fluid from the capsule of a salamander that the capsular fluid is identical in composition with the blood, except that the proteins and blood cells have been filtered out. If fluid is now collected by micropipette from various regions of the nephron tubule and analyzed, it is found that the salt concentration remains unchanged in the proximal portion, but it decreases in the distal portion of the tubule. We may conclude that salt is reabsorbed from the distal tubule. As in the crayfish, there is a copious flow of this relatively salt-free urine, which serves to dispose of the water which enters the animal by osmosis. When the salt concentration of the water is increased, the regulatory mechanism adjusts somewhat at low salt concentrations but fails to accommodate at higher levels in most cases. An exception is the eel, in which the blood osmotic concentration is held almost constant over a wide range of external concentrations.

Elasmobranchs

A remarkable situation is encountered in the elasmobranchs. Nearly all of these animals are marine forms, and the blood, in sharks or rays living in sea water, is always slightly hypertonic to the medium. If the sea water is diluted, the blood remains hypertonic, and the osmotic concentration of the blood decreases less rapidly than that of the medium. In the few species of fresh-water elasmobranchs the osmotic concentration of the blood is somewhat more than half of what it is in marine forms, and this in turn is somewhat above the concentrations found in most fresh-water vertebrates. If, however, we examine the ion concentration of the blood of the elasmobranchs which live in the sea, we find that the concentrations of all the ions are lower than those in the surrounding medium (Table 14.2). The hypertonicity of the blood is accounted for by an unusually high concentration of urea, which in certain marine elasmobranchs is present at a concentration over 2%, as compared with a typical value in mammals of 0.02%; the urea in the blood of a typical marine elasmobranch accounts for more than 50% of the osmotic concentration of the blood. In the fresh water elasmobranchs the urea level is much less,

TABLE 14.2
Electrolytes in Blood Plasma of Vertebrates, mM per liter

Group	Na^+	K^+	Ca^{2+}	Mg^{2+}	Cl^-	HCO_3^-	HPO_4^{2-}	SO_4^{2-}
Mammals	140–150	4.2–6.2	2.5–5.2	1.2–1.8	103–116	20–50	1.6–4.1	1.2–2.5
Birds (Chicken)	164	6	5.6	2.3	122	–	–	–
Reptiles								
Crocodilidae	140–149	3.5–7.9	2.6–3.4	1.1–1.9	108–117	11–18	1.1	0.5
Lizards	157–159	2.9–4.6	2.7–2.9	0.8–1.0	118–133	2–18	2.0–2.6	–
Snakes	141–176	3.5–5.9	2.2–4.3	1.0–2.3	89–143	6–14	1.2–3.9	–
Turtles	113–163	2.4–7.8	1.5–5.5	0.5–4.8	81–122	25–47	1.0–3.5	0.2–1.3
Amphibians (anurans)	86–128	1.7–7.4	1.5–2.0	0.6–3.8	70–80	5–25	1.9–3.1	–
Fishes, marine	141–215	3.8–9.8	2.7–6	1.7–5	117–189	–	–	2.3
freshwater (trout)	149	5.1	–	–	141	–	–	–
Elasmobranchs (*Raja*)	254	8	6	2.5	255	–	–	–
Cyclostomes, marine	450–558	9.6	6.25	19.4	500–576	–	–	–
freshwater	120	3.2	2.0	2.1	96	–	–	2.7
Sea water	470	10.0	10.2	53.6	548	2.34	–	28.3

Data from *Blood and Other Body Fluids*, Fed. Am. Soc. Exp. Biol., Washington, and Prosser and Brown, *Comparative Animal Physiology*, 2nd ed., Saunders, Philadelphia.

falling to 0.6%. This level of urea, however, still adds to the osmotic concentration of the blood and increases the problem of osmotic regulation over what it would otherwise be, since the salt concentration of the blood in fresh water elasmobranchs appears to be at least as much as that of other fresh water vertebrates.

The explanation which has been suggested for this curious situation is that the ancestors of the elasmobranchs were at one time residents in fresh water, with presumably the typical mechanisms of salt regulation characteristic of other fresh-water forms. Certainly the general structure and functioning of the elasmobranch nephron is similar to that of the same structure in the other vertebrates, and the urine of all elasmobranchs studied is hypotonic to the blood. It is not known whether the elasmobranch has any ability to transport salt actively across the gill membranes in either direction, but the rectal gland of the dogfish excretes sodium chloride actively.

At some time in the history of the elasmobranchs, one or more species migrated to the sea and found themselves confronted with a hypertonic medium. One mechanism that appears to have evolved is a physiological uremia, which is probably mediated by a special portion of the nephric tubule capable of reabsorbing urea from the urine and thus conserving the urea in the blood. The rectal gland may supplement this mechanism by eliminating excess salt, as does the teleost gill. The specific regulatory mechanisms that enabled elasmobranchs to colonize the sea, then, include the regulation of the urea concentration of the blood as well as, in some species at least, the salt concentration. This colonization was presumably so successful that the marine elasmobranchs became quite abundant, while the fresh-water ancestors of the group became extinct. The present fresh-water elasmobranchs are presumably descended from marine ancestors who have re-entered fresh water and have retained to some extent the uremia which is actually a handicap. It has been shown that the heart of a marine elasmobranch must have a certain minimum urea concentration to function normally; hence the tissues of the elasmobranchs have become adapted to a level of urea concentration which would be harmful to the tissues of other vertebrates. We shall note later that amphibians also have the ability to develop a physiological uremia in response to water loss or to hypertonic media.

Marine Teleosts

The marine teleost fishes offer another curious situation with respect to salt and water regulation. The osmotic concentration of the blood of a marine teleost is always less than that of the surrounding sea water. There is thus a continual osmotic loss of water across the gills, which must be replaced if the animal is to survive. It can be shown that the water is replaced by absorption through the digestive tract by blocking the esophagus; when this is done, the fish rapidly becomes dehydrated and dies. The normal fish drinks considerable quantities of sea water and absorbs the sea water, salts and all, through the walls of the stomach and intestine. This replenishes the water lost by osmosis but introduces an excess of salt into the body. The salt cannot be eliminated by the kidney, which in marine fishes forms only a very scanty amount of urine, normally isotonic, or nearly so, with the blood, and never hypertonic. Evidence that the route of salt excretion is across the gill membrane was obtained by a particularly ingenious experiment using the eel. A preparation of the head of an eel was made, including the heart and gills, so that fluid could be pumped through the gills by the heart action while water was passed across the gill surface, and both fluids could be analyzed for chloride ion. It was found that, when the external fluid was sea water, there was a continual elimination of chloride across the gill membrane from the blood, even though the concentration of chloride in the sea water is well above that in the blood. By analogy with other similar situations, we may suppose that the actual active transport is a transport of sodium ion and that the chloride follows along a potential gradient, but this has not been proved for the fish gill.

The explanation for this rather complex regulatory mechanism is similar to that for the elasmobranchs. It is assumed that the ancestors of present marine teleost fishes were fresh-water fishes, with the typical regulatory mechanisms now found in such animals, namely salt absorbing mechanisms in the gills and in the nephric tubules. When the teleosts first migrated into the sea, they were enabled to do so by developing the ability to reverse the direction of the salt pump in the gills, which now pumped salt outward instead of inward. In those fishes which today migrate freely from fresh water to the sea and back again, the ability to reverse the pump persists. The eel breeds in the sea, and the larval development of the fish takes place there. The young eels then migrate into fresh water, and

most of their growth takes place in this medium. At sexual maturity they return to the sea to breed. The fresh-water eel retains the ability to regulate salts in either hypertonic (sea water) or hypotonic (fresh water) media. The various species of salmon breed in fresh water, and the young fish migrate to the sea; after one or more years of feeding and growth here, they return to fresh water to breed. They too are able to change with relative ease from hypertonic to hypotonic regulation.

In permanently marine teleosts, kidney function tends to change, since the kidney loses its important function in salt regulation. In the typical marine fish, the glomerulus degenerates, and the scanty urine is formed in the tubule entirely by secretion. Such a fish has lost one of the essentials for hypotonic regulation, and so cannot return to fresh water. It seems probable that in anadromous fish (salmon) and in catadromous fish (eel) there is some hormonal control over the change from hypertonic to hypotonic regulation, or the reverse. This has not been investigated in detail as yet, but it is clear that the thyroid gland, and possibly other endocrine glands, are concerned in the preparation of the young salmon for downstream migration. The various osmoregulatory mechanisms of aquatic vertebrates are summarized in Figure 14.5.

Amphibians and Other Semi-terrestrial Forms

In terrestrial animals, the problem of water loss becomes pre-eminent, and osmotic regulation related to salt regulation is less important. Many animals that live in terrestrial habitats can regulate their water loss only by behavioral means. The pulmonate

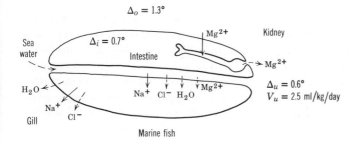

$\Delta_o = 1.3°$

Sea water

$\Delta_i = 0.7°$

Intestine

Mg^{2+} Kidney

H_2O

Na^+ Cl^- H_2O Mg^{2+}

$\rightarrow Mg^{2+}$

$\Delta_u = 0.6°$
$V_u = 2.5$ ml/kg/day

Na^+

Cl^-

Gill

Marine fish

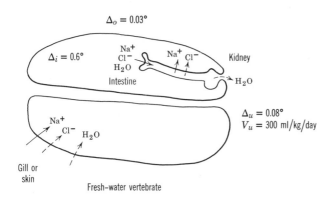

$\Delta_o = 0.03°$

$\Delta_i = 0.6°$

Na^+
Cl^-
H_2O

Na^+ Cl^- Kidney

Intestine

$\rightarrow H_2O$

Na^+
Cl^- H_2O

$\Delta_u = 0.08°$
$V_u = 300$ ml/kg/day

Gill or skin

Fresh–water vertebrate

Fig. 14.5 Mechanisms for ionic and osmotic regulation in a fresh-water vertebrate (fish, frog) and in a marine teleost fish. Active transport processes and filtration processes, requiring energy, are shown by solid arrows; passive diffusion processes are shown by broken arrows. Δ_o, Δ_i, Δ_u represent the depression of the freezing point, in deg. C, for external medium, body fluid, and urine respectively. V_u = volume of urine.

gastropods confine their activity to times of day and seasons of the year when the relative humidity of the atmosphere is sufficient to retard evaporation from the moist body surface. It is notable that the clue utilized by certain slugs, for example, to determine whether they will stay in their moist habitat under a rock or emerge to feed, is not humidity, but temperature; they are active when the temperature falls, inactive when it rises. This insures that they will normally be active at night, when the humidity is higher, and inactive during the day. The pulmonate gastropods with shells, such as the snail *Helix pomatia,* have developed the habit of estivation. When the temperature rises sufficiently, they withdraw into their shells and seal the opening with a mucous secretion which serves to retard evaporation. The operculate terrestrial snail

of India, *Pila virens,* estivates with the shell closed by the operculum, and during this period its metabolism must be predominantly anaerobic.

Such adaptations place a severe limitation on activity, especially in dry climates. The amphibians are in most cases limited in this same way to moist environments, or to activity during the more humid hours of the day, but the degree of tolerance of various species to dry environments and the degree of dependence on an aquatic environment vary considerably. Moreover, some of the amphibians, notably certain salamanders such as *Taricha torosa,* spend a part of each year in the water and then emerge to undertake a considerable terrestrial migration, often in rather dry climates. This change in activity must involve a considerable change in the arrangements for regulation of water loss. The return of some of these animals to fresh water is brought about by behavioral changes consequent on secretion of LTH by the anterior pituitary; whether this hormone also induces changes in water and salt regulation is not known.

The regulatory processes for salt and water, and their control, have been studied rather extensively in frogs, which offer special advantages for such study. When the frog is in fresh water, water diffuses into the animal across the skin, which has a relatively low permeability to water and to salts. The blood is filtered through the glomerulus of the nephron, and Na^+ (along with other substances) is actively reabsorbed by a "pump" mechanism across the tubule wall; Na^+ reabsorption is normally almost complete. The small losses of Na^+ in urine, feces, and through the skin are compensated for by active uptake of Na^+ across the skin. It will be recalled that the frog skin provided the material for the first unequivocal demonstration of active transport of an ion. The principal regulatory mechanisms, then, are the salt pumps specific for sodium ion in kidney, skin, and in some species in the bladder wall as well.

If the common green frog, Rana pipiens, is transferred to a sodium chloride solution, isotonic with the blood, the sodium level in the plasma rises somewhat to reach a steady level somewhat higher than that in the environment. The "marine" frog of southeast Asia commonly enters sea water to feed on crustaceans, and in this animal, the plasma sodium level remains below that of the medium. The blood, however, is hypertonic to the medium, so that water still diffuses in; the difference is made up by urea, as in the elasmobranchs. Apparently these frogs, like the elasmobranchs, have made use of a widely distributed mechanism for adaptive urea synthesis and possibly retention as well. Both processes have been demonstrated as a response to desiccation or saline media in several amphibian species. Terrestrial species also often have a sodium-reabsorbing mechanism in the urinary bladder; water is also reabsorbed from the hypotonic urine by osmosis, a process which is further aided by the salt uptake.

In frogs, exposure to isotonic salt solution is followed within a short time by a marked decrease in the rate of Na^+ uptake across the skin, and in Rana pipiens, at least, across the wall of the kidney tubule as well. In terrestrial species, exposure to salt solutions, or desiccation, is followed by a decrease in urine volume; it is not entirely certain whether this is a result of changes in kidney function, bladder function, or both.

The controlling mechanisms in the response to exposure to salt solution in R. pipiens involve a sequence of neurosecretory and endocrine mechanisms (Figure 14.6). The neurohypophysial hormone of amphibians is arginine vasotocin; a small amount of oxytocin has also been found. The content of vasotocin in the neurohypophysis is reported to decrease following exposure to salt solution, and vasotocin has been shown to stimulate sodium transport by the isolated skin, when applied directly to the skin. Exposure to salt solution also alters the staining properties of neurosecretory cells in the preoptic nucleus. These observations, then, lead to the conclusion that the preoptic neurosecretory cells are active when the frog is in fresh water and that their activity results in vasotocin secretion, which in turn maintains the sodium pump in an active condition. Exposure to salt solution stops the neurosecretion and the formation and liberation of vasotocin, with a resulting decrease in the activity of the sodium pump.

This is not, however, the whole mechanism. Removal of the adenohypophysis, without damage to the neurohypophysis, is followed by a decrease in sodium transport by the skin. This effect can be reversed by injection of ACTH into the frog, suggesting that the interrenal bodies (corresponding to the adrenal cortex of mammals) are involved. This is further confirmed by the fact that injection of aldosterone or cortisol will also reverse the effects of hypophysectomy. Exposure of frogs to salt solution results in characteristic histological changes in the interrenal tissue, most notably an increase in the number of Stilling cells, eosinophil cells of unknown function; the same effect is produced by hypophysectomy.

If the interrenal bodies are severely damaged by cautery, the sodium transport by the skin decreases. ACTH will no longer restore this function, but adrenal steroids will. In toads exposed to salt solution, the aldosterone content of the blood decreases, as does sodium transport across the bladder wall; aldosterone injection increases sodium transport across the bladder wall but does not appear to do so in the kidney tubule of these animals. The connection between the changes in neurosecretory activity and interrenal function, which in turn evidently has a role in regulation of sodium transport, is not established. Sodium transport in the skin recovers its normal level within about three weeks after removal of the adenohypophysis; there is no significant recovery in sodium transport or interrenal histology during exposure to isotonic saline for a

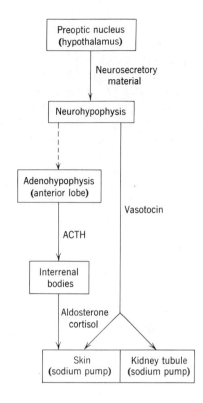

Fig. 14.6 Factors in the neuroendocrine control of the ionic regulatory mechanisms in the frog, *Rana pipiens.*

month. This suggests the probability that the neurohypophysial mechanism exerts a control over both processes, in response to the stimulus of exposure to salt solution. The relation of these hormonal mechanisms to the production or retention of urea remains to be established.

Terrestrial Animals

The truly terrestrial animals—insects, arachnids, reptiles, birds, and mammals—all have integuments that are almost impermeable to water. Except for those mammals in which evaporation of water from the body surface plays a part in temperature regulation, the major loss of water in terrestrial animals takes place in the excreta, and by evaporation from the respiratory organs. The tracheal respiratory system of insects minimizes water loss by providing a long diffusion path; the respiratory surfaces of the other forms are enclosed within the body, with access to the air through relatively limited apertures. Loss of water through the excreta is minimized in all the terrestrial forms by absorption of water from urine and feces. In insects, the Malpighian tubules open into the intestine, and the hindgut is provided with a special region which can reabsorb water from feces and urine alike. The urine is formed in the Malpighian tubules by secretion, rather than by filtration and reabsorption as in aquatic animals. The principal nitrogenous end product is uric acid, which is relatively insoluble, and some of the water which is secreted with the uric acid into the proximal end of the tubule is reabsorbed before the urine reaches the distal end, so that the urine voided into the intestine is sometimes semi-solid in consistency. Uric acid offers a considerable advantage for reabsorption of water, since it precipitates out before the osmotic concentration of the solution reaches any large value, and the work of reabsorption is thereby much reduced. Arachnids excrete the purine guanine as their nitrogenous end product, and it has properties similar to those of uric acid. Terrestrial reptiles and birds also excrete uric acid. In reptiles and birds the urine passes into the cloaca, where water may be abstracted from both urine and feces. Birds, in addition, have a segment in the kidney tubule capable of reabsorbing water from the urine. This same segment is present in mammals, but mammals do not have

the cloaca; the large intestine, however, is able to remove water from the feces. In desert mammals, the ability of the kidneys to reabsorb water from the urine is highly developed, and these animals can excrete a very hypertonic urine; the respiratory water loss is also reduced.

The function of the water-reabsorbing segments of the mammalian kidney has recently been worked out in considerable detail using micropuncture studies, in which minute amounts of fluid are withdrawn from the various segments of the nephron and analyzed. As a standard of comparison, the inulin content of the samples is used. Inulin is a polysaccharide which is filtered through the glomerulus, but is not reabsorbed or metabolized to any appreciable extent. Consequently, its concentration in the tubular fluid after injection into the blood is a good indication of the withdrawal or addition of water, and comparisons of its concentration with those of other substances permit deductions concerning the absorption of the other substances. Samples of fluid withdrawn from the proximal convoluted tubule prove to be isotonic with blood over a wide range of blood concentrations; however, when the blood contains inulin, the concentration of inulin in the proximal tubule increases steadily as samples are taken farther from the glomerulus. Calculations suggest that as much as 75% of the water filtered through the glomerulus is removed in the proximal tubule. Since the tubular fluid remains isotonic, salt must be removed as well, and there is independent evidence showing that the tubule wall can transport Na^+ actively from lumen to blood. This evidence rests on microelectrode studies showing that there is a potential gradient across the tubule wall, with the lumen negative and on "stopped flow" measurements, showing that when the tubule is blocked with an oil drop, sodium chloride is removed from the lumen.

The specific structure found in mammals and birds, but not in lower vertebrates, and hence associated with water reabsorption is the loop of Henle, a thin U-shaped tube connecting the proximal convoluted tubule with the distal convoluted tubule. It was not possible to obtain samples from this structure, but samples of fluid taken from the first portion of the distal tubule, immediately beyond the loop, proved to be hypotonic to the blood; the inulin concentration, on the other hand, was only slightly higher than that in the last portion of the proximal tubule. These observations support the conclusion that the walls of the loop of Henle absorb salt, but not water. In the distal tubule, the inulin concentration and the osmolar concentration increase, while the salt concentration decreases, suggesting that the walls of this structure are permeable to water, but do not take up Na^+.

The fluid at the distal end of the distal tubule, where it joins the collecting ducts, has about 15 times the inulin concentration of the blood and 0.6 times the sodium concentration, and is essentially isotonic with the blood. The urine which enters the bladder has an inulin concentration almost 700 times that of the blood. Considerable changes therefore must occur in the collecting tubules, the walls of which have been shown to absorb sodium and, along with it, considerable water. The efficiency of the whole process is greatly increased by the arrangement of the tubules and the associated blood vessels, in the kidney, as shown in the diagram (Figure 14.7). The system constitutes an effective counter-current exchange mechanism, in which the driving forces are the circulation of blood and urine in opposite directions and the sodium pump in the proximal tubule, the loop of Henle, and collecting tubules. It is clear that the older view, which ascribed the water reabsorbing function to the loop, was only partially correct.

There is, in spite of the efficiency of the kidney mechanism, some loss of water in urine, as well as some in the feces. The sources of water available to replace this loss are liquid water for drinking, water present in the food as such, and the metabolic water formed by oxidation of foodstuffs. In certain insects and desert mammals, which feed on dry seeds primarily, the conservation mechanisms are so effective that the metabolic water alone suffices to replace the normal loss. Other terrestrial forms must depend on moist food or on liquid water as well. There is evidently a nervous regulation of liquid intake in the thirst mechanism of mammals, but the receptors of this mechanism, and their mode of operation, remain uncertain.

The primary regulation of water loss in mammals appears to reside in the antidiuretic hormone (ADH) of the posterior pituitary, which has been identified with vasopressin. This hormone, like vasotocin in lower vertebrates, is formed in certain neurosecretory cells, whose axons terminate in the posterior or neural lobe of the pituitary. Histologically identifiable materials have been observed in the cell bodies of these cells, which are located in the hypothalamic region of the midbrain, and movement of these materials from the cell bodies along the axons into the posterior lobe of the pituitary has been seen. Moreover,

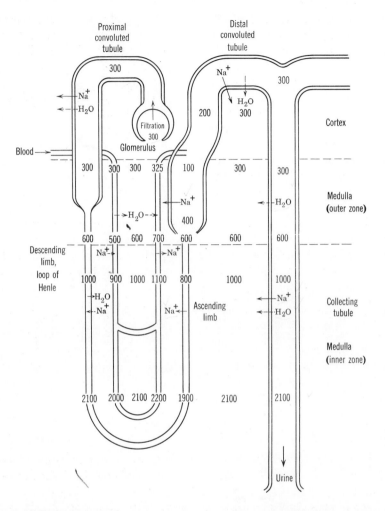

Fig. 14.7 A current concept of the osmoregulatory function of the mammalian nephron. The numbers represent hypothetical values of the osmolar concentration of the fluid in the nephron, the blood, or the tissue fluid of the kidney. Solid arrows indicate active transport or (in the glomerulus) filtration processes, broken arrows represent passive diffusion. The diameter of the tubules is exaggerated by comparison with their lengths. The ascending limb of the loop of Henle is assumed to be relatively impermeable to water, while the proximal tubule, distal tubule, and collecting tubule walls are permeable to water. In these latter regions, water uptake therefore accompanies Na transport and vasopressin, the antidiuretic hormone probably increases the rate of both processes. (After Gottschalk, 1961, *The Physiologist* 4 35.)

blockage of this movement by lesions in the axons or damage to the cell bodies leads to a marked increase in the urine volume in consequence of the failure of water reabsorption. The major question remaining is the rela-

tion between these histologically identifiable neurosecretory materials and the antidiuretic hormone itself, which can be extracted from the posterior pituitary.

A still more important matter is the

way in which the secretion of ADH is controlled. The evidence so far available suggests but does not prove that the receptors which initiate the process leading to discharge of ADH are located in the prosencephalon and are activated by an increase in the osmotic concentration of the blood. Presumably in the normal animal, this system is continuously active, and the rate of water reabsorption is kept high by a continuous liberation of ADH into the circulation. When a large volume of fluid is taken in, or when the neurosecretory system forming ADH is damaged, the ADH secretion decreases, and there is a sharp increase in the elimination of water, due primarily to a decrease in the rate of water reabsorption in the kidney tubules. The bulk of current evidence favors the view that ADH, like vasotocin, acts on membrane pore diameter, thus increasing Na^+ uptake; the uptake of water follows Na^+ uptake osmotically in the countercurrent system of the kidney and is accelerated by the increased pore diameter of the tubule cell membranes.

The only source of salts for terrestrial animals is in the food and, to a very limited extent, the drinking water. Loss is primarily through the excreta, especially from the kidneys, and the kidneys are the primary regulatory agents. However, in mammals, at least, there is considerable internal regulation of salt balance in the blood, mediated primarily by the action of specific hormones on the kidneys and on the other tissues of the body to some extent. The major endocrine organs concerned are the parathyroid glands and the adrenal cortex. The parathyroids, located in close association with the thyroids in the neck region, are concerned with the regulation of calcium and phosphate metab-

olism, and are of particular importance in mammals in relation to the formation of the skeleton. Removal of the parathyroids is followed by a rapid decrease in the calcium concentration in the blood, with consequent increase in excitability of nervous tissue, and is consequently fatal. The evidence now points to the kidneys as one primary site of action of the parathyroid hormone, where the hormone controls the excretion of phosphate by increasing the reabsorption of phosphate from the urine across the tubular wall. In the absence of the hormone, phosphate is lost from the blood and is consequently withdrawn from the bones. Calcium appears to move along with the phosphate, but there is also evidence of a direct action of the hormone favoring calcium deposition in bone. Parathormone secretion is probably normally controlled by a direct influence of the calcium or phosphate level of the blood on the secreting cells, but the details of the control are not established.

Removal of the adrenal cortex is followed by an increased loss of sodium ion from the blood via the kidneys, due to decreased reabsorption by the kidney tubules and by an altered salt balance in the body cells as well. One important agent responsible for the kidney effect has recently been identified as aldosterone, which is formed by the cells of the zona glomerulosa of the adrenal cortex. This hormone appears to act by increasing the reabsorption of sodium ion in the kidney tubules. Several other steroids are formed in the zona fasciculata cells of the adrenals, and there is evidence that these may influence the salt balance of body cells independently of the action on the kidney of aldosterone. The regulation of aldosterone secretion in mammals probably involves the adrenocortico-trophic hormone (ACTH) of the anterior pituitary in part, but there is evidence of a control of aldosterone secretion by a substance formed in the diencephalon and by another hormone formed in the kidney.

Marine Mammals and Birds

Marine mammals have a problem in water regulation similar to that of terrestrial mammals; the sea contains plenty of water, but it is in the form of a salt solution, hypertonic to the blood, and so cannot be used to replace water lost in the excreta or by evaporation, without some additional device for salt removal. Relatively little study has been given to this problem, but it is clear that those marine mammals which feed upon fish can obtain enough water from the food to replace the relatively small loss in urine and feces and by evaporation in respiration. The water regulation of those whales which feed on crustaceans, for example, has not been studied. Marine birds, which habitually drink sea water, have a special nasal gland that contains an active sodium transport mechanism and forms a salt solution hypertonic to the blood. This mechanism serves to eliminate the extra salt taken in with the food.

Regulation of pH

Related to the problem of salt regulation is that of the control of the pH of the blood. This has been studied only in the mammals, and to a limited extent in a few other vertebrates. The concentration of hydrogen ion in the blood is very small compared with that of other ions. The pH of 7.0, near that commonly maintained in the blood, represents a concentration of 10^{-7} M. Nevertheless, a very small change in this concentration, amounting to a few tenths of a pH unit, may have large consequences in the physiology of the animal, and especially in the activities of the central nervous system. The reason for the sensitivity of the central nervous system to pH changes has never been adequately explained.

Very little is known about the pH of the cell interior. Attempts to determine this quantity accurately by means of indicators, indirectly by calculations from the concentrations of bicarbonate ion or directly by use of microelectrodes, have generally led to values near pH 7, or somewhat less; the different methods do not agree entirely, and the reasons for the differences are not well enough known to permit evaluation of the methods. In any case, very little attention has been given to the nature or extent of physiological variations in intracellular pH; from what we do know, we may conclude tentatively that some regulatory mechanisms exist, and that the pH within the cell usually does not deviate much from neutrality.

The pH of the blood of mammals is also held very near neutrality, but here we know much more, both of the extent of the variation and the mechanism by which this variation is kept small. The factors in pH regulation in mammals are (1) the buffer systems of the blood, (2) the respiratory exchange in the lungs, and (3) the regulatory activity of the kidneys. The factors tending to disturb the pH of the blood are (1) products of metabolism such as CO_2, lactic and other organic acids, and ammonia; (2) secretory activities such as the secretion of HCl in the stomach and of $NaHCO_3$

in the pancreas, and (3) the absorption of acidic or alkaline substances in the food. The major buffers of the blood are the bicarbonate ion and the blood proteins. These participate in equilibrium reactions

$$H^+ + HCO_3^- \rightleftharpoons H_2CO_3$$
$$H^+ + H_2N - R - COO^- \rightleftharpoons$$
$$^+H_3N - R - COO^-$$
$$H^+ + {}^+H_3N - R - COO^- \rightleftharpoons$$
$$^+H_3N - R - COOH$$

such that any production of H^+ leads to a shift in the equilibria to the right, and any removal of H^+ shifts the equilibria to the left, thus tending to preserve the H^+ concentration unchanged. This is a passive adjustment and is probably found to some extent in all animals.

The role of the lungs in the regulation of the pH of the blood is primarily in removing carbon dioxide from the blood and hence in increasing the pH. The rate of CO_2 removal is directly related to the rate of ventilation of the lungs, that is, to the rate and depth of the respiratory movements. These movements are under control of a complex of nervous centers in the medulla oblongata, known collectively as the respiratory center. This center normally exhibits a pattern of rhythmic spontaneous discharge, leading to alternate contraction and relaxation of the muscles involved in the respiratory movements, such as the diaphragm, the intercostal muscles, abdominal muscles, and others. The level of activity of the center, in mammals, is determined largely by the concentration of carbon dioxide in the blood. If this concentration increases, as after exercise, the activity of the respiratory center increases, and this increases the rate and depth of respiration, hence the amount of ventilation of the lungs.

If the CO_2 decreases in the blood, the respiratory center becomes less active, and by flushing CO_2 out of the blood in "overbreathing," for example, we can cause the center to become inactive, when respiratory movements stop altogether. Since the major buffer system in the blood is the bicarbonate system, any increase in acidity will effectively increase the CO_2 content of the blood and stimulate the respiratory center to increased activity, thus eliminating the CO_2. It is not clear to what extent this mechanism operates in animals other than mammals, but in many aquatic animals the respiratory center seems to be sensitive to oxygen lack, rather than to carbon dioxide excess, and consequently the respiratory center can play only an indirect role in regulation of blood pH.

The kidneys can alter the pH of the blood in two ways: by altering the amount of ammonia eliminated, and by altering the amount of bicarbonate eliminated. In the mammal, most of the ammonia formed by deamination of amino acids is converted into urea in the liver; ammonia is alkaline, but urea is essentially neutral. When an animal ingests substances such as sodium bicarbonate, or the sodium salts of organic acids, for example, the anion (bicarbonate or the oxidation product of the organic anion) may be eliminated as CO_2, but the cation (sodium ion) remains behind to contribute to the alkalinity of the blood; the total amount of such non-metabolizable cations in the blood is consequently known as the "fixed base." The kidney may decrease the alkalinity (decrease the pH) of the blood by eliminating this fixed base in combination with bicarbonate ion, which is constantly produced by metabolism and hence is readily available. Alternatively the kidney may decrease the acidity of the blood (increase the pH) by excreting chloride ion in place of bicarbonate, or by eliminating ammonium ion instead of sodium or potassium ion. Again ammonium ion is readily available from the deamination of amino acids in the kidney. It is well established that the kidney varies its elimination of bicarbonate and ammonium ions according to the pH of the blood and according to the concentration of fixed base in the blood, but the mechanism of this regulation is not clear. Presumably the cells of the kidney tubule react directly in response to the composition of the fluid in the tubule, but there may be some external control as well.

Regulation of Blood Flow

In the vertebrates, and especially in mammals, the supply of oxygen and certain foodstuffs to the cells is regulated. It is probable that this same regulation operates to some extent in other animals as well, but it has been little studied. The regulation in mammals depends on a number of factors: the regulation of blood flow to the various tissues and organs, the regulation of the oxygen level in the blood, and the regulation of the blood-sugar level are the three most thoroughly understood.

Blood Pressure

The basic regulatory phenomenon in the circulation is the regulation of the arterial blood pressure; the regulation of blood flow to individual organs and tissues depends on this basic regulation. As we learned earlier, the hydrostatic pressure measurable in the arteries is a consequence of the force of the contraction of the heart, forcing fluid into the blood vessels against the frictional resistance to flow offered by the vessels. The blood pressure at any one time will then depend upon the cardiac output and upon the frictional resistance of the blood vessels.

We have seen that the cardiac output is dependent only on inflow, and this is in general not subject to regulation but depends upon the activity of the animal. The major frictional resistance occurs in the arterioles and is inversely related to the diameter of these vessels. The primary factor in the regulation of blood pressure is therefore the control of arteriolar diameter. Arteriolar diameter is influenced primarily by local effects of substances formed during tissue activity, which cause dilation, and by vasoconstrictor nerves, which cause constriction by producing contraction of the circular muscles of the arteriolar walls. The vasoconstrictor nerves are activated through a cardiovascular center in the medulla, which is in turn activated through several reflex pathways. The most important of these begins in stretch receptors in the aorta, which are stimulated to discharge impulses with each heartbeat as the blood flowing into the aorta causes the walls of that vessel to stretch. The amount of stretch, and hence the intensity of the nervous discharge, is directly related to the blood pressure. As the blood pressure increases, the discharge of vasoconstrictor impulses from the cardiovascular center decreases, and the dilation of the arterioles, which follows, results in a lowering of the blood pressure. This mechanism is normally in continuous tonic action. A supplementary mechanism of the same sort arises in stretch receptors in the carotid sinus, insuring that the blood pressure in the arteries leading to the brain will remain constant.

Blood Flow

With the exception of the brain, where there is little or no variation in blood flow as long as the blood pressure remains constant, the flow of blood to the other organs of the body may vary considerably at constant pressure. Wherever a blood vessel branches the fraction of the total flow which enters each branch is proportional to the diameters of the branches. Thus, dilation of the arterioles in a particular organ will result in considerable increase in the flow to that organ, if the arterial pressure remains constant. The central reflex mechanism described above acts upon all the arterioles, and its action is sufficient to hold the blood pressure within relatively narrow limits, but the degree of dilation of the vessels in a particular organ is the result of an interaction between local effects of metabolites from the activity of the organ and the central influence of the vasoconstrictors. In consequence, though the total blood pressure remains constant, the flow of blood to any organ will vary in accordance with the activity of the organ.

In addition, there are numerous reflexes and other nervous influences, and some hormonal influences as well, which act to alter blood flow to various regions of the body. Emotional stimuli of various sorts excite the sympathetic vasoconstrictors in the intestines particularly, with the result that blood is diverted from the splanchnic area into other parts of the body, especially to the muscles. Blood flow to the skin depends on emotional factors, which induce constriction of skin vessels through stimulation of the sympa-

thetic nervous system, and on changes in body temperature. An increase in body temperature causes dilation of the skin vessels, while a decrease causes constriction. The amount of blood thus diverted to or from the skin may be considerable. The sympathetic vasoconstrictors act by liberating the neurohumor norepinephrin from their endings. This neurohumor may also be liberated by the adrenal medulla in consequence of vigorous sympathetic stimulation, as in fear or rage, with the result that widespread vasoconstriction, especially in the skin and splanchnic areas, occurs.

Oxygen Supply

The oxygen supply to the cells depends on the rate of blood flow and on the oxygen content of the blood. The regulation of the latter is both passive and active. The passive regulation is comparable to the buffer mechanism regulating the pH of the blood. The respiratory proteins help in the maintenance of a constant oxygen supply by maintaining a reservoir of oxygen in chemical combination from which large amounts of oxygen can be withdrawn in consequence of relatively small changes in oxygen tension. This factor clearly operates in the regulation of oxygen supply in many animals which have respiratory proteins in the blood. The active factor in oxygen regulation is the regulation of respiratory ventilation. In many aquatic animals there appears to be a direct effect of the level of the oxygen content in the blood on the respiratory center in the brain, such that a decrease in blood oxygen causes an increase in the activity of the center and hence an increase in ventilation of the gills. In terrestrial animals, where the oxygen content of the air is always high, the effective agent is not oxygen but carbon dioxide; an increase in CO_2 content of the blood stimulates the center, as we have seen. This works well enough in insuring an adequate oxygen supply with one exception; when mammals, including man, are exposed to air at high altitudes or where the oxygen content of the air is reduced, there is no response of the respiratory mechanism to this oxygen lack, and anoxia may develop through inadequate ventilation.

Regulation of Carbohydrate Metabolism

The control of the concentration of glucose in the blood of mammals has been thoroughly studied; the same mechanisms appear to operate in other vertebrates as well, but in the lower vertebrates the rate of action of the various controlling agents is so much reduced that one can speak only of regulation of glucose utilization, not of blood-glucose concentration. In order to understand the control of blood sugar in mammals, we must first recall some aspects of carbohydrate metabolism. When foodstuffs, especially carbohydrates, are absorbed from the intestine they pass first into the hepatic portal circulation and are carried to the liver. Here they are largely removed from the blood. The carbohydrates may be converted into glycogen (glycogenesis), or oxidized. Most of the amino acids (the glucogenic amino acids) are either converted into glycogen (gluconeogenesis) after deamination, or oxidized. The other amino acids are either oxidized or converted into fat. Absorbed fatty acids are not converted directly into carbohydrate, but the glycerol arising from hydrolysis of lipids may be. The store of

glycogen which is built up in the liver may be broken down to glucose (glycogenolysis) and liberated as such into the blood, or it may be broken down further (glycolysis) to pyruvic acid (aerobically) or lactic acid (anaerobically). In general, the tissues of the body other than the liver cannot absorb carbohydrates, other than glucose, nor can they carry out gluconeogenesis. The glucose which they do absorb may be used for glycogenesis, glycolysis, or oxidation; the lactic acid which arises from anaerobic glycolysis during vigorous muscular activity, for example, is generally liberated into the blood, from which it is removed by the liver and used in gluconeogenesis.

To summarize the factors which can influence the concentration of glucose in the blood, we may indicate by a + sign that the particular factor tends to increase blood glucose, and by a − sign that it tends to decrease blood glucose. The four major factors are:

(1) Absorption from the intestine (+).
(2) Glycogenesis in the liver (−).
(3) Glycogenolysis in the liver (+).
(4) Utilization of glucose by the tissues (−).

A fifth factor, gluconeogenesis in the liver, does not influence blood glucose directly, but in the absence of glucose absorption from the intestine it may be necessary to insure an adequate supply of glycogen for (3). Processes (1) and (4) above are variable, depending on the activities of the animal, and must be balanced by appropriate variations in (2) and (3) if the blood-sugar level is to be maintained constant. The liver cells, themselves, without external influence, will take up glucose (2) or give it off (3) depending on the glucose level in the blood, and this serves as the basis of the regulation of blood sugar.

Hormonal Control

The level of blood-sugar concentration at which glycogenesis predominates over glycogenolysis is normally determined in the mammal by the interaction of several hormonal influences. The first of these is the hormone insulin, secreted by specialized endocrine cells—the beta cells of the islets of Langerhans in the pancreas. The first indication that the pancreas has a role in carbohydrate metabolism came as an accidental result of experiments aimed at the study of the role of the pancreas in digestion. The pancreas was surgically removed from dogs, and an observant animal caretaker noted that the urine of the depancreatized dogs attracted insects. This led to an examination of the urine, which was found to contain glucose; the appearance of glucose in the urine is characteristic of the disease diabetes mellitus, which at the time of these observations was incurable. The glucose appears in the urine in diabetes because the level of glucose concentration in the blood is abnormally high, and the kidney mechanism that reabsorbs glucose completely from the urine in the proximal tubule of the nephron at normal blood-sugar levels is unable to cope with the high concentration. It was subsequently shown that if the pancreatic duct is ligated the exocrine portion of the pancreas degenerates, leaving only the islets, but this operation does not produce diabetes. The next step was to prepare an extract of the islet tissue and show that this will lower the blood sugar of diabetics. This discovery demonstrated beyond doubt the existence of a hormone in the islet tissue, and this hormone has since been purified, isolated, and its complete structure determined, as we have seen earlier.

The basic effect of insulin, in the normal or diabetic organism, is to promote the utilization of glucose by the tissues, including the liver. In the liver, the level of blood sugar at which glycogenesis predominates over glycogenolysis is lowered, and in the tissues, the removal of glucose from the blood is increased. There is also, apparently independently, some effect of insulin in stimulating the degradation of glucose in the tissues. The net effect of insulin administration is, then, a decrease in the level of blood glucose, in consequence of increased removal of glucose from the blood.

The second hormonal factor active in the normal control of blood sugar arises from the pituitary. It was found that, in animals rendered diabetic by removal of the pancreas, removal of the anterior lobe of the pituitary restored the blood sugar to essentially normal levels. On the other hand, injection of extracts of the anterior pituitary into normal animals resulted in an increased blood sugar. These effects were attributed to a "diabetogenic factor" in the anterior pituitary, which had the effect of decreasing the utilization of glucose by the tissues. With progress in the purification of the hormones of the anterior pituitary, however, it became evident that no single substance was responsible for the diabetogenic effect. Instead, mixtures of the growth hormone (somatotrophic hormone or STH) and the adrenocorticotrophic hormone (ACTH) will duplicate the diabetogenic effects of anterior pituitary extracts. The growth hormone appears to act directly upon the liver and other tissues to depress glucose utilization, while the action of ACTH is indirect and is exerted through its influence on the adrenal cortex.

Following extirpation of the adrenal cortex, an animal which is well fed with adequate carbohydrate supplies and kept on a carefully balanced salt regime may show no serious effects. Even a short fast, however, or a diet containing little carbohydrate will cause an abnormally rapid fall in blood-sugar levels. This condition can be remedied by injections of one of several steroid hormones, of which cortico-sterone and cortisol are probably the most important occurring naturally in the secretion of the gland. These hormones act to promote gluconeogen-esis from amino acids and hence to permit maintenance of normal glycogen levels in the liver during fasting or while on a diet low in carbohydrates.

The diabetogenic action of ACTH appears to arise primarily from its action in stimulating the adrenal cortex to form and liberate these steroids. The normal secretion of ACTH by the anterior pituitary is under neurosecre-tory control from the hypothalamo-hypophysial system which connects the midbrain with the posterior pitui-tary. The control of the secretion of growth hormone and of insulin has not been definitely established, but it ap-pears probable that the blood-sugar level influences the secretion of one or both of these hormones. The end result of the operation of the con-trolling factors is that the blood-glucose concentration of the blood of most mammals is maintained near 0.1%, regardless of variations in food intake or activity.

There is, however, a regulatory fac-tor which tends to cause deviations from the normal blood-sugar level under certain conditions. This is the hormone epinephrin, secreted by the adrenal medulla. Intense emotional stimulation results in liberation of this hormone into the blood, and its pri-mary action is to increase glycogenoly-sis in the liver, and hence increase the blood sugar. This response to emotion has been interpreted as an adaptive phenomenon, in that the increased blood sugar places the animal in a better position for "flight or fight" in response to the situation which aroused the emotional excitement in the first place.

A third factor in the regulation of blood sugar is the hormone glucagon. For some time, the functional signifi-cance of glucagon was uncertain, but it now appears clear that it shares with insulin in the control of normal blood-sugar levels, and more important, of normal rates of tissue utilization of glucose. Comparative studies have given us some extremely interesting insights into the roles of the two hor-mones glucagon and insulin in the var-ious vertebrate groups.

In most vertebrates, the islet cells of the pancreas contain both alpha and beta cells in varying proportions; the most striking exceptions are the uro-dele amphibians (salamanders, newts), which have only beta cells, and certain birds, which have largely or entirely alpha cells. Removal of the pancreas, where this operation has been per-formed, generally is followed by an increase in the glucose level in the blood and often by the other symptoms of diabetes as well; the exceptions are (1) the squamate reptiles (lizards, snakes), in which the operation is fol-lowed immediately by a decrease in blood sugar, though diabetes ulti-mately ensues and (2) birds such as the duck, in which the decrease in blood sugar is often the only effect seen, and this is transitory. The injection of insulin generally causes hypoglycemia, but this may be preceded in anuran amphibians and squamate reptiles by hyperglycemia. In birds, insulin is often ineffective in changing blood sugar when the pancreas is intact, or in curing the hyperglycemia which sometimes follows removal of the pancreas. Removal of the adenohypophysis alone usually has little effect on blood-glucose levels or else results in a slight decrease, but in diabetic animals this operation alleviates the diabetes; again the birds are exceptions, since hypophysectomy intensifies the hypoglycemia, which follows removal of the pancreas. The effect of glucagon injection is typically to increase blood sugar in all the vertebrates tested, but the sensitivity varies considerably; in urodele amphibians, very large doses are required to produce any effect, while birds by contrast are extremely sensitive.

This survey—which represents results on only a few species in each of the groups mentioned—suggests that the relative roles of insulin and glucagon vary considerably in the vertebrate group. The extremes are the urodele amphibians with no alpha cells and a very low sensitivity to glucagon, where insulin must the main regulatory factor, and certain birds with few beta cells and a low sensitivity to insulin, where glucagon must be the regulatory factor. Further study of these extreme cases would be of great interest in elucidating the normal actions of the two factors which occur together in mammals, a fact which makes detailed study more difficult.

One other point of importance emerges from comparative studies. In the poikilotherms (e.g., the alligator),

the effects of insulin injection, though qualitatively similar to those in mammals, develop very slowly, over a period of hours or even days, and persist for a long period. This means in turn that rapid changes in blood sugar cannot be regulated, hence the main function of insulin must be in the long-term regulation of glucose utilization by the tissues. This was, in all likelihood, its primitive function. This conclusion is further illustrated by the nervous effects of insulin injection. In mammals, insulin, partly by lowering blood sugar drastically and rapidly, produces a condition of nervous shock, in which convulsions due to widespread muscular contraction are observed. In the lower vertebrates, these convulsions are either much reduced in intensity or do not occur at all, even though the blood sugar level is greatly reduced. It seems likely that, in mammals and other higher vertebrates, the nervous system has become dependent on a constant glucose level for its normal functioning, but in the lower vertebrates this dependence is less, and the regulatory mechanisms are directed more at constant cellular activity than at a constant internal environment.

Regulation of Body Temperature

As a final instance of regulation, we shall discuss the control of body temperature in birds and mammals. The cells and tissues of most animals operate at the same temperature as that of the external environment; unusually active animals may, during periods of activity, develop body temperatures somewhat above the environmental temperature, but this is rare. Chemical reactions in general—and metabolic processes are chemical reactions—occur at rates which are dependent on the temperature; the rate of many chemical processes, including metabolic ones, is doubled or tripled by an increase in temperature of 10°C. In consequence, the activity of most animals will depend very much on the temperature, and normal activity can occur only within a relatively restricted range of external temperatures. Many animals can, over a period of time, undergo an adaptive change such that the rate of activity at a low temperature will gradually increase and may nearly attain the rate which earlier prevailed at a higher temperature; and animals which normally live at or near 0°C in polar waters may have rates of respiration and movement not very different from those which live at 30°C in tropical waters. However, adaptation of this sort takes time and in extreme cases may even involve evolutionary changes. Adaptation is not able to deal with the normal diurnal temperature variation on land, for example.

Birds and mammals, by contrast, are nearly all able to maintain body temperatures at a constant level of 35 to 40°C when the external temperature is very much lower or somewhat higher than this range. This means that a bird or mammal can continue normal activities at temperatures which would paralyze a lower vertebrate or invertebrate, and they can resist high temperatures which might be lethal to an animal accustomed to life at 10°C or below. Animals which can maintain relatively constant body temperatures regardless of the external temperature are spoken of as homeothermous; this term is scientifically preferable to the more popular "warm blooded," since in the tropics the body temperature of a homeotherm might well be below that of a poikilotherm—which we commonly speak of as "cold-blooded."

In any animal, heat may be gained primarily from the heat produced by metabolic activity or by radiation from warm objects. In an environment with a higher temperature than the body, it may also be gained by conduction and radiation from the environment. Heat may be lost by evaporation of water, and in an environment cooler than the body temperature it may be lost by radiation and conduction to the environment. In poikilothermous animals, radiation, evaporation, and conduction normally serve to dissipate the metabolic heat as rapidly as it is produced. In homeothermous animals, radiation, conduction, evaporation, and heat production are all more or less regulated, with the result that the body temperature is usually held quite constant.

The control of heat production is normally seen only at the extremes of the temperature range. In most homeotherms, there is a relatively wide range of external temperatures, within which the metabolic rate does not vary with the temperature. Outside this range, at lower temperatures, the rate increases, and at higher temperatures the rate also increases; in the poikilotherm, the metabolic rate increases regularly with temperature over the entire range of tolerance. The major factor in the variation of metabolic rate with temperature in homeotherms is muscular activity. At low temperatures the muscle tonus increases, and clonic contractions (shivering) may occur; at high temperatures, muscle tonus and general bodily activity decrease. The control over these changes is primarily nervous, mediated through a thermoregulatory center in the brain. In addition, there is probably a hormonal control of the metabolism of the tissues through the thyroid and other glands, which appear to be involved in the increased metabolism at lower temperatures, before shivering appears. The activity of the thyroid is mediated through one or more hormones related to thyroxin, and the secretion of these hormones is regulated by the thyrotrophic hormone, secreted by the anterior pituitary. The secretion of thyrotrophin is probably in turn regulated through neurosecretory connections with the brain.

Within the ordinary range of temperatures, however, the regulation in most birds and mammals is of heat loss rather than heat production. The following factors are involved; we shall indicate factors increasing heat loss by +, those decreasing heat loss by −.

(1) Erection of hair or feathers (−).
(2) Increased skin circulation (+).
(3) Decreased skin circulation (−).
(4) Secretion of sweat (+).
(5) Panting (+).

Of these, the most widely used in normal regulation of body temperature are those which alter the circulation. The other factors are used at extreme low (1) or high (4, 5) temperatures, and most animals have only one of the two last mechanisms. In addition, there are a great variety of behavioral factors which enter into temperature regulation; in animals such as reptiles, behavioral mechanisms alone may result in an effective temperature control, within relatively narrow limits.

References

Cellular Regulation and General References

Adolph, E. F. 1957. Ontogeny of physiological regulations in the rat. *Quart. Rev. Biol.* **32** 89–137.

Barcroft, J. 1932. "La fixité du milieu intérieur est la condition de la vie libre" (Claude Bernard). *Biol. Rev.* **7** 24–87.

Adolph, E. F. 1959. How specific are physiological regulations? *Pers. Biol. Med.* **3** 55–69.

Barcroft, J. 1934. *Features in the Architecture of Physiological Function.* Univ. Press, Cambridge, England.

Boxer, G. E., and Devlin, T. M. 1961. Pathways of intracellular hydrogen transport. *Science* **134** 1495–1501.

Cannon, W. B. 1939. *The Wisdom of the Body.* Norton, New York.

Chance, B., and Hess, B. 1959. Spectroscopic evidence of metabolic control. *Science* **129** 700–708.

Davis, B. D. 1962. The teleonomic significance of biosynthetic control mechanisms. *Cold Spring Harbor Symp. Quant. Biol.* **26** 1–10.

Hess, B., and Chance, B. 1959. Über zelluläre Regulationsmechanismen und ihr mathematisches Modell. *Naturwiss.* **46** 248–257.

Horecker, B. L. 1958. Le cycle des pentoses et sa signification physiologique. *Bull. Soc. Chim. Biol.* **40** 555–578.

Ingle, D. J. 1954. Permissibility of hormone action. *Acta Endocrinol.* **17** 172–186.

Knox, W. E., Auerbach, V. H., and Lin, E. C. C. 1956. Enzymatic and metabolic adaptations in animals. *Physiol. Rev.* **36** 164–254.

Krebs, H. A. 1957. Control of metabolic processes. *Endeavour* **16** 125–132.

Lardy, H. A., Lee, Y. P., and Takemori, A. 1960. Enzyme responses to thyroid hormones. *Annals N.Y. Acad. Sci.* **86** 506–511.

Lehninger, A. L. 1960. Thyroxine and the swelling and contraction cycle in mitochondria. *Annals N.Y. Acad. Sci.* **86** 484–493.

Monod, J., and Jacob, F. 1962. Teleonomic mechanisms in cellular metabolism, growth and differentiation. *Cold Spring Harbor Symp. Quant. Biol.* **26** 389–401.

Wolstenholme, G. E. W., and O'Connor, C. M. (eds.) 1959. *Ciba Foundation Symposium on the Regulation of Cell Metabolism.* Churchill; London.

Young, J. Z. 1954. Some requirements for the study of the organization of cellular processes. *Proc. Royal Soc. London B* **142** 137–140.

Regulation of Salts and Water; Excretion

Chew, R. M. 1961. Water metabolism of desert-inhabiting vertebrates. *Biol. Rev.* **36** 131.

Fraser, E. A. 1950. The development of the vertebrate excretory system. *Biol. Rev.* **25** 159–187.

Gottschalk, C. W. 1961. Micropuncture studies

of tubular function in the mammalian kidney. *The Physiologist* **4** 35–55.

Jones, I. C., and Eckstein, P. (eds.) 1956. *The Comparative Endocrinology of Vertebrates part II: The Hormonal Control of Water and Salt-electrolyte Metabolism in Vertebrates.* Univ. Press, Cambridge, England.

Kitching, J. A. 1953. Contractile vacuoles. *Biol. Rev.* **13** 403–444.

Lafon, M. 1953. Quelques faits concernant l'équilibre hydrominéral et sa regulation chez les invertébrés. *Arch. Sci. Physiol.* **7** C39–53.

Leaf, A., and Hays, R. M. 1961. The effects of neurohypophyseal hormone on permeability and transport in a living membrane. *Rec. Progr. Horm. Res.* **17** 467–487.

Manery, J. F. 1954. Water and electrolyte metabolism. *Physiol. Rev.* **34** 334–417.

Marshall, E. K. Jr. 1934. The comparative physiology of the kidney in relation to theories of renal secretion. *Physiol. Rev.* **14** 133–159.

Morel, F. 1954. Le contrôle hormonal de la fonction renale, element de la regulation de l'equilibre hydrominéral. *Arch. Sci. Physiol.* **8** C163–174.

Muller, A. F. 1961. Some aspects of the hormonal control of water and electrolytes. *Symp. Water Electrolyte Metab.* 64–75.

Noble, R. L. 1955. Physiology of the adrenal cortex. *The Hormones* **3** 685–819.

Potts, W. T. W. 1954. The energetics of osmotic regulation in brackish and fresh-water animals. *J. Exp. Biol.* **31** 618–630.

Robertson, J. D. 1957. The habitat of the early vertebrates. *Biol. Rev.* **32** 156–187.

Robertson, J. D. 1959. The origin of vertebrates, marine or fresh-water? *Adv. Sci.* **15** 516–520.

Sawyer, W. H. 1961. Comparative physiology and pharmacology of the neurohypophysis. *Rec. Progr. Horm. Res.* **17** 437–461.

Sayers, G. 1950. The adrenal cortex and homeostasis. *Physiol. Rev.* **30** 241–320.

Schmidt-Nielsen, B. 1958. The resourcefulness of nature in physiological adaptation to the environment. *The Physiologist* **1** 4–20.

Schmidt-Nielsen, K., and Schmidt-Nielsen, B. 1952. Water metabolism of desert mammals. *Physiol. Rev.* **32** 135–166.

Selkurt, E. E. 1954. Sodium excretion by the mammalian kidney. *Physiol. Rev.* **34** 287–333.

Smith, H. W. 1936. The retention and physiological role of urea in the elasmobranchs. *Biol. Rev.* **11** 49–82.

Smith, H. W. 1956. *Principles of Renal Physiology.* Oxford Univ. Press, New York.

Vogt, M. 1954. The role of the adrenal gland in homeostasis. *Quart. J. Exp. Physiol.* **39** 245–252.

Winton, F. R. (ed.) 1956. *Modern Views on the Secretion of Urine.* Churchill, London.

Wirz, H. 1961. Newer concepts of renal mechanism in relation to water and electrolyte excretions. *Symp. Water Electrolyte Metab.* 100–108.

Zwemer, R. L. 1953. Water and electrolyte metabolism. *Biochem. Physiol. Nutr.* **1** 39–56.

Carbohydrate metabolism

Ashmore, J., and Weber, G. 1959. The role of hepatic glucose-6-phosphatase in the regulation of carbohydrate metabolism. *Vitamins and Hormones* **17** 92–132.

MacLeod, J. J. R. 1926. *Carbohydrate Metabolism and Insulin.* Longmans, Green, London.

Miller, L. L. 1961. Some direct actions of insulin, glucagon and hydrocortisone on the isolated perfused liver. *Rec. Progr. Horm. Res.* **17** 539–564.

Park, C. R., Morgan, H. E., Henderson, M. J., Regen, D. M., Cadenas, E., and Post, R. L. 1961. The regulation of glucose uptake in muscle as studied in the perfused rat heart. *Rec. Progr. Horm. Res.* **17** 493–529.

Soskin, S. 1941. The blood sugar: its origin, regulation and utilization. *Physiol. Rev.* **21** 140–193.

Respiration and Body Temperature

Bronk, J. R. 1960. The influence of thyroxine and related compounds on oxidative rate and efficiency of phosphorylation in liver mitochondria and submitochondrial particles. *Annals N.Y. Acad. Sci.* **86** 494–505.

Irving, L. 1959. Heterothermous operation of warm-blooded animals. *The Physiologist* **2** 18–32.

Smith, R. E., and Hoijer, D. J. 1962. Metabolism and cellular function in cold acclimation. *Physiol. Rev.* **42** 60–142.

Strom, G. 1961. Central nervous regulation of body temperature. *Hdbk. Physiol. I: Neurophysiol.* **3** 1173–1196.

15 Progressive and cyclic regulation

The orderly sequence of events in the development of an animal from a fertilized egg has attracted the attention and excited the wonder of scientists since Aristotle first observed and described the development of the chick. Aristotle ascribed the orderly character of development to an *entelechy,* an internal guiding principle directing events in the egg to their ultimate goal, the chicken. This view has the advantage of offering a complete and, in a sense, an indisputable explanation, but to a modern scientist it is not acceptable because it fails to fulfill the major aim of science, the relation of one phenomenon to other, usually simpler, phenomena. The entelechy is at least as complex a concept as development itself and in the ultimate logical analysis can be seen to be merely a word, essentially equivalent to the process which it purports to explain.

The analysis of development in terms of efficient causes, on the other hand, offers some of the greatest difficulties yet encountered by science. These difficulties arise out of the complexity of the process and its small scale. In this book, where our purpose is to summarize some of the main points of physiological knowledge, we shall have relatively little to say about embryonic development, other than to state a few of the leading concepts and ideas. Most of this chapter will be devoted to phenomena in the later development of the organism, phenomena which are far better understood in many cases than are those in the embryo.

One of the necessary bases of the analysis of development is the fact that development and heredity are closely interrelated. There is little reason to doubt that the ultimate determination of each stage in development must be in the genes. In a sense, the chromosomes of the zygote nucleus represent, better than anything else, the Aristotelian entelechy in that the chromosomes must contain, in coded form, the whole plan for embryonic and later development. Geneticists have for good reasons devoted their attention largely to the inheritance of characteristics which are apparent only late in development. The difficulties of relating genes to the crucial events in early development that have most interested experimental embryologists are considerable, but it is at this point that the geneticist and the experimental embryologist must one day meet.

Differentiation and Development

In some animals the early events of differentiation in the cleavage of the fertilized egg are determined, not by the genes, but by the constitution of the egg itself, which in turn depends fortuitously on the position of the egg when it was formed in the ovary and oviducts. Most embryos, however, experience their first differentiation in the early stages of cleavage. Some mollusks, for example, show differentiation at the first cleavage; if the two blastomeres formed at this stage are separated, each develops into a partial embryo. In the sea urchin, this kind of differentiation does not occur until the third cleavage, and it is not complete even then. The embryo can be split into two halves, each of which will form normal embryos even at the 64-cell stage. The basis for the early differentiation of the sea urchin has been extensively explored by a variety of techniques. It is clear from these studies that the differentiation rests on differences between the "animal"

and "vegetal" pole of the egg. This has been most brilliantly demonstrated by Hörstadius' experiments, in which blastomeres from the different regions of the egg in the 32- and 64-cell stages have been separated and recombined in various arrangements. A normal embryo results only when the proportions of animal and vegetal material are roughly the same as in the original embryo (Figure 15.1). These experiments suggest that the regulation of development at this early stage depends on distribution of materials. However, development can be altered towards the animal or vegetal direction (that is, with a predominance of structures derived from the respective poles) by a variety of chemical treatments of the egg, suggesting that processes, rather than or in addition to substances, may be involved. We may hazard the hypothesis at this stage that the genes which control the very earliest stages in development do so by influencing the arrangement in the egg of specific enzyme systems.

The transplantation technique has been used with great success in amphibian embryos at the stage of gastrulation. These experiments are now well known to most students of biology and will not be described in detail here. The conclusions from the experiments should, however, be summarized briefly. The cells of the embryo begin by being pluripotent; that is, they can, under suitable influence, develop in any of several directions. The direction in which they do in fact develop depends primarily on the position they occupy in the embryo; that is, the development of any cell is influenced by its surroundings. After development of any cell has proceeded beyond a certain stage the original pluripotency is lost, and the fate of this cell is partly or

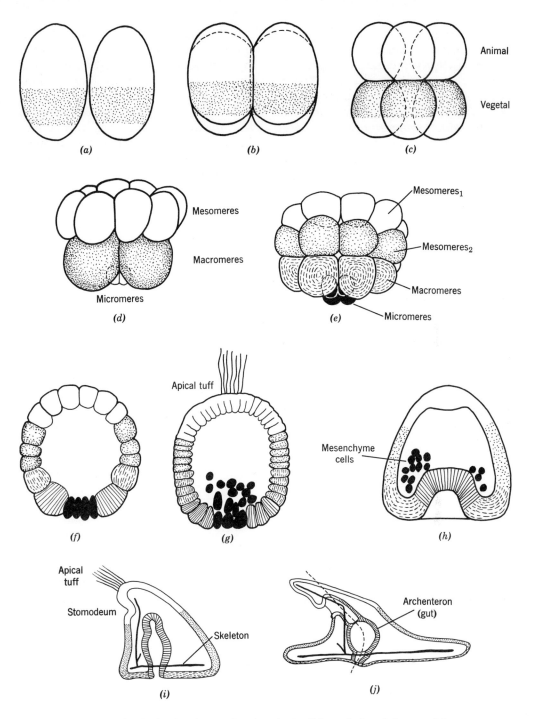

Fig. 15.1 (*A*)   The role of animal and vegetal regions in the differentiation of the egg of the sea urchin. This figure shows the normal pattern of early development. The shading indicates the fate, in the later stages, of cell groups from the first cleavage stages (*a*) through (*e*).

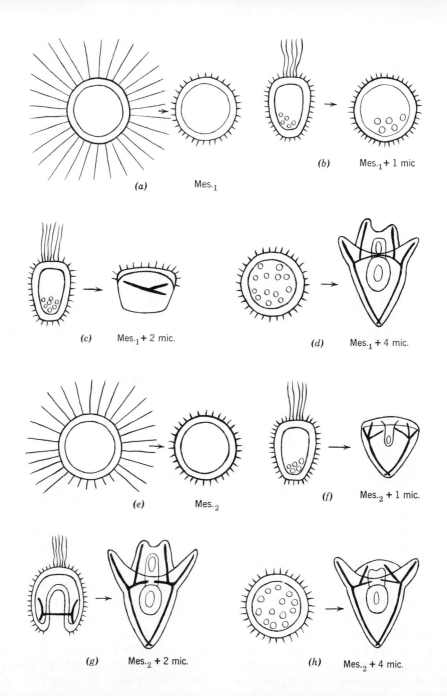

Fig. 15.1 (*B*)   The development of cell layers isolated from the 32- or 64-cell stages.   Mes.$_1$ = upper layer of mesomeres.   Mes.$_2$ = lower layer of mesomeres.   Mac.$_1$ = upper layer of macromeres.   Mac.$_2$ = lower layer of macromeres.   Mes.$_1$ + 1 mic. = Mes.$_1$ with one micromere added.   Note that normal larvae (*d, g, h*) can be produced by a suitable proportion of mesomeres and micromeres, while other combinations produce abnormal larvae of various sorts.   (After Hörstadius, 1950, *L'Année Biol.* **26** 381.)

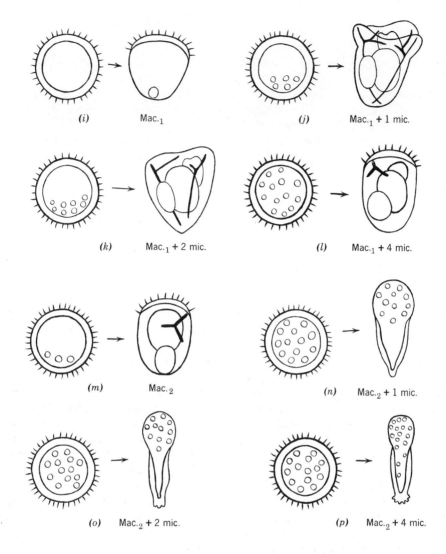

(i)   Mac.$_1$

(j)   Mac.$_1$ + 1 mic.

(k)   Mac.$_1$ + 2 mic.

(l)   Mac.$_1$ + 4 mic.

(m)   Mac.$_2$

(n)   Mac.$_2$ + 1 mic.

(o)   Mac.$_2$ + 2 mic.

(p)   Mac.$_2$ + 4 mic.

entirely determined; it is no longer susceptible to influence from the surroundings, or at least becomes much less susceptible to such influence. Some cells or regions in the embryo, when they have lost their pluripotency and acquired the ability to carry out a particular course of development (an ability known as self-differentiation), also exhibit the ability to induce changes in the development of other pluripotent cells. Thus, certain regions in the embryo early take on the function of organizing the development of cells in their immediate vicinity.

This picture, based on a series of brilliant investigations in the first quarter of the present century, raises a number of important questions for which as yet we have no answer. What happens in a cell to change it from a pluripotent to a self-differentiating condition? What is the nature of the influence that the organizing regions of the embryo exert on adjacent cells to cause the differentiation? How do the genes, presumably the same in all cells, control the varieties of differentiation seen in the various cells and tissues of the embryo? There is a steadily growing body of experimental evidence relating to these questions, but little purpose would be served in reviewing this evidence here, because at present it provides no more than general hypotheses not verifiable by direct experimental study. Problems of differentiation and the control of embryonic development remain among the most important of the unsolved problems of biology.

Postembryonic Development: Insects

One group of animals, the insects, affords us an unusual opportunity for the study of developmental processes at a stage where experiments are more readily performed and interpreted than is the case in the embryo. The embryonic development of insects, as with many other invertebrates and some vertebrates as well, leads to a larval form, which is often quite different in appearance from the adult. In consequence, this larva must undergo a further developmental process before attaining the adult stage. The advantage which the insects offer is that, for many species, it is quite easy to keep the larvae in culture in the laboratory, and moreover these forms are extraordinarily resistant to experimental manipulation.

There are three common patterns of postembryonic development in insects. In some primitive groups development is direct. The animal which hatches from the egg is essentially similar in form to, though smaller than, the adult, and postlarval changes involve mostly an increase in size. In other groups, of which the Orthoptera

(roaches, grasshoppers, etc.) are the best known, the animal which emerges from the egg is called a nymph. It usually differs substantially from the adult in structure, though it has the characteristic three pairs of thoracic limbs. The nymph increases in size, with relatively little change in form, through a series of larval molts. It then undergoes a final molt with more extensive changes in form to reach the adult or sexually mature stage (imago). This type of development is known as hemimetabolous. The third type of postlarval development, known as holometabolous, involves three distinct body forms, with substantial metamorphosis between. Holometabolous development is most familiar in Diptera (flies), Hymenoptera (ants, bees), and Lepidoptera (butterflies, moths), but occurs in other groups as well. The animal emerges from the egg as a worm-like larva (maggot, caterpillar), not resembling in the least the adult of the same species. The larva grows without change in form through several instars (stages separated by molt) and then undergoes a pupal molt, in which the form changes completely to that of an inactive pupa encased in a resistant cuticle. The pupal stage is terminated by the final or imaginal molt, in which the adult winged form emerges from the discarded pupal integument in one of the most dramatic of all biological processes.

In all insects the growth which occurs in the course of development is discontinuous; that is, the body size remains constant during an instar or larval stage, and then increases suddenly, often within an hour or less, at the time of molting. The molting process itself follows a substantial period of preparation. At a certain well-defined point in each instar, the cells of the epidermis—which in insects lies below the firm cuticle—are activated. This activation is first evident in the appearance of mitotic activity in localized regions of the epidermis, and subsequently in the onset of secretory activity in the epidermal cells. These cells secrete the protein matrix of a new cuticle beneath the old and at the same time secrete enzymes which dissolve away part of the inner layers of the old cuticle. The result is the formation of a new cuticular matrix below the old and a separation of the old cuticle from the epidermis. When the separation is complete the molt proper occurs. The old cuticle is split by muscular activity, an increase in body size is produced typically by intake of air into the body, and the insect works its way out of the old cuticle. On emergence the new cuticle is soft, and the insect enlarges its body further by swallowing air and pumping blood into limbs and other appendages.

Soon after emergence the cuticle begins to harden. The hardening is brought about primarily by a process known as phenolic tanning. Polyphenols are secreted into the cuticle by the epidermal cells, and they form cross linkages with the protein molecules of the cuticular matrix. As the polyphenols are oxidized by atmospheric oxygen, these cross linkages become firm, and the protein becomes hardened. At the same time the polysaccharide chitin is synthesized and deposited in the cuticle, further strengthening this structure. Finally, a waxy epicuticle is secreted through canals in the cuticle proper and spreads over the outer surface of the cuticle as a waterproofing layer. When this process is complete, the size of the animal is fixed until the next molt. True growth in the sense of increase of living tissues

takes place in the period following the molt, when new tissue is laid down to replace the air or water taken in rapidly at the time of molting.

The process of molting in itself may provide only for an increase in size, but in many cases developmental changes occur as well. In the simplest case, these changes involve merely local variations in mitotic activity of special regions of the epidermis, so that after molting the structure of the body surface is changed by enlargement of these regions. At the other extreme is the set of changes involved in the conversion of a pupa to an imago in holometabolous insects. Here the larval organs are completely broken down and replaced by a new set of organs, differentiated from small clumps of cells which have remained in an undifferentiated condition through the larval stages. This rather special case of differentiation offers some unusual advantages for experimental study, especially since in certain insects the techniques of genetic study are highly developed, and a great deal of genetic knowledge has been accumulated.

Humoral Control

The study of the control of the related processes of molting and metamorphosis began with some simple experiments, in which threads were tied tightly around various parts of the body of larvae of holometabolous insects. Ligatures which separated the brain from the rest of the body were, if performed early enough, effective in preventing a molt. Ligatures which separated the thorax from the abdomen prevented molting of the abdomen, while permitting the head and thorax to molt. The inference was that molting is controlled by two centers, one in the head and the other in the thorax.

This inference was confirmed and extended by Wigglesworth, using an especially favorable experimental animal, the bloodsucking bug, *Rhodnius prolixus*. This animal is hemimetabolous. If nymphs are not fed, they do not molt, though they may survive for considerable periods in a fasting condition. When they are fed blood, they then molt at a definite time after feeding. The time differs for each larval instar, but is quite definite in any one instar. The animals will survive such drastic operations as decapitation for considerable periods. Wigglesworth showed that, if the animal was decapitated soon after feeding, the body failed to molt at the normal time, though it remained alive. On the other hand, decapitation shortly before the normal time of molting did not prevent the molt. By performing the operation at various times between feeding and molting, Wigglesworth was able to establish for each instar a critical time before which decapitation prevented the molt. He then examined the body regions histologically and showed that this critical period coincides with the development of neurosecretory activity in a group of cells in the brain. Subsequent studies showed that these cells send axons to the corpora cardiaca and liberate their product from these end organs.

Rhodnius proved suitable for another type of experiment as well. Decapitated bugs can be joined together by small tubes so that their blood mixes (parabiotic union). In this situation, bugs which have been decapitated after the critical period will induce molt in bugs decapitated before the critical period. More important is the fact that when a young bug (early larval instar) is joined to a bug in the last larval instar, and hence ready to metamorphose to the adult stage, the molt induced in the older bug is not an imaginal molt; instead, the older bug molts to form an extra large nymph. The normal developmental changes leading to the adult condition fail to occur. This led Wigglesworth to postulate the existence of a juvenile hormone that restrains developmental changes, without interfering with the other processes leading to a molt. Histological and experimental studies led him to suggest the corpora allata as the site of origin of this hormone.

The conclusive identification of the thoracic center involved in the molt was made by Williams at Harvard University, using another very favorable experimental material, the cecropia silk worm. This animal, like many other insects, enters into a condition called diapause, while in the pupal stage. In diapause, the metabolic rate falls to a low level, and developmental processes are arrested. The animal normally passes the winter in this condition. Termination of diapause, normally occurring in spring, can be brought about experimentally by first chilling the animals (e.g., to 5°C) for a period, and then exposing them to warmer temperatures (e.g., 20–25°C). The chilling is essential; animals kept continually at warm temperatures remain in diapause. Williams showed that chilling affects the brain primarily. Brains from chilled animals implanted into diapausing animals at room temperature will induce termination of the diapause. They will do this, however, only if a structure in the anterior part of the thorax, the prothoracic gland, is present. Implantation of brains from chilled pupae into abdomens isolated from diapausing pupae does not terminate diapause in the abdomen, but parabiotic union of such abdomens with chilled head-thorax preparations of chilled pupae does terminate diapause.

The termination of diapause is, of course, followed by developmental changes, and ultimately by the imaginal molt. Williams has tried to establish the first event involved in termination of diapause and has good evidence that this event is the synthesis of cytochrome oxidase. The diapausing pupa has a low rate of oxygen consumption, resulting from complete inactivity of the cytochrome system; this in turn is a consequence of the absence of cytochrome oxidase. Treatments which terminate diapause induce, as the first identifiable change, resynthesis of cytochrome oxidase. Unfortunately, this phenomenon seems to be confined to the cecropia silkworm and a few related species, and will not provide a basis for a general interpretation of hormone action in insects.

Van der Kloot has given an excellent account of the events in the brain that are associated with the onset and termination of diapause. In diapause, the brain becomes completely inactive electrically; this change is associated with the disappearance from the brain of the enzyme acetylcholinesterase. Chilling is followed by accumulation of acetylcholine, and this in turn is followed by reappearance of cholinesterase and then of electrical activity. This sequence suggests that the reappearance of cholinesterase is an induction phenomenon, brought about by the presence of the substrate (Figure 15.2). Again, there is no reason to suppose that this series of phenomena has general significance for the activation of neurosecretion. Rather, it

appears that the mechanisms of diapause termination are highly specialized adaptations in the particular species studied.

On the other hand, the basic mechanisms in the control of diapause and of molting seem to be much the same, and the molt control mechanism in particular appears to be universal among insects. In summary, this mechanism is as follows: The initial stage identified thus far is activation, by any of several means, of a special group of neurosecretory cells in the protocerebrum. The secretion of these cells passes along axons to the corpora cardiaca, to be liberated from these structures into the blood stream. The brain hormone activates the thoracic gland, an endocrine structure derived from embryonic regions adjacent to those that will form the salivary glands. The secretion of the thoracic gland activates the epidermis, inducing mitosis and cuticular secretion. It has been shown that the thoracic gland is necessary for both these epidermal processes, independently. The substance ecdyson, isolated from whole insects by Karlson in Germany, duplicates the actions of the thoracic gland and is thought by many to be the thoracic gland hormone.

In larval insects, a second hormone, known as the juvenile hormone, is secreted during the activation of molting by the corpora allata. This hormone restrains developmental processes in the epidermis and elsewhere, without interfering with the molt as such. Its chemical nature is unknown, but it is soluble in ether and similar solvents, and its actions are duplicated by farnesol, an intermediate in steroid synthesis. Farnesol may not be the hormone, but it may be closely related to it. In the imaginal molt, and in holo-

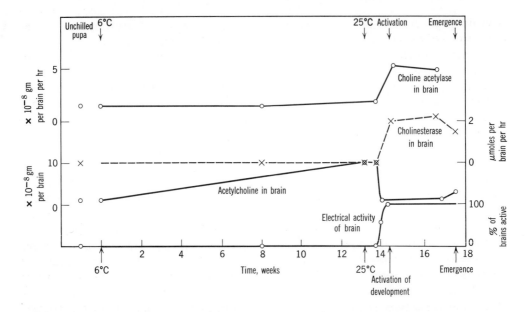

Fig. 15.2 Diapause release in the cecropia silkworm. At zero time, the diapausing pupa is transferred from 25°C to 6°C. During 13 weeks of chilling, the acetylcholine concentration increases gradually. After 13 weeks, the pupa is returned to 25°C. On the 5th day thereafter, cholinesterase appears, the concentration of choline acetylase increases, and electrical activity reappears. On the 8th day, the first signs of adult development appear. (After Van der Kloot, 1955, *Biol. Bull.* **109** 276.)

metabolous insects in the pupal molt as well, the corpus allatum is inactive, and little or no juvenile hormone is secreted. The diverse nature of the actions of both ecdyson and the juvenile hormone have led Williams and Karlson to propose that these substances act, not on specific enzyme systems, but on the cellular mechanisms which transfer information from the genes to the synthetic processes. Recent evidence in support of this view is a stimulation of structural changes in the chromosomes, normally occurring in specific developmental stages, by treatment of pupae with ecdyson.

Postembryonic Development:
Amphibians

A somewhat parallel case to the metamorphosis of insects is the meta-

morphosis of anuran amphibians from the larval (tadpole) to adult body form. This change appears somewhat less spectacular than insect metamorphosis, because it requires more time for completion. As we have seen, the appearance in insects is deceptive, since most of the changes occur within the opaque pupal cuticle. In the frog the obvious external changes are the growth of limbs and the loss of the tail. These changes, which involve extensive development internally in the skeleton and the muscles, are accompanied by structural and functional changes internally as well, in growth of the liver, development of enzyme systems for urea synthesis, formation of new blood proteins (albumin, hemoglobin), conversion of the visual pigment from porphyropsin to rhodopsin, and many others.

It has been known since 1912 that

thyroid preparations or pure thyroid hormone will bring about this complex of changes. In the normal sequence of events the thyroid is stimulated to activity by the thyrotrophic hormone of the adenohypophysis, and removal of this structure prevents metamorphosis, as does removal of the thyroid. The tissues of the late embryo and early larva, before the beginning of feeding, are insensitive to thyroid treatment. Sensitivity to thyroid appears long before thyroid secretion begins; hence thyroid extracts or hormones will induce premature metamorphosis. The sensitivity to thyroid appears earlier in some tissues than in others, and each tissue has a threshold of responsiveness. At thyroxin concentrations above the threshold, the amount of development and the time required for development depend on the thyroxin concentrations. There is no evidence at present to suggest that any one of the many changes produced by thyroxin is primary, and we must again suppose that the hormone may act on the information transfer system of the cells. These two examples of the control of postembryonic development have been selected as the best known. They have the common feature of a hormone system with a wide variety of developmental effects. It seems quite unlikely that similar mechanisms act in embryonic development. The specific hormones of adults do not in general occur in the embryo, since the endocrine glands develop relatively late and attain functional activity even later. The known hormones, moreover, do not in general have much effect on the tissues of embryos. Finally, the observed interactions among embryonic tissues generally occur only when the interacting tissues are in relatively close contact.

The study of postembryonic development, then, cannot be expected to throw more than a general light on the problems of embryonic development. Postembryonic development, especially in insects, does offer some outstanding opportunities for the correlation of genetic and developmental study. The classic example is the study by Beadle and colleagues of eye-color development in *Drosophila,* showing that the specific pigmentation of the eyes is controlled by the synthesis of specific precursors, and that each stage in this synthesis is under the control of a specific gene. This approach, applied to other significant events with the aim of elucidating principles of development rather than principles of gentics, might prove very illuminating.

Growth

In the postlarval and adult organs development as such is greatly restricted as compared with the embryo, being confined to the maturation of the gonads, development of secondary sexual characters, and the process we call aging in most animals. On the other hand, growth may continue for some time after the final body form is attained. If we restrict the term growth to the increase in cellular organic material, excluding storage material and the mere accumulation of water, it is clear that there are two basic processes underlying growth; protein synthesis and cell division. The latter results in growth only when accompanied by the former, and we shall not discuss mitosis in detail here. The mechanisms of protein synthesis have already been discussed. The factors which normally control this process are by no means clearly understood. In vertebrates the principal control seems to be the somatotrophic or growth hormone of the adenohypophysis, which has a general stimulatory effect on protein synthesis. The mechanism of action of STH and the normal control of its secretion are so poorly understood that there is no point in our discussing it further here.

Most quantitative studies of growth have been essentially descriptive and confined to a study of the time course of some quantity (Figure 15.3). Such time studies invariably disclose a pattern in which the time differential of the parameter studied (e.g., body mass m) is a linear function of the same parameter, thus

$$\frac{dm}{dt} = km$$

Many species attain a maximum weight m_m, and the last phase of growth takes the form

$$\frac{dm}{dt} = k(m_m - m)$$

Extensive studies of relative growth— the relation of the growth of one part

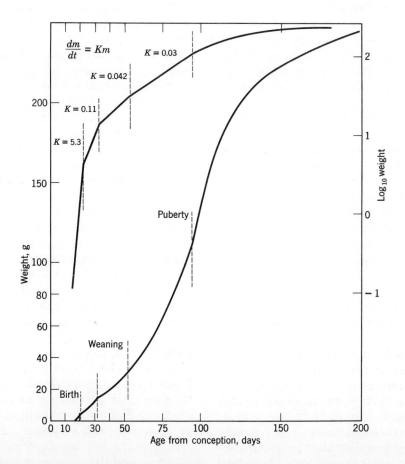

Fig. 15.3 Growth of the rat. Upper curve plotted on the logarithmic scale shown to the right; lower curve on the linear scale shown to the left. (Data from Brody, *Bioenergetics and Growth*, Reinhold, New York, 1945.)

to that of the whole—have led to simple empirical formulas describing the relationship, but to no general principles. In summary, the study of growth has as yet provided no real insight into the basic problems of the cause of growth or the cause of its cessation.

Discontinuous Growth: Crustaceans

One special case of postlarval growth is of peculiar interest, namely, the periodic growth of crustaceans. Like insects, these animals are enclosed in a rigid cuticle; hence growth must be periodic, with regular molts. The basic pattern of control of the initiation of postlarval molting appears to be much the same as in larval insects, but the details are less well understood in crustaceans. There is a molting gland, the Y-organ of Gabe, which is essential to the initiation of the molt, and ecdyson has been isolated from a crustacean. Many crustaceans form, in the eyestalk, a molt-inhibiting hormone, which inhibits the activity of the molt gland during a prolonged period between molts (anecdysis). Anecdysis is characteristic of those crustaceans which molt seasonally. Studies of neurosecretory events in relation to the intermolt cycle suggest that the control of the cycle involves a relatively complex sequence of events, in which at least three distinct groups of neurosecretory cells are concerned. Evidence for a hormone activating the secretion of the molt gland is thus far incomplete.

The regular cycle of events which separates one molt from the next in crustaceans must involve a rather elaborate sequence of metabolic changes. The following have been identified: Immediately before and after the molt there is a vigorous uptake of water.

This is responsible for the rapid increase in body size at molting, and there is some evidence that it is under hormonal control by a factor from the eyestalk. Following the molt, the processes of phenolic hardening and chitin synthesis occur, as in insects. Chitin is synthesized primarily at the expense of glycogen stores laid down before the molt. In addition, a mucopolysaccharide is synthesized and laid down in the cuticle, probably as a matrix for calcification of the cuticle. Calcification begins soon after the phenolic hardening is complete. In involves absorption of calcium from the sea water in marine forms, or utilization of calcium stores laid down as gastroliths in the walls of the stomach in fresh-water forms. When the cuticle is hard enough to permit normal body movements, feeding begins, and the water taken in at the time of molting is replaced by tissue.

The predominant metabolic process during early intermolt is protein synthesis. Later this process is replaced by the synthesis of reserve stores of carbohydrate and lipid. The synthesis of glycogen is controlled by an eyestalk hormone. This factor was first noted as a "diabetogenic" factor; injection of eyestalk extracts in crabs causes an increase in blood sugar level. The increase results from a decreased utilization of glucose by the tissues, and removal of the eyestalks is accompanied by an increase in carbohydrate content of the tissues. Eyestalk extracts have an inhibitory action on the enzyme UDP-glycogen transglucosylase, normally involved in the synthesis of glycogen in the tissues. The increase in tissue carbohydrate which follows eyestalk removal in the intermolt period is comparable to that which normally occurs in the first stages of preparation for the molt, and eyestalk removal in the premolt period does not cause further increase in tissue carbohydrate. These facts suggest that the molt-inhibiting and diabetogenic hormones may be related.

The first sign of the approach of molt is the appearance of epidermal growth in the appendages. Mitosis has been detected in one instance. In those species which form gastroliths, calcium is reabsorbed from the old cuticle and deposited in gastroliths. The protein matrix for the new cuticle is laid down, and carotenoid pigments are mobilized from the hepatopancreas into the blood to be deposited in the cuticle. All these processes are accelerated by eyestalk removal in the intermolt period, as is growth of the molt gland. The whole set of processes from one molt to the next constitutes a cycle, and it seems likely that each of the many events may be controlled by a complex of neurosecretory and endocrine factors.

Reproduction

Another group of cyclical phenomena of importance is seen in reproduction. Reproductive activities of most animals are periodic and are regulated by nervous and hormonal factors. We shall confine our attention here to cases selected from the arthropods and the higher vertebrates to illustrate the control mechanisms involved.

Egg Development in Insects

Among insects there are several species in which the final development of the egg—deposition of yolk and subsequent events—is dependent on some specific stimulus. In the viviparous roach, *Leucophaea maderae*

(Orthopt.), eggs do not develop in fasting females, in fed virgin females, or in pregnant females. Feeding followed by copulation or parturition induces egg development. In the milkweed bug, *Oncopeltus fasciatus* (Heteropt.), feeding alone is an adequate stimulus. In certain mosquitoes (*Aedes aegypti, Anopheles stevensi, Culex pipiens pipiens*), eggs develop only after the insect feeds on blood; fruits, which are taken as food in the absence of suitable sources of blood, do not permit egg development. In other mosquitoes (*Culex pipiens molestus*), the eggs develop even when the animals are on a fruit diet.

The failure of egg development arises from an inhibition originating in the brain. Egg development without other stimulus follows removal of the whole brain or of the pars intercerebralis (*O. fasciatus*), or the lateral protocerebrum (*L. maderae*)—regions with abundant neurosecretory cells—or of a specific group of neurosecretory cells from the pars intercerebralis (*O. fasciatus*). The axons from the neurosecretory cells extend from the brain through the corpus allatum to the corpus cardiacum, and section of the nerve tracts connecting these regions will also activate egg development. In addition, in the case of pregnant *L. maderae,* the embryos themselves liberate something which inhibits egg development.

The fact that the axons of inhibitory neurosecretory cells extend into the corpus allatum suggests a role for this organ, and it can be shown that ligation of the head of newly emerged autogenous mosquitoes (those whose eggs develop without a feeding stimulus) or of recently fed anautogenous forms (which require a blood meal) will prevent egg development. Implants of corpora allata from auto-genous mosquitoes, or from fed anauto-genous forms, will then activate egg development. There is, moreover, a clear correlation between the size of the corpus allatum and its effectiveness in inducing egg development. The normal activation of the corpora allata apparently involves nervous stimuli reaching this structure through the subesophageal ganglion and arising from receptors in the gut (stimulated by distention of the gut after feeding) or the external genitalia (stimulated by copulation and parturition). These stimuli probably also reach the brain and inhibit the secretion there of the neurosecretory material which keeps the corpora allata inactive. The na-ture of the corpus allatum hormone concerned in activation of egg develop-ment is not clear, but it could well be the juvenile hormone. The larval cor-pus allatum is active in stimulating egg development, but is apparently opposed by the secretion of the tho-racic gland.

Sex Determination and Development

In insects, sex is determined geneti-cally and is fixed during the reproduc-tive life, which usually involves only one reproductive cycle, occasionally two or more. The same is true for many crustaceans, but others show the phenomenon of consecutive pro-tandric sexuality, in which the animal begins adult life as a male and then later reverses sex to become a female. The eyestalk of crustaceans forms an ovary-inhibiting hormone in a special group of neurosecretory cells. This hormone apparently also stimulates testis development in some species. The androgenic gland, an endocrine organ found in the walls of the vas

deferens in most crustaceans, stimu-lates development of male secondary sexual characteristics and also stimu-lates testicular development. Implants of the gland into females can cause conversion of ovaries into testes; the reversal of sex from male to female which occurs in many crustaceans is preceded by degeneration of the vas deferens gland; the cause of this degen-eration is not known.

In the vertebrates, sex is normally determined genetically, but the embryo is often ambisexual relatively late in development. The manner in which the genetic mechanisms ultimately determine the development of an ovary or a testis remains unknown, but estrogens and androgens can influence development when applied experimen-tally, and may in some cases induce reversal of the genetic sex. Late in development, usually after a postem-bryonic juvenile stage, the secretion of gonadotrophins by the adenohypophy-sis increases, and the gonads are stim-ulated to activity. The three known gonadotrophins (the follicle-stimulat-ing hormone FSH, the luteinizing or interstitial cell-stimulating hormone ICSH, and the luteotrophic hormone or prolactin LTH) are found in all the vertebrates, and both FSH and ICSH are involved in gonadal stimulation in both sexes. The role of LTH is not generally established. As the gonads develop under this stimulation they begin to secrete their characteristic hormones. The testicular hormone is the steroid testosterone and is formed by the interstitial cells of the testis. Its most characteristic action is a gen-eral stimulation of development of male secondary sexual characteristics, which vary greatly with species. It also stimulates growth of the testis and accessory male ducts and glands, and can in some species effect transformation of a genetic female into a functional male. This hormone also induces in either sex the characteristic male behavior, and it stimulates protein synthesis.

The ovary forms two hormones, the estrogen estradiol and progesterone, which are also steroids. The differences in structure of the three sex hormones are small, but the differences in physiological effect are considerable. Estradiol appears to be primarily responsible for the development of secondary sex characteristics, and in many cases for typical female behavior, especially that directly related to copulatory activity in mammals and possibly in other vertebrates. Detailed study of estrogen effects in intact animals is greatly complicated by the existence of feedback interactions with the pituitary, in which estrogens inhibit secretion of FSH and stimulate secretion of ICSH. The details of these interactions will be discussed later. Estrogens are formed by the interstitial cells of the ovary. Progesterone is formed by the mammalian ovary only when corpora lutea are present; the corpora lutea are formed after an egg is discharged from the ovarian follicle in ovulation. They are found in mammals and in certain viviparous reptiles and amphibians. The known functions of progesterone are related to the maintenance of pregnancy and will be discussed in that connection.

Reproductive Cycles

Many vertebrates have seasonal sexual cycles, in which the gonads are inactive during most of the year and become active at a specific season. The most common stimulus for activation is light, usually a change in the length of the day. This in turn activates the hypothalamic neurosecretory cells, and their secretion stimulates the adenohypophysis to form the gonadotrophins. The nature of the neurosecretory material responsible for this stimulation is not known. In most mammals, the females show cyclic reproductive activity. Cycles are seasonal in many species, but independent of season in others.

The details of the control of the female reproductive cycle have been thoroughly examined in a number of mammalian species. In most species the cycle involves periods of estrus, during which the female shows typical copulatory behavior, alternating with periods in which copulation is not permitted. Exceptions are primates and rabbits, which accept the male at any time. As we shall see later, these animals differ in other respects from one another. In rodents, among the most thoroughly studied of mammals, the cycle begins with a period of anestrus in which the uterus is small and shows no spontaneous activity. This state passes into one of diestrus as a result of secretion by the pituitary of FSH and small amounts of ICSH. FSH stimulates growth and ripening of the ovarian follicle, and ICSH stimulates estrogen secretion. The estrogen in turn stimulates growth and muscular activity in the uterus; it also inhibits FSH secretion and increases ICSH secretion. The result is a positive feedback cycle with progressively increasing levels of estrogen and of ICSH, and a negative feedback cycle of FSH secretion. When the estrogen level is sufficiently high, the animal enters the estrus stage and copulation may occur.

In the cat, rabbit, and some other mammals the stimulus of copulation causes ovulation through adrenergic stimulation of hypothalamic neurosecretion, which in turn causes release of ICSH from the adenohypophysis; this in turn causes estrogen release from the ovary. The combination of ICSH and estrogen action probably is responsible for ovulation, some 10 to 14 hours after copulation in these species. In most mammals, however, ovulation occurs without this specific stimulus. High levels of estrogen apparently inhibit ICSH secretion; moreover, the ruptured follicle develops into a corpus luteum under ICSH stimulation and begins to secrete progesterone under the influence of LTH. Progesterone causes development of the uterine endometrium and also inhibits ICSH secretion in a negative feedback cycle, if implantation of a fertilized egg in the endometrium does not occur. The corpus luteum degenerates and the animal returns to a condition of anestrus, with regression of the uterus. In the rabbit there is no cycle, and the female is in a condition of constant estrus. In primates the cycle begins with the massive breakdown of the endometrium and the consequent uterine bleeding of menstruation. As soon as this breakdown is complete, follicular development under FSH stimulation begins, with no pause comparable to the anestrus condition of other mammals. Ovulation occurs midway in the cycle, and the corpus luteum persists longer, relative to the length of the cycle, than in other mammals.

If an embryo is implanted in the endometrium, it begins to produce chorionic gonadotrophin. This is an ICSH different chemically from that of the pituitary, with similar but not identical physiological action. Like ICSH it maintains the corpus luteum, but unlike ICSH it also stimulates the pituitary to form FSH. The result is that the endometrium is stimulated to further growth and development. The chorion also produces LTH, which maintains progesterone secretion, and ultimately with the collaboration of progesterone and estrogen stimulates development and secretion of the mammary glands. In primates and some other mammals with long gestation periods the placenta also secretes progesterone and estrogen. The various hormonal controls are summarized in Figure 15.4.

Conclusions

In this chapter we have brought together a few instances of regulatory mechanisms concerned in the control of progressive processes such as growth and development, and cyclic process such as molting and reproduction. Many more examples could be cited. Most of these processes extend over relatively long periods of time. The control mechanisms are primarily humoral, with nervous mechanisms entering to initiate the cycle or alter its character at a critical point. In many cases the cyclical process depends on feedback interactions which first reinforce and then inhibit specific processes or activities. Our understanding of progressive processes is in general quite poor and limited to the description of events. The causal analysis of the control mechanisms in these processes remains an outstanding problem in biology.

In closing, we should merely mention one aspect of cyclic activity which is also poorly understood, namely spontaneous temperature-independent activity cycles. These have been widely observed in all kinds of living material.

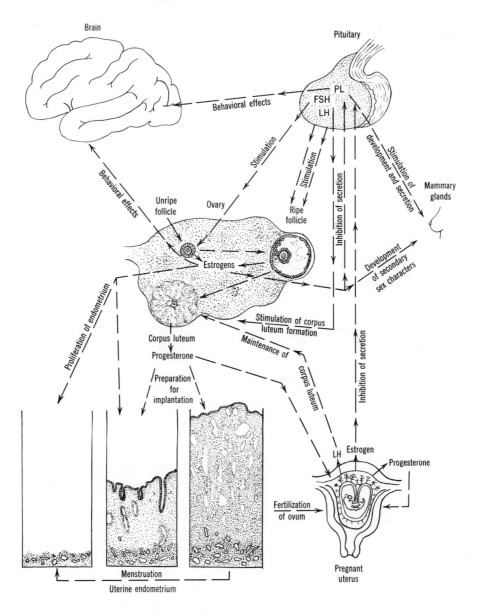

Fig. 15.4 Hormonal regulation of reproductive cycles in the vertebrates. PL = prolactin; FSH = follicle-stimulating hormone; LH = luteinizing hormone.

They are most often diurnal, or follow a lunar or tidal cycle. Typically they remain constant under rather extensive environmental alterations. They must depend on phenomena at the cellular or subcellular level, in some cases at least, since they are found in unicellular forms. Our information about control mechanisms remains scanty and debatable, but these cycles have considerable potential importance and offer challenging problems.

References

Allen, B. M. 1938. The endocrine control of amphibian metamorphosis. *Biol. Rev.* **13** 1-19.

Bullough, W. S. 1961. *Vertebrate Reproductive Cycles.* (2nd ed.) Wiley, New York.

Bodenstein, D. 1954. Endocrine mechanisms in the life of insects. *Rec. Progr. Horm. Res.* **10** 157-179.

Brown, F. A., Jr. 1959. The rhythmic nature of plants and animals. *Am. Scientist* **47** 147-168.

Cowie, A. T., and Folley, S. J. 1955. Physiology of the gonadotropins and the lactogenic hormone. *The Hormones* **3** 309-387.

De Bodo, R. C., and Altszuler, N. 1957. The metabolic effects of growth hormone and their physiological significance. *Vitamins and Hormones* **15** 205-258.

Fontaine, M. 1954. Du déterminisme physiologique des migrations. *Biol. Rev.* **29** 390-418.

Harvey, L. A. 1960. Rhythmic periodicities in animals. *Sci. Progr.* **48** 106-113.

Grobstein, C. 1959. Differentiation of vertebrate cells. *The Cell* **1** 437-496.

Hörstadius, S. 1939. The mechanisms of sea urchin development studied by operative methods. *Biol. Rev.* **14** 132-179.

Karlson, P. 1956. Biochemical studies on insect hormones. *Vitamins and Hormones* **14** 227-267.

Lees, A. D. 1955. *The Physiology of Diapause in Arthropods.* Univ. Press, Cambridge, England.

Maqsood, M. 1952. Thyroid functions in relation to reproduction of mammals and birds. *Biol. Rev.* **27** 281-319.

Pincus, G. 1955. The physiology of ovarian and testis hormones. *The Hormones* **3** 665-684.

Weiss, P. 1935. The so-called organizer and the problem of organization in amphibian development. *Physiol. Rev.* **15** 639-674.

Wigglesworth, V. B. 1954. *The Physiology of Insect Metamorphosis.* Univ. Press, Cambridge, England.

Witschi, E. 1950. Zur biologischen Charakterisierung der gonadotropen Hormone. *Naturwiss.* **37** 81-85.

16 Reactive integration

In the two preceding chapters, we were concerned with regulatory processes in which the activities of the parts of the organism were held at a steady level (conservative) or directed along a well-defined course of growth and development (progressive) or directed through a sequence of changes to return, ultimately, near to the starting point (cyclical). We now turn to the complex of activities known as behavior, in which the animal still acts as an integrated whole, but in which the aims or goals are quite various and less clearly defined.

The study of behavior can be approached from two directions: One approach starts with the objective description of behavior itself; this approach has been very little used. The psychologists, who might be expected to use it, have either been concerned

with experimental study or in their descriptive work have been influenced by *a priori* theories of behavior. Recently, under the name of ethology, the objective study of animal behavior has been undertaken by Lorenz and Tinbergen among others.

The other approach to behavior, which we may call physiological, begins with the analysis of the basic processes underlying behavior—the properties of nerve cells, muscle cells, and their interconnections—and attempts to build up the elements of behavior from these units. The classical use of this approach is seen in the work of Sherrington, who concerned himself especially with the nervous mechanisms underlying posture in mammals. In principle, the two methods should meet in the middle and permit an analysis of objectively described behavior in terms of the properties of the units. It is unlikely that this end will ever be fully realized because of the complexity of behavior on the one hand and the enormous number of units and the possible interconnections on the other.

Our task in this chapter is further complicated by the fact that during the last few decades the availability of important new research techniques has given rise to a great increase in the amount and extent of research in neurophysiology, to the point where it is difficult for one whose interests are not confined to this field to follow and evaluate all the many lines of investigation. In consequence, we shall be concerned here only with some of the main outlines of the major concepts at the physiological rather than the behavioral level. Moreover, we shall present these concepts primarily from the comparative point of view, abstracting from many results those which seem to have some general significance.

The types of activities we might include under reactive integration, from a biological point of view, involve responses to environmental factors of a potentially harmful nature—that is, protective responses—and activities related to specific goals of the organism such as feeding or reproductive activities. The latter category will include responses to external stimuli related to the presence of food or mates, and internal drives leading the animal to seek these things actively even in the absence of stimuli. Both categories of activity will be related to the conservative and cyclical processes described earlier, but in this chapter we shall be concerned with rapid responses to stimuli, particularly with motor responses involving muscular contraction. These are mediated largely or entirely by the nervous system and do not involve endocrine factors directly as primary elements, though endocrine factors may influence or even initiate some of the nervous processes.

The Coelenterate Nerve Net

The simplest nervous system we know from the viewpoint of structure is the nerve net of the coelenterates. This simplicity was recognized in the late nineteenth century by the morphologists, and the study of coelenterate responses has continued to attract the attention of zoologists ever since. Among the leaders in this field in our own century is Professor Pantin of Cambridge University; his work has directly inspired or influenced most of the younger men now active in the field. In the United States G. H. Parker of Harvard has played a similar role in his earlier studies of sea anemones, though his interest turned elsewhere in later years.

The nerve net has sometimes been envisioned as a true network of anastomosing nerve fibers without synaptic connections, but the most recent studies have verified the earlier observations of Hertwig, showing that the axons do not in fact fuse but merely come into intimate contact. Physiologically the system acts as a net, in that a state of excitation aroused at one point is conducted in all directions through the system and if strong enough, it ultimately excites the whole system. This suggests that the synapses between neurons may not in general be polarized. On the other hand, they often require facilitation before synaptic transmission can occur. Pantin showed that in the sea anemone, *Calliactis parasitica*, a single electrical shock was never effective in exciting a muscular contraction, whereas two shocks in general were effective if they were administered sufficiently close together in time. The size of the muscular contraction resulting from trains of stimuli depends on the number and frequency; the distance the excitation spreads from the point of stimulation also depends on number and frequency of stimuli. The same properties have been observed in many other coelenterates, with considerable qualitative and quantitative variation in the different species.

The simplest nerve net, as seen for example in the simple hydroid polyps, exhibits varying degrees of differentiation in the larger coelenterates. One of the most general forms taken by such differentiation is the development of through-conduction pathways, specialized regions of the nerve net in which conduction is more rapid than it is in the net generally. The basis for such pathways seems to be, primarily, an arrangement of axons parallel to the direction of conduction, so that the state of excitation travels for a longer distance before encountering a synapse. A section through a conducting pathway shows also a higher concentration of nerve fibers in the conducting region. In the sea anemones such pathways are found especially in the circumference of the oral disc and in the vertical mesenteries dividing the coelenteron into compartments. These pathways function especially in the excitation of contractions in the muscles that shorten the column of the anemone body and retract the oral disc in response to potentially harmful stimuli. In medusae there is a similar through-conduction pathway in the margin of the bell. This path is concerned in transmission of the impulses which cause the rhythmic contractions of the bell in swimming.

Spontaneous Activity

The existence of spontaneous activity in the nervous system of the medusae has been evident in the swimming movements these animals carry out, but the early observations of Parker and more detailed recent study by Batham and Pantin have shown that sessile sea anemones also engage in spontaneous activity. Still more recently, electrophysiological studies have disclosed nervous activity, even in the simple hydroid nerve net, in the absence of specific external stimuli. Such spontaneous nervous activity is apparently characteristic of all nervous systems and may be regarded as among their fundamental properties. Its origin is still not fully understood, but we do know that nerve or muscle cells can be brought, by various experimental treatments, into a condition in which they discharge impulses rhythmically without specific external stimulus. It is possible to imagine a number of types of feedback circuits which would convert such inherent rhythmicity into a pattern of rhythmic activity at a lower frequency, in which bursts of impulses are followed by relatively quiet periods, but the details of such circuits have not been worked out for any system.

This sort of rhythmic activity is seen in the ganglia of medusae. Coelenterate polyps have no multicellular sense organs or aggregates of nerve cell bodies, but in the medusae the margin of the bell contains clusters of sense organs of many types, mostly mechanoreceptors and photoreceptors, placed at regular intervals. Each of these sense organs is associated with a cluster of nerve cell bodies—that is, a ganglion. Experimental studies, some carried out by von Uexküll near the turn of the century and many more since, show that the sensory ganglia originate the impulses which cause the regular rhythmic swimming contractions of the bell. Moreover, the rate of the beat is influenced by sensory stimulation of the sense organs; study of the effects of such stimulation, on intact medusae and on medusae in which the individual ganglia have been isolated by cuts through the marginal nerve ring, lead to the conclusion that at any one time one of the ganglia is acting as pacemaker for the swimming movements. Such a pacemaker must act by sending out, at regular intervals, bursts of nerve impulses. These spread rapidly around the nerve ring, exciting the other ganglia and spreading in turn into the nerve net of the bell, to arouse muscular contraction in the circular muscles of the margin and then in turn in the radial muscles of the bell.

Even the hydroid polyp shows electrical signs of rhythmic nervous activity, though there is no evidence of an aggregation of nerve-cell bodies in hydroids. The pacemaker mechanism must therefore be one which can operate in a diffuse nerve net. In addition to regular rhythmic activities of relatively high frequency, coelenterates show spontaneous and induced patterns of behavior of greater complexity. Batham and Pantin have described a regular and spontaneous pattern of activity in the sea anemone, *Metridium senile,* extending over several hours. The anemone first extends its column to full extent and expands the oral disc. It then engages in waving movements of disc and column for a period. This is followed by shortening of the column and retraction of the oral disc. Then the mouth is opened, and the contents of the coelenteron are largely expelled, leaving the anemone flaccid and collapsed. Gradually, the coelenteron is filled with water by ciliary action in the siphonoglyph, and the column extends to repeat the cycle. The cycle is interrupted by feeding, but when the coelenteron is evacuated after completion of digestion the cycle is again resumed.

Another kind of spontaneous activity is seen in the slow locomotor movement of an anemone over a smooth surface. This movement involves a complex and integrated sequence of contractions in the pedal disc. Finally, a Pacific Coast anemone, *Stomphia micrococcinea,* shows a most remarkable response on exposure to a large starfish or to extracts of starfish. The pedal disc is detached from the substratum, and the anemone begins a series of active swimming movements of a complex nature.

These various examples are introduced here to demonstrate that the relatively undifferentiated nerve net is nevertheless capable of organizing relatively complex behavior, involving the coordinated activity of many muscles. As an aid to defining the problems of neurophysiology we may also note from our examples two properties in the nerve net, which must ultimately be analyzed in terms of the activity of the units in the net. These are: (1) dominance, the ability of one part of the system to control the activities of the other parts, as seen for example in the pacemaker phenomenon; (2) spontaneity, the ability to initiate patterns of activity without external stimulation, or to carry through a complex pattern of activities in response to a stimulus long after the stimulus itself has ended.

Ganglionic Nervous Systems

The trend in the evolution of nervous systems has been largely in the direction of ganglionization, with aggregation of nerve-cell bodies and synapses into definite ganglia, communicating with the receptors and effectors by axons which tend to run in definite tracts or nerves. In the remainder of this chapter we shall trace some of these developments and examine the properties of some of the systems which have evolved in relation to the properties of the units and their structural relations where possible.

The ganglia of the coelenterate medusae are closely associated with sense organs, and we may suppose that ganglia originated essentially as aggregations of cell bodies of sensory neurons. The most effective integration of sensory information can be brought about if this information, of various sorts, can be brought into a single center, and there into contact with the motor units which are to initiate the response to the information. As we have noted, the ganglia of the medusae originate the rhythmic discharge of impulses responsible for locomotor movements, and hence these ganglia are motor as well as sensory centers and have in addition a mechanism for spontaneous rhythmicity. These three mechanisms, sensory, motor, and spontaneous activity, are characteristic of most ganglia, and the absence of one or another is probably to be regarded as a specialization.

The development of ganglia is closely associated with locomotion. The sessile polyps have no ganglia; the motile medusae have. The free-living flatworms, with a general level of nervous organization similar to that of the coelenterates, also have ganglia. Moreover, these relatively active bilaterally symmetrical animals have the ganglia located in the anterior region, closely associated with the photoreceptors and with the mechanoreceptors of the snout. The advantages of a set of receptors in the front end of an actively moving organism are clear, and this arrangement of cephalic sense organs and of a cephalic integrating center will generally be found in actively motile animals.

Planarians

The relation of sense organs and cephalic ganglia of the planarian flatworm to its behavior has been studied in a number of interesting experiments. The characteristic eyespots of this animal consist of a pair of cup-shaped organs lined with photosensitive cells, which are backed by opaque pigment. The cells on one side of the animal therefore are affected only by light coming from that side. Moreover, there is some functional differentiation among the sense cells, in that the effect of the illumination of the anterior cells on locomotor activity is different from the effect of illumination of the posterior cells. If the animal, moving in the dark or in low-intensity diffuse light, is suddenly exposed to a thin beam of light from one side, the head is sharply turned toward or away from the beam, and locomotion is subsequently oriented parallel to the beam in such a way that the illumination of the two eyespots becomes equal. Studies of orientation in a gradient of diffuse light show that the sensitivity of the eyespots varies in accordance with previous exposure, and that this variation in sensitivity, together with specific responses to changing intensity, finally results in selection of a particular intensity level by the worm.

Historically the study of responses (taxes) to directed stimuli such as beams of light had a great vogue early in the present century, and reactions

368   Integrative Functions in Animals

similar to those described in planarians were found throughout the animal kingdom. Their role in behavior and their value in interpreting nervous mechanisms, however, have proved less significant than was originally supposed.

The feeding responses of planarians depend on chemoreceptors, but the way in which these are used depends on the species and its normal habitat. Planarians inhabiting a lake were able to locate food particles, using the chemical sense alone, in quiet water. Planarians inhabiting a flowing stream could not do this but always moved upstream against the current when a current flowed. Presence of a food particle upstream from the worm increased the rate of movement, presumably by stimulating chemoreceptors, but orientation was primarily related to current. Each pattern of response is probably adequate in the normal habitat.

Mollusks

The extent of possible variation in ganglionic arrangement within a single phylum is probably best seen among the mollusks (Figure 16.1) and one can correlate this variation with the activities of the animals to a considerable extent. The simplest and doubtless most primitive condition is seen in the amphineurans. Here the nervous system consists essentially of a circumesophageal ganglionic ring from which arise nerve trunks extending to the various regions of the body and connecting with a general nerve net. There are no extensive or elaborate multicellular sense organs, and the behavior of the animal, aside from reproductive activities, is confined in some species to brief feeding excursions from a home niche, to which it often returns when feeding is completed. The circumesophageal nerve ring probably serves to coordinate the feeding activities of the radula, but these and other aspects of behavior and control have been little studied.

In the pelecypods the nerve ring is replaced by a series of rather well-defined ganglia, each associated with one of the specific response mechanisms. These animals typically have two well-developed adductor muscles, which close and hold shut the bivalve shell, and a relatively complex set of muscles in the foot. Each of these muscle groups has its ganglion, and there are, in addition, cephalic and visceral ganglia concerned in feeding and the regulation of circulatory and digestive activities, respectively. The ganglia are interconnected by the nerve cords, and there are, besides, traces of a nerve net in many of the tissues. The functions of the pedal ganglion vary in an interesting way in different species. In the mussel, where the foot functions primarily in the rather complex activities of spinning, attaching, and detaching the byssus fibers which fasten the animal to the substratum, the pedal ganglion is relatively autonomous and can organize these activities even when separated from the other ganglia. In the razor shell clam, by contrast, the foot is used almost entirely in rapid and relatively simple digging activities, which serve primarily as mechanisms of escape from predators. In these animals the pedal ganglion has no integrative functions. Sensory axons pass through it without synapse to the cephalic ganglion, and motor impulses arising in cephalic ganglion are merely relayed through the pedal ganglion to the motor axons of the foot.

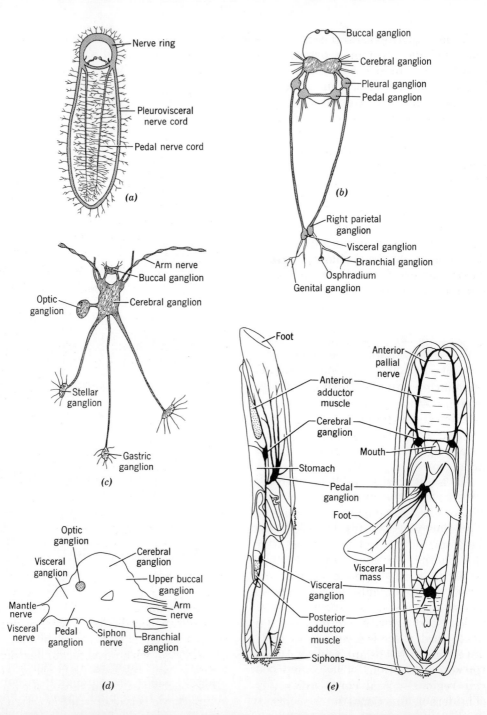

Fig. 16.1 The ganglionic nervous system of mollusks. (*a*) Amphineuran. (*b*) Gastropod. (*c*) Cephalopod. (*d*) Brain of a cephalopod. (*e*) Razor clam, *Ensis*. (From Scheer, *Comparative Physiology,* 1948, Wiley, New York.)

In both gastropods and cephalopods the cephalic ganglia are relatively much larger in size and functionally much more important than the peripheral ganglia. The latter, like the pedal ganglia of the razor clam, are generally only motor relay centers, and the cephalic ganglia—which generally incorporate the visceral ganglia as well—are the major integrating centers. We shall have more to say about the cephalopods later since they have the most elaborate brain of any invertebrate, but in both of these classes the development of the cephalic ganglia is clearly associated with active locomotion.

Segmental Nervous Systems

In the annelids and arthropods we see another pattern of ganglionic evolution, starting from a system of paired segmental ganglia in the elongate segmented body of the annelid worm. The arthropods have a closely similar arrangement of ganglia, and in general there is no marked tendency for the anterior ganglion to develop to a position of complete dominance over more posterior ganglia. Instead, with the development of limbs in arthropods, the thoracic ganglia often become larger than the cephalic ganglia and retain a considerable degree of functional autonomy. In the vertebrate series, starting with a dorsal tubular nerve cord, there is a very substantial development of the anterior portion of the cord—the brain. The more posterior regions—spinal cord—still retain considerable functional autonomy and, in the paired spinal nerves, evidence of segmentation. We shall examine the functional aspects of some of these systems in more detail later.

Integration in Locomotion and Posture

In the classical study of neurophysiology the unit of function has been the reflex arc, comprising a receptor, an afferent axon, a central synapse, an efferent axon, and an effector. We have already followed a state of excitation aroused in the receptor through such an arc and examined the significant events in its passage. For our present purposes, this picture is too specialized, since a reflex arc in this sense can be found only in echinoderms, mollusks, arthropods, and vertebrate animals in which muscles are differentiated as organs. Even in these animals, the picture is an oversimplification, since every motor neuron receives preganglionic fibers from many sources, both peripheral (i.e., sensory) and central.

Motor Innervation

In most of the lower animals, and many tissues of higher animals as well, the motor unit is a body of muscle tissues containing a nerve net. The central nervous system then exerts its actions through influences fed into the nerve net, which in turn has a considerable degree of autonomy. Examples include the nerve plexus of the vertebrate intestine and a similar plexus in the arm of an octopus. The intestinal plexus can coordinate peristaltic and segmentation movements in the course of digestion without external nervous stimuli, and can be influenced to greater activity by stimulation of parasympathetic nerves or to lesser activity by stimulation of the sympathetic nerves. The plexus of the arm of a cephalopod mollusk such as an octopus is a nerve net which alone can coordinate movements of the arm and of the suckers effectively, but which is also under influence from the central nervous system. When we know more about the properties of nerve nets, it may be possible to explore the relations of these nets with their central controlling mechanisms.

Even in animals with well-differentiated muscles that have lost their nerve nets and their autonomy, the reflex arc is an oversimplification as far as our present interests are concerned. We shall instead start with consideration of the motor center for a particular muscle, by which we mean the group of motor neurons innervating that muscle, and their synapses. This is also the classical operational unit from the experimental viewpoint, since the simplest sort of experiment we can do is to record the contraction of the whole muscle in response to various kinds of stimuli. This unit is also the functional unit since, in all normal activities, the whole muscle is the effector unit.

The detailed study of muscular contraction in response to nervous stimulation has disclosed the existence of two sorts of motor innervation. One of these is characteristic of the rapidly-contracting striated muscles of the vertebrates. Neuromuscular transmission here is an all-or-nothing process. Each muscle fiber receives a single motor fiber branch in a specialized motor end-plate, and transmission of excitation across the endplate is followed by a maximal contraction of the fiber. Each motor axon branches in the muscle to innervate a relatively small number of muscle fibers, of the order of 10 to 1000, depending on the muscle. Gradation of contraction in the whole muscle in this system can be accomplished only by variation in the number of muscle fibers excited at any one time.

The other pattern of excitation, as seen in the muscles of echinoderms, mollusks, and arthropods, and in some vertebrate muscles, has been studied in full detail only in the arthropods, though the physiological evidence suggests a similar pattern in other groups. In the arthropods a single muscle may be innervated only by two to five motor neurons. Each of these neurons branches extensively, and the branches ramify over the whole muscle in such a way that each muscle fiber is innervated at many points by branches of each of the motor fibers. Experimental study of muscular responses to stimulation of single motor fibers shows that these are of two types in insects, or of three types in crustaceans. The first type, known as a slow fiber, produces a slow partial contraction of the muscle, the extent of which depends on the frequency of impulses from the motor axons. The second type of axon, known as a fast fiber, produces all-or-nothing twitches of the whole muscle, similar to those seen on maximal stimulation of a vertebrate striated muscle (Figure 16.2). A third type of axon, found only in crustaceans, causes no contraction when stimulated alone but will inhibit contractions which might otherwise result from stimulation of one or both of the other kinds of fibers. Present evidence suggests that double innervation of the fast-slow type is found in echinoderms and mollusks as well. Here, however, the number of nerve fibers innervating a single muscle is greater than in arthropods.

Motor Centers

If we now return to the center and examine the requisites for control of

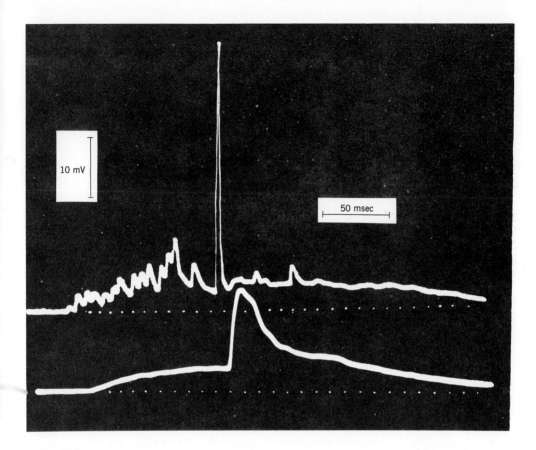

Fig. 16.2 "Slow" and "fast" contractions in the extensor tibiae muscle of the cockroach. The upper trace shows the electrical activity of the muscle, recorded with an intracellular electrode, in response to stimuli applied to the ventral nerve cord. The many small peaks in the first part of the curve are junctional potentials; note that the membrane is progressively depolarized to a "plateau." The sharp peak is a "spike" potential. The lower record shows the mechanical response, recorded electrically by means of a transducer. During the first part of this curve, the tension gradually rises in a "slow" contraction. The spike is associated with a more vigorous "fast" contraction. (T. Smyth and G. Hoyle, unpublished results.)

muscular contraction, we can visualize three kinds of function. The first is to produce a rapid, vigorous, all-or-nothing contraction (twitch) in the muscle. This can be accomplished in the arthropod system simply by excitation of the fast fiber to that muscle. In the vertebrate system, all the motor units must be excited simultaneously to produce a maximal twitch. The second kind of function is to produce a submaximal twitch, in which the muscle contracts to less than its full extent for a short period. This can be done in the vertebrate by excitation of a fraction of the motor units. The size of the contraction will depend on the ratio of excited to quiescent units. Such differential excitation could be provided for by differences in threshold of the different units. In the arthropod system a submaximal contraction would have to result from excitation of the slow fibers, and the extent of the contraction would depend on the frequency of impulses in the fiber. This in turn might depend primarily on the degree of depolarization (that is the postsynaptic potential) in the cell body of the slow axon.

A third and very important task of the motor center is to produce and maintain a constant level of partial contraction in the muscle, a state known as tonus. In pelecypod mollusks, tonic contraction is the primary function of the shell adductor muscles, which must hold the shell closed against the elastic force of the hinge for prolonged periods. In these muscles there appears to be a "catch" mechanism. When the muscle contracts in response to normal nervous stimuli, it can then enter into a state of maintained contraction or tonus that requires little expenditure of energy and can be maintained by a very low rate of nervous stimulation. This mechanism is not found elsewhere, and in arthropods tonus must be maintained by a continuing discharge of impulses along the single slow fiber, a mechanism which is especially liable to fatigue.

In the vertebrate system, on the other hand, tonus can be maintained only by the continual rotation of activity among motor units, so that at any instant a fraction of the units are in the state of maximal contraction, and the rest of the units are relaxed. This state of contraction then passes on to another set of units in a regular rotation. Such a rotation has been demonstrated experimentally; it must be centrally maintained by some mechanism in the motor center involv-

ing a regular circulation of a state of excitation among the cell bodies of the center. Moreover, external influences must somehow alter the fraction of cell bodies excited at any instant, as the extent of the tonus is to be changed. The nature of this mechanism remains to be established, but the fact that in mammals most of the muscles are in a state of constant partial tonic contraction is well established, and most movements involve a change in the degree of tonus rather than a twitch.

In animals with movable jointed limbs (arthropods, higher vertebrates), the control of movements assumes further complexity. Opposing movements in a particular plane (for example, extension and flexion) involve antagonistic sets of muscles. Smooth performance of such movements requires carefully adjusted relaxation of one set while the antagonistic set is contracting. This in turn involves some kind of reciprocal connection between the motor centers for the antagonistic muscle sets. In the mammal, experimental studies demonstrated that excitation of the extensor muscles of the leg, for example, causes simultaneous inhibition of the flexors (Figure 16.3). This inhibition is of course central, and as we have seen involves basically a hyperpolarization of the flexor motor cell bodies. The actual operation is not as simple as this, of course, because of the rotation of activity among the motor cell bodies in tonic contractions. In crustaceans, the central control mechanisms for reciprocal innervation can be much simpler because of the existence of peripheral innervation. It suffices to have a connection which will excite the inhibitory neuron of the antagonist when the excitatory neuron of the

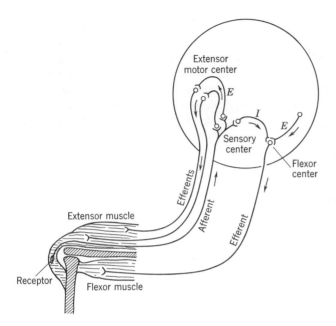

Fig. 16.3 Nervous and muscular elements in the reciprocal innervation of flexor and extensor muscles in a vertebrate. *E* and *I* are excitatory and inhibitory interneurons, respectively. (From Scheer, 1953, *General Physiology*, Wiley, New York.)

agonist is stimulated. In insects central inhibition will be required. These central processes have been little studied in arthropods as yet.

Locomotion

If we move upward in the scale of complexity from the reciprocal innervation of antagonistic muscles we come to the problem of posture, the maintenance over long periods of fixed positions, often requiring coordination of many muscle groups. The problem of posture is, however, an important one only in those land animals which are supported by limbs. Aquatic animals are supported largely by the dense medium they inhabit, and creeping and crawling terrestrial animals are supported by the substratum. From the evolutionary viewpoint, posture becomes a special case of locomotion, and the neural mechanisms involved clearly demonstrate this relation. The postural mechanisms are special adaptations of the locomotor mechanisms.

As we noted earlier in this chapter, locomotor movements of considerable complexity can be integrated by the nerve net in coelenterates such as the sea anemone. In many higher animals this kind of integration remains the basis for a part, at least, of locomotion. In the amphineuran and gastropod mollusks, for example, locomotion involves a coordinated action of the musculature of the thick flat foot, in which successive portions of the foot are raised from the substratum, moved forward, and attached again to the substratum. This operation progresses over the surface of the foot in a wave or in two or more parallel waves. The direction of the wave motion may be the same as that of the locomotion, opposed to it, or at some angle to it. The process can be coordinated by the nerve plexus of the foot.

In the starfish, locomotion involves a stepping movement of each of the hundreds of tube feet. The foot is raised from the substratum by contraction of longitudinal muscles and relaxation of the ampulla (reciprocal action), pointed by further contraction of one of the five sets of longitudinal muscles, and then extended to make contact with the substratum by contraction of the ampulla in coordination with relaxation of the longitudinal muscles. This process can be coordinated by the intrinsic nerve net, but is initiated only in response to the stimulus of stretch of the longitudinal muscles produced, for example, by pulling on the tube foot—a stimulus which would occur naturally in locomotion as the whole animal moves along. In the starfish we can see one role of the ganglionic nervous system—that of coordinating the movements of the many tube feet. In the intact starfish all the tube feet carry out their stepping movements in the same direction. If the circumoral nerve ring is cut, this coordination is lost, but the activities of the tube feet in any one limb are still coordinated. The result may be that the limbs move off in diverse directions with such vigor that the starfish pulls itself apart. The explanation proposed for normal coordination is that, in the nerve ring, there are five major centers. Each of these controls the longitudinal muscles on one side of all the tube feet. Thus when center A is the pacemaker for locomotion, the pointing movement is made by contraction of longitudinal muscle on side A of all the tube feet, side A being oriented with respect to the whole animal, not to the individual limb, and the animal moves off with side A in advance.

The role of the ganglionic centers in gastropod mollusks is similar, but here there is evidence for a control of the initiation of locomotion as well. Typi-

cally, in all those forms which have a circumoral nerve ring, removal of the upper portion—usually developed into a supraesophageal or cerebral ganglion mass—results in continuous locomotion by the animal. Removal of the subesophageal ganglion mass as well stops locomotion unless the animal is stimulated vigorously. Evidently normal locomotor activity is initiated spontaneously in the subesophageal ganglion but is kept under inhibition by the supraesophageal ganglion. This gives us a clear example of the two properties already noted in the coelenterates as spontaneity and dominance, in a more specialized relation.

In annelids, such as the earthworm, the locomotor coordination in individual segments may involve the segmental ganglia, and coordination between successive segments certainly does. Classical studies on earthworms have shown that the muscles of each segment exhibit a stretch response. When the longitudinal muscles are stretched by stretching the worm lengthwise, these muscles contract. This in turn stretches the circular muscles and they in their turn contract. Thus a continuous stretch applied to the worm induces regular alternating rhythmic contractions in the antagonistic muscle sets. These contractions can also be elicited in the unstretched worms by tactile stimuli, such as those produced by drawing a fine brush over the body surface. The result is that coordination of locomotion can occur in two halves of an earthworm which have been joined merely by a piece of thread. On the other hand, if the body wall is removed from several segments in the center of the worm, and these segments are immobilized by pinning this part of the worm to a board, leaving the nerve cord attached between the segments, locomotor activity can be transmitted from the anterior to the posterior portion of the worm through the nerve cord alone.

A similar coordination of locomotor activity has been observed in insects, where a severed limb with its ganglion attached can execute coordinated stepping movements if stimulated by pulling it along the substratum. This local coordination is so effective that locomotor activity is readily resumed in arthropods from which one or more limbs have been removed experimentally or accidentally, without the necessity of learning a new pattern of leg movements. The requisite pattern is put into operation at once by the automatic action of the ganglionic coordinating mechanisms.

In the vertebrates there is generally less autonomy of the spinal motor centers, but fish, in which the connection of spinal cord and brain has been severed, will execute coordinated swimming movements when exposed to a current of water; other lower vertebrates can carry out limited locomotor activity with the spinal cord alone. The coordinating function of the brain is, however, of considerable importance in most vertebrates, and even in the invertebrates the cerebral ganglion gives direction to locomotion as well as holding it under restraint.

Higher Centers

At the beginning of this discussion we said that the motor center is our unit of action. We must now examine the influences which act upon this center to determine its activity. Some of these are purely local, consisting of sensory impulses originating in or near the effector itself. Such impulses arise from mechanoreceptors responsive to sudden stretch or to continued tension. In the vertebrates they are located in the muscle itself or in the tendons attaching the muscle to a bone. Such receptors are widespread in animals. In arthropods, they may occur as well in or associated with the joint which is bent by the action of a muscle. The function of these receptors is evident and has been confirmed experimentally as that of providing information on the state and extent of activity of the muscle. This information is fed back into the center where it modifies the activity of the center in either a positive or negative feedback cycle. In most muscles, the result of a sudden stretch is a contraction. This response is called the stretch reflex, and it is the basis of posture in terrestrial vertebrates and of locomotion in insects, earthworms, and starfish, for example. Evidently any tendency for departure from erect posture will stretch the extensor muscles, leading to a corrective response. The stretch reflex persists when the brain is removed from mammals, but it is not effective in maintaining posture, for reasons to be discussed below. In the other animals mentioned, we have already seen that when tension is placed on the stepping muscles of an isolated unit, the unit responds to this stretch by executing a stepping movement.

The basic feedback circuits in the motor center are, however, subject to influences from other parts of the nervous system. We noted one instance of this in the initiation of locomotion in, for example, the earthworm, when the cerebral ganglion is removed and the subesophageal ganglion left intact. Clearly, the latter ganglion sends out instructions which activate the segmental ganglia to carry out their patterns of locomotor activity. There is, moreover, considerable evidence, for earthworms and other animals as well, that the normal locomotor activity results from intrinsic patterns of nervous activity, which are reinforced by but not dependent on the stretch reflexes and other peripheral coordinating mechanisms. The role of the anterior ganglia may then be to release or to inhibit these intrinsic patterns of activity. One of the most striking demonstrations of this concept is seen in certain forms of the praying mantis. In these animals the male clasps the female to initiate copulation. Further copulatory behavior in the male occurs either in response to neurosecretory stimuli from the corpora cardiaca, or when the female eats the male's head. The anterior ganglia normally inhibit copulatory behavior coordinated by the last abdominal ganglia; the neurosecretory stimuli, or removal of the anterior ganglia, release the abdominal ganglia from inhibition.

These observations lead us to the concept of higher centers—regions of the central nervous system that have an influence over motor centers and are in general located in the anterior portion of the central nervous system. Thus the supraesophageal ganglia or brain of annelids and arthropods is essential for feeding movements, though the reflexes involved are centered in the subesophageal ganglia. In cephalopod mollusks there are well-defined areas in the supraesophageal ganglia controlling large groups of muscles.

The development of the higher centers of vertebrates is the most extensive and the best known among animals, and we shall discuss this, first, in relation to locomotion and posture, returning to a consideration of other brain functions later. The basic mechanism in posture in mammals appears to be the stretch reflex centered in the motor center for each of the postural muscles. When any muscle is stretched, the receptors in that muscle and its tendon respond to the stretch and send impulses to the center, resulting in increased contraction of the same muscle. This reflex, under the various other controls to be noted later, results in a delicate adjustment of tension in all postural muscles that can be maintained for considerable periods. The second basic reflex is crossed extension. Contraction of flexor muscles on one side results in stimulation of extensors on the other side, to increase the contraction. This, again under central control, permits adjustments of posture without loss of balance. For each of these reflexes, we must keep in mind also that opposed extensors and flexors acting on the same part of the skeleton are reciprocally innervated in such a way that the increased activity in an extensor center inhibits activity in the center controlling the opposed flexor and vice versa. A third reflex is the positive supporting reaction, in which extensor contraction is increased by pressure on the sole of the foot and by stretching of the foot muscles.

The onset of locomotion involves a more elaborate intersegmental reflex correlated with the crossed-extension reflex. Contraction of the flexors in a limb—for example, the left hindlimb— is associated with contraction of extensors in the other limb on the same side (left forelimb), as well as with contraction of extensors in the opposite limb (right hindlimb). Thus one can trace, in terms of basic reflexes, machinery for the elementary operations of posture and locomotion. These reflexes, however, appear to be manifestations of a basic pattern of integrated activity in the spinal cord, and the posture and movements are coordinated by this pattern rather than being completely dependent upon external stimuli. The external stimuli serve rather to correct and adjust the basic pattern than to initiate it.

The basic pattern is, moreover, under control from a series of higher centers (Figure 16.4). The first of these is found in the cervical portion of the spinal cord, where the tonic neck reflexes are centered. The receptors for these reflexes are in the stretch receptors in the neck muscles, stimulated by head movements. Thus dorsal flexion of the head causes extension of the forelimbs and flexion of the hindlimbs; ventral flexion of the head has

the opposite effect. Lateral rotation of the head increases the tonus in the extensors of the limbs on the side toward which the head is rotated, and decreases extensor tonus on the opposite side. The next controlling center is the vestibular nucleus in the medulla. Impulses reach the center from the vestibular apparatus of the inner ear, and the effects of head movements mediated through this nucleus are the same as those of the same movements mediated through the neck reflexes.

These centers are all, thus far, reflex centers in which a specific set of receptor inputs acts upon motor outputs, to produce specific states of tonic activity. The ultimate state of con-

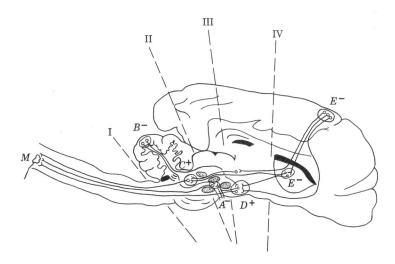

Fig. 16.4 Postural centers in the brain of a cat. The motor center for an extensor muscle is shown at *M*. This center is inhibited by the vestibular center at *A*, which receives information from the vestibular nerve and from an inhibitory center in the cerebellum at *B*. The motor center is excited by a center at *C*, the activity of which is normally modulated by inhibitory centers *E* in the anterior part of the reticular formation and in the motor cortex. These higher centers also act on a midbrain center at *D*, which alone is excitatory; it communicates with the center *B* in the cerebellum as well as with the motor center directly. A section through the brain at I results in flaccidity of all postural muscles. Section II is the classical decerebration section of Sherrington, resulting in extensor rigidity under the influence of center *C*, and removal of the influence of *A* and *E*, and the indirect influence of *B*. A section at III results in relaxation of the extensor muscles, with persistence of the vestibular reflexes. A section at IV produces some extensor contraction, but not true rigidity; reflexes are present, but voluntary control of movement is lacking.

traction in a particular muscle depends presumably on a balance of all the sensory input effects playing upon the motor center for that muscle, and the motor center is thus the site of integration. In the cerebellum we find the first center capable of a higher order of integration. The cerebellum receives nerve tracts from the proprioceptors in the body musculature, from the vestibular nerve and from higher centers to be noted later. Its function is apparently to integrate this information to provide a fine control over the locomotor and balancing activities of the entire peripheral musculature. It is especially well developed in birds and mammals; in birds its removal virtually abolishes locomotor activity, while in mammals and other vertebrates the effects are less marked and are mainly seen in loss of ability to balance. The cerebellum acts on the motor side largely through the vestibular center, but it also sends tracts upward to higher centers in the brain.

A second integrative region is located in, or rather dispersed through, the reticular formation. This extends from the medulla through the pons, midbrain (mesencephalon), and diencephalon, and it appears to contain at least three integrative regions for posture and locomotion. The lowest of these is influenced primarily by the cerebellum. A second anterior region near the red nucleus of the diencephalon is influenced by cerebral motor centers, and a third, between these two, is acted upon by the red-nucleus center. The role of the red-nucleus center was first demonstrated by Sherrington in his famous decerebration experiment. A section through the brain of a mammal, which passes behind the cerebrum and cuts the brain stem just posterior to the red nucleus, produces a state of extensor rigidity—extreme contraction of all extensors—which is called decerebrate rigidity. Apparently the vestibular center is excitatory on the whole extensor system and is normally restrained by the red-nucleus center. The interactions are in fact doubtless more complex than this; the reticular formation as a whole is a complex network of small neurons and conducting tracts, receiving branches from all the sensory tracts to the brain and acting in turn on all motor activities. Its general function will be discussed in more detail later.

The highest integrating centers for posture and locomotion are located in mammals in the cerebral cortex in the motor areas. These areas receive, by projection tracts, information from all the sensory areas, and from the cerebellum and reticulum. In turn they have descending connections directly with the spinal centers, and with the higher centers in the medulla, reticulum, and cerebellum as well. These centers can be shown by ablation and stimulation experiments to be the sites of the entire voluntary control over motor activity.

In this brief and highly condensed account of control of posture and locomotion we wish to emphasize primarily the complexity of the control system and the fact that this system consists of a hierarchy of centers, extending from the motor center for a single muscle up through centers of increasing complexity to the cortical centers which have as their tasks complete integration of the whole pattern of movements of the body. The physiological analysis of the activities of these centers has made great progress, but it is nevertheless only at the beginning. It is an analysis which must proceed on many levels, using many techniques, and calling upon a high order of intellectual effort. Its aim is an understanding of the essentials of central nervous activity, which in turn lie at the base of all intellectual effort.

Brains

In closing this section and the book we may turn briefly to a consideration of brain function as a whole. To a very large extent this consideration must still be confined to a survey of the localization of brain function. The analysis of this function still is at its beginning. A systematic survey of the evolution of brain function has two main points of interest: it shows us how the elaborate function of the mammalian and especially the primate brain may have developed out of simpler functions, and it may suggest suitable materials for more detailed study of some of these functions.

The primitive vertebrate brain (Figure 16.5), as seen in the cyclostomes, elasmobranchs, and fishes, is a more or less linear elaboration of the swollen end of the dorsal tubular nerve cord of the embryo, and probably of the even more primitive brain of the ancestral vertebrates now extinct. At its anterior end the brain is primarily an olfactory sensory center, and its removal produces no serious effects in behavior, nor does its stimulation elicit motor responses. In fishes, however, the rhinencephalon does exhibit spontaneous rhythms, and in its absence some instinctive behavior may be lost. The role of the diencephalon in the lower vertebrates has been little explored, and this is unfortunate in view of the importance of that region in the higher vertebrates. The hypothalamus is, however, the site of numerous neurosecretory cell bodies, with axons

leading to the neurohypophysis and directly involved in the control of osmoregulatory and probably other functions. The midbrain of the lower vertebrates is generally regarded as the highest integrative center. It consists of the dorsal tectum, which is the terminus of the optic fibers and exhibits a close correspondence to the retinal receptor pattern, and the ventral tegmentum, including the oculomotor and other motor centers.

The relation of midbrain to diencephalon in the lower vertebrates deserves special attention. The cerebellum is absent from the cyclostomes and appears merely as a small commissure in elasmobranchs, but in fishes it appears as the archicerebellum, receiving the vestibular input. It appears to have some function in coordinating position and locomotor functions. The medulla contains the respiratory centers, generally two in number, coordinating the alternating movements of inspiration and expiration. The inspiratory center is a swallowing center in the lower vertebrates. The circulatory center for cardiac and vasomotor reflexes is also found here. The medulla also has the important vestibular center, which is the main center for locomotor integration in the lower vertebrates. In fishes, the nervous center for regulation of color change is also found here. One has the general impression that the brain of the lower vertebrates contains a set of motor centers in the midbrain, sensory centers in the forebrain, and an integrative region between.

In the amphibians some notable differences appear. Most notable is a movement of integrative functions from midbrain to diencephalon. The latter appears to have some motor control, and in the habenular region it has many

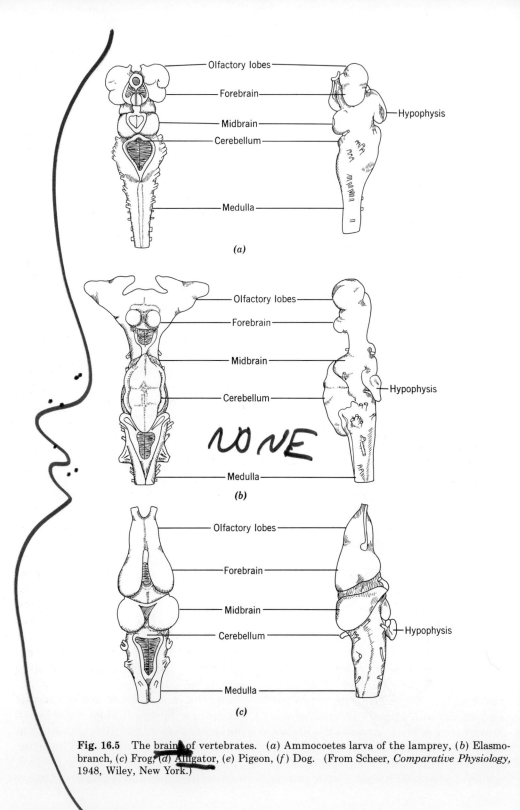

Olfactory lobes

Forebrain

Midbrain — Hypophysis

Cerebellum

Medulla

(a)

Olfactory lobes

Forebrain

Midbrain

Cerebellum — Hypophysis

NO NE

Medulla

(b)

Olfactory lobes

Forebrain

Midbrain

Cerebellum — Hypophysis

Medulla

(c)

Fig. 16.5 The brain of vertebrates. (*a*) Ammocoetes larva of the lamprey, (*b*) Elasmobranch, (*c*) Frog, (*d*) Alligator, (*e*) Pigeon, (*f*) Dog. (From Scheer, *Comparative Physiology,* 1948, Wiley, New York.)

382

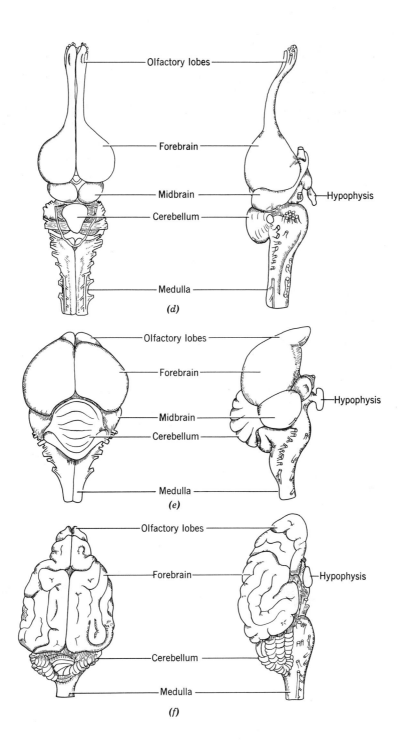

Olfactory lobes

Forebrain

Midbrain

Cerebellum

Hypophysis

Medulla

(d)

Olfactory lobes

Forebrain

Midbrain

Cerebellum

Hypophysis

Medulla

(e)

Olfactory lobes

Forebrain

Hypophysis

Cerebellum

Medulla

(f)

connections to sensory and motor centers elsewhere. Moreover, the optic termini have moved from the optic lobes to the diencephalon. The midbrain retains its function in coordination of proprioceptive and exteroceptive information into motor patterns and has been shown to control aspects of reproductive behavior.

The functional aspects of the reptilian brain have been little studied. This is unfortunate since these animals offer a variety of interesting questions. They lie between amphibians and the higher vertebrates in the evolutionary scale and they show a great deal of adaptive radiation within the class. The brain of the bird shows extensive structural differences from brains of the lower vertebrates, especially in the well-developed cerebrum and cerebellum. The cerebrum of birds appears to be primarily a sensory projection area with limited motor function. The cerebellum is highly developed, as the paleocerebellum, and has extremely important functions in locomotor and postural coordination. The diencephalon of birds has a well-developed center for control of body temperature and, as a part of this, higher centers controlling respiration and the vasomotor functions closely related to temperature control. The red nucleus and an extensor function in the vestibular center appear first in the reptiles and are well developed in birds as well.

Finally, in the mammals the cerebrum comes to dominate, in size and function, the entire brain. It contains projection areas for all the sensory functions, hence is the terminus for all sensory information. In general, there are three sensory areas with varying degrees of definition for each type of sensation. The cerebrum also contains extensive motor areas dominating and coordinating all the voluntary aspects of movement. The extent of the motor areas and their functional importance vary among the mammals, being most highly developed in the primates. Finally, the cerebral cortex contains, in the prefrontal region, association areas not directly involved in either sensory or motor function but concerned with the functions of association, learning, and memory. The rhinencephalon, which was the whole of the cerebrum in the lower vertebrates, persists as the olfactory center. It is also concerned in memory and in the emotions and, through its connections with the reticular system, with activation of the other cerebral functions. We are led to wonder whether these functions precede the higher coordinating functions of the cortex in evolution.

The diencephalon, as in birds, has a temperature center and, as in the lower vertebrates, centers for communication with the endocrine system through the neurohypophysis. The reticular formation, which extends from the medulla to the rhinencephalon, has recently attracted extensive study. Through this region, with its extensive sensory, cortical, and motor connections, sweep the regular rhythms which are connected with sleep, arousal, and intellectual activity. Experiments with implanted electrodes show that the reticulum contains "pleasure" centers, stimulation of which clearly gives gratification to rats, as well as a few "pain" centers. One gains an impression, still vague and poorly defined, that here may be the seat of emotions and consciousness, if there is in fact any such localized seat.

By contrast, the midbrain, in lower vertebrates the highest integrative center, becomes in the mammals only a relay for sensory information, and the locomotor centers of the medulla are subordinated to the cortex, diencephalon, and cerebellum. The cerebellum is more elaborate in mammals than in birds, with the lateral hemispheres constituting the neocerebellum, where sensory information is coordinated with information from all parts of the brain related to movement.

Conclusion

The task of physiology, to interpret in rational terms the nature of life, nowhere seems more attractive and more difficult that here in the brain. There is work ahead for many generations of students working at all levels, from the molecular to the behavioral. The goal is a great one, for it is only by knowing ourselves that we fully realize our relation to the universe, animate and inanimate.

References

Blum, H. F. 1954. Photoorientation and the "tropism theory." *Quart. Rev. Biol.* **29** 307–321.

Bonin, G., von. 1960. *The Cerebral Cortex.* Thomas, Springfield, Ill.

Bullock, T. H. 1947. Problems in invertebrate electrophysiology. *Physiol. Rev.* **27** 643–664.

Eccles, J. C. 1953. *The Neurophysiological Basis of Mind.* Clarendon Press, Oxford.

Fessard, A. 1959. Brain potentials and rhythms. *Hdbk. Physiol. I: Neurophysiol.* **1** 255–259.

Florey, E. (ed.) 1961. *Nervous Inhibition.* Pergamon, London.

Gerard, R. W. 1960. Neurophysiology: an integration. *Hdbk. Physiol. I: Neurophysiol.* **3** 1919–1965.

Hoagland, H. (ed.) 1957. *Hormones, Brain Function and Behavior.* Academic Press, New York.

Lashley, K. S. 1949. Persistent problems in the evolution of mind. *Quart. Rev. Biol.* **24** 28–42.

Magoun, H. W. 1958. *The Waking Brain.* Thomas, Springfield, Ill.

Maxwell, S. S. 1923. *Labyrinth and Equilibrium.* Lippincott, Philadelphia.

McCulloch, W. S. 1944. The functional organization of the cerebral cortex. *Physiol. Rev.* **24** 390–407.

Oberholzer, R. J. H., and Tofani, A. O. 1962. The neural control of respiration. *Hdbk. Physiol. I: Neurophysiol.* **3** 111–1130.

Pitts, R. F. 1946. The organization of the respiratory center. *Physiol. Rev.* **26** 609–630.

Prosser, C. L. 1952. Problems in the comparative physiology of nervous systems. *Mod. Trends Physiol. Biochem.* 323–336.

Sherrington, C. S. 1947. *The Integrative Action of the Nervous System.* (2nd edn.) Yale Univ. Press, New Haven, Conn.

Sherrington, C. S. 1951. *Man on His Nature.* Univ. Press, Cambridge, England.

Smith, J. E. 1945. The role of the nervous system in some activities of starfishes. *Biol. Rev.* **20** 29–43.

Uvnas, B. 1961. Central cardiovascular control. *Hdbk. Physiol. I: Neurophysiol.* **3** 1131–1162.

Walsh, E. G. 1957. *Physiology of the Nervous System.* Longmans, Green, London.

Walter, W. G. 1953. *The Living Brain.* Duckworth, London.

Welsh, J. H., and Schallek, W. 1946. Arthropod nervous systems. *Physiol. Rev.* **26** 447–478.

Wells, M. J. 1961. What the octopus makes of it: our world from another point of view. *Adv. Sci.* **17** 461–471.

Whitteridge, D. 1956. Machinery of posture. *Adv. Sci.* **13** 104–110.

Young, J. Z. 1951. *Doubt and Certainty in Science.* Clarendon Press, Oxford, England.

Index

Bulbus arteriosus, 234
Bullfrog (see *Rana catesbeiana*)
Bundle of His, 240
Busycon canaliculatum, 218, 219
Butenandt, A., 307
Butterfly, 277, 350
Butyryl coenzyme A, 48

C_1 cycle, 258–259, 262, 266
Caecum, 192
Cajal, Ramon y, 157
Calcification, 357
Calcium, in blood, 320–321, 324, 333
  excitability effect of, 316
  metabolism of, 171, 292, 301, 333, 358
  in nerve, 77
Caldwell, P. C., 102
Calliactis parasitica, 365
Calorie, 12
Calorigenic effect, 249
Calorimeter, 10, 18, 20
Calorimetry, 246–247
Camera-type eye, 138, 142–143
Cancer, 218
Cannon, W. B., 282
capacitance, membrane 98, 101
Capillary, air in, 208–209
  blood in, 203, 226, 241, 243
  electrode of, (see Microelectrode)
  lymph in, 243
Capsule, Bowman's, 323
Carbamino compound, 223
Carbamyl phosphate, 269, 314
Carbohydrates, 11
  metabolism of, 39, 251–255, 266, 275, 303, 338
  oxidation of, 33, 36
  synthesis of, 11, 48, 252–253, 257, 313
  transport of, 251–255
Carbon dioxide, Bohr effect, 216, 219
  in blood, 209–211, 222, 335, 338
Carbon monoxide, 221
Carbon source, 175
Carbonic acid, 209
Carbonic anhydrase, 209
Carboxylase, 173
Carboxylation, 171
Carboxylation oxidative, 172
Carboxypeptidases, 195, 196
Cardiac output, 215, 230, 238, 240–241, 243, 248, 336
Cardiovascular center, 336
Carlson, A. J., 235
Carnitine, 174
Carotenoid pigments, 178, 358
Carotid sinus, 336
Carp, blood of, 210, 217, 218
Caspersson, T., 69
Cat, 126, 132, 147, 153, 210, 217, 360, 379
Catabolism, regulation of, 311
Catadromous fish, 326
Catalyst, 23

Catalytic function in vitamins, 172–173
Catch mechanism in muscle, 374
Caterpillar, 350
Catfish, 217–218
Cathode ray oscilloscope, 94, 95
Cation effects, 316
Cause, efficient, 282, 345
  final, 281
Cavy, 178
Cecropia, 352–354
Cell, galvanic, 76, 89
  muscle, 88
  pigment, 139, 141
  sensory, 131
Cell body, neuron in, 164
Cell theory, 282
Cellular division, 355
Cellular ion concentration, 76
Cellular lipid, 54
Cellular membrane, 53–56, 82, 320
Cellular metabolism, 251
Cellular oxidation, 21, 58, 300
Cellular permeability, 301
Cellular pH, 334
Cellular regulatory mechanisms, 252, 311–315
Cellular structure, 52–64
Center, cardiovascular, 336
  circulatory, 381
  higher, 377–379
  integrative, 284, 286, 368, 371, 381
  locomotor, 385
  motor, 371–372, 377–378, 380–381
  nervous, 286, 368
  olfactory, 381, 384
  pain, 384
  pleasure, 384
  postural, 379
  reflex, 285
  respiratory, 335, 337, 381
  sensory, 381
  spinal, 377
  thermoregulatory, 342
  vestibular, 379–381, 384
Central nervous system, 161, 334, 366, 385
Cephalic ganglia, 368–371
Cephalin, 17
Cephalochordates, 108
Cephalopods, blood of, 321
  circulation of, 227–228, 236
  excretion of, 271
  eye of, 132, 138, 142, 144, 149
  feeding and digestion in, 192
  nervous system of, 370–371, 378
  respiration in, 203, 219
Cerebellum, 379, 382, 384, 385
Cerebral cortex, 380, 384
Cerebral ganglion, 376, 377
Cerebroside, 17, 55
Cerebrospinal fluid, 201
Cerebrum, 380–384
Ceriodaphnia, 218

FAD (see Flavine-adenine dinucleotide)
Faraday, M, 89
Farnesol, 353
Fast contraction, 373
Fasting, 262
Fat, absorption of, 197
  body, 253–254
  metabolism of, 274–276
  oxidation of, 33, 276
  synthesis of, 48
Fat depot, 276
Fatigue, 109
Fatt, P., 163
Fatty acids, 16
  free, 275–276
  oxidation of, 34, 36, 47, 49, 58, 252
  pool, 275–276
  synthesis, 194, 257, 262, 264–266
Feathers, 343
Feedback, 286, 299, 301–302, 360, 366
Feedback amplifier, 98
Feedback cycle, 377
Feedback inhibition, 295, 313–314
Feeding, 181, 185
  filter, 186
  mechanism of, 181, 183, 187, 200
  movements in, 378
  response of, 369
Female reproductive cycle, 360
Fermentation, 23
Ferments (see Enzymes)
Fetal blood, 220
Fiber, nerve, inhibitory, 372
  slow, 374
Fick's law, 73
Filaments, 118
Filter feeding, 186
Filter, mucous, 189
Filtration, kidney, 323, 327, 332
First law of thermodynamics, 105, 245
Fish, blood of, 214, 232, 324
  body fluid of, 201
  brain of, 381
  circulation in, 234–235, 237–238
  hemoglobin of, 217–219
  motor centers of, 377
  nitrogen excretion by, 267
  osmoregulation in, 323, 325, 327
  respiration of, 203–204, 208
  sense organs of, 132, 133, 144
Fixed base, 335–336
Flagellates, 174–177, 179, 183
Flatworms, 135, 368
Flavine, 19, 28
Flavine adenine dinucleotide, 19, 28, 30
Flavoprotein, 28, 31, 32, 172
Fletcher, W. M., 105
Flies, 350
Flight muscle, 313
Flow birefringence, 110
Fluids, body, 200–202, 226, 310

Fluids, cerebrospinal, 201
  compartments, 201
  extracellular, 201
  synovial, 201
  tissue, 202, 226, 227
  volume, 201
Focusing mechanism, 144
Follicle, ovarian, 362
Follicle-stimulating hormone (FSH), 291, 296, 299, 359, 360, 362
Fontana, F. G. F., 92
Food cup, 183
Food energy, 246
Food groove, 189
Food utilization, 197
Food vacuole, 112–113, 190
Foodstuffs, 10
Foot, tube, 376
Forebrain, 381, 382
Formic acid, 262, 266
Fovea, 143
Fox, D. L., 188
Foxon, G. E. H., 240
Francis, E. T. B., 240
Free amino acids, 264
Free energy, 42–43
Frequency, 123, 142
Fresh-water animals, 320, 325
Frictional resistance, 225, 241, 336
Frog, blood of, 211
  blood pressure of, 239
  brain of, 382
  heart of, 159
  metamorphosis in, 354
  muscle of, 89, 106, 109, 252
  neuromuscular transmission in, 156–157
  nitrogen excretion by, 267, 273–274
  osmoregulation in, 323, 327–329
  proteins in, 217
  respiration of, 207
  sense organs of, 126, 132, 150, 152–153
  skin of, 78, 80, 305
Fructo-aldolase, 41
Fructose, 11, 251, 253–254
Fructose-6-phosphate, 40, 251, 253
Fructose-1,6-diphosphate, 40
FSH (see Follicle-stimulating hormone)
Fuel, 10–18, 20
  oxidation of, 34
Fumarase, 37
Fumarate, 26, 33, 36, 37, 49, 264–266
Fungi, 174, 179

Gabe's Y-organ, 290, 357
Gadus, 217
Galactogen, 252
Galactose, 11, 17, 253
Galactose phosphate, 251, 253
Galactosidase, 66, 67
Galactoside permease, 66
Gall bladder, 290

Kleiber, M., 248, 249
Kneejerk reflex, 284
Krebs, H. A., 34
Krebs cycle (see Tricarboxylic acid cycle, Ornithine cycle)
Krogh, A., 80, 208
Kynurenate, 261–262
Kynurenin, 261–262

Labyrinth, 322
Lactate (lactic acid), 33, 42, 105–107, 109–110, 216, 252, 358
Lactate dehydrogenase, 33, 42
Lactation, 294
Lacteal, 274
Lactogenic hormone (see Prolactin)
Lactose, 12, 66–67, 253
Lacunae, 225, 230
Lamprey, 144, 300, 382
Langerhans, islets of, 291, 302
Larva, ammocoetes, 300
    insects 350
Larval molt, 350, 354
Lasioderma serricorne, 178–180
Latent period, 90, 142
Lavoisier, A. L., 9
Law, Fick's, 73
    of the heart, 237
    Poiseuille's, 228, 241
    Starling's, 237
    surface, 246
    of thermodynamics, 42
Learning, 384
Lecithin, 17
Leech, 274
Length-tension curve, 116–117
Lens, 137–138, 143–144
Lepidoptera, 350
Lepidosteus, 208
Leptophlebia, 250
Leucine, 13, 49, 262–263, 266
Leucocytes, 303
Leucophaea maderae, 358
LH (see Luteinizing hormone)
Li, C. H., 297
Ligaments, suspensory, 230
Light, 134
    adaptation, 134
    polarized, 141
    ultraviolet, 142
Limax, 274
Liminal intensity, 92
Limnaea stagnalis, 191
Limulus, 126
L. polyphemus, 141, 212, 235
Linoleic acid, 16, 180
Linolenic acid, 16
Lipase, 275
Lipids, 15–18
    absorption of, 197
    cellular, 54, 56, 57–58, 60–61

Lipids, membrane, 73
    metabolism in, 274–276, 301
    oxidation of, 33–34, 36, 47, 49–50, 252, 276
    solubility of, 73
    storage of, 276
    synthesis of, 48, 194, 257, 262, 264–266, 313
Lipoic acid, 30, 34–35, 46, 172
Lipoprotein, 30, 82, 275–276
Littorina, 274
Liver, circulation in, 243
    endocrine control of, 291, 295
    growth of, 354
    metabolism of, 251, 255, 274–276, 314, 338–340
    octopus, 192
    secretion by, 195
Lizard, 239, 324, 340
Ljubimova, V. M., 112
Lobster, 132, 211, 222, 231–232
Local potential, 97
Locomotion,202–204, 368, 375–378, 381, 384–385
Loewi, O., 159
Loligo, 218–219, 222
L. pealii, 211
Loop of Henle, 331–332
Lorenz, 364
Loxorhynchus grandis, 211, 222
LTH (see Luteotrophic hormone)
Lumbricus, 108, 221
Lundsgaard, E., 107
Lung, 203, 206–209, 334–335
    capacity of, 208
    circulation in, 239, 243, 334–335
    in fish, 206–208, 232
Luteinizing hormone (see Interstitial cell-stimulating hormone)
Luteotrophic hormone (LTH), 291–292, 295–296, 299, 328, 362
Lwoff, A., 175, 177
Lymnaea, 274
Lymph, 201, 243, 274
    circulation of, 244
Lymph duct, 274
Lymph flow, 243
Lymph formation, 243
Lymph hearts, 244
Lymphatic capillaries, 243
Lymphatic system, 197
Lymphatic vessels, 274
Lymphocytosis, 290
Lysine, 13, 49, 77, 257, 262, 266

MacGinitie, G. E., 188
Mackerel, 217–218
Maggot, 350
Magnesium, 77, 316, 320–321, 324
Maja squinado, 211, 319
Malate (malic acid), 28, 33, 36, 37, 266
Malate dehydrogenase, 28, 30, 37
Malpighian tubules, 330
Maltose, 11, 48, 255
Mammalian nephron, 332

Mollusks, digestion in, 186–193
excretion by, 267, 271, 274
metabolism of, 253–254
muscles of, 88, 107–108
nervous system of, 369–372, 374–376, 378
photoreceptors of, 135, 139, 142
respiration of, 203
respiratory proteins in, 214, 218–219
Molt, 282
control of, 351, 353
crustacean, 357
imaginal, 350, 353
inhibiting hormone, 305, 308, 357, 358
insect, 350–351
pupal, 350, 354
Molt gland, 307–308, 357
Monarch butterfly, 277
Monas vestita, 183
Monkey, 298
Monod, J., 66–68
Monosaccharides, 11
Morgan, T. H., 63
Mosquitoes, 358
Moths, 350
Motor neurons, activity of, 249
center of, 368, 371–372, 377–378, 380–381, 384
cortex of, 279–280
endplate of, 159, 163, 372
innervation of, 371–372
unit, 371
Mouse, 217
Movement, voluntary, 379
MSH (see Melanocyte-stimulating hormone)
Mucopolysaccharide, 11, 56, 253, 357
Mucosa, 291
Mucus, 11, 187–189, 327
Müller, J., 122
Muscles, antagonism in, 374–375
cell, 80, 88
circulation in, 243
energetics of, 118
excitation in, 92, 301
fiber of, 82, 113
flight of, 313
in frog, 89, 106, 109
glycolysis of, 106
metabolism in, 252
models of, 112
postural, 378
proteins in, 107, 110, 112
smooth, 118, 292
spindle, 123–124, 126
striated, 104, 113, 372
structure of, 113, 115–116
tension in, 116–117
Mussel, 186, 188, 228, 319, 369
Mutants, 63
Mutations, 64, 68, 177
Mya, 136, 190
Myelin, 55, 126
Myocardium, 234–235

Myofibril, 119
Myogenic heartbeat, 235
Myoglobin, 214, 223
Myosin, 110–113, 115–118
Myristic acid, 16
Mytilus californianus, 188, 319

Na$^+$ (see Sodium)
NAD (see Nicotinamide-adenine dinucleotide)
NADP (see Nicotinamide adenine dinucleotide phosphate)
Nasal gland, 334
Nebenkern, 53
Neck reflexes, 379
Needham, D. M., 111, 112
Needham, J., 267, 268, 272
Nematocyst, 184–185, 284
Nemerteans, 108
Neocerebellum, 385
Nephridial canal, 322
Nephridium, 322
Nephron, 323, 325, 332
Nereis diversicolor, 108, 221
Nerve, 89, 368
excitation of, 92, 301, 316
muscle preparation of, 89
optic, 145, 149
vagus, 158,
vasoconstrictor, 336
Nerve axon, 76
Nerve impulse, 90, 121
Nerve net, 365–367, 369, 371–372, 375–376
Nerve plexus, 371
Nerve ring, 369, 376
Nervous activity, 378
Nervous centers, 286
Nervous code, 285
Nervous mechanisms, 286
Nervous system, 341
autonomic, 158
central, 121, 161, 334
coelenterate, 365–367
control, arterioles, 241
ganglionic, 367–371, 376
parasympathetic, 158
segmental, 371
shock, 341
sympathetic, 158, 161, 289, 337
Neural lobe (see Neurohypophysis)
Neuroeffector junction, 285
Neuroendocrine system, 305–308
Neurogenic heartbeat, 235
Neurohumor, 288, 337
Neurohypophysis, 289, 293–294, 296–297, 329, 331, 381, 384
Neuromotor system, 88
Neuromuscular system, 87
Neuromuscular junction, 159, 163, 285, 372
Neurons, 157
motor, 88
sympathetic, 291

Neurosecretion, 288-289
  crustacean, 357
  insect, 305-306, 352-354, 358, 378
  vertebrate, 292-297, 328-329, 331, 360-361, 381
Neurosecretory end organs, 289, 305-306
Neurospora sitophila, 63, 64, 177
Newt, 217, 299, 340
Niacin, 171, 173, 174, 262
Nicotinamide-adenine-dinucleotide, 19, 30, 34, 35, 37, 41, 48, 173, 300, 313
Nicotinamide-adenine-dinucleotide dehydrogenase, 28, 30
Nicotinamide-adenine-dinucleotide oxidation, 46
Nicotinamide-adenine-dinucleotide phosphate, 19, 297, 300
Nicotinate, nicotinic acid (see Niacin)
Nitrate, 175-177
Nitrogen, nonprotein, 194
Nitrogen excretion, 267, 271-274
Nitrogen pool, 255, 256, 266
Nitrogen source, 175, 194
Nitrogenous base, 18
Nocturnal animals, 134
Node of Ranvier, 129, 130
Noise, 283
"Nonelectrogenic" pump, 81
Noradrenalin (see Norepinephrin)
Noradrenin (see Norepinephrin)
Norepinephrin, 163, 288, 289, 291, 337
Nuclear membrane, 62
Nucleic acids, 18, 65
Nucleolus, 53, 61, 63, 69, 70
Nucleoprotein, 53
Nucleosides, 18-19
Nucleotides, 18-19, 64, 313
  phosphates, 68-69
  pyridine, 19, 173
  synthesis of, 270
  uridine, 48
Nucleus, cell, 52-53, 61, 65, 69
  paraventricular, 293
  red, 380, 384
  supraoptic, 293
  vestibular, 379
Nutrition, 169-180, 188
Nymph, 350

Ocellus, 136-138
Octopus, 192, 204, 218, 228-230, 371
Odontophore, 190-191
Oleic acid, 16
Olfactory lobes, 381-384
Oligochaetes, 226
Oligosaccharides, 48
Omasum, 194
Ommatidia, 139, 140
Oncopeltus fasciatus, 358
Open circulation, 225-228, 230-233
Operculate snail, 327
Operculum, 204, 327

Ophiuroids, 108
Opsin, 134
Optic lobes, 384
Optic nerve, 145, 149
Optic termini, 384
Organ of Bellonci, 306
Organ of Gabe (Y-organ), 306
Organ of Hanström (X-organ), 307
Organization, embryonic, 349
Orientation, 138, 368
Ornithine, 49, 77, 262, 266, 268-269
Ornithine cycle, 268
Orthopterans, 350
Oscilloscope, cathode ray, 94, 95
Osmoregulation, 274, 316-334, 381
Osmosis, 72
Osmotic concentration in blood, 273, 319, 323, 325
Ostium, 230-231
Output, 286
  cardiac (see Heart, output)
Ovarian follicle, 291
Ovary, 291-292, 360-362
Overton, 54
Ovulation, 361
Ox, 298
Oxaloacetate, 28, 33-37, 49, 255, 266
Oxalosuccinate, 26, 35, 266
Oxidation, 10, 26
  of amino acids, 34, 47-49
  beta, 34
  of carbohydrates, 11, 34, 291
  energy yield, 11, 15, 18, 47
  enzymes, 23, 26, 58
  of fat, 18, 33, 47
  of fatty acids, 34, 47, 246
  in mitochondria, 59
  in muscle, 110
  of protein, 15, 34
  of pyruvic acid, 34-36
  regulation of, 313
  of succinic acid, 26
  tissue, 21, 26-37, 292, 295, 300
Oxidative carboxylation, 172
Oxidative deamination, 34
Oxidative decarboxylation, 34-35, 45
Oxidative metabolism, 312
Oxidative phosphorylation, 41, 45, 47, 58-59, 300, 313
Oxygen affinity, 217-218, 223
Oxygen capacity, 222
Oxygen consumption, 246, 248, 250, 300-301
Oxygen dissociation, 213, 221
Oxygen effects, 313-314
Oxygen lack, 335
Oxygen pressure, 250
Oxygen storage, 213, 222
Oxygen supply, 337
Oxygen transfer, 220
Oxygen transport, 211-223
Oxytocin, 289, 292, 294-295, 297, 299
Oyster, 186

Rhythmicity, 237, 367, 381, 384
Riboflavin, 172–174
Ribonucleic acid (RNA), 18, 50, 57–58, 60, 63, 65–70
  messenger, 67–69
  repressor, 67
  ribosomal, 68
  soluble, 67–69
  synthesis of, 68, 70
Ribose, 11, 18
Ribosomes, 57–58, 65, 67–69
Rice polishings, 170
Rickets, 170
Rigidity, decerebrate, 379–380
Rittenberg, D., 225–226
RNA (see Ribonucleic acid)
Rock lobster, 211, 222
Rod, visual, 131–134, 143–145, 149, 151
Rodent, 302, 360
Rouget cells, 241
Roundworms, 214
Royal Society of London, 5, 9
Rubner, M., 246, 249
Rumen, 194
Ruminants, 194–195

s-a node (see Sinu-atrial node)
Sabella pavonina, 221
Sabellidae, 212, 214
Salamander, 323, 327, 340
Saliva, 192
Salmo salar, 217
Salmon, 217–218, 238, 326
Salt, permeability to, 317, 328
Salt bonds, 13
Salt excretion, 326
Salt metabolism, 303
Salt pump, 75, 317, 322, 326
Salt regulation, 315–334
Salt transport, 80, 325
Salting-out, 31
Salvelinus fontinalis, 217
Sarcodina (see Rhizopods)
Sarcolemma, 113
Sarcomere, 114, 115, 116
Sarcoplasm, 113, 115
Scallop, 137
Scharrer, E. 288, 294
Schoenheimer, R., 255–256, 311
Scomber scombrus, 217–218
Scotopsin, 131–133
Scurvy, 170
Sea anemone, 365–367, 375
Sea robin, 218
Sea urchin, 74, 346–347
Sea water, 77, 90, 211, 324
Secondary sex characters, 291–292, 360, 362
Secretin, 195–196, 292
Secretion, 58, 290
  control of, 194–196, 301, 305, 333
  cuticular, 353

Secretion, gastric, 291
Segmental nervous system, 371, 376
Self-differentiation, 349
Self-duplication, 64
Selachians (see Elasmobranchs)
Semi-permeability, 73
Sensation, 122
Sense cells, primary, 123, 131
  secondary, 123
Sense organ, 123, 366, 368
Sensitivity, color, 151
  light, 134
  wavelength, 142, 152–153
Sensory center, 368, 381, 384
Sensory papilla organ, 307
Sepia, 138
Septum, atrial, 239
  ventricular, 239–240
Serine 13, 17, 49, 179, 256–258, 260, 266
Serological techniques, 113
Serpulidae, 212, 214
Sex, secondary characters of, 291–292, 295, 308, 360, 362
Sex gland, 308
Sex hormones, 295, 299
Sexuality, consecutive, 359
SH-groups (see Sulfhydryl groups)
Shark, 323
Sherrington, C. S., 157, 364, 379–380
Shock, nervous, 341
Short-circuit current, 78
Silkworm, cecropia, 353–354
Sinu-atrial node, 235, 237, 240
Sinu-atrial valve, 234
Sinus, blood from, 225, 227, 230
  carotid, 336
Sinus gland, 305, 307
Sinus node, 240
Sinus venosus, 234
Siphon, 204
Sipunculids, 108, 214, 226
Sipunculus, 218
Skate, 210–211
Skeleton, hydrostatic, 227–228
Skin, 206, 210–211, 337
  of frog, 207, 305, 323, 328–229
Sleep, 384
Sliding-filament hypothesis, 117
Slow contraction, 372–374
Slow fiber, 372–374
Slug, 201, 227–228, 274, 327
Snail, 137, 191, 214, 274, 327
Snake, 132, 144, 152, 153, 239, 267, 324, 340
Sodium bicarbonate, 195
Sodium concentration, in blood, 321, 324
  in cells, 76–77, 81, 164–165
  effect of, 130, 316
Sodium, permeability to, 101
Sodium pump, 78, 80–81, 98, 102, 165, 328–329
Sodium transport, 78, 80, 164, 290, 292, 294, 305, 320, 322, 325–326, 330, 332–334

68